T

i

Of

and

Compiled by Owen Wells

Shaw & Sons Limited
in association with

napo

NATIONAL PROBATION SERVICE

Published by
Shaw & Sons Limited
Shaway House
21 Bourne Park
Bourne Road
Crayford
Kent DA1 4BZ

tel   01322 621100
fax   01322 550553

www.shaws.co.uk

© 2009 Shaw & Sons Limited

Published January 2009

ISBN 978 0 7219 1751 1
ISSN 0142-1328

Page make-up by Groundwork, Skipton
Printed in UK by
CPI William Clowes, Beccles NR34 7TL

The Editor

The Probation Directory is compiled by a retired probation officer, Owen Wells. If you have any suggestions or questions about the directory, please contact him on:

(01943) 602270
07951 436126 (mobile)

e-mail o.r.wells@gmail.com

Introduction

The Probation Directory is compiled each October. Wherever possible, changes that occur after October are included in the text up to 20th December. The very short time between compilation and publication means that the Probation Directory is probably the most up-to-date book of its kind published anywhere. Errors will, of course, occur; any that are notified to the publisher will normally be corrected in the *Probation Bulletin*.

Acknowledgement

Without the help of the Chief Officers and their administrative staff, NOMS and Prison Department, and many others this directory could not have been produced. The publisher wishes to thank them all.

Abbreviations

Where a person has no designation after their name, they can be presumed to be a Probation Officer

aco	Assistant Chief Officer
cclo	Crown Court Liaison Officer
co	Chief Officer
js	Job-sharing
p	Part-time
pao	Principal Administrative Officer
psa	Probation Service Assistant
pso	Probation Service Officer
qa mgr	Quality Assurance Manager
spo	Senior Probation Officer
ssw	Senior Social Worker
sw	Social Worker
vlo	Victim Liaison Officer

Other job titles are explained in the text. In general, job titles in the Probation Service are becoming ever longer and more obscure. In the text they are usually abbreviated, but hopefully in a manner that will allow the reader to make an intelligent guess as to what they mean.

CONTENTS

PROBATION SERVICE & PROFESSIONAL ORGANISATIONS

Napo

4 Chivalry Road, London SW11 1HT
020-7223 4887 *fax 020-7223 3503*

e-mail initialsurname@napo.org.uk
www.napo.org.uk

General Secretary: Jonathan Ledger
Asst Gen Secy (campaign & pr): Harry Fletcher
Asst Gen Secy (conditions of service):
Ian Lawrence
Asst Gen Secy (er, training, prof): Cordell Pillay
National Official (Health & Safety):
Mike McClelland
National Official (TUO):Ranjit Singh
HR & Office Manager: Keith Waldron
Admin (ICCJ monograph, publications, training):
Jeannie Ah-Fong (p)
Admin (gen sec, neg & st, website): vacant
Admin (resources & receptn): Margaret Pearce
Admin (ags, neg & tuo): Cynthia Griffith
Admin (ags, er, pr): Shireena Suleman
Admin (ags, cam & pr): Kath Falcon
Admin (membership): James Carpenter
Admin (membership): Alison Bonner
Admin (nec & officers): Chris McGarry
Admin (reception): Jacqueline Paryag (p)
Admin (finance): Theresa Boorman
Chair: Tim Wilson
Vice Chair (Probation): Dino Peros
Vice Chair (Probation): Deborah Borgen
Vice Chair (Probation): Mike Quinn
Vice Chair (CAFCASS): Paul Bishop
Treasurer: Duncan Hume

Probation Association

83 Victoria Street, London SW1H 0HW
020-3008 7930 *fax 020-3008 7931*

E-mail: association@probationassociation.co.uk
www.probationassociation.co.uk

Chief Executive: Christine Lawrie
Employment Relations, Pay & Policies
Manager: Chas Dowden
Governance Manager: Mike Caldwell
Communications Manager: Vacancy
Board Secretary: Vacancy
Interim Board Secretary: Nigel Spencer
Accountant: Duncan Gaskell
Office Manager: Liz Hogan
Admin Officer: Agnes Andrade

Admin Officer/LCCS Administrator:
Yasmin Jankowski-Doyle
Office Assistant: Helen Ben-Rejeb

National Approved Premises Association (formerly NAPBH)

NAPA, P.O. Box 13682, Cradley Heath, B62
2DY. tel 0121-550 6444
e-mail: office@napa-uk.org www.napa-uk.org

The national organisation working to support
and promote all Approved Premises (hostels)
both within probation and the voluntary
managed sector. The Association works in
partnership with other bodies concerned with
residential facilities for offenders and tackling
crime.

Director: Mike Short
Chair: Judith Poole

Association of Black Probation Officers

The Association's definition of Black is a
political one, which emphasises the common
experiences and common determination of
people of African, African-Caribbean and Asian
origin to oppose the effects of racism.

1st Floor, Mitre House, 223/237 Borough High
Street, London SE1 1JD
tel 020-7740 8537 *fax 020-7740 8450*

Chair: Davlin Brydson 0121-464 6259
Vice Chair: Abdallah Nagib-Ali (01753) 537516
National Co-ordinator: Susan Roye 020-7740
8537
Treasurer: Sharon Clarke 020-8652 9670
Information Officer: Carl Morgan 0121-246 6650
Midlands Region Convenor: Chelsea Cameron
0115-845 5218
N. Regional Convenor: Trevor Bernard 0161-
862 9881
S. Regional Convenor: Mervyn Parris (01727)
847787

National Association of Asian Probation Staff

Encourages and maintains a support group of
members promoting an Asian perspective on
professional issues. Initiates and campaigns
for changes within the CJ System to adjust
the imbalance of disadvantage suffered by all
minority ethnic groups.

National Administrator: Room 102a, 1st Floor,
Mitre House, 223/237 Borough High Street,
London SE1 1JD

tel 020-7740 8563 *fax 020 7740 8450*

Chair:
Savina Badhan 020-7740 8584/0191 262 9211
Vice Chair: Pervez Sadiq 0115 841 5630
Treasurer: Shamim Khan 020-8808 4522
Membership Secretary: Sudeep Bone 0116-270 8327

N Region co-ords
Azra Sharif 01274 704612
Davinder Singh 0161-620 4421
Ishtiaq Ramzan 01274 704503
W Midlands co-ord
Gurpreet Kaur 0121-248 3660
E Midlands co-ord
Gurdev Singh 0115-908 2900
London & S co-ord
Navinder Subherwal 020-7740 8455

LAGIP for lesbians, gay men, bisexuals and transgendered staff
working in probation & family courts

Co-Chair: Helen Dale, Greater Manchester
Co-Chair: Libby Wrighton, West Yorkshire
Vice Chair: Keri Summers, South Wales
Treasurer Administrator: Suzanne Brooks, Greater Manchester
Communications Officer: Vacancy
Conference Organiser: Brian Rich, West Midlands
Regnl Co-ord Wales & West: Amanda Watts, South Wales
Regnl Co-ord North East: Libby Wrighton, West Yorkshire
Regnl Co-ord North West: Suzanne Brooks, Greater Manchester
Regnl Co-ord Midlands: Paula Whelan, West Midlands
Regnl Co-ord East: Vacancy
Regnl Co-ord South-East: Eleanor Levy, Surrey
Regnl Co-ord London: Vacancy

all e-mail addresses are @(area name).
probation.gsi.gov.uk

National Disabled Staff Network

Working to identify and remove institutional barriers and to empower disabled staff and service users in the Probation Service, MoJ, NOMS and CAFCASS.

1st Floor, Mitre House, 223/237 Borough High Street, London SE1 1JD
tel 020 7740 8556 *fax 020 7740 8450*

Co-Chair: Desiree.Leete@devon-cornwall.
probation.gsi.gov.uk tel 01392 861538

Co-Chair: David Quarmby quarmby@ntlworld.com
tel 07736 087019
Vice Chair: Sarah.Chapman@warwickshire.
probation.gsi.gov.uk tel 02476 482841

National Co-ord & Treasurer: Maria.Lenn@
london.probation.gsi.gov.uk tel 020 7740 8556
ABPO rep: Grace.Powell@surrey.probation.gsi.
gov.uk
CAFCASS rep: Margaret.Longson@cafcass.gov.uk

Regional Co-ordinators:
South East: Grace.Powell@surrey.probation.
gsi.gov.uk
South West: Sheila.Hawken@avon-somerset.
probation.gsi.gov.uk
Yorkshire and Humberside: Chris.Lewis@
north-yorkshire.probation.gsi.gov.uk
North East: Barbara.Randall@Northumbria.
probation.gsi.gov.uk
East of England: Lauren.Bleach@norfolk.
probation.gsi.gov.uk
North West: Karen.Lavelle@manchester.
probation.gsi.gov.uk
West of Midlands: Sarah.Chapman@
warwickshire.probation.gsi.gov.uk
East Midlands: Gilly.Hagen gillyflower50@
hotmail.com
Wales: Marie.Young@south-wales.probation.
gsi.gov.uk
London: Anne.Lescombe@london.probation.
gsi.gov.uk

Probation Service Christian Fellowship

Open to all Christian probation staff, current and retired, and others working with offenders and their families. Supporting local prayer networks, relating the Christian faith to probation practise, linking with other related agencies, regular newsletter, prayer days, and fellowship weekends. Affiliated to the Evangelical Alliance.

Chair: Simon May, Probation Office, 70 London Road, Southampton, SO15 2AJ,
tel 02380635011 or 02380248694 (direct line).

email: simon.may@hampshire.probation.gsi.gov.uk
or enquiries@pscf.org.uk *www.pscf.org.uk*

The Edridge Fund

The Edridge Fund of the National Association of Probation Officers is a Registered Charity that gives financial help to those in need. All members of the service who are members of Napo, or are eligible to be members of Napo, can benefit as can retired staff and bereaved partners and dependants of either of the above. Each Napo Branch has its own Edridge Representative. Applications are generally made through those Representatives and passed on to the Trustees who sit about 5 times a year to consider applications. These applications have to be based on financial need. The Secretary of the Fund is:

Richard Martin, The Limes, Lynn Road, Gayton, King's Lynn, Norfolk PE32 1QJ (01553) 636570 e-mail edridge@btinternet.com www.edridgefund.org

IMPACT Probation Officers' Branch (Ireland)

Probation Officers in the Republic of Ireland are a branch of IMPACT, the Public Services Trade Union

N.B. When dialling from UK dial 00 353 and omit first 0 of Irish dialling code

IMPACT, Nerney's Court, Dublin 1 01-817 1512 fax 01-817 1501 Asst Gen Sec (working with the branch): Ray Ryan e-mail moneill@impact.ie

Branch Officers

Chair: Tom Ryder, Probation Service, Friary House, Friars Mill Road, Mullingar, Co Westmeath. tgryder@probation.ie

Vice Chair: Mary McDonald, Probation Service, Gov't Buildings, Alphonsus Road, Dundalk, Co Louth. mbmcdonald@probation.ie

Secretary: Judy Quinlan, Probation Officer, Probation Service, Castlerea Prison, Castlerea, Co Roscommon. jaquinlan@probation.ie

Treasurer: Frank Cahill, Probation Service, Limerick Prison, Mulgrove Street, Limerick fgcahill@probation.ie

Minutes Secretary: Carolyn Fahey, Probation Service, Government Buildings, Portlaoise, Co Laois cfahey@probation.ie

Equality Officer: Aine Morris, Probation Service, Mountjoy Prison, N.C.Road, Dublin 7 aemorris@probation.ie

Health & Safety Officer: Joan Condon, Probation Service, Limerick Prisno, Limerick jmcondon@probation.ie

Membership Secretary: Aine Morris, Probation Service, Mountjoy Prison, N.C.Road, Dublin 7 aemorris@probation.ie

PR Officer: David Williamson, Probation Service, Mountjoy Prison, N.C.Road, Dublin 7 dgwilliamson@probation.ie

Respect

1st Floor, Downstream Building, 1 London Bridge, London SE1 9BG 020-7022 1801 fax 020-7022 1806 e-mail info@respect.uk.net www.respect.uk.net

The UK wide membership organisation promoting best practice amongst statutory and independent sector projects and individual practitioners, trainers and consultants who work with perpetrators of domestic violence and their (ex)partners.

Respect Phoneline 0845 122 8609 an information and advice line for domestic violence perpetrators, their (ex)partners as well as frontline workers phoneline@respect.uk.net

Men's Advice Line 0808 801 0327 a helpline for male victims of domestic violence www.mensadviceline.org.uk or info@mensadviceline.org.uk

Social Care Councils

The General Social Care Council is the regulatory body for the social care profession in England. Similar organisations exist in Northern Ireland, Scotland, and Wales (see below). It issues codes of practice, registers social care workers and regulates social work education and training.

England

General Social Care Council, Goldings House, 2 Hay's Lane, London SE1 2HB. 020-7397 5100 fax 020-7397 5101. Information service: 020-7397 5800 e-mail info@gscc.org.uk www.gscc.org.uk

General Social Care Council, Myson House, Railway Terrace, Rugby CV21 3HT. (01788) 572119 fax (01788) 532474

Northern Ireland

Northern Ireland Social Care Council, 7th Floor, Millennium House, 19-25 Great Victoria Street, Belfast BT2 7AQ. 028-9041 7600 fax 028-9041 7601 textphone 02890 239340 e-mail info@nisocialcarecouncil.org.uk

Scotland

Scottish Social Services Council, Compass House, Discovery Quay, 11 Riverside Drive, Dundee DD1 4NY. (01382) 207101 fax (01382) 207215

Information service 0845 6030891 e-mail enquiries@sssc.uk.com www.sssc.uk.com

Wales
Care Council for Wales, 6th Floor, West Wing, South Gate House, Wood Street, Cardiff CF10 1EW 029-2022 6257 *fax 029-2038 4764* e-mail info@ccwales.org.uk www.ccwales.org.uk

International Social Service of the United Kingdom

International Social Service (ISS) is a voluntary organisation, staffed by specialist intercountry social workers, linking social services around the world. It exists to help individuals and families with problems requiring social work intervention in more than one country. ISS is used regularly by social workers, family court welfare officers and individuals who require information, advice or a social work service from abroad.

If advice or service is required, it is helpful if ISS can be consulted as early as possible. A duty officer is available to discuss cases on the telephone. A referral guide is available on request. ISS works through its overseas network of branches and correspondents - thus the service is normally provided by, or in consultation with, a national social worker of the overseas country. A charge is levied for the service

International Social Service of the UK, Canterbury Court, Unit 1.11 1-3 Brixton Road London SW9 6DE 020-7735 8941 or 020-3176 0253 *fax 020-3176 0259* e-mail info@issuk.org.uk

The National Organisation for Practice Teaching

NOPT is an organisation created to provide quality practice teaching in social work. Membership of about 250. Provides members for several national committees and influences social work education. Annual, workshop based, conference plus regional workshops

Membership Administrator: Liz Munro, 2 Green Bank, Simmondley, Glossop, Derbyshire SK13 6XT   e-mail admin@nopt.org

NATIONAL OFFENDER MANAGEMENT SERVICE (MINISTRY OF JUSTICE)

The contact details below are for the units which made up the National Probation Directorate prior to it's amalgamation with NOMS Headquarters in January 2007, and additional NOMS contact details that will be of use to NPS staff. Under each unit name appears where the unit currently fits within the NOMS structure.

Director of Probation's Office
Director of Probation: Roger Hill 020-7217 0650
Staff Officer: Bettina Crossick 020-7217 8445
Higher Executive Officer: David Millett 020-7217 8484
Diary Mgr /PA: Jan Pogmore 020-7217 0737
fax 020 7217 0660

Communications Team
(NOMS Corporate Services Directorate)
1st Floor Abell House, John Islip Street, London, SW1P 4LH

NPS Communications
Head of Communications: Susan Lord 020-7217 8696
Communications Mgr: Phil McDonough 0191 284 7628 (based at ROM's NE office)
Communications Officer: Joeleen Anderson 020-7217 1363
Communications Officer: Jay Das 020-7217 0653
fax 020 7217 0660

Specification, Benchmarking & Costing Programme (Probation)
(NOMS Commissioning and Operational Policy Directorate)
Room 703 Cleland House, Page Street, London SW1P 4LN

Head of Unit: Martin Copsey
020 7217 5842/07789 921 790
Martin.copsey@hmps.gsi.gov.uk
Deputy Head of Unit: Sue Carrie
020 7217 5608/07876 478 683
Sue.carrie@hmps.gsi.gov.uk
Asst to Martin Copsey & Sue Carrie/ Programme Communications & Enquiries: Paddy Salter
020 7217 2963/07739 986 883
Patrick.salter@hmps.gsi.gov.uk

Operational Leads
Suki Binning: suki.binning@hmps.gsi.gov.uk

Janet Corcoran: janet.corcoran@hmps.gsi.gov.uk
Tony Grapes: tony.grapes@hmps.gsi.gov.uk
Jonathan Martin: jonathan.martin@hmos.gsi.gov.uk
Peter Rogers: peter.rogers@hmps.gsi.gov.uk
Stephen Spurden: Stephen.spurden@hmps.gsi.gov.uk
Martin Walpole: martin.walpole@hmps.gsi.gov.uk

Project Team Admin & Supt/Info Mgr: Stephen Pulker
020 7217 5661
Stephen.pulker@hmps.gsi.gov.uk
Finance Manager: Alison Hamer
0161 952 4373/07768 526242
Alison.hamer@justice.gov.uk

Probation Change Programme
(NOMS Performance & Improvement Directorate)
1st Floor Abell House, John Islip Street, London, SW1P 4LH

Programme Director: Anton Obholzer 020-7217 0759
Programme Director's PS/Training & Devpt Support: Arlene Munir 020-7217 8095
Programme Mgr: Iain Anderson 020-7217 0758
Programme Support: Alan Pinel 020-7217 8261
Project Mgr: Workforce Remodelling, Training & Devpt: Sandra Boyd 020-7217 0733
Project Support: Training & Devpt: Shukri Gesod 020-7217 8812
Project Mgr: Productive Time: Graham Taylor 020-7217 5131
Transition Mgr: Frank Treble 020-7217 1305
Transition Mgr: Sue Power 020-7217 0655
Programme Co-ordinator (p): Danny Robinson 020-7217 8933
Project Mgr: Lynne Last 020-7217 1884
Project Mgr: Value for Money: Avril Hall 020-7217 5892
Projects Mgr: Trusts: Angie Munley 020-7217 5594
fax 020-7217 8986/0693

NOMS Offender Assessment & Management Unit
(NOMS Performance & Improvement Directorate)
3rd Floor Abell House, John Islip Street, London, SW1P 4LH

Head of Unit: Sarah Mann 020-7217 0727
Secretary: Julie Taylor 020-7217 8546
Head of Intensive Offender Mngmnt: Phil Bowen 020-7217 8646
Policy Devpt Mgr: Robin Brennan 020-7217 0916
Offender Assessment System (OASys) Team
Head of OASys: Laura Fairweather 020-7217 0680

PS to Head of OASys: Ann Saddington 020-7217 5958
OASys Operational Mgr: Janet Corcoran 020-7217 8908
Personal Secretary to Janet Corcoran and Tony Grapes: Marjorie Baker 0700
OASys R Project: Trisha Borrows 020-7217 5825
OASys Operational Supt Mgr: Pauline Hill 020-7217 0690
OASys Operational Supt Mgr: Denise Kenealy-Fox 020-7217 0697
OASys Operational Mgr: Vicki Quilliam 020-7217 1889
OASys HMPS Operational Supt Mgr: Caroline Nowell 020-7217 5825
OASys Policy Devpt Advisor: Maureen Onyejeli 020-7217 5935
OASys Policy Devpt Officer: Robert Hatch 020-7217 5404
Office Mgr: Bunmi Abidoye 020-7217 5872
fax 020 7217 5750

OASys Data Evaluation & Analysis Team (O-DEAT)
Head of O-Deat: Mia Debidin 020-7217 0699
Snr Research Officer: Philip Howard 020-7217 0698
Snr Research Officer: Robin Moore 020-7217 0703
Snr Research Officer: Sarah Morton 020-7217 8165
Research Officer: Wendy Smith-Yau 0207 217 8050
Beyond Systems: David Reid 020-7217 1329
fax 020 7217 5750

Offender Management Team
Head of NOMS Offender Mngmnt: Paul Hindson 020-7217 5167
OM Implementation Mgr: Karen MacLeod 020-7217 2082
OM Implementation Mgr: Bobbie Jones 020-7217 8208
OM Implementation Mgr YAO: Claire Harvey 020-7217 5951
OM Implementation Mgr: Jo Chilvers 020-7217 1871
OM Implementation Mgr: Joe Woods 020-7217 2240
OM Project Advisor: Gareth Mercer 020-7217 8499
OM Project Advisor: Robin Dickens 020-7217 8604
OM Policy Support Officer: Ola Haruna 020-7217 8607
FNP Support: Nick Hammond 020-7217 1824
Head of PrOMPT: Tony Grapes 020-7217 8985

OASys Operational Mgr: Jackie Seaton 020-7217 8018
Support Officer: Carol Sylvester 020-7217 0708

Interventions & Substance Abuse Unit
(NOMS Commissioning & Partnerships Directorate)
1st Floor Abell House, John Islip Street, London, SW1P 4LH

Community Reintegration Team
Head of Community Reintegration: Jill Shaw 020-7217 0673
Project Implementation Mgr: Roger Stevens 020-7217 8283
CSAP Secretary/EIB: Carole Wham 020-7217 5714
Unpaid Work Programme Mgr: Neil Martin 020-7217 8877
Unpaid Work Scheme Mgr: David Mead 020-7217 5120
Administration Support: Olubusola Shokan 020-7217 8448
Learning & Skills Advisor: Ian Henshaw 020-7217 0682
Policy Advisor: Marcus Smart 020-7217 0766
Events Organiser: Mark Chidwick 020-7217 0681
PS Plus Mgr: David Preston 020-7217 8323
fax 020 7217 8496

Intensive Interventions Team
Secretary: Marie Malone 020-7217 0686
Drug & Alcohol Devpt Officer: Robert Stanbury 020-7217 0767
Drugs/Alcohol Policy Advisor: Elaine Castle 020-7217 8003
fax 020 7217 0693

Attitude, Thinking and Behaviour Team
Head of Attitude, Thinking & Behaviour Programmes: Danny Clark 020-7217 0675
Business Support & Communications Mgr: John MacGregor 020-7217 8520
Project Implementation Mgr: Philip McNerney 020-7217 8895
Head of Psychology & Evaluation: Liz Bird 020-7217 8418
Senior Psychologist: Karl Williams 020-7217 8991
Principal Psychologist: Jo Day 020-7217 8999
Trainee Research Psychologist: Sinead Bloomfield 020-7217 8813
Data Management Research Officer: Joe Longman 020-7217 0676
Psychological Asst: Nicola Garrick 020-7217 2238
Senior Research Officer: Liz Calvert 020-7217 8815

Progr Implementation Mgr: Phil Mackin 020-7217 8044
Progr Implementation Mgr: Penny Rickman 020-7217 8044
Progr Implementation Mgr: Jonathan Martin 020-7217 8081
Progr Implementation Mgr: Elizabeth Hayes 020-7217 8401
Training Devpt Advisor: Alex Law 020-7217 8068
Training Devpt Advisor: Eileen Davis 020-7217 8211
Training Devpt Advisor: Anita McLeod 020-7217 0674
Training Devpt Advisor: Karen Townend 020-7217 8211
Admin Officer: Ali Moghal 020-7217 0679
Office Mgr: Ruth Taylor 020-7217 1779
Executive Officer: Lesley Smith 020-7217 8336
fax 020 7217 0693

Drug Strategy Team (Custodial)
3rd Floor SE Quarter, Fry Building, 2 Marsham Street, London, SW1P 4DF

Head of Drug Strategy Team: Martin Lee 020-7035 6156
Secretary to Martin Lee: Michelle Sandilands 020-7035 6155
Head of Treatment Policy: Matthew Bullard 020-7035 6148
Secretary to Neil Irving, Matthew Bullard & Caroline Bonds: Rebecca Kamara: 020 7035 6154
Snr Treatment Policy Mgr: Firoza Saloo 020-7035 6152
Research Officer: Kim Tyler 020-7035 6150
Head of Treatment Policy Mgr: Caroline Bonds 020-7035 6149
Treatment Policy Mgr: Abena Baffoe-Bonnie 020-7035 6132
Treatment Policy Mgr: Simon Pannell 020-7035 6130
MDT Programme Mgr: Rupert Woods 020-7035 6138
Supply Reduction & VDT Policy Mgr: Carlo Azzopardi 020-7035 6139
MDT Database & Policy Mgr: Jeffrey Tribe 020-7035 6137
Drug Supply Reduction Policy: Lesley Franklin 020-7035 6140
Head of Strategic, Aim 5 Liaison & Ministerial Briefing: Neil Irving 020-7035 6153
Programme & Finance Mgr: Lai Pedro 020-7035 6133
Finance Mgr: Carleen Protain 020-7035 6136
Finance & Management Officer: Kevin Brown 020-7035 6135

fax 0870 336 9189 & 020 7035 6131

Performance Area Co-ordination Unit (PACU)
(NOMS Performance & Improvement Directorate)
1st Floor Abell House, John Islip Street, London, SW1P 4LH

Head of PACU: Richard Cullen 020-7217 0731
Executive Asst: Toby Cottrell 020-7217 0654
Head of Training & Devpt: Paula Cairney 020-7217 0728
Training Project Mgr: Mandy Pointon 020-7217 0791
Workforce Planning: Helen Smith 020-7217 0738
Workforce Planning: Mark Gray 020-7217 2004
Head Pay & Reward: Iain McIntosh 020-7217 8768
Policy Devpt Mgr: Nick Jones 020-7217 8362
Policy & Devpt Officer: Kishwar Hyde 020-7217 8589
Policy & Devpt Support: Beverly Warren 020-7217 8343
Leadership & Devpt Mgr: Ingrid Wheeler 020-7217 8556
Senior Business Supt Mgr: Diane Battershield 020-7217 8879
Business Support Mgr: Dermott O'Gorman 020-7217 8879
Business Support Officer: Roger Davis 020-7217 0730
Business Support Asst: Vishal Thakrar 020-7217 0788
Health, Work & Wellbeing Mgr: Kathryn Ball 020-7217 8954
Chiefs & Chairs Mgr: Martin Murphy 020-7217 8089
Asst Mgr (Chiefs & Chairs): Kelly Collins 020-7217 0741
Chiefs & Chairs Support: Simon Edwards 020-7217 0740
Chief & Chairs Recruitment Asst: Davinder Rai 020-7217 8803
Corporate Risk Mgr: Ayodele Kayode 020-7217 8395
Quality Assurance Officer: Joanne Trevitt 07988 607 891
Workload Mngmnt Tool: Martin Walpole 020-7217 8164
fax 020 7217 0660

Prospects Unit
(NOMS Perfomace & Improvement Directorate)
Room 417, Abell House, John Islip Street , London, SW1P 4LH

Acting Programme Director: Denis McGlade 0771 754 0984
Finance Co-ordinator: Susan Mehmet 020-7217 8572
fax 020 7217 0823

Performance Improvement Unit
(NOMS Performance & Improvement Directorate)
1st Floor Abell House, John Islip Street, London, SW1P 4LH

Head of Performance & Improvement Unit: Ben Emm 020-7217 8244
Performance & Quality Mgr: Sonia Crozier 020-7217 8293/07734 845 295
Performance & Quality Mgr: Kevin Robinson 07717 662 383

Improvement & Development Mgrs
National Devpts: Ian Fox 07818 077250
Wales: Ged Bates 07818 016458
South East England and London: Sue Carrie 020-7217 8218
Yorkshire & Humberside: Kath Morris 07859 009 332
East Midlands: Sharon Higson 07770 941 745
North East: Stuart McPhillips 07876 478 687
East of England: Tom McQuillan 07876 478 691
North West: Andrew Underdown 07876 478 685
West Midlands: Colin Pinfold 07770 940 505
South West: Meg Blumsom 07789 921 811
fax 020 7217 0660

Performance Management Unit
(NOMS Performance & Improvement Directorate)
3rd Floor Fry Building, NE Quarter, 2 Marsham Street, London, SW1P 4DF

Head of Performance Management Unit: Paul Ibrahim 020-7035 3165
Head of Probation Performance: Paris Mikkides 020-7035 8732
Head of Reporting: Ed Stradling 020-7035 6145
Information Mgr: Keith Ward 020-7035 6144
Executive Officer: Lulu Robbani 020-7035 4379
Information Officer: Everlyne Shimbalia 020-7035 3429
Information Officer: Allan Greedharee 020-7035 8740
Head of Data & Information Technology: John Swallow 020-7035 0325
Head of Prisons & NOMS System Performance: Rebecca Hall 020-7035 0341
Head of Metrics Devpt: Natasha Garnham 020-7035 0333
SSO: Natasha Trasi 020-7035 0331
HSO: Richard Boorman 020-7035 0336
SO: Ingela Hansson 020-7035 3431

Project Mgr: Stephen Harbron 020-7035 3318
Prison Sponsor Function: Charles Adcok 020-7035 3097
Senior Executive Officer: Maureen Nwafor 020-7035 4378
Prison & Probation Policy Sponsor: Paul Wray 020-7035 0329
Higher Executive Officer: Philip Tucker 020-7035 0328
fax 0870 336 9180

Enforcement Improvement Team
(NOMS Performance & Improvement Directorate)
1st Floor Abell House, John Islip Street, London, SW1P 4LH

Enforcement Policy Mgr: Helen West 020-7217 8680/07770 635 303
Performance: Mgr (end to end enforcement): Anthony O'Kane 020-7217 8814/07824 599 267
Performance: Mgr (end to end enforcement): Andy Frost 07767 770 213
Performance: Mgr (end to end enforcement): Joanne Trevitt 07798 607 891
Performance: Mgr (end to end enforcement): Liz Holden 07909 902 960
Performance Mgr: Helen Ward 07884 440 835
fax 020 7217 8986

Equality & Diversity Unit
1st Floor Abell House, John Islip Street, London, SW1P 4LH

Equality & Diversity Mgr: Rory Heap 020-7217 8009
Equality & Diversity Mgr: Omar Ralph 020-7217 5693
Equality & Diversity Mgr: Alethea McIntosh 020-7217 8878
Business Support Mgr: Azi Eniasoro 020-7217 8562
Equality & Diversity Admin: Verona Walcott 020-7217 8669
Equality & Diversity Admin: Neil Stanesby 020-7217 8609
fax 020-7217 8986

Public Protection Unit
(NOMS Performance & Improvement Directorate)
Ground Floor, Abell House, John Islip Street, London, SW1P 4LH.

Head of Public Protection: Gordon Davison 020-7217 0754
Senior Personal Secretary: Agnes Harris 020-7217 8681

Finance & Corporate Support Team
Head of Team: Noeleen Verner 020-7217 8823
Deputy Head of Team: Musharraf Khan 020-7217 0752
Correspondence & HR: Mgr Norman Beckwith 020-7217 8573
Finance Mgr: Jennifer Lawrence Wynne 020-7217 8058
Accounts Payable: James Mills 020-7217 8597
Corporate Support: Keith Miller 020-7217 0824

Approved Premises & Dangerous Offenders
Head of Team: Sean Langley 020-7217 8226
Senior Policy Adviser: Paul Douglas 020-7217 0773
Policy Adviser: Mark Rollason 020-7217 5216
fax 020 7217 0799

Critical Public Protection Casework Team
Head of Team: Ian Sammut-Smith 020-7217 0750
Case Mgr: Janet Gregory 020-7217 0637
Admin Support: Gita Ladva 020-7217 0749
fax 020-7217 0756

Serious Further Offences
Head of Team: Richard Pearce 020-7217 0695
Senior Caseworker: Anna Beddis 020-7217 5282
Case Mgr: Damian Angelis 020-7217 0744
Caseworker: Monuara Ullah 020-7217 0748
Casework Admin: Philip Cogram 020-7217 0746
fax 020 7217 0756

Victim Policy
Head of Team: Felicity Hawksley 020-7217 0670
Senior Policy Adviser: Robert Lawman 020-7217 0639
Policy Support: Archana Patel 020-7217 8031
fax 020-7217 0799

MAPPA, Child Probation & Sex Offender Treatment
Head of Team: Claire Wiggins 020-7217 8514

MAPPA
Head of MAPPA Team: Penny Barker 020-7217 5551
MAPPA Police Policy Lead: Jennifer East 020-7217 0747
Public Protection Devpt Mgr: George Woolsey 020-7217 5267
Leads on HMPS Public Protection Manual: Terry Collins 020-7217 8565
MAPPA Policy Developer: Chris Potter 020-7217 0692
MAPPA Policy Support: Brian Chapman 020-7217 5136
MAPPA Support: Paul Maidment 020-7217 8547

Domestic Abuse
Senior Policy Advisor: Angela Colyer 020-7217 0702

Sex Offender Team
Head of Sex Offender Team: Mark Farmer 020-7217 0672
Team Support: Maria Duraes 020-7217 8576

Risk of Harm & Indeterminate Sentence Prisoners (ISP)
Head of Team: Tony Robson 020-7217 0935
ACO: Helen Preston 020-7217 8561
Parole & Post Sentence ISP Policy: Diana Bartram 020-7217 8052
Team Support: Andrew Collymore 020-7217 8750
fax 020 7217 0799

Supported Witness Section
Head of Section: Malcolm Ayers 020-7217 8612
Office Mgr: Daniella Parascandolo 020-7217 8612
Team Support: James Keen 020-7217 5677
fax 020 7217 0842

Pre Release Section: PPU
(NOMS Performance & Improvement Directorate)
4th Floor, Fry Building, 2 Marsham Street, London, SW1P 4DF

Head of Pre-Release Section: Alistair McMurdo 020-7035 3890
Personal Secretary: Geraldine Nolan 020-7035 3607

Team Leader: Lisa Burrell 020-7035 3999
Caseworker: Navid Abassi 0207 035 3994
Caseworker: John Ahern 0207 035 3898
Caseworker: Simon Alderman 020-7035 3587
Caseworker: Shahida Ali 020-7035 3997
Caseworker: Cheryl Anson-McAndrew 020-7035 3586
Caseworker: Samuel Asiedu 020-7035 3899
Caseworker: Michele Bent 020-7035 3895
Caseworker: Timothy Bowden 020-7035 3584
Tariff Caseworker: Kevin Breame 020-7035 3767
Caseworker: Francoise Brudey-Elwin 020-7035 3599
Caseworker: Sue Bryant 020-7035 3992
Caseworker: Darren Butler 020-7035 3874
Caseworker: Jane Daws 020-7035 3880
Caseworker: Daniel Donkoh 020-7035 3995
Caseworker: Jenny Dyer 020-7035 3993
Administration & Support: Mark Ferrigan 020-7035 3005
Team Leader: Sue Gambling 020-7035 3999
Caseworker: Rishi Ganguly 020-7035 3960
Caseworker: Mike Gray 020-7035 3596

Caseworker: Anne Hailstone 020-7035 3871
Caseworker: Nicola Halse 020-7035 3597
Caseworker: Kevin Hampton 020-7035 3585
Team Leader: James Hough 020-7035 3879
Caseworker: Chris Hughes 020-7035 3900
Caseworker: Sherifat Idris
Caseworker: Bobbi Ingram 020-7035 3590
Casework Policy: Paul Jackson 020-7035 3002
Caseworker: Bill John 020-7035 3996
Caseworker: Baljit (Bob) Khangura 020-7035 3591
Caseworker: Jill Leff020 7035 3959
Caseworker: Jan Mahmut
Caseworker: Joss Mistry 020-7035 3586
Caseworker: Sylvia Mitchell 020-7035 3894
Caseworker: Lynda Morley 020-7035 3758
Caseworker: Adebukola Bukie Oduola
Caseworker: Philip Ojiako
Caseworker: Emete Osman
Caseworker: Lesley Paterwson 020-7035 3956
Caseworker: Elle Pepperdine
Caseworker: Clare Pope 020-7035 3998
Caseworker: Puvi Puvirajah 020-7035 3592
Caseworker: Simon Quinn 020-7035 3958
Casework Policy: Vicky Quinn 020-7035 3003
Caseworker: Phil Ransom 020-7035 3594
Caseworker: Rosalind Read-Leah 020-7035 3588
Team Leader: Khatija Seedat 020-7035 3608
Caseworker: Michelle Shippie
Head of Casework & Corporate Issues: Duncan Smith
Team Leader: Howard Smith 020-7035 3892
Casework Support: Gary Steel 020-7035 3004
Caseworker: Abu Sufian
Caseworker: Irum Syed
Caseworker: Tony Turrell 020-7035 3872
Caseworker: Joseph Ubom
Caseworker: Jeannine Vambe
Caseworker: Richard Walden 020-7035 3609
Head of Casework: Steve Watson 020-7035 3998/07790 840667
Admin Support: Malcolm Willis 020-7035 3006
Caseworker: Neil Wright 020-7035 3583
fax 020 7035 3583

Post Release Section: PPU London
(NOMS Performance & Improvement Directorate)
4th Floor, Fry Building, 2 Marsham Street, London, SW1P 4DF

Head of Post Release Section, and Parole & Public Protection Policy Section: Russell A'Court 020-0735 3022
Head of Post Release Policy & Performance Mngmnt: Jo Thompson 020-7035 3891

Head of Casework Team: Jim Watts 020-7035 3662
Personal Secretary: Saira Morarji 020-7035 4892
Senior Executive Officer: Akile Osman 020-7035 1712
Senior Executive Officer: Kerry Adams 020-7035 3700
Senior Executive Officer: Lucy Derilo 020-7035 3710
Higher Executive Officer: Paul Walsh 020-7035 3603
Asst Officer: Marj Carnegie-Riley 020-7035 3713
Asst Officer: Nazima Baubony 020-7035 3708
Asst Officer (temp): Kam Flora 020-7035 3873
Asst Officer (temp): Bunmi Oyewumni 020-7035 3605
Asst Officer: Ryan Phelps 020-7035 3878
Asst Officer: Dannette Simpson 020-7035 3882
Asst Officer: Anu Mojid 020-7035 3883
Asst Officer: Laurence Cashman 020-7035 3598
Public Protection Advocate: Elizabeth Stokes 020-7035 3888
Executive Officer: Jas Bansal 020-7035 3728
Executive Officer: Gareth Hunter 020-7035 3727
Executive Officer: Jeff D'Cruz 020-7035 3600
Executive Officer (temp): Mendel Maass 020-7035 3604
Executive Officer (temp): Sodienye Jaja 020-7035 3602
fax 020 7035 0821

Executive Officer: Laura Gould 020-7035 3712
fax 0870 336 9134

Public Protection Advocate: Polly Gilbert 020-7035 3886
Public Protection Advocate: Susan Kelly 020-7035 3884/07920 213752
SEO Presenting Officer/Team Mgr: Nuzhat Razvi 020-7035 3714
HEO Public Protection Advocacy Team Officer Mgr: Sean Coles 020-7035 3715
HEO Public Protection Advocate: Michael Fox 020-7035 3885
HEO Public Protection Advocate: Zela Mulligan 020-7035 3883
HEO Public Protection Advocate: Celeste Myrie 020-7035 3886
Higher Executive Officer: Lesley Case 020-7035 3887
Higher Executive Officer: Amanda Smith 020-7035 3888
Executive Officer: Julie Dennis 020-7035 3721
Executive Officer: Ayo Adeosun 020-7035 3716
Executive Officer: Ann Carter 020-7035 3723

Executive Officer (temp): Selina Barker 020-7035 3718
Asst Officer: Gavin Harrison 020-7035 3722
Asst Officer: Karen Duke 020-7035 3720
Asst Officer: Nicola Priestley 020-7035 3721
fax 0870 336 9198

HEO: Eileen Drummond 020-7035 3877
Executive Officer: Charles Kapita 020-035 3719
Executive Officer: Shirley Hamilton 020-7035 3728
Executive Officer: Claire Nelson 020-7035 3737
Asst Officer: Kalbir Bains 020-7035 3729
Asst Officer: Christine Amoako 020-7035 3877
Asst Officer (temp): Lawrence Kirby 020-7035 3730
Asst Officer: Chris Hatzar 020-7035 3726
fax 0870 336 9199

Post Release Section: PPU Croydon
(NOMS Performance & Improvement Directorate)
7th Floor, AMP House, Dingwall Road, Croydon, CR0 2LX

Head of Casework Mgrs for Recall Teams: John Townley 020-8760 1749
HEO: Kim Fitzgerald 020-8774 0243
HEO: Christine Handley 020-8760 1856
Executive Officer: Emma Thompson 020-8774 0238
fax 0208 774 0244

Executive Officer: Lynn Thurgood 0208 760 1837
Executive Officer: Hayley Chalkley 020- 774 0226
Asst Officer: Candice Barholomeusz 020-8774 0265
Asst Officer: Claire McIlroy 020-8760 1859
Asst Officer: Verity Hayward 020-8774 0263
Asst Officer: Rebecca Almond 020-8774 0269
Asst Officer: Michael Strange 020-8760 1859
Asst Officer: David White 020-8760 1712
fax 0208 774 0268

HE Casework Mgr: Sarah Harold 020-8774 0264
Executive Officer: Daniel Bainbridge 020-8774 0227
Asst Officer: Zahida Brown 020-8760 1874
Asst Officer: Joanne McCormick 020-8774 0262
Asst Officer: Sue Theedam 0208 774 0267
Asst Officer: Iram Shahzad 020-8774 0274
Asst Officer: Nicholas Parkinson 020-8774 0261
Asst Officer: Lauren Hemstead 020-8774 0272
Asst Officer: Daniela Donatantonio 020-8774 0266
fax 020 8760 1766

Asst Officer: Nicola White 020-8774 0226

Asst Officer: Marcello Di Zenzo 020-8760 1713
Asst Officer: Jennifer Hutchinson 020-8760 1759
fax 0208 760 1746

HEO: Brigid Edwards 020-8774 0291
Asst Officer: Glenda Dennis 020-8774 0294
Asst Officer: Noor Din 020-8774 0296
Asst Officer: Nicola Mclean 020-8774 0293
Asst Officer: Rick Curum 020-8774 0293
fax 0208 774 0298

Executive Officer: Dee Nair 020-8760 1737
Asst Officer: Anieka Cummings 020-8760 1806
Asst Officer: Sulemana Yesufu
Asst Officer: Barbara Dow 020-8774 0221
Asst Officer: Vimbai Mauwa 020-8760 1847
Asst Officer: Chris Young
fax 0208 760 1849

Asst Officer: Victoria Okine 020-8760 1840
Asst Officer (temp): Lee-Ann De Villers 020-8760 1716
fax 0208 760 1840

Executive Officer: Shams Ahmed 020-8774 0228
Asst Officer: Mathew Edwards 020-8760 1794
Asst Officer: Gavin Henry 020-8774 0233
Asst Officer: Julie Brown 020-8760 1851
Asst Officer: Lynn Webb 020-8774 0273
Asst Officer: Keith Hood 020-8774 0234
Asst Officer: Vicki Goodburn 020-8774 0222
fax 0208 760 1729

SPO: Megan Jones 020-8760 1822
Asst Officer: Noami Cardinez 020-8774 0297
Asst Officer: Gareth Boon 020-8774 0240
Asst Officer: Tara-Marie Fennessey 020-8760 1787
Asst Officer: Andrew Martynski
fax 0208 760 7860

Corporate Support, Finance & Corporate Team
Gareth Boon 020-8774 0240
Kim Fitzgerald 020-8774 0243
Angela Fitzsimons 020-8774 0237
fax 0208 774 0244

Probation related NOMS Offender Information Services Unit
(NOMS Corporate Services Directorate)

Head of Operations: Paul Curley 020-7217 2824 / 07968 909 907
Personal Secretary: Pam Oakley 020-7217 8105

Contracts and Competitions Unit
Head of CCU ICT: Claire Henson 07973 701 555
OMNI Project Mgr: Mark Brett 020-7217 0802 / 07887 540 099

Contract Mgr: Samantha Madhoo 020-7217 5711
Commercial and Contracts: Mgr (Quantum): Stephen Percival 020-7217 8825
Commercial and Contracts: Mgr (Quantum): Ivan Stein 020-7217 6640 / 07968 909 045
Contract Mgr: Michael Taylor 020-7217 6089 / 07952 236 089
Commercial & Contracts Mgr: Richard Woodward 020-7217 6870
OMNI Contract Mgr: Peter Worth 020-7217 2166

OMNI Transformation
OMNI Transformation Mgr: Christopher Gray 07981 917 914
Security & Assistive Technology
Head of Security & AT (Probation): Bob Nicholls 020-7217 8062 / 07818 427 682
Natnl Info Security Adviser (Probation): Anna Cevidalli 020-7217 0671
Natnl Info Security Adviser (Probation): Stan Cook 07768 811 932
Assistive Technology Mgr: Trevor Roberts 020-7217 8023 / 07899 922 543
Assistive Technology Co-ordinator: David Quarmby 020-7217 8023 / 07736 087 019

Service Delivery: OMNI
OMNI Service Mgr: Cilay Turker 020-7217 0651 / 07748 906 867
Service Level Mgr: Amanda Rollison 020-7217 2824 / 07966 114 817
Data Mgr: Aida Bakalovic 020-7217 6415
Service Introduction Mgr: Alistair Brown 020-7217 8190 / 07766 781 615
Service Introduction Mgr: Sue Gravener 020-7217 6815 / 07968 907 726
Service Introduction Mgr: Brian Whitnall 020-7217 6894 / 07968 909 252
Service Introduction Supt: Steve Palmer 020-7217 8785 / 07921 785 458
Service Level Mgr: Sharron Cumberbatch 020-7217 8662 / 07909 948 330
Service Delivery Supt Officer: Jane Hummerston 020-7217 0669

Service Support: Operations
Head of Service Support: David Pick 020-7217 8628 / 07884 113 681
RFS Mgr: Jim Brown 020-7217 8176 / 07956 278 416
Operational Projects Mgr: Dennis Chalk 020-7217 8441 / 07875 221 751
Service Mgr: Tony Smalley 020-7217 0778 / 07772 560 263
OMNI Service Mgr: Tony Fisher 020-7217 6804 / 07973 457 344

Service Mgr: Mus Ali 020-7217 0665 / 07917 081 797
Change & Release Mgr: Nick Dowsett 020-7217 5767 / 0780 509 765
Head of Probation Case Management Systems: Ken Ades 020-7217 8193 / 07803 269 283
IT Administrator: Darren Faulkner 020-7217 8939 / 07971 766 665
Executive Officer: Gerard Parry 020-7217 0613 / 07726 833 193
Executive Officer: Edward Cummins 020-7217 5767

NOMSNet
NOMSNet Administrator: Derrick Horslen 020-7217 1043 / 07966 114 638

OASys
OASys Service Mgr: Mike Barrett 020-7217 6816 / 07970 242 308
OASys Service Mgr: Kate Negus 020-7217 6535 / 07973 457 403
fax 020 7217 0663

General Property
Home Office Property-General, 2 Marsham Street, London SW1P 4DF

Accommodation Help Desk 0871 641 2135

Head of Unit: Tony Edwards
Secretary to Head of Unit: Suzanne Sheldon
For further assistance consult relevant Facilities Delivery Team:

Head of Facilities Delivery Teams National: Steve Evans

Facilities Delivery: London and Anglia region
GeneralPropertyLondonEstate@homeoffice.gsi.gov.uk.
Responsible for London, Suffolk, Cambridgeshire, Essex, Hampshire, Hertfordshire, Leicestershire, Norfolk.

Facilities Delivery: North East region
facilitiesdeliverynortheast@homeoffice.gsi.gov.uk
Responsible for Cheshire, County Durham, Cumbria, Gtr Manchester, Lancashire, Merseyside, Northumbria, Teeside, West Yorkshire, North Yorkshire, South Yorkshire.

Facilities Delivery: North West
hogeneralpropertynw@homeoffice.gsi.gov.uk
Responsible for: Bedfordshire, Cambridgeshire, Derbyshire, Humberside, Leicestershire & Rutland, Lincolnshire, Norfolk, Nottinghamshire, Northamptonshire, Suffolk.

Facilities Delivery Wales & South West region
facilitiesdelivery@homeoffice.gsi.gov.uk
Responsible for West Midlands & Wiltshire, Warwickshire, Dorset, Devon & Cornwall, Dyfed Powys, Avon, Somerset, Gloucestershire, South Wales, Gwent, West Mercia.

Programme Delivery & Estates Management
Head of Programmes and Estates: David Laurence

Programme Delivery
Programme Delivery Mgr: John Morgan 020-7035 0164 /7850 760 707
(Projects in London, East & South East)
Programme Delivery Mgr: Jon Windass 07768 708 965 (Projects in the North).
Programme Delivery Mgr: Fred Fairclough 020-7035 0163 /7850 760 707
(Projects in the West of England and Midlands).

Estates Management
Estate Surveyor: Ian Nicolas
Responsible for: Properties in all counties/areas of England and Wales.

Sustainable Development
Sustainable Development: Julia Wright/Eileen Aldridge 020-7035 0157

Planning
Email: HOPGPlanning@homeoffice.gsi.gov.uk
Head of Team: Denis Hassett
Accountant: Edith Egbuna
HOPG Health and Safety
Health and Safety advisor: Bill Wood 07713 214850

Probation Finance Team
(NOMS Corporate Services Directorate)

For all enquires please contact Lalita Shah on the helpdesk number 020-7035 0803
or email:npd.finance@homeoffice.gsi.gov.uk

Assisted Prison Visits Scheme

PO Box 2152, Birmingham, B15 1SD

Public enquiries 0845 3001423 (10.15 to 11.45 & 14.15 to 15.45, Monday to Friday)
Textphone 0845 3040800 (for people with hearing difficulties)
Application forms 0121626 2206

Head of Unit: Alan Jones 0121-626 2208
Team leaders: 0121-626 2740

e-mail: assisted.prison.visits@hmps.gsi.gov.uk

Information available at www.hmprisonservice.
gov.uk

Prisoner Location Service

PO Box 2152, Birmingham B15 1SD

Prisoner location enquiries *fax 0121-626 3474*
Probation enquiries 0121-626 2742 (24 hour
answer machine)
Public enquiries 0121-626 2773 (24 hour
answer machine)

Team leader 0121-626 3331

e-mail: prisoner.location.service@hmps.gsi.gov.uk
Information available at www.hmprisonservice.gov.uk

Victim Helpline

NOMS Victim Helpline, PO Box 4278,
Birmingham B15 1SA
tel 08457 585112 Monday to Friday 9am to 4pm
(24 hour answer machine at other times)
Team leader 0121-626 3331
Information available at www.hmprisonservice.gov.uk

HER MAJESTY'S INSPECTORATE OF PROBATION

Functions

HM Inspectorate of Probation is an independent
inspectorate funded by the Ministry of Justice
and reporting directly to the Secretary of
State. HM Inspectorate of Probation's aims
are to report to the Secretary of State on
the effectiveness of work with individual
offenders, children and young people aimed
at reducing reoffending and protecting the
public; to contribute to improved performance
by the organisations whose work we inspect;
to contribute to sound policy and effective
service delivery, especially in public protection,
by providing advice and disseminating good
practice; to promote actively race equality and
wider diversity issues; and to contribute to the
overall effectiveness of the Criminal Justice
System, particularly through joint work with
other inspectorates.

HM Inspectorate of Probation is based in two
locations, in London and Manchester, at the
addresses indicated below. London staff are
listed together with their extension number.
Staff based in Manchester are indicated by
'mcr', and the main Manchester number, as

below should be used for contacting them.

London
2nd Floor, Ashley House, 2 Monck Street,
London SW1P 2BQ
enquiries 020-7035 2202 *fax 020-7035 2237*
enquiries about reports 020-7035 2207
Staff - 020-7035 + ext

Manchester
6th Floor, Trafford House, Chester Road,
Stretford, Manchester M32 0RS
0161-869 1300 *fax 0161-869 1350*

General enquiries to HMIP.enquiries@
hmiprobation.gsi.gov.uk
website: htpp://www.inspectorates.justice.gov.
uk/hmiprobation/

Staff
HM Chief Inspector of Probation:
Andrew Bridges ext 2200
Personal Secretary: Ann Hurren ext 2202

Assistant Chief Inspectors
YOT Inspection Programme: Julie Fox mcr
Alan MacDonald mcr

Offender Mngmnt Inspection Prog:
Krystyna Findley ext 2234
Joint Inspection Programme: Liz Calderbank
mcr
Support Services & Devpt: Peter Ramell ext
2233

Inspectors
Jane Attwood mcr
Helen Boocock mcr
Mark Boother ext 2222
Rose Burgess ext 2213
Lisa McDowell ext 2214
Sandra Fieldhouse mcr

Jude Holland mcr
Sally Lester mcr
Ian Menary mcr
Joy Neary mcr
Anthony Rolley ext 2225
Nigel Scarff ext 2217
Joe Simpson ext 2219
Andy Smith ext 2218
Ray Wegrzyn mcr
Steve Woodgate mcr
Yvonne McGuckian mcr
Les Smith ext 2215

Practice Assessors
Stephen Hubbard mcr
Sarah Ashworth mcr

Inspection Support
Programme Manager: Andy Bonny mcr

Services Delivery Mgr: Lynn Carroll mcr
Inspection Supt Mgr: Rob Turner mcr
Inspection Supt Officer: Pippa Bennett mcr
Inspection Supt Officer: Maura O'Brien mcr
Inspection Supt Officer: Andy Doyle mcr
Publications & Manchester Office Mgr:
Alex Pentecost mcr
Proof Reader: Debbie Hewitt mcr
Information Manager: Kevin Ball mcr
Asst Information Manager: Oliver Kenton mcr
Finance & London Office Mgr: Charles Luis ext
2208
Finance Supt Officer: Nicholas Channell ext
2209
Information Asst: Paul Cockburn ext 2207

REGIONAL TRAINING CONSORTIA

1. **East of England Probation Training & Development Consortium**
   Crowland House, Withersfield Road,
   Haverhill, Suffolk CB9 9LA
   tel (01440) 705875 *fax (01440) 761399*
   e-mail firstname.surname@essex.
   probation.gsi.gov.uk

   Dermot McCarthy (director)
   Elizabeth Morgan (learning & devpt mgr)
   Vacancy (learning & devpt mgr)
   Michael Butcher (eff pract training mgr)
   Graham Fitchett (regnl trainer)
   James Jasper (regnl trainer)
   Nikki Middleton (regnl trainer)
   Janeen Sengendo (regnl trainer)
   Lesley Kibble (admin)
   Vacancy (admin)
   Charmian Thompson (admin)
   Emma Wright (admin)

2. **London Probation Regional Training Consortium**
   Mitre House, 223-237 Borough High St
   London SE1 1JD
   tel 020 7740 8500 *fax 020 7740 8448*
   e-mail firstname.surname@
   london.probation.gsi.gov.uk

   Pagan, Tim (director) 020-7740 8513
   Coleman, Judy (exec asst)
   020-7740 8505 *fax 020-7740 8447*

   Idusohan, Vicki (HRD mgr, NVQ
   centre & PSO training) 8527
   Jones, Mike (HRD mgr, qual
   training) 8533
   Anderson, Delise (HRD mgr,

learning & devpt) 8512
Duke, Michaela (HRD mgr,
effective practice) 8588
Kelly, Andrea (HRD mgr,
IT training) 8565
Bixby, Kay (HRD mgr, admin) 8506

Devpt & Assessment Centre
Sayeed-Hussain, Nushrat (NVQ centre
quality assurance co-ord) 8561
Horlock, Jo (snr IV/staff trainer) 8562
LSW/trainers
Epie, Pat 8568
Felgate, Cheryl 8568
Lynch, Peggy 8568
Raison, Peter 8569
Ramsey, Joanne 8567
PSO trainer/assessors
Agdomar, Lisa 8567
Kelly, Steve 8567
Power, Julie 8567
Purryag, Sharmila 8567

Qualifying Training
Pilinski, Krystyna (PDA mgr) 8545
Smith, Keith (PDA mgr) 8553
Wheeler, Graham (PDA mgr) 8521
Whittaker, Anne-Marrie (peri PDA) 8552

Management & Admin, Staff Devpt
Learning & Development Advisers
Cives-Enriquez, Rosa-Maria 8546
Harris, Laurice 8524
Koch, Shula 8511
Read, Jan 8531

Effective Practice
Forbes, David (OASys training mgr) 8542
Reilly, Sigrun (MAPPA, OASys &
risk training mgr) 8504
Crews, Ray (OASys trainer) 8554
EP trainer/developers
Edmead, John 8452
Granata, Judith 8456
Hosegood, Claire 8452
Subherwal, Navinder 8455

Admin
fax 0207 740 8448
Carcavella, Susan (snr HRD admin) 8547
Flynn, Daniel (HRD admin) 8538
Rai, Pree (HRD admin) 8549
Stuart, Elizabeth (HRD admin) 8507
Leadbetter, Victoria (librarian) 8590

IT
*based at 71/73 Great Peter Street
London SW1P 2BN
fax 020-7960 1188
IT trainer/developers*

Kalembo, Masote 020-7960 1873
Morris, David 020-7960 1874
Reis, Siobhan 020-7960 1874
Spraggs, Andrew 020-7960 1873

3. **North East Probation Training
    & Development Consortium**
    c/o Northumbria Probation Area
    Dene House, Durham Road
    Low Fell, Gateshead NE9 5AE
    tel 0191-491 1693 *fax 0191-491 3726*

    Angus McIntosh (director)
    Mary E Smith (eff pract training mgr)
    Martyn Shakespeare (DipPS mgr)
    Peter Faill (nvq assessment centre mgr)
    Julie Peaden (co-ord)
    Dawn Shacklady (accred progs admin)
    Maria Burl (DipPS admin)
    e-mail firstname.secondname@
    northumbria.probation.gsi.gov.uk

4. **North West Training Consortium**
    Sefton House, 1 Molyneux Way
    Old Roan, Liverpool L10 2JA
    tel 0151-526 1346 *fax 0151-526 0692*
    e-mail firstname.surname@merseyside.
    probation.gsi.gov.uk

    Lesley Thompson (director)
    Julia Summerfield (rdac mgr)
    Irene Doyle (consortium admin)
    Peter Fright (learning & devpt manager)
    Jon Lear (regional L and D and ept mgr)
    Sushma Parmar (quality manager)
    sushma.parmar@manchester.probation.
    gsi.gov.uk
    Pam Whittaker (pda manager)
    pam.whittaker@lancashire.probation.gsi.gov.uk

5. **South East Regional Probation
    Training Consortium**
    College House, Woodbridge Road
    Guildford, Surrey GU1 4RS
    tel (01483) 304963 *fax (01483) 440601*

    Avtar Singh (director)
    Chas Smith (nvq centre mgr)
    Sally Barrett (effective pract training mgr)
    Naomi Claxton (learning & devpt mgr)
    Jill Tonks (pso devpt mgr)
    Peter Hilling (business mgr)
    Sandra Stevens (nvq/tpo co-ord)
    Jenny Pullen (accredited progs co-ord)
    Helen Holdaway (pso/accredited progs
    co-ord)

6. **South West Training Consortium**
    c/o Gloucestershire Probation Area
    Oakes House, 55-57 London Road
    Gloucester GL1 3HF
    tel (01452) 551221 *fax (01452) 551210*

    Martin Smith (director)
    Gill Steadman (admin)

    NVQ Centre
    c/o Avon & Somerset Probation Area
    The Old Convent, 35 Pulteney Road
    Bath BA2 4JE
    tel (01225) 324965 *fax (01225) 324979*

    Jane McLaughlin (qualifications L&D mgr)
    mobile 07891 475398
    e-mail jane.mclaughlin@avon-somerset.
    probation.gsi.gov.uk
    Geunor Taverner (nvq centre mgr)
    mobile 0794 152 3377
    e-mail gtaverner@yahoo.com
    or geunor.taverner@gloucestershire.
    probation.gsi.gov.uk
    Helen Spurrell (admin)

    Effective Practice Training
    c/o Dorset Probation Area HQ
    Forelle House, Marshes End
    Upton Road, Creekmoor, Poole
    Dorset BH17 7AG

    Barry Cooney (eff pract training mgr)
    tel (01202) 664089 mobile 07813 715 519
    Wendy Towers (admin)
    tel (01202) 664088 *fax (01202) 664061*

    Liz Playle (regional training officer)
    mobile 07859 391791
    email: liz.playle@devon-cornwall.
    probation.gsi.gov.uk

7. **Midlands Consortium
    Lichfield**
    Stowe Court, Stowe Street, Lichfield
    Staffs WS13 6AQ
    tel (01543) 416776 *fax (01543) 419361*
    e-mail firstname.surname@staffordshire.
    probation.gsi.gov.uk

    Ian Macnair (director)
    Ellen Wallace (ops mgr)
    Joanna Bell (eff pract trg mgr east)
    John Richards (eff pract trg mgr west)
    Dawn Bakewell (office mgr)
    Natalie Ryan (rgnl trg off eff pract)
    Natalie Cole (pa)
    Hannah Barrett (admin off acc progs)
    Laura Grose (admin off acc progs)
    Natalie Noon (admin ass acc progs)
    Jane Cook (finance & clerical off)

Lesley Rawlinson (clerical off)

Atherstone
1 Market Street, Atherstone, Warks CV9
1ET
tel (01827) 713813 *fax (01827) 718677*
e-mail firstname.surname@warwickshire.
probation.gsi.gov.uk

Michelle Walters (learning & devpt mgr
qual trg)
Eve Brown (learning & devpt mgr voc
awards)
Alan Clark (learning & devpt mgr qual trg)
Sally Cherry (learning & devpt mgr man
dev)
Rob Hodgson (rgnl trg off)
Brendon Flint (rgnl trg off)
Sheelah Carpenter (rgnl trg off)
Elaine Blewitt (admin off learning & devpt)
Sarah Walker (admin off learning & devpt)
Maureen Nicholls (admin off man devpt)

8. **Yorkshire & Humberside Consortium**
    2nd Floor, Devonshire House
    38 York Place, Leeds LS1 2ED
    tel 0113-244 6044 *fax 0113-245 1394*
    e-mail yhpcgen@yhpc.co.uk

    Steve Cosgrove (consortium director)
    Roger Geeson (learning & devpt mgr)
    Sue Lawson (learning supt mgr)
    David Atkinson (eff pract training mgr)
    Phil Clare (DipPS progr mgr)
    Nicola Woodward (office mgr)
    Janet Marchant (admin)
    Janette Ridsdale (admin)
    Claire Beier (nvq admin)

9. **Wales Training Consortium**
    Consortium Hyfforddiant Cymru
    4-7 The Broadway, Pontypridd CF37 1BA
    tel (01443) 494333 *fax (01443) 494285*
    e-mail firstname.surname@south-wales.
    probation.gsi.gov.uk

    Julia Attwell (consortium director)
    Jackie Leggett (hrd mgr)
    Nigel Miller (eff pract training mgr)
    Rob Thomas (qualifications mgr)
    Ceinwen Gwilyn (rto qualifications)
    Sheryn Anthony (rto hrd)
    Lyn Fox (rto ept)
    Kairen West (office mgr)
    Chris Metcalfe (admin)
    Huw Price (admin)
    Cara Chapman (admin)
    Janet Humphreys (admin)
    Sarah Smith (finance admin)

CIRCLES OF SUPPORT AND ACCOUNTABILITY

Circles of Support and Accountability (Circles)
are a highly effective community contribution
to reducing re-offending by medium to high
risk sex offenders living in our communities.
Volunteers are recruited, trained and supervised
to support, monitor and maintain these men
and women, helping to reduce emotional
loneliness and isolation. Working in partnership
with Police, Probation and the Prison Service
there are now a number of Circles Projects
established around England and Wales. The
umbrella organisation, Circles UK, was
launched in 2008, and is an authorised service
provider to the Ministry of Justice supporting
the development of local projects and working
to ensure consistency of national standards
across England and Wales.

1. **Head Office**
    Circles UK
    1 St Giles Court
    Southampton Street, Reading RG12QL
    tel 0118-950 0068 *fax 0118-950 0064*
    info@circles-uk.org.uk
    www.circles-uk.org.uk
    e-mail: firstname.lastname@circles-uk.org.uk

    Hanvey, Stephen (chief executive officer)
    Wilson, Chris (national devpt mgr)
    Langford, Cara (national support officer)
    Curnow, Heather (office mgr)

2. **Devon & Cornwall Circles**
    c/o NSPCC, Devon Child Protection
    Centre
    Brunswick House, 1 Brunswick Road
    Cattedown, Plymouth PL4 0NP
    tel (01752) 235120 *fax (01752) 235125*

    Stephenson, Jamie (circles co-ord)
    jamiestephenson@NSPCC.org.uk

3. **Greater Manchester Circles**
    c/o Greater Manchester Probation Area
    Oakland House, Talbot Road
    Manchester M16 0PQ
    tel 0161 -872 4802 *fax 0161-872 3483*

    Phillips, Annette (circles co-ord)
    annette.phillips@manchester.probation.
    gsi.gov.uk

4. **Hampshire & Thames Valley Circles**
    Ridgeway House, 1A Hagbourne Road
    Didcot OX11 8ER

tel (01235) 816050 *fax (01235) 517873*
firstname.lastname@htvcircles.org.uk

Saunders, Becky (chief executive)
Macrae, Ron (circles co-ord)
Williams, Dom (circles co-ord)
Webb, Carrie (circles co-ord)
Holmes, Anne (office mgr)

5. **Leicestershire Circles**
    Leicestershire Probation Area
    The Probation Centre, 2 Cobden Street
    Leicester LE1 2LB
    tel 0116-2620400 *fax 0116-253 0819*

    Looby, Clair (circles co-ord)
    clair.looby@leicestershire.probation.gsi.gov.uk

6. **Lucy Faithfull Foundation**
    Wolvercote Centre, 46 - 48 East Street
    Epsom, Surrey KT17 1HB
    tel 0870 774 6354 *fax (01372) 847162*
    tlffwol@lucyfaithfull.org.uk

    Sauze, Simon (progrs mgr)
    ssauze@lucyfaithfull.org.uk
    Parrott, Blair (circles co-ord)
    bparrot@lucyfaithfull.org.uk

7. **North Yorkshire Circles**
    c/o North Yorkshire Probation Area
    Union Lane, Selby YO8 4AU
    tel (01757) 707241 *fax (01757) 213911*

    Powell, Anne (circles co-ord)
    ann.powell@north-yorkshire.probation.
    gsi.gov.uk

8. **North Wales Circles**
    c/o North Wales Probation Area
    Plas y Wern (Approved Premises)
    Llangollen Road, Ruabon
    Wrexham, LL14 6RN
    tel (01978) 814949 *fax (01978) 810435*

    Ennis, Juliet (project devpt mgr)
    juliet.ennis@north-wales.probation.gsi.gov.uk

OFFENDER MANAGEMENT AND SENTENCING – ANALYTICAL SERVICE (OMS AS)

2nd Floor Fry Building, 2 Marsham Street, London SW1P 4DF

Head of Unit (Assistant Director): Dr Chloë Chitty 020-7035 3421

OMS Research Programme
Programme Director:
Programme Director: Dr Nisha de Silva 020-7035 3485

Heads of Sections/Teams:
Reducing Re-Offending Research: Robin Elliott-Marshall/David Brown (Joint Heads of Section) 020-7035 3423/3439
Public Protection Research: Charlotte Allen 020-7035 3422

OMS Strategy and Regulation Programme
Programme Director:
Programme Director: Dr Gemma Harper 020-7035 3414

Heads of Sections/Teams:
Regulation: Vacant
Economic Adviser: Andy Healey 020-7035 3480
Strategic Research/Analysis: Rachel Walmsley 020-7035 3440

OMS Sentencing, Prison and Probation Statistics Programme
Programme Director: Pat Dowdeswell 020-7035 3454

Heads of Sections/Teams
Prison & Probation Statistics: Jo Peacock/Vacant (Joint Heads of Section) 020-7035 3413/3455
Sentencing Statistics & NOMS Projections: Paul Cowell 020-7035 3464
MoJ Modeling & Cross Cutting: Vincent Chinegwundoh 020 7035 3453

OMS Re-offending and Criminal Career Statistics Programme
Programme Director: Ian Knowles 020-7035 8385

Heads of Sections/Teams
Reconviction Analysis: Mike Cornish 020-7035 3467
Reconviction Analysis: Vacant (Joint Head of Section)

PRISONS AND PROBATION OMBUDSMAN

Ashley House, 2 Monck Street, London SW1P 2BQ
020-7035 2876 fax 020-7035 2860
e-mail mail@ppo.gsi.gov.uk

Function
To provide independent investigation of complaints from all prisoners, those subject to community penalties, those who have reports written on them by the National Probation

Service, and those in immigration detention, who have failed to obtain complete satisfaction through the internal complaints systems of the Prison, Probation and Immigration Services, and to make recommendations to those services to help resolve justified complaints.

To investigate the circumstances of the deaths of prisoners, residents in NPS approved premises and those held in immigration detention or under UKBA managed escort.

Staff

Prisons & Probation Ombudsman: Stephen Shaw 020-7035 2851

Snr Personal Secretary: Jennifer Buck 020-7035 2851

Deputy Ombudsman: Rhian Evans 020-7035 2834 (shared line)

Deputy Ombudsman: Tony Hall 020-7035 2040

Deputy Ombudsman: Jane Webb 020-7035 2154 or 07766 422297 (mobile)

Acting Deputy Ombudsman: Ali McMurray 020-7035 2869

Personal Secretary: Janet Jenkins 020-7035 2282

Asst Ombudsman: Louise Baker 020-7035 2272

Asst Ombudsman: John Cullinane 020-7035 2279 (shared line)

Asst Ombudsman: Vacancy 020-7035 2881

Asst Ombudsman: Gordon Morrison 020-7035 2702 or 07827 369786 (mobile)

Asst Ombudsman: Olivia Morrison-Lyons 020-7035 2870

Asst Ombudsman: Colleen Munro 020-7035 2846

Asst Ombudsman: Thea Walton 020-7035 2835

Asst Ombudsman: Nick Woodhead 020-7035 2865

Head of HR & Business Devpt: Caroline Smith 020-7035 2845

Head of Central Services: Eileen Mannion 020-7035 2836

Senior Research Officer: Sue Gauge 020-7035 2834 (shared line)

Information Manager: John Maggi 020-7035 2854

Asst Information Manager: Jay Mehta 020-7035 2852

Finance Manager: Geoff Hubbard 020-7035 2855

Finance Officer: Mark Chawner 020-7035 2825

Requisitions Officer: Samantha Torrington 020-7035 2885

Investigators

Christina Arsalides 020-7035 2872

Terry Ashley 020-7035 2878

Tamara Bild 020-7035 2941

David Cameron 020-7035 2035

Karen Chin 020-7035 2837

Steve Clarke 07717 747979 (mobile)

Althea Clarke-Ramsey 020-7035 2858

Paul Cotton 020 7035 2838

James Crean 020-7035-2152

Lorenzo Delgaudio 020-7035 2832

Rob Del-Greco 020-7035 2278

Susannah Eagle 020 7035 2705 (shared line)

Angie Folkes 020-7035 2831

Andrew Fraser 020-7035 2887

Ann Gilbert 020-7035 2157

Kevin Gilzean 020-7035 2726

Alan Green 020-7035 2164

Natasha Griffiths 020-7035-2862

Helena Hanson 020-7035 2853

Diane Henderson 020-7035 2701

Ruth Houston 020-7035 2286

Sarah Hughes 020-7035 2153

Joanna Hurst 020-7035 2041

Karen Jewiss 020-7035 2034

Lisa Johnson 020-7035 2857

Mark Judd 020-7035 2844

Razna Khatun 020-7035 2829

Madeline Kuevi 020-7035 2886

Lisa Lambert 020-7035 2882

Anne Lund 020-7035 2863

Steve Lusted 020-7035 2242

Lisa Mcilfatrick 020-7035 2829

Steven McKenzie 020-7035 2155

Beverley McKenzie-Gayle 020-7035 2827

Kirsty Masterton 020-7035 2864

Tracey Mulholland 020-7035 2149

Anita Mulinder 020-7035 2879

Peter Nottage 020-7035 2833

Amanda O'Dwyer 020-7035 2868

Ben Rigby 07833 314048 (mobile)

Robin Shone 020-7035 2826

Anna Siraut 020-7035 2859

Amanda Steyn 020-7035 2283

Kevin Stroud 020-7035 2883

Rick Sturgeon 020-7035 2842

Anne Tanner 020-7035 2877

Jonathan Tickner 020-7035 2279 (shared line)

Steve Toyne 020-7035 2867

Ian Truffet 020-7035 2861

John Unwin 020-7035 2848

Louisa Watkins 020-7035 2821

Karl Williamson 020-7035 2843

Bryan Woodward 020-7035 2705 or 07798 581283 (mobile)

Saj Zafar 020-7035 2874

Senior Family Liaison Officer: Demelza Penberth 020-7035 2703

Family Liaison Officers:

Abbe Dixon 020-7035 2280
Joanne Howells 020-7035 2125
Jennifer Howse 020-7035 2704 or
07917 232068 (mobile)
Laura Stevenson 020-7035 2828

Admin Mgr (Fatal Incident Team): Mandy Edler
020-7035 2841
Admin Officers: David Gire-Mooring 020 7035
2839
David Kent 020-7035 2887
Tony Soroye 020-7035 2849
Laura Spargo 020-7035 2124
Transcriber/Typist: Durdana Ahmed 020-7035
2156
Esther Magaron: 020-7035 2706

Assessment Team
Head of Team: Anna Siraut 020-7035 2859
Veronica Beccles 020-7035 2840
Sarah Buttery 020-7035 2875
Antony Davies 020-7035 2043
Verna McLean 020-7035 2830
Ranjna Malik 020-7035 2884
Emma Marshall 020-7035 2871
Alison Stone 020-7035 2285
Melissa Thomas 020-7035 2797
Tracy Wright 020-7035 2856

PAROLE BOARD OF ENGLAND AND WALES

The Parole Board for England and Wales
Grenadier House, 99-105 Horseferry Road,
London, SW1P 2DX
tel 0845 251 2220 *fax 0845 251 2221*
DX: 155620, Victoria 17

Senior Management Team
Vacancy (chairman)
tel 020-7217 0582

Christine Glenn (chief exec)
tel 020-7217 0582
e-mail christine.glenn5@paroleboard.gsi.gov.uk

Sally Parkin (exec asst to chair & CEO)
tel 020-7217 0582
e-mail sally.parkin4@paroleboard.gsi.gov.uk

Senior Mgmnt Team fax 020-7217 0454

Sarah Lightfoot (director of performance &
devpt)
tel 020-7217 0152
e-mail sarah.lightfoot2@paroleboard.gsi.gov.uk

Martha Blom-Cooper (director of quality &
standards)
tel 020-7217 0563

e-mail Martha.Blom-Cooper@homeoffice.gsi.gov.uk

Terry McCarthy (head of casework)
tel 020-7217 0419
e-mail terry.mccarthy12@paroleboard.gsi.gov.uk

Peter Grant (head of operations)
tel 020-7217 0517
e-mail peter.grant24@paroleboard.gsi.gov.uk

Tim Morris (head of communications)
tel 020-7217 0564
e-mail tim.morris5@paroleboard.gsi.gov.uk

Paul Ketchley (training mgr)
tel 020-7217 0214
e-mail paul.ketchley@paroleboard.gsi.gov.uk

Pat Boshell (head of corp services)
tel 020-7217 0111
e-mail patrick.boshell3@paroleboard.gsi.gov.uk

Andy Cobbett (head of finance)
tel 020-7217 0240
e-mail andy.cobbett3@paroleboard.gsi.gov.uk

Casework Teams

Oral Hearings Team
Responsible for all casework relating to oral
hearings for life sentence prisoners, including
representations against recall.

Bernadette Beckett (team mgr)
tel 020-7217 0061
e-mail Bernadette.Beckett5@paroleboard.gsi.gov.uk

Suzie Goodman (team mgr)
tel 020-7217 0110
e-mail Susan.Goodman5@paroleboard.gsi.gov.uk

Oral Hearings Casework
tel 020-7217 0129/0201
fax 020-7217 0338

Oral Hearings Panel Advisors
tel 020-7217 0458/0038/0155/0507/0449/0489
/0566
fax 020-7217 0344

Paper Hearings Team
Responsible for all tasks relating to the
processing of determinate sentence cases
including checking dossiers, obtaining additional
paperwork and managing deferred cases.

Bhupinder (team mgr)
tel 020-7217 0203

Silvana (team mgr)
tel 020-7217 0034

Paper Hearings Administrative Support
tel 020-7217 0197/0198/0271/0209/0537/0549
fax 020-7217 0339

Representations Against Recall (RARE) Team

Responsible for arranging oral hearings to consider representations against recall from determinate sentence prisoners.

Martin Longley (team mgr)
tel 020-7217 0222
e-mail martin.longley3@paroleboard.gsi.gov.uk

Panel Administrators/Caseworkers
tel 020-7217 0191/0457/0185/0194/0193
fax 020-7217 0227

Post Panel Team

Responsible for all post-panel casework related to Parole Board decisions and recommendations, including judicial reviews complaints regarding decisions.

Vince Peters (team mgr)
tel 020-7217 0217
e-mail vincent.peters10@paroleboard.gsi.gov.uk

Post Panel Casework
tel 020-7217 0064/0174/0540/0436
fax 020-7217 0342

Listings Team

Responsible for the listing and rescheduling of all oral hearings and allocating members to panels

Angela Forbes (team mgr)
tel 020-7217 0106
e-mail angela.forbes3@paroleboard.gsi.gov.uk

Panel Listings
tel 020-7217 0521
fax 020-7217 0338

Cassie Histed (panel membership co-ord)
tel 020-7217 0187
fax 020-7217 0338
e-mail Catherine.Histed@paroleboard.gsi.gov.uk

Support Teams

Human Resources Team

Responsible for all human resources issues including secretariat staff recruitment, but not member recruitment.

Karen Simeon (team mgr)
tel 020-7217 0183
e-mail karen.simeon2@paroleboard.gsi.gov.uk

Finance Team

Responsible for financial management, including the payment of invoices, fees and expenses claims.

Andy Cobbett (head of finance - see above)

IT Team

Responsible for maintaining the Parole Board website, maintaining all databases and providing IT support to members and staff.

Jacob Asare (team mgr)
tel 020-7217 0579
e-mail jacob.asare4@paroleboard.gsi.gov.uk

Corporate Services Team

Responsible for corporate governance issues, supporting the Management Board, producing performance statistics and dealing with complaints.

Pat Boshell (head of corp services - see above)

THE OFFENDER HEALTH RESEARCH NETWORK

Hostel 1, Ashworth Hospital, Maghull, Merseyside L31 1HW

The Offender Health Research Network (OHRN) is a Department of Health funded initiative, led by the University of Manchester. It comprises a multi-disciplinary team of researchers with strong clinical and research credentials in offender healthcare.

The aim of the Network is to develop the infrastructure needed to sustain a programme of research and development across all criminal justice settings, based on the notion that offenders are entitled to services of equivalent scope and quality as those available to the wider population. Other organisations are actively encouraged to join OHRN and contribute to its work.

OHRN works to identify research and development priorities in offender health care, supporting researchers to undertake work to address gaps in knowledge and practice, thus improving service delivery.

OHRN has four main areas of work pertinent to offender health research: mental health, primary care, substance misuse, public health.

In addition to undertaking and supporting specific projects in these areas, OHRN works to:

a) establish discrete regional networks of clinicians, professionals and academics interested in undertaking offender health research;

b) outline clear pathways to successfully undertake research in offender health settings, incorporating considerations such as research quality, ethics and research governance.

c) maintain a website at www.ohrn.nhs.uk highlighting offender health care research and clinical best practice, detailing ongoing work, research findings, funding and training opportunities

d) host an annual national conference and other regional training events.

Contacts
Jenny Shaw (Academic Lead)
jenshaw@dsl.pipex.com

Jane Senior (Research Project Manager)
jane.senior@merseycare.nhs.uk

Angela Cookson (Administrator)
angela.cookson@merseycare.nhs.uk

telephone contact (general): 0151-471 2417

CAFCASS – CHILDREN AND FAMILY COURT ADVISORY & SUPPORT SERVICE

1. **Cafcass**
   6th Floor, Sanctuary Building
   Great Smith Street, London SW1P 3BT
   tel 0844 353 3350 *fax 0844 353 3351*
   e-mail webenquiries@cafcass.gov.uk
   www.cafcass.gov.uk

Regional Offices

N1 North & South of Tyne

2. **North of Tyne Office**
   3rd Floor, Parkview House
   Front Street, Benton
   Newcastle upon Tyne NE7 7TZ
   tel 0191-270 1897 *fax 0191 270 0363*

3. **South of Tyne Office**
   Haybourne House
   Cambell Park Road
   Hebburn, S Tyneside NE31 2SS
   tel 0191-483 4611 *fax 0191-428 4404*

N2 Teesside and Durham

4. 38 Saddler Street
   Durham DH1 3NU
   tel 0191-383 9279 *fax 0191-370 9741*

5. Alport House
   35 Old Elvet **Durham** DH1 3HN
   tel 0191-386 9426 *fax 0191-386 6211*

6. 2nd Floor, Prudential House

31-33 Albert Road
Middlesbrough TS1 1PE
tel (01642) 251555 *fax (01642) 211582*

N3 Lancashire and Cumbria

7. Capital Building, Hilltop Heights
   Carlisle CA1 2NS
   tel (01228) 549130 *fax (01228) 510911*

8. The Court House, Catherine Street
   Whitehaven CA28 7PA
   tel (01946) 62031/62544 *fax (01946) 69237*

9. 711 Cameron House
   White Cross, South Road
   Lancaster LA1 4XQ
   tel (01524) 586300 *fax (01524) 581455*

10. 241 Church Street
    Blackpool FY1 3PB
    tel (01253) 294780 *fax (01253) 292553*

11. 18 Winckley Square
    Preston PR1 3JJ
    tel (01772) 203999 *fax (01772) 204999*

12. St John's Court, Ainsworth Street
    Blackburn BB1 6AR
    tel (01254) 272450 *fax (01254) 677533*

N4 North & East Yorkshire & Humberside

13. 1 Westbourne Grove
    Scarborough YO11 2DJ
    tel (01723) 341083 *fax (01723) 341084*

14. 37 Fishergate
    York YO10 4AP
    tel (01904) 641488 *fax (01904) 651032*

15. The Deep Business Centre
    Hull HU1 4SA
    tel (01482) 388060 *fax (01482) 609212*

N5 West Yorkshire

16. 1 Park Cross Mews
    Park Cross Street **Leeds** LS1 2QH
    tel 0113-394 7474 *fax 0113-247 0929*

17. PO Box 92, Kenburgh House
    28a Manor Row **Bradford** BD1 4WR
    tel (01274) 386100 *fax (01274) 735019*

18. West House
    Hanover Street **Batley** WF1 5DZ
    tel (01924) 479066 *fax (01924) 442403*

19. Bull Ring House
    3rd Floor, 23 Northgate
    Wakefield WF1 3BJ
    tel (01924) 204410 *fax (01924)201855*

N6 South Yorkshire

20. 32 Park Street
     Wombwell **Barnsley** S73 0HF
     (01226) 754646 *fax (01226) 751297*

21. Kings Mews
     1 Frances Street **Doncaster** DN1 1JB
     tel (01302) 327202 *fax (01302) 349641*

22. Osborn House
     1/2 Highfield, Doncaster Road
     Rothertham S65 1EA
     tel (01709) 786200 *fax (01709) 839010*

23. 3 Dragoon Court
     Hillsborough Barracks
     Pennistone Road **Sheffield** S6 2GZ
     tel 0114-231 6119 *fax 0114-231 6120*

N7 Greater Manchester

24. 6th Floor, Byrom House
     Quay Street **Manchester** M3 3JD
     tel 0161-830 5720 fax *0161-835 2246*

25. 3 Great Moor Street
     Bolton BL1 1NS
     tel (01204) 370831 (private law)
     tel (01204) 548200 (public law)
     fax (01204) 382385

26. **Rochdale (public law)**
     91 Manchester Road
     Rochdale OL11 4JG
     tel (01706) 525774 *fax (01706) 347985*

27. **Rochdale (private law)**
     87/89 Manchester Road
     Rochdale OL11 4JG
     tel (01706) 341529 *fax (01706) 713527*

28. 1st Floor, Edward House
     Edward Street
     Stockport SK1 3DQ
     tel 0161-480 5450 *fax 0161-476 1522*

N8 Cheshire & Merseyside

29. 24 Lathom Road
     Southport PR9 0YZ
     tel (01704) 513880 *fax (01704) 513849*

30. 3rd Floor, State House
     Dale Street **Liverpool** L2 4TR
     tel 0151-224 8330 *fax 0151-236 5498*

31. 21/31 Barrow Street
     St Helens WA10 1RX
     tel (01744) 630245 *fax (01744) 630246*

32. Quattro House, Buttermarket Street
     Warrington WA1 2NL
     tel (01925) 428900 *fax (01925) 634829*

33. 55 Hoole Street
     Chester CH2 3NJ
     tel (01244) 348201 *fax (01244) 400427*

34. 10 Congleton Road
     Sandbach CW11 1WJ
     tel (01270) 760658 *fax (01270) 759462*

C1 Derbyshire Nottinghamshire

35. New Enterprise House
     St Helen's Street
     Derby Derbyshire DE1 3GY
     tel (01332) 290214 *fax (01332) 292268*

36. 5/7 Brimington Road
     Chesterfield S41 7UG
     tel (01246) 221082 *fax (01246) 278118*

37. Clumber House, 7 Clumber Street
     Mansfield NG18 1NU
     tel (01623) 466880 *fax (01623) 466881*

38. 2A Castlebridge Office Village
     Castle Marina Road
     Nottingham NG7 1TP
     0115-853 2500 *fax 0115-941 0929*

C2 Lincs, Cambridge, Herts & Beds

39. 2nd Floor, Hamilton House
     1/3 Clasketgate **Lincoln** LN2 1JG
     tel (01522) 580750 *fax (01522) 580751*

40. 71 London Road
     Peterborough PE2 9BB
     tel (01733) 312159 *fax (01733) 344138*

41. Southway
     290 London Road
     Bedford MK42 0PY
     tel (01234) 269274 *fax (01234) 261499*

42. 1st Floor, Cresta House
     Alma Street **Luton** LU1 2PU
     tel (01582) 735265

C3 Leics, Northants Warwickshire

43. Riverside House
     49 Western Boulevard
     Leicester LE2 7HN
     tel 0116-249 5600 *fax 0116-247 0175*

44. Greyfriars House
     2 Greyfriars Road **Coventry** CV1 3RY
     tel 02476 553601 *fax 02476 553408*

45. Newlands House, Campbell Square
     Northampton NN1 3EB
     tel (01604) 608000 *fax (01604) 608001*

C4 Staffordshire, Shropshire, Worcestershire, Herefordshire

46. 13 Hartshill Road
Stoke on Trent ST4 7QT
tel (01782) 747127 *fax (01782) 745106*

47. Marsh Court
Tillington **Stafford** ST16 2RE
tel (01785) 236260 *fax (01785) 236288*

48. Suite 3, Prospect House
Belle Vue Road
Belle Vue **Shrewsbury** SY3 7NR
tel (01743) 276080 *fax (01743) 276099*

49. Virginia House
The Butts **Worcester** WR1 3PZ
tel (01905) 723601 *fax (01905) 725855*

C5 Birmingham, Black Country, Solihull

50. 1 Printing House Street
Birmingham B4 6DE
tel 0121-710 1830 *fax 0121-710 1831*

51. 1st Floor, The Citadel
190 Corporation Street
Birmingham B4 6QD
tel 0121-248 6270 *fax 0121-248 6271*

52. Gough Street
Wolverhampton WV1 3LG
tel (01902) 576076 *fax (01902) 453304*

53. Midlands Road
Walsall WS1 3QE
tel (01922) 720665 *fax (01922) 746421*

C6 Norfolk, Suffolk, Essex

54. St Mary's House, 90 Victoria Road,
Chelmsford Essex CM1 1RD
tel (01245) 255600 *fax (01245) 505235*

55. St Clements House
St Clements Alley
Colegate **Norwich** NR3 1BQ
tel (01603) 226600 *fax (01603) 767920*

56. 6 Merchants Court
7a Foundation Street
Ipswich IP4 1BN
tel (01473) 236128 *fax (01473) 254193*

S1 Avon, Wiltshire, Gloucestershire, Somerset

57. Northgate House
19 London Road
Gloucester GL1 3HB
tel (01453) 311888 *fax (01452) 386474*

58. Units 1a & 1b, York House

Edison Park **Swindon** SN3 3RB
tel (01793) 612299 *fax (01793) 613399*

59. Unit 9 York Court
Wilder Street **Bristol** BS2 8QH
tel 0117-923 2070 *fax 0117-923 2075*

60. 35 Pulteney Road
Bath BA2 4JE
tel 0117-923 2070 *fax (01225) 335168*

63. 6 Mendip House
High Street **Taunton** TA1 3SX
tel (01823) 340224 *fax (01823) 323821*

S2 Thames Valley

64. Clyde House, 10 Milburn Avenue
Oldbrook **Milton Keynes** MK6 2WA
tel (01908) 359420 *fax (01908) 359421*

65. 1st Floor, 2 Cambridge Terrace
Oxford OX1 1TP
tel (01865) 728421 *fax (01865) 245938*

66. Glasson Centre
319 Oxford Road **Reading** RG30 1AU
tel (01189) 566322 *fax (01189) 502618*

67. 1st Floor, Regal Court
42/44 High Street **Slough** SL1 1EU
tel (01753) 215260 *fax (01753) 518588*

S3 Greater London

68. 1st Floor **55/65 Wells Street**
London W1A 3AE
tel 020-7255 1555 *fax 020-7255 1556*

69. 5th Floor, First Avenue
42/49 High Holborn London WCV1V 6NP
tel 020-7947 6054 *fax 020-7430 1232*

70. Academy House
75 High Street **Uxbridge** UB81JR
tel (01895) 251398 *fax (01895) 251299*

71. 13th Floor **Archway Tower**
2 Junction Road, London N19 5HQ
tel 020-7210 4100 *fax 020-7210 4129*

72. 2nd Floor, Charter House
450 High Road **Ilford** IG1 1UF
tel 020-8553 0535 *fax 020-8478 6031*

73. 3rd Floor, Carolyn House
22/26 Dingwall Road
Croydon CR0 9XF
tel 020-8603 2620 *fax 020-8681 1271*

74. 125 Richmond Road
Kingston upon Thames KT2 5BX
tel 020-8541 0233 *fax 020-8547 0915*

S4 Kent

75. 9 New Road Avenue
     Chatham ME4 6BB
     tel (01634) 815855 **fax (01634) 811262**

76. Lesser Knowlesthorpe
     Barton Mill Road **Canterbury** CT1 1BP
     tel (01227) 763263 *fax (01227) 763818*

S5 Sussex & Surrey

77. 2nd Floor, Blenheim House
     1/2 Bridge Street **Guildford** GU1 4RY
     tel(01483) 543300 *fax (01483) 543301*

77. Map House, 34/36 St Leonard's Road
     Eastbourne BN21 3UT
     tel (013323) 4331000 *fax (01323) 438647*

78. The Law Courts, Hurst Road
     Horsham RH12 2DE
     tel (01403) 265445 *fax (01403) 272903*

79. 38 Southgate
     Chichester PO19 1PD
     tel (01243) 531764 fax (01243) 531767

S6 Hants, Dorset, Isle of Wight

80. 1st Floor, Grosvenor House
     Basing View **Basingstoke** RG21 4HG
     tel (01256) 392770 *fax (01256) 392771*

81. Grove House, 7 Ocean Way
     Meridians Cross
     Southampton SO14 3TJ
     tel 02380 630996 *fax 02380 235597*

82. 30 Quay Street **Newport**
     Isle of Wight PO30 5BA
     tel (01983) 528867 *fax (01983) 528771*

83. The Law Courts, Hanham Road
     Wimbourne BH21 1AS
     tel (01202) 881416 *fax (01202) 840876*

84. 2 Poundbury Business Centre
     Poundbury DT1 3WA
     tel (01202) 881416 *fax (01305) 215929*

S7 Cornwall & Devon

85. Minerva House
     Pynes Hill **Exeter** EX2 5JL
     tel (01392) 354600 *fax (01392) 447369*

86. 8 Ford Park Lane
     Mutley **Plymouth** PL4 6RR
     tel (01752) 229124 *fax (01752) 254919*

87. 62 Fore Street
     Bodmin PL31 2HR
     tel (01208) 262900 *fax (01208) 269373*

88. Southview House
     Unit 2 St Austell Enterprise Park
     Carclaze Downs **St Austell** PL25 4EJ
     tel 0844 353 4920 *fax 0844 353 4921*

Wales

The functions of Cafcass in Wales are
functions of the Welsh Assembly.

TRAINING & CONSULTANCY ORGANISATIONS

Organisations that feel they should be included
in this section are invited to contact the
Editor. The descriptions included are those
of the organisations. The Editor accepts no
responsibility for any statements made in this
section nor for the violence sometimes inflicted
on the English language.

Skills for Justice

Head Office Centre Court, Atlas Way, Sheffield
S4 7QQ
0114-261 1499
email info@skillsforjustice.com
www.skillsforjustice.com

Wales Office 2 Court Road, Bridgend, Mid
Glam CF31 1BN
(01656) 750 133

Scotland Office 140 Causewayside, Edinburgh
EH9 1PR
0131-662 5234
Northern Ireland Office 7th Floor, 14 Great
Victoria Street, Belfast, BT2 7BA
02890 25 8028

Skills for Justice is the Sector Skills Council
covering all employers, employees and
volunteers working in the UK justice system.
This includes: community service; court
services; custodial care; policing and law
enforcement; prosecution services

Skills for Justice provides the support necessary
to enable the justice sector to identify its
current and future learning needs, to engage
more effectively with learning providers in
order to meet these needs with high quality
development programmes, and to link the
acquisition of learning to reputable and valuable
qualifications.

Ad Esse Consulting Ltd

St Paul's House, Warwick Lane, London EC4M 7BP
0844 8266162
email seriousfun@ad-esse.com *www.ad-esse.com*

Ad Esse's UK-wide scope covers the entire criminal justice system from top to bottom and from arrest through to resettlement. Its has delivered hundreds of Criminal Justice projects and working in partnership probation staff and managers. It aims to fit the tools used to the unique circumstances of each client. It will help you in delivering improvement, transferring skills to staff to ensure improvement is sustainable, year after year. 'You don't need yet another consultancy report, teams of consultants camped in your organisation, or performance which collapses when business drivers and priorities change. Join the rest of our clients and have some serious fun delivering sustainable improvement for your clients, stakeholders, shareholders and communities.'

BUSEC

Suite 2, Spain Buildings, 28 The Spain, Petersfield, Hants GU32 3LA
01730 710055 *fax 01730 710066*
e-mail admin@busec.co.uk *www.busec.co.uk*

Provides professional assessment as a route to Membership of the Chartered Institute of Personnel and Development (CIPD). This is specifically designed for personnel and training practitioners with at least five years middle/senior management experience and three years in HR. Candidates meet the CIPD professional standards by demonstrating practical application of competence through a variety of assessment methods. Professional assessment is an alternative to the academic, exam-based, route to membership.

Delivery of ILM endorsed programmes (e.g. recruitment and selection, employment law, performance management, and train the trainer). Also provides a range of NVQs. Busec has worked with a number of CJ agencies, including probation

Catherine Fuller Training & Development

Cop Castle, Bringsty Common, Worcs WR6 5UN
(01886) 821403 mobile 07805 803 133
e-mail catherine.fuller@talk21.com

Author of NPD Toolkit of Motivational Skills and trainer of national and European Union trainers and staff. 30 years experience in criminal justice agencies. Skills based, interactive training that values diversity. Specialising in motivational skills training including introductory training, group work, advanced motivational skills and coaching skills for staff development. Copies of the second edition of the Toolkit of Motivational Skills (2008) are also available providing a step by step approach to developing motivational skills and exercises to use with service users to build commitment and confidence to change stuck patterns of behaviour

The Centre for Public Innovation

32/36 Loman Street, London SE1 0EH
020-7922 7822 fax 020-7922 7821
e-mail info@publicinnovation.org.uk
www.publicinnovation.org.uk

The Centre for Public Innovation (CPI) is a social enterprise working to develop innovation, better performance and outcomes in health, social care and criminal justice. Its aim is to improve service outcomes for end users, in particular, end users from disadvantaged communities. It specialises in innovation and outcome management that is delivered through training and consultancy services.

Child Bereavement Charity

Aston House, High Street, West Wycombe, Bucks HP14 3AG
(01494) 446648 *fax (01494) 440057*
UK Info & Support line 01494 446648 (weekdays 9am-5pm)
e-mail enquiries@childbereavement.org.uk
www.childbereavement.org.uk

The Child Bereavement Charity (formerly The Child Bereavement Trust) provides support to families and professionals when a child dies or when a child is bereaved of someone important in their lives. Services offered include an information and support line, interactive website, resources and Professional Training Programme.

Paul Cooper Consultants Ltd

19 Mossley Hill Road, Mossley Hill, Liverpool L18 4PT
0151-724 4133 mobile 07734 108 753
e-mail paulcooper@radicalguru.co.uk

Specialises in the application of law to criminal

justice practice and management (compliance, enforcement, breach, court skills, witness skills, indeterminate detention (IPP's) lifers, oral hearings, Human Rights Act, Data Protection and new legislation and case law). Courses offered also include, Report Writing, Hate Crime, and Sentence Planning. Also specialises in the application of law and policy to the work of the Youth Offending Service. Offers comprehensive programmes of management development for middle managers and customised courses for senior managers that include performance management, change management, planning, leadership, recruitment and selection and discipline and capability. Customized management programmes may also be developed for charitable organizations. Accredited with the Open College Learning Network. E learning and web-based programmes can be developed to meet client needs.

Delight Training Services Ltd

19 Chestergate, Macclesfield, Cheshire SK11 6BX
0044 1625 421045, fax 0044 1625 42106
e-mail admin@delight.co.uk   *www.delight.co.uk*

Delight Training has fifteen years experience of working in criminal justice and forensic mental health across the UK and overseas. Has worked with every probation area in England and Wales, Social Services in Scotland, and prisons across the UK, in Scandinavia, and Australia. Work has involved significant national initiatives including the provision of a range of nationally accredited training programmes and associated staff and trainer training.

Delight Training is able to provide training and consultancy service across a wide range of generic delivery areas including, Motivational Interviewing, Groupwork Skills, and other Intervention skills for a range of staff including TPO, PSO, Management, and main-grade staff. Alongside this generic delivery is a continued commitment to both facilitator and management training across a range of accredited programmes including Think First, ASRO, and COVAID (alcohol and violence), the latter in close collaboration with Professor Mary McMurran.

Web-site includes a full range of available provision including areas of team development, team building, and management of change that have been core areas of Delight Training private sector delivery over the last 16 years.

Equality Works

London office Shepherdess Walk Buildings, 2 Underwood Row, London N1 7LQ 0207 251 4939
Manchester office 10th Floor, Bridgewater House, Whitworth Street, Manchester, M1 6LT 0161 200 8540
email info@equalityworks.co.uk
www.equalityworks.co.uk

A consultancy and training company specialising in integrating equalities into workplace learning and staff development. The approach is based on integrating a clear professional analysis of equalities and the way discrimination is embedded in organisations. Currently working with several probation areas, providing services including: core equalities training; recruitment and selection training; performance management training; impact assessment; facilitation; training for mentors of black and Asian offenders; and providing consultancy advice to senior management.

Forensic Psychology Practice Ltd

The Willows Clinic, 98 Sheffield Road, Boldmere, Sutton Coldfield B73 5HW
0121-377 6276 *fax 0121-377 6027*
email info@forensicpsychology.co.uk
www.forensicpsychology.co.uk

Provides forensic and clinical psychology expertise in direct work with clients or in support of statutory and voluntary agencies; advice, support, consultancy and training on all aspects of forensic and clinical psychology; specialist assessment and design and implementation of treatment programmes. Experienced in developing and running treatment programmes for sex offenders with learning disabilities in both health and criminal justice settings. Provides specialist training in working with sex offenders for practitioners in Probation and NHS settings; acts as consultant to National Probation Service in managing high risk offenders in the community; and currently contracted to provide Psychological Life Sentenced Prisoner Reports to HM Prison Service. Experienced in working with mentally disordered offenders and developing risk assessment protocols for private and criminal justice agencies.

GB Learning Consultancy

3 Basildon Close, Sutton, Surrey SM2 5QJ

0790 661 3081 or 0791 439 7701
email jim@gblearningconsultancy.co.uk or
mandy@gblearningconsultancy.co.uk
www.gblearningconsultancy.co.uk/contact

Specialist management, leadership, and learning
and development consultancy. Developers of
the Living Leadership Toolkit with an excellent
reputation for leadership and management
development in the public sector, including both
the NPS and NOMS. Specialists in the design of
open and e-learning materials.

Grey Cell Training Ltd

Cherrybrook, 12 Lakeside, Irthlingborough,
Northants NN9 5SW
phone & fax (01933) 653845
email enquiries@greycelltraining.co.uk
www.greycelltraining.co.uk

Grey Cell has provided strategy consultation
and generic training programmes for national
and local government customers for over
six years. Over 90 courses are offered,
targeted to reflect both the needs of the CJ
and local government systems and each
individual organisation. All grades of staff are
trained, with courses covering personal and
management development. Particular focus on
performance enhancement and improvement
through staff motivation. Courses include
Management Development Programme, Sex
Offender Awareness, Practitioner, PSO and
similar grade core programmes, Appraisal and
Supervision, Interviewing Skills and Report
Writing, Court Skills Training, many courses
based on Cognitive Behaviour principles, and
group and communication skills. All courses
compliant with NVQ competences and qualities
of excellence.. All courses compliant with Home
Office circulars and directives. Contact Susan
Rawden, Director.

Groupwork Consultation & Training Ltd

PO Box 363, Southsea, Hants PO4 0YP
phone/fax 02392 750030
email: simon@groupct.co.uk
www.groupworktraining.co.uk

Groupwork Consultation & Training Ltd
(GCT Ltd) is an accredited and established
National Groupwork Training Organisation
founded in 1987. It specialises in providing
theoretical and practical social group work
training to group work practitioners primarily
in the public sector: Probation Areas, Social
Service Departments, Health Authorities,

Drug Projects, and Voluntary Organisations.
Courses are held in London and in-house all
over the British Isles. They include Foundation,
Intermediate and Certificate level groupwork
courses. Also Two Day courses in Anger
Management and CBT. GCT Ltd is a Member of
the Institute for Learning and Development.

Grubb Institute

Cloudesley Street, London N1 0HU, 020-7278
8061 *fax 020-7278 0728*
e-mail info@grubb.org.uk *www.grubb.org.uk*

Works with leaders, managers and professionals
on role and institutional transformation, using
a systemic and group relations approach and
applied Christian theology. Offers consultancy,
development and learning opportunities in one-
to-one role consultation, teams and groups, and
whole systems. The Institute works across the
community in a range of organisations, and has
a track record within the criminal justice field.

HealthCV

3 Beckside Gardens, Huddersfield, W Yorks
HD5 8RS
0845 4601032 *fax (01484) 304614*
e-mail info@healthcv.com *www.healthcv.com*

Works with probation services providing
employee assistance programmes, health risk
screening and stress management courses. Also
specialises in employee well-being schemes,
stress audits, health profiles, ergonomics, risk
assessment, and relaxation techniques. Member
of International Stress Management Association
(Validated Trainer).

Ignition Creative Learning Ltd

21 Donald Street, Roath, Cardiff CF24 4TJ
0700 394 6217 *fax 029-2045 1823*
e-mail info@ignition-learn.com
www.ignition-learn.com

The company is a national and international
provider specialising in domestic violence
and abuse work. Ignition is outside consultant
to several probation areas running IDAP
and delivers essential staff supervision and
consultancy. The company also offers a range
of one-day practical training courses for IDAP
facilitators, 'Aspects of Excellence', which focus
on enhancing core practice, such as improved
conduct of critical dialogue or structuring skills
practise to develop non-abusive behaviours (in
session three of IDAP modules) meaningful

and effective. These courses are compliant with guidelines on programme integrity and treatment management. Ignition provides supervision for IDAP Women's Safety Workers and training for case managers on effective work with men sentenced to IDAP or otherwise showing evidence of domestic violence or abuse issues.

Linda Gast Training

Somersbourne House, 54 Somers Road, Malvern, Worcs WR14 1JB
tel/fax (01684) 564363
e-mail training@lindagast.co.uk
www.lindagast.co.uk

Leader of a very established training network working across the criminal justice sector. A proven track record in all aspects of diversity, particularly from a management perspective, offering up to date workshops and courses for working with Hate Crime Offenders. A continuing focus on 'people' skills; Performance Management, Supervision and Appraisal Skills and Sentence Planning and Objective Setting events are all offered with detailed handbooks to support the training. Also PSO training on how to deliver effective supervision using a cognitive behavioural framework. New for 2008: ILM Coaching and Mentoring Qualifications at levels 3, 5, and 7, offering an opportunity to enhance supervision skills leading to a nationally recognised qualification. Also ILM Management Qualifications at levels 3 and 5, along with training in a range of management issues. All events individually tailored to commissioners' requirements.

Link Training and Development

Oldacre House, Court Drive, Shenstone, Lichfield, Staffs WS14 0JG
tel (01543) 481884 mobile call David Shepherd on 07793 726227
email info@linktraining.co.uk
www.linktraining.co.uk

Link Training is a network of 3 established, independent trainers. All have experience of working in the probation service, helping to develop best practice, and recognise the value to customers of linking their knowledge and skills to deliver quality training. The workshops are focussed around the skills necessary for effective engagement with offenders, the courts, other services providers and meeting the new challenges of NOMS.

The practical application of models, research and ideas is encouraged and developed. The workshops will be tailor made to meet the varying skills development requirements of Offender Managers and Supervisors, Key Workers and Case Administrators.

Lucy Faithfull Foundation

Bordesley Hall, The Holloway, Alvechurch, Birmingham B48 7QA
tel (01527) 591922 *fax (01527) 591924*
e-mail bordesley@lucyfaithfull.org
www.lucyfaithfull.org

A national charity providing specialist assessment and treatment for sexual abusers of children, their families and victims. Provides consultancies and training to social service departments, probation and YOTs. Takes referrals from agencies, courts and solicitors (not from clients directly).

LMT Training and Consultancy

Ellaston House, Maenclochog, Pembrokeshire SA66 7LQ
(01437) 532888 *fax 05601 146100* Mobile: 077721 955216
e-mail info@lmt.uk.com *www.lmt.uk.com*

A well established provider of tailor made training, mentoring and consultancy for practitioners and managers working in the crime and disorder arena. Practice areas covered include: risk assessment and management; offence behavioural and cognition analysis; pro-social modelling; motivational enhancement; groupwork; diversity; cognitive behavioural methods. Management provision includes all aspects of staff, cultural and transition management and team building. The Pathway Plus programme is available for YOTs and other services working with young people. Refer to website for more information.

New Leaf Training and Counselling – Becky Wright

PO Box 4, Taunton, Somerset TA21 9FN
tel & fax (0759 0684888
email new.leaf@virgin.net *www.newleaf.uk.com*

A well established provider of anger and stress management services. Held a contract with Avon & Somerset Probation Area for many years providing post traumatic stress counselling. Now offers individual counselling and group work for those who have difficulty in managing anger and stress. Individuals can self refer to the service. MBACP (accredited) counsellor & UKRC registered independent counsellor. Has also delivered workshops within the prison system.

Risk Shifters

Ground Floor, 3 Westminster Court, Hipley Street, Old Woking , Surrey GU22 9LG
01932 351617 email mail@riskshifters.co.uk

A management consultancy providing support to regional and senior management teams Risk Shifters works with managers to assess the dangers from failing to manage the risks drugs and alcohol can present in the workplace and offers a range of ways to reduce them. Its services include, Risk Assessment, Policy Formulation, Driver Assessment and Training, Training in Alcohol Awareness and Drug Recognition, Help-line, counselling and rehabilitation, Drug and Alcohol Screening and Test Kits, Drug Test Management Services, Breathalysers, Alcohol Interlocks

The company's principal is a former Assistant Chief Officer with more than 15 years experience working at board level in probation, the NHS, the not-for-profit sector and the private sector.

Strategic People

Bank Chambers, 15 High Road, Byfleet, Surrey KT14 7QH
tel & fax 01189 771159
e-mail marylou.lousvet@strategicpeople.co.uk
www.strategicpeople.co.uk

Focuses on organisational change and activities to achieve successful change including: leadership development, flexible and mobile working, work life balance, planning for mergers and reorganisation, facilitated strategic planning workshops, leadership skills, management skills, team building, effective implementation of performance management and appraisal. Over 15 years experience of working with the probation service, CAFCASS and other public and private sector organisations. Specialist knowledge of public sector procurement and contract management, including service level arrangements.

Tavistock Centre for Couple Relationships

120 Belsize Lane, London NW3 5BA
020-8938 2353 *fax 020-7435 1080*

e-mail tccr@tccr.org.uk *www.tccr.org.uk*

Offers training and consultation services in the field of relationships. As well as training directly involved with couples, the Tavistock consult to managers and supervisors who work in agencies involved with family relationships. A course on 'Working with relationship breakdown' is run annually, as is 'Effective Staff Supervision'.

TMQ Consulting

6 North Street, Southminster, Essex, CM0 7DF
(01621) 772417 mob 0787 647 8691
e-mail Tom.McQuillan@btconnect.com
www.tmqconsulting.co.uk

Built upon substantial experience and expertise in probation and wider criminal justice senior management. TMQ Consulting is able to offer a comprehensive range of services that are tailored to meet the specific requirements of customers. Specialising in leadership & management development, team building, coaching & mentoring, and with an embedded emphasis on valuing diversity, services can be delivered across all organisational levels and roles.

Also provides particular expertise in business and organisational development, coupled with change management and business process engineering. These services can range from a single development event to a full organisational programme. Project and whole programme management is available, as is the undertaking of inquiries and investigations. TMQ Consulting works collaboratively with a range of other well established providers that enhances its ability to meet customer requirements.

TQMI Ltd

The Heath Business & Technical Park, Runcorn, Cheshire WA7 4QX.
(01928) 513171 *fax (01928) 513174* email info@ tqmi.co.uk *www.tqmi.co.uk*

A specialist improvement consultancy. Established in 1987 TQMI is an organisation of 20 people with a wide network of associates. Consultants located throughout the UK supported by central office staff at Runcorn. For nearly 21 years, has worked with organisations determined to improve their performance in the light of challenges facing them from customer expectations, technology, government, competition and cost effectiveness. Helps clients to bridge the performance gap between current and future aspirations by providing support that is relevant and appropriate. Has worked extensively over the last 8 years with Probation Areas and with the NPD. The projects include implementing and using the European Excellence Model, streamlining processes to generate time or cost savings and conducting research projects.

Tuklo Orenda Associates

55 Courtlands Avenue, Lee, London SE12 8JJ
020-8852 1207
e-mail info@tuklo.co.uk

Tuklo Orenda has been working with the Probation Service and other elements of the Criminal Justice System for 20 years. Their expertise and commitment lies particularly in the field of Diversity in the widest sense. They offer training, consultancy, mediation, conference organising, development of good practice guides and long term work with staff support groups. As well as training on the general understanding of diversity; they offer applied training for practitioners in such issues as Working with Asylum Seekers, Disability and Literacy. They are particularly interested in the relationship between Diversity and aspects of practice such as Motivational Interviewing, Programme Work and Unpaid Work. As well as offering courses for mixed groups of staff, they work with specialist groups such as YOTs, Unpaid Work, DTTO etc.

Charlie Watson Staff Development & Training

Mulberry Barn, Main Road, Stanton in Peak, Derbyshire DE4 2LW
tel/fax (01629) 636986 mobile 07739 468351
e-mail charlie.watson@virgin.net
www.offendermentoring.co.uk

Offers learning and development programmes in the criminal justice, voluntary and higher education sectors concentrating on: Interactional skills, involving engagement and motivation techniques; diversity; management development, including supervision and appraisal; presentation skills; groupwork; teambuilding; managing conflict; risk and public protection; academic delivery and placement supervision. NVQ assessor and verifier practice training. CJNTO endorsed.

ELECTRONIC MONITORING SERVICES

The Ministry of Justice contractors are responsible for the management and enforcement of Home Detention Curfew, Curfew Orders and other applications of electronic monitoring within the criminal justice system of England and Wales.

1. **Serco Home Affairs (Monitoring)**
    Austin House, Stannard Place,
    St Crispins Road, Norwich NR3 1YF
    tel (01603) 428300 fax (01603) 428311

    Terry Harris (contract director)
    Dave Weston (asst director field services)
    Andy Homer (asst director operations support, agency/customer liaison)
    Colin Flynn (finance & commercial mgr)
    Martin Elvin (asst director monitoring centre)

    Serco Home Affairs Monitoring Centre
    PO Box 45, Norwich, Norfolk NR3 1BF

    Monitoring Centre 24 Hours Helplines for all Enquiries regarding Electronic Monitoring for HDC, Court Orders, Bail, Immigration Monitoring, Tracking, Control Orders, Service Delivery Support (office hours): 08080 965124
    e-mail: sdo@serco-moniotring.com
    Legal Enquiries: 08080965124
    e-mail: breachdept@serco-monitoring.com

    London and Eastern
    tel 08080 965124 fax 08700 700321
    West Midlands and Wales
    tel 08080 152369 fax 08700 700321
    Secure e-mail neworders-amendments@ serco-monitoring.com.cjsm.net

    Field Regional Manager London & Eastern
    Roop Kalyan (01638) 554353

    Areas Covered
    Bedfordshire, Cambridgeshire, Essex, Hertfordshire, London (Metropolitan), Norfolk, Suffolk
    Field Service Managers London & Eastern
    East Anglia
    Alastair Read (01638) 554357

    North London
    Maggie Melvin 0208-364 4756

South London
Kevin Fleary 0208-668 9429

Regional Manager West Midlands & Wales
Rob Spear 02920 498520

Areas Covered
Dyfed-Powys, Gwent, North Wales, South Wales, Staffordshire. Warwickshire, West Mercia, West Midlands.

Field Service Managers West Midlands & Wales
North Wales
Derek Mosforth (01743) 465673

West Midlands
Dave Beech (acting mgr) 0121-236 5547

South Wales
Nick Doherty (02920) 491077

2. **G4S Care & Justice Services**
PO Box 170, Manchester, M41 7XZ
0161-862 1000 *fax 0161-749 9022/7620*
e-mail em.comms@uk.g4s.com

Richard Morris (director)
John Wheater (chief operations off)
Claire Sims (communications director)
Mark Preston (commercial director)
James Gill (business devpt director) 07841 966563

Communications Team
Helen Sanderson Walker (communications mgr, press enquiries)
Lindsay Frize (marketing mgr)

National Contacts
Julian Cross (business development mgr)
Stuart Featherstone (customer relationship mgr)

Notifications and Processing Department (National)
Contact for information and enquiries relating to new orders and variations to orders and licences
Secure email lpadmin@uk.g4s.com.cjsm.net
fax 0161-876 5331
Simon Fennell (NPT mgr)
0161-862 1700

Control Centre (National)
Contact for any general enquiries. Centre available 24 hours, 7 days a week
PO Box 170, Manchester, M41 7XZ
0161-862 1200 *fax 0161-749 8358* (24 hours)

Diane O'Brien (control centre mgr) 0161-862 1205

Operations (Branch Based)
For all operational enquiries relating to monitoring:
Contact Branch Mgr or Regional Operations Mgr

Customer Liaison Officers (Branch Based)
Contact for compliance reports, specific enquiries relating to individual subjects

Manchester Shirley Jones (branch mgr) 0161 864 6270
Graham Eadie (regional operations mgr) 0161 862 1200
Customer Liaison Officer e-mail
manchester.helpdesk@uk.g4s.com
CJ Areas: Greater Manchester; Cheshire

Rainford Phil Wilson (branch mgr) 01744 887120
Graham Eadie (regional operations mgr)
Customer Liaison Officer e-mail
rainford.helpdesk@uk.g4s.com
CJ Areas: Lancashire; Merseyside

Washington Christine Wright (branch mgr) 0191 416 9957
Graham Eadie (regional operations mgr)
Customer Liaison Officer e-mail
washington.helpdesk@uk.g4s.com
CJ Areas: Cleveland; Cumbria; Durham; Greater Humberside; Northumbria

Leeds Lisa Flynn (branch mgr) 0113 201 1200
Dee Hampson (regional operations mgr)
Customer Liaison Officer e-mail leeds.helpdesk@uk.g4s.com
CJ Areas: South Yorkshire; West Yorkshire

Nottingham Jude Woods (branch mgr) 0115 924 5855
Dee Hampson (regional operations mgr)
Customer Liaison Officer e-mail
nottingham.helpdesk@uk.g4s.com
CJ Areas: Derbyshire; Leicestershire; Lincolnshire; North Yorkshire; Northamptonshire; Nottinghamshire

Swindon Chris West (regional operations mgr) 01793 514646/544
Customer Liaison Officer e-mail
swindon.helpdesk@uk.g4s.com
CJAreas: Avon and Somerset; Devon and Cornwall; Dorset; Gloucestershire; Hampshire; Kent; Surrey; Sussex; Thames Valley; Wiltshire

Interagency Team (Regional)
Our field based Interagency Team

work with partner agencies to provide greater understanding of technology and applications of electronic monitoring. They are available to attend presentations, provide training sessions, demonstrate equipment and support agency events.

Natalie Chesney (07764 442 949) Cheshire, Greater Manchester, Derbyshire

John Coy (07739 777 418) Cumbria, Lancashire, Merseyside

Sharon Ballantine (07739 777 420) Northumbria, Durham, Isle of Man, North Yorkshire, Teesside

Tracy Eadie (07734 331 060) Humberside, West & South Yorkshire

John Simpson (07801 809 336) Leicestershire, Lincolnshire, Northamptonshire, Nottinghamshire

Paul Grainge (07841 966 572) Avon & Somerset, Devon & Cornwall, Gloucestershire, Jersey

Tristan Shaw (07841 965 921) Dorset, Hampshire, Isle of Wright, Thames Valley, Wiltshire

Andrea Jones (07841 969 280) Kent, Surrey, Sussex

Court Team (Regional)
For all queries relating to enforcement of single and multiple curfew requirements, contact the relevant Team Leader:

Alan Mercer (0161 864 6287) Greater Manchester, South Cheshire

Jason Whitehouse Strudwick (01744 889074) North Cheshire, Merseyside, Lancashire, South Cumbria

Angela Franciosi (0191 419 8158) Teeside, North Yorkshire, Humberside, Durham, North Cumbria, Northumbria

Steve Doyle (0113 201 1201) West Yorkshire, South Yorkshire

Aisha Haq (0115 985 8283) Leicestershire, Nottinghamshire, Derbyshire, Lincolnshire, Northamptonshire

Joanne Howard (01793 514 573) Avon and Somerset; Devon and Cornwall; Dorset; Gloucestershire;

Stuart Smith (01793 514 573) Hampshire; Kent; Surrey; Sussex; Thames Valley; Wiltshire

GLOSSARY OF COMMONLY USED ABBREVIATIONS AND SLANG

The following is a glossary of abbreviations and slang commonly used in the Probation and Prison Services. It is hoped that it will be of use to trainees and others struggling to understand contact records and referral forms. This glossary does not claim to be comprehensive. It has been compiled by the editor from his personal experience and with extra help from Terry Bond, Rod Pickin, Keith Norton and Angela Brown. Abbreviations particularly associated with NVQs, CRAMS or prisons are indicated, but there is obviously some cross over between categories. Any suggestions from colleagues will be gratefully received.

A1	assessor award (nvq)
AA	acceptable absence, Alcoholics Anonymous
ABH	actual bodily harm (or AOBH)
ACR	automatic conditional release (prison)
ADAs	additional days awarded (internal prison punishment)
AKA	also known as
AOBH	assault occasioning actual bodily harm (or ABH)
APD	approved parole date
APEL	accreditation of prior experience and learning (nvq)
ARD	automatic release date (prison)
ART	aggression reduction training
ASRO	addressing substance related offending (programme)
ASW	approved social worker (mental health)
AU or UA	unacceptable absence
AUR	automatic unconditional release (prison)
bilking	making off without payment
BWNB	bench warrant no bail
Br	breach (of order/licence)
C&G	City & Guilds (nvq)
CAR	cumulative assessment record (nvq)
CALM	controlling anger & learning to manage (programme)
CARATS	counselling, assessment, referral & throughcare services
CJ	community justice (nvq)
CJNTO	community justice national training organisation (nvq)
CM	case manager
CPS	Crown Prosecution Service
CPU	child protection unit
CRAMS	case recording and management system
CRD	conditional release date
CRN	client reference number
CRO	Community Rehabilitation Order (formerly Probation Order)
CSCP	cognitive self change programme
CS	community service (now unpaid work)
DCR	discretionary conditional release (prison)
Deps	depositions (witness statements)
D/H	dwelling house
DIDs	drink impaired drivers (programme)
Dipping	pick pocketing
DipSW	Diploma in Social Work
DLP	Discretionary Lifer Panel (prison)
DNA	did not attend
DO	duty officer
DoB	date of birth
DRR	Drug Rehabilitation Requirement
DTTO	Drug Treatment & Testing Order (now DRR)
DV	domestic violence
DWD	drive whilst disqualified
EDR	earliest date of release (prison)
EEM	European excellence model
ETS	enhanced thinking skills (programme)
ETE	education, training and employment
EV	external verifier (nvq)
F2050	code name for main prison file on prisoner
F2052SH	section of F2050 relating to self harm (prison)
F75	progress report on lifer (now obsolete) (prison)
FLED	facility licence eligibility date (in open prisons)
FTA	fail to attend
FTS	fail to surrender (to bail)
FWW	formal/final written warning
GBH	grievous bodily harm
GOAD	good order and discipline (prison)
HDC	home detention curfew (prison)
HDCED	home detention curfew eligibility date (prison)
HOC	Home Office circular
HV	home visit
IEP	integrated employability programme
IG54/94	prison service instruction relating to Schedule 1 offenders

IPP	intensive probation programme
IV	internal verifier (nvq)
kiting	issuing dud cheques
LDR	latest date of release (prison)
LED	licence expiry date (prison)
LIDS	local inmate database system (prison computer system)
LJA	Local Justice Area (formerly Petty Sessional Area)
LSP	life sentence plan (prison)
LSP3E	progress report on lifer (formerly F75) (prison)
MAPPP	multi agency public protection panel
MAPPPA	multi agency public protection panel arrangement
MALRAP	multi agency lifer risk assessment panel (prison)
MDT	mandatory drug test
MOWOP	make off without payment (bilking)
MPSO	Money Payments Supervision Order
NA	next appointment, not applicable
NAI	non accidental injury (to child)
NBW	bench warrant no bail (BWNB)
NEO	no evidence offered
NFA	no fixed abode
No DL	no driving licence
No Ins	no insurance
nonce	(offensive) prison term for sex offender
NPD	non parole date (prison)
NS	Home Office National Standards
OASys	offender assessment system
OCR	Oxford, Cambridge, Royal Society (nvq)
OGRS	offender group reconviction score
on the game	Prostitution
on the rule	prisoner segregated under Rule 43 (prison)
OPL	over the prescribed limit (drunk driving)
OV	office visit
Page 16	prison service version of contact sheet
PDA	practice development assessor
PDH	plea and directions hearing
PED	parole eligibility date (prison)
Perp	perpetrator of sexual offence
PH	preliminary hearing (Crown Court)
POA	Public Order Act, Prison Officer's Association
PPU	public protection unit
PSD	pre-sentence disclosure
PSI	prison service instruction

PSO	probation service officer, prison service order
PSO 4400	prison service instruction relating to child protection and harassment
PSR	pre-sentence report
RMIS	resource management information system
ROTL	release on temporary licence (home leave) (prison)
R & R	reasoning and rehabilitation (programme)
RTO	road traffic offence
Rule 43	prison rule enabling prisoner to request segregation for their own protection
Sch 1	offence listed in Schedule 1 1993 Children & Young Persons Act (a sexual or violent assault on a child)
SED	sentence expiry date (prison)
SEU	Sentence Enforcement Unit (Home Office)
SOTP	sex offender treatment programme
SPO	senior probation officer
SSSO	Suspended Sentence Supervision Order
SSR	specific sentence report
TC	telephone call/contact
TDA	take (motor vehicle) and drive away
TICs	offences taken into consideration
TOPs	Targeted Offenders Project
TPO	trainee probation officer
TWOC	take (motor vehicle) without owners consent
UAL	unlawfully at large (prison)
V1	verifier award (nvq)
VDT	voluntary drug test
VLO	victim liaison officer
VOU	victim offender unit
VP	vulnerable prisoner
Wt no bail	warrant issued not backed for bail
YJ	youth justice
YOT	youth offending team

1 TEESSIDE
2 MERSEYSIDE
3 GREATER MANCHESTER
4 NOTTINGHAMSHIRE
5 WEST MIDLANDS
6 WARWICKSHIRE
7 NORTHAMPTONSHIRE
8 BEDFORDSHIRE
9 HERTFORDSHIRE
10 GLOUCESTERSHIRE

AVON & SOMERSET PROBATION AREA

Out of hours emergency contact point
Glogan House (01278) 424165

Victim enquiries contact number
0117-930 3732

e-mail Firstname.Surname@avon-somerset.probation.gsi.gov.uk

1. Queensway House
    The Hedges, St Georges
    Weston-super-Mare
    North Somerset BS22 7BB
    tel (01934) 528740 *fax (01934) 528797*
    direct dial (01934) 52 + ext

Board
Kuipers, Joe (chair) 8711
Berk, Elaine (lead pa and pa to board) 8711

Chief Officer's Group
Lewis, Sally (co)
Dauncey, Debbie (pa to co) 8708
Hambleton-Ayling, Dean (aco, hr) 8718
Neale, Danielle (dir of finance) 8705
Doust, Michelle (pa to D Hambleton-Ayling & D Neale) 8707
Thomas, David (aco) 8703
Davies, Martin (aco) 8702
Heaton, Maria (pa to D Thomas & M Davies) 8712
McAdam, Diane (aco) 8711
mobile 07917 464 550

Area Business Managers
Bristow, Brenda 8715
Kelly, Mel 8714

Information & Quality Manager
Allen, Dave 8706

Human Resources/Payroll
Taylor, Alison (hr mgr) 8726
Scarbro, Anna (snr hr off) 8725
Richards, Anna (hr off) 8729
Willcocks, Sue (hr off) 8723
Downey, Nicola (asst hr off) 8724
Mercer-Matthews, Gill (asst hr off) 8730
Baxemdale, Chloe (asst hr off) 8727

Communications
Geake, Rachael (comms off) 8728
Peglar, Richard (comms asst) 8728

Information Technology
Helpdesk 01934 528780

Thompson, Bruce (systems mgr) 8781
Bennett, Lee 8790

Carter, Trevor 8783
Edwards, Ed (assistive tech co-ord) 8791
El Hack, Yasir 8789
Gleed, Nick 8782
Goddard, Peter 8785
Harrison, Peter 8788
Motlow, Ben 8787
O'Shea, Chris 8792
Pannila, Niluka 8786
Quelch, Sara (info off) 8795
Shepherd, Scott 8784
Thompson, Shirley (IT trainer) 8793

Finance
Clark, Jane (finance mgr) 8738
Joyce, Karen (finance mgr) 8733
Ridley, Victoria (finance off) 8734
Heydenrych, Desiree (temp finance asst) 8709
Parker, Sue (temp finance asst) 8736
Young, Alison (temp finance asst) 8735
Lawson, Lucy (mgmnt accountant) 8737
Woodey, Dawn (finance asst) 8744

Health & Safety
Andrews, Ben (mob 07920 774 595)

Staff Development
Wilson, Jim (lead training off) 8746
Kent-Probert, Fleur (training off) 8745

Victim Liaison Team
Summerhayes, Alex (vlo) 8748

General
Duce, Lesley (office supt) 8742
Pearce, Jane (catering asst) 8742

2. The Old Convent
    35 Pulteney Road **Bath** BA2 4JE
    tel (01225) 315809 *fax (01225) 324979*

Direct dial (01225) 32 + ext

Local Business Manager
Reed, Liz 4935

Admin
Fox, Diane (dep office mgr) 4934
Acres, Carole 4933
Barling, Bridget 4931
McKellan, Lyndsey 4932
Pearson, Margaret 4930

Area Performance Manager
Hull, Sue

Offender Mgmnt Assessment Team
Day, Kevin (middle mgr) 4948
Brazier, Tony (middle mgr) 4949
Higgins, Frank (snr pract) 4950
Breckenridge, Allyson 4969

Denne, Emily 4958
Martin, Deborah 4957
McCaffrey, Mary 4943
Ring, Lisa 4959
Spinney, Jo-Anne 4955
Summers, Claire 4961
Torczuk, Ray 4971
Stredder, Lesley 4956
Gill, Rebecca (pso) 4944
Love, Di (pso) 4939
Quinn, Lorraine (pso) 4940
Silver, Deborah (pso) 4945

Programmes
Rakoczi, Jenny (middle mgr) 4951
Henry, Olivia (treatment mgr) 4975
Billingsley, Jennifer (pso) 4941
Harris, Elaine (pso) 4976
Mountford, Guy (pso) 4974
Barker, Paul (progrs driver)

ASPOS/DRRs
Hawken, Sheila 4968

Unpaid Work Unit
Prior, Martin (supvr/plcmnt mgr) 4942
Coltman, Frank (sess supvr)

Consortium
Spurrell, Helen 4965

Trainees
Rymell, Alison (pda) 4964

Women's Safety Worker
Butler, Alice 4942

3. **Central Office**
    Marlborough Street, Bristol, BS1 3NU
    tel 0117-930 2500 *fax 0117-9302525*
    direct dial 0117-930 + ext

    Area Performance Manager
    King, Anne 2500

    Local Business Manager
    Hudson, Sarah 2526

    Admin
    Witts, Catherine (asqo) 2529
    Kelley, Jo (allocations off) 2532
    Ashworth, Victoria 2514
    Church, Keith 2534
    Dempster, Sarah 2527
    Fox, Nicola 2530
    Nobrega-Collins, Stella 2535
    Paterson, Ella 2538
    Stevens, Diane 2533
    Wilson, Adam 2537
    Phull, Gurdarshan Kaur (staff devpt supt)
    2500

Offender Mgmnt & Assessment Team
Hanbidge, Matthew (middle mgr) 2549
Cragg, Rachael (middle mgr) 2551
Chapman, Charlotte
Brown, Diane (pso) 2545
Cook, Bev (pso) 2539
Groom, Hannah (pso) 2500
Palmer, Daniel (pso) 2500
Yates, Ina (pso) 2543

OMAT PSR Authors
Davies, Neal 2562
Ealey, Emma 2561
Fagg, Pat 2420
Jackson, Audrey 2560
Middleton, Jayne 2561
Nava, Andrew 2554
Parry, Enfys 2555
Sula, Ssali 2437
Vincent, Susan 2558
Whitefield, Nicholas 2557
Young, Carrie 2556

Breaches Unit
Bryant, Carla (pso) 2541
Knill, Lisa (pso) 2546
Phillips, Beth (pso) 2542

MAPPA Co-ordinator
Wise, Mair (apm) 2512
Ealei, Emma 2500

Trainees
Watson, Sybil (practice devpt mgr) 2548
Dawson, Andrew (trainee) 2449
Jenkinson, Liam (trainee) 2463
Weldon, Clive (trainee) 2464

Victim Liaison Team
Harvey, Bridgette (vlo) 2520
Stuart, Wendy (vlo) 2520
Edwards, Sarah (p, dep office mgr) 2500
D'Arcy, Jason (p, admin) 2520
Smith, Dawn (admin) 3732

4. **Bristol Crown Court Liaison Office**
    Small Street, Bristol BS1 1DA
    tel 0117-976 3071/2 *fax 0117-976 3073*

    Court & Assessment Team
    Comerford, Joanne (pso) 0117 9302 539

    Administration
    Taynton, Colin (dom) 0117 9763071
    Marshall, Sheralyn 0117 9763071

5. **Decourcy House**
    Upper York Street **Bristol** BS2 8QN
    tel 0117-944 7200 *fax 0117-944 7220*
    direct dial 0117-944 + ext

Local Business Manager
Szczelkun, Emma 7204
Tye, Sarah 7204

Admin
Coombs, Holly 7200
Dinnis, Jane 7207
Gainey, Alan 7295
Gifford, Stacey 7215
Glanville, Amy 7206
Green, Jennifer 7208
Jenner, Polly Ann 7200
Kerr, Anyha-Maria 7200
Mace, Julie 7200
Mogridge, Robyn 7200
Nansimbi, Cynth
Quaynor, Natalie 7200
Ramakrishnan, Bhuvaneswari 7208
Ransom, Benjamin 7218
Williams, Aleysha 7212

Drug Management Team
admin 0117-944 7215 *fax 0117-942 9285*

Scott, Robin (middle mgr) 7277
Fitzgerald, Declan 7294
Pasco, Mark 7241
Romain, Maria 7200
Walsh, Jonathan 7289
Nutt, Lisa (pso) 7200
Reid, Rebecca (pso) 7244
Scott, Marvre (pso) 7200
Wildish, Kate (pso) 7200

Unpaid Work
Britton, Jeremy (middle mgr) 7275
Bartlett, Keith (supvr/plcmnt mgr) 7200
Mullins, Kevin (supvr/plcmnt mgr) 7200
Wainwright, Paul (supvr/plcmnt mgr) 7200

ETE
O'Connor, Dan (middle mgr) 7272
Dunstan, Nicky (middle mgr) 7242
Bromham, Paul (admin mgr) 7246
Cain, Paulette (ete off) 7274
Damsell, Mark (ete off) 7296
Griffiths, Michaela (ete off) 7271
McAllister, Gerry (ete off) 7223
McMeechan, Adam (ete off) 7296
Ngozi, Kwesi (ete off) 7200
White, Vicky (ete off) 7200
Williams, Michael (ete off) 7200

ETE Admin
Miles, Karen 7218
Scott, Debbie (partnership devpt mgr) 7291

Offender Mgmnt Assessment Team
0117-944 7250
Harrison, Marilyn (middle mgr) 7292

Hook, Mike (middle mgr) 7284
Lane, Russell (mddle mgr) 7236
Daly, Clare 7262
Fisher, Rachel 7238
Atchison, Jane 7250
Birch, Fiona 7283
Brewitt, Helen 7230
Burgess, Lucy 7250
Darts, Caroline 7250
Farrelly, Richard 7250
Forbes, Angela 7250
Hall, Becky 7230
Parker, Sarah 7247
Reilly, Debbie 7251
Ridewood, Denise 7250
Russell, Ruth 7259
Stewart-Gentle, Angela 7269
Sutherland, Luke 7250
Ufumwen, Frank 7283
Webb, Richard 7250
Wellman, Tom 7268
White, Emma 7250
Woodroffe, Emma 7250
Wray, Nicky 7250

Boulton, Gemma (pso) 7239
Campbell, Mary (pso) 7278
Clark, Sarah (pso) 7228
Clifford, Helen (pso) 7261
Franklin, Leanne (pso) 7250
Handley, Ceris (pso) 7247
Harewood, Sheila (pso) 7218
Heckbert, Murray (pso) 7250
Hill, Abigail (pso) 7281
Martin, Alison (pso) 7231
Norton, Nicholas (pso) 7250
O'Brien, Catherine (pso) 7238
Sunderland, Rachel (pso) 7265
Thomas, Katherine (pso) 7250
Wakefield, Daniel (pso) 7276

Programmes /Groupwork
Bristol, Tiggy (middle mgr) 7288
Cormack, Rita (p, tutor) 7210
van der Eerden, Barbara (trtmnt mgr) 7235
Calderwood, Islay 7200
Goedhart, Adriana 7229
Harley, David 7243
McBride, Odette 7291
Sayer, Richard 7267
Banfield, Rose (pso) 7234
Mountford, Guy 7200
Potter, Brian (pso) 7244
Pretty, Kelly (pso) 7200
Windle, Debra (pso) 7227
Waller, Barbara (prog mgr) 7214

Trainees
Jenner, Sue (pda) 7200
Austin, Matthew (trainee) 7200
Boulnois, Helen (trainee) 7200
Cross, Harriet (trainee) 7200
Faulkner, Melissa (trainee) 7200
Gregory, Hannah (trainee) 7200
Thompson, Sarah (trainee) 7200

Volunteers
Galena, Cherry 7258

Women's Safety Officers
Banfield, Rosemary 7234
George, Rebecca 7234

Admin
Green, Paula (asqo) 7289

6. 70 Crossways Road
    Knowle Park Bristol BS4 2SP
    tel 0117-983 0050/316 0680/1
    fax 0117-983 0051

    direct dial 0117-316 + ext

Local Business Manager
Beeson, Lesley 0688

Admin
James, Susan 0050
Osbiston, Faye 0050
Williams, Margaret 0705
Wring, Carol 0682

Offender Mgmnt Assessment Team
Miners, David (middle mgr) 0689
Yates, Tony (middle mgr) 0689
Allen, Angie 0296
Dickins, Andrew 0696
Hooper, Lois 0050
Jenkins, Vaughan 0699
Lane, Susan 0050
Lewis, Beverley 0690
Martin, Clive 0691
Murray, Graeme 0050
Pace, Alexandra 0698
Pengelly, Janna 0707
Richards, Matthew 0694
Clark, Colin (pso) 0709
Hopton, Natalie (pso) 0708
Kenyon, Caroline (pso) 0697
Roberts, Michelle (pso) 0050

ETE
Bricker, Marcia (ete tutor) 0685
Pole, Tony (project for work tutor) 0684

Unpaid Work Unit
Mulholland, Simon (supvr plcmnt mgr) 0686
Reed, Nick (supvr plcmnt mgr) 0686

Sabin, Shelia (supvr plcmnt mgr) 0687
Simmonds, Dorian (supvr plcmnt mgr) 0687

Trainee
Mudzamiri, Stephen (trainee) 0500

7. **North Bristol**
    Greystoke Avenue, Westbury on Trym
    Bristol BS10 6AD
    tel 0117-950 9105 *fax 0117-959 1933*
    direct dial (0117) 959 + ext

Local Business Manager
Matthews, Christian 7272

Admin
McLeod, Jamie (asqo) 7282
Allison, Nichola 9105
Cook, Rita 7286
Taylor, James 7283

Unpaid Work Unit
Searle, Alison (qa mgr) 7274
Wellman, Stewart (qa mgr) 7272
Hoskins, David (supvr plcmnt mgr) 9105
Scott, Michael (supvr plcmnt mgr)
(mobile 07774 968 672)
Ward, Richard (supvr plcmnt mgr) 7261
Griffin, Colin (sess supvr) 9105

Offender Mgmnt Assessment Team
Sanyasi, Marcia (middle mgr) 7273
Hunt, Allason (middle mgr) 7273)
Bennett, Bridget 7269
Dobbs, Nicky 7270
Faulkner, Melissa 9105
Gaskin, Sarah 9105
Goodhind, Ben 7268
Hall, Andy 7281
Hathaway, David 7267
Hutchinson, Stuart 7279
Keaney, Sarah 7276
Moreton, Amanda 7277
Preston, Boyce 7265
Thompson, Bridget 7269
Cesenek, Debbie (pso) 7280
Griffin, Annie (pso) 7270
Hillier, Graham (pso) 7284
Meas, Kim (pso) 7266
Targett, Vanessa (pso) 7263

Trainees
Goodhall, Margaret (pda) 7275
Anglin, Victoria (trainee) 9105
Raja, Ruby (trainee) 9105
Wedmore, Rachel (trainee) 7292

ETE Middle Mgr
Thompson, Suzanne (p) 7272

8. Riverside House, West Quay
    Bridgwater Somerset TA6 3HW
    tel (01278) 423977 *fax (0127\8) 453941*
    direct dial (01278) 72 + ext

Local Business Manager
Denslow, Shelley 7247

Offender Mgmnt Assessment Team
Spencer, Liz (middle mgr) 7118
Elliot, Jennifer (middle mgr) 423977
Brooks, Marie 423977
Carver, Adrian 7154
Clark, Roger 423977
Darbin, Steve 7124
Grover, Maggie 7137
Harper, Sandra 7100
Hole, Gemma 423977
Jones, Kevin 7130
Knott, Christopher 7145
Smith, Chantelle 7107
Symons, Karen 423977
Ward, Catherine 7143
Price, Carol (area accom off) 7111
Hale, Lyn (pso) 7120
Kirby, Anna (pso) 7119
Madelin, Chris (pso) 7117
Sanchez, Paula (pso) 7152
Tuke, Mark (pso) 7105

Programmes
Heyworth, Elaine (apm, ete, upw) 7121
Barrie, Collette 423977
Harper, Sandra 7100
Vale, Alan 7110
Miller, Clare (pso) 7155
Samotyj, Carly (pso) 7155

Unpaid Work Unit
Harris, Tracey (upw co-ord) 7117
Wellman, Stewart (upw co-ord) 7117
Emest, Peter (supvr plcmnt mgr) 7113
John, Trevor (supvr plcmnt mgr) 7128
Wilkinson, Dave (supvr plcmnt mgr) 423977
Stretch, Sharon (upw admin) 7146
Bickham, Denis (sess supvr) 423977

DIP
fax 01278 434648
Carver, Aileen (pso) 7147
Kingsbury, Marian (admin mgr) 7139
TP & SDS indicate Partner Agencies

ETE
Mobsby, Melayn (pso) 7129
Hampson, Sandra (case admin) 7133

Trainees
Chin, Mike (pda) 7131
Baxter, Katherine (trainee) 423077

Burrows, Jacqueline (trainee) 423977
Hayes, Jillian (trainee) 423977
Watson, Zoe (trainee) 7122

Business Development Unit
Meadows, Frank (middle mgr) 7101
Brandt, Peter (apm) 7113

Case Administrators
Bright, Leanne 7103
Cayley, John 7125
Chorley, Ruth 7103
Foreman, Christine 7127
Skinner, Gail 7102
Speakman, Emily 7125

Admin
Reeve, Jacqui (asqo) 7103 (also 11)

9. 11 Canon Street
    Taunton TA1 1SN
    tel (01823) 251351 *fax (01823) 321724*
    direct dial (01823) 34 + ext
    Minehead report centre (07974) 109850

Local Business Manager
Fensom, Pat 6425

Case Administrators
Ariannejad, Chantel 6451
Curtis, Amanda 6401
Locke, Joanne 6443
Jeffries, Joyce 6426
Reitman, Tessa 6453

DIP
Penelhum, Margaret 6438
Baker, Jane (pso) 6404

Unpaid Work Unit
Day, Denise (qa mgr) 6423
Bowden, Joe (supvr/placmnt mgr) 6423
Searle, Daniel (supvr/plcmnt mgr) 6415
Stretch, John (supvr/ plcmnt mgr) 6415

Offender Mgmnt Assessment Team
Hamilton, Liz (middle mgr) 6416
Foy, Tom 6432
Bawden, Kerrie 6441
Lewis, Lis 07974 109850
Powell, Angie 6402
Roberts, Paul 6434
Waugh, Nicola 6436
Webster, Robin 6429

Booth, Simon (pso) 6415
Ferrero, Marion (pso) 251351
Rawles, Colette (pso) 6403
Munday, Rachel (pso) 6459

Programmes
Boxer, Liz 6457

Cook, Adam 6455
Bradley, Steve (trtmnt mgr) 6418
Cartright, Faith (trtmnt mgr) 6424
Rexworthy, Frances (trtmnt mgr) 6417
Shepherd, Jane (IDAP co-ord) 6458
Rosewarne, Pauline (progs admin, S Area) 6420
Hembery, Julie (pso) 6417
Packman, Heidi (pso) 6430

Employment, Training & Education
Cornelius, Simon (APM) 6411
West, Jackie (ete off) 6421

IT
Hosie, Freda (admin info off) 6410

Trainees
Ashton, Richard (pda) 6435
Dryland, Lauren (trainee) 6431
Freer, Stephen (trainee) 6449
Hammacott, Elizabeth (trainee) 6456
Pickup, Lynne (trainee) 6439
Pike, Kate (trainee) 6405
Thomson, Matthew (trainee) 6445

10. **Taunton Crown Court**
Shire Hall, Taunton TA1 1EU
tel (01823) 338599 *fax (01823) 338946*

Crown Court Administrators
Radford, Kathy (p, pso) 338599
Smith, Maxine (p, pso) 6408

11. **North Somerset Magistrates' Court**
North Somerset Court House
The Hedges, St Georges
Weston-Super-Mare
North Somerset BS22 7BB
tel (01934) 528640 *Main fax (01934) 528595*
Court/PSR fax (01934) 528588
direct dial (01934) 52 + ext

Local Business Manager
Clarke, Annette 8622 (also 12)

Admin
Reeve Jacqui (asqo) (also 8)

Case Administrators
Druce, Marion 8621
Gotsell, Susan 8640
Hector, Elizabeth 8645
Mitchell, Tracy 8640
Newbon, Letitia 8637
Reay, Diane 8642

Offender Mgmnt & Assessment Team
Harris, Andy (middle mgr) 8631
Woods, Doug 8625

Berry, John 8642
Birt, Judy 8624
Holgate, Kerensa 8640
Hector, Katherine 8640
Hooley, Rachel 8640
Kitusa, Lillian 8628
Lockwood, Daniel 8640
Somerville-Ashby, Helen 8643
Tiernan, Joe 8634
Turner, Katie 8640
Walkley, Julia 8640
Coveney, Helen (pso) 8627

Court & Assessment Team
Bessant, Matthew (pso) 8638
Coltham, Joy (pso) 8619
Daniells, Sue (pso) 8618

12. 50 The Boulevard
Weston-super-Mare BS23 1NF
tel (01934) 623526 *fax (01934) 621111*
direct dial (01934) 64 + ext

DIP 528753
Greenway, Karen (pso) 7416
Herowych, Trina (pso) 7415

Programmes
Thatcher, Sally (middle mgr) 7412
Burnett, Laurence 7403
Camish, Marilyn (treatment mgr) 7422
McGreevy, Lisa (pso) 7406
Hewart, Michael (prog driver) 623526
Pask, Lyndon (supvr/plcmnt mgr) 623526

ETE
Hawley, Janice (learning link officer) 7423

Trainees
Clarke, Christopher (trainee) 623526
Hood, Colette (trainee) 623526

13. Court Ash House
Court Ash **Yeovil** BA20 1AG
tel (01935) 476461 fax *(01935) 475290*
direct dial (01935) + ext

Local Business Manager
Hole, Kate 709101

Admin
Taylor, Lesley (asqo) 709102
Ashford, Kay (admin) 476461
Gulliford, Wendy (admin) 476461
Hallet, Vicky (admin) 709104
Hughes, Sarah (admin) 476461
Strickland, Janette (admin) 709103

Unpaid Work
Roberts, Joy (p, qa mgr) 709112
Binns, David (supvr plcmnt mgr) 709112

Shoemark, Robin (supvr plcmnt mgr) 709119

Round, Roger (supvr plcmnt mgr) 709119

Boice, Peter (sess supvr) 476461

DIP
Piggott, Jane 01749 679058
Bushell, Karen (pso) 709125
Harper, Joe (pso) 01749 679058

ETE
Janas, Emily (learning link & ete off) 709116

White, Deanne (ETE XL caseworker) 709119

Keane, Melody (ETE link off) 709116

Offender Mgmnt & Assessment Team
Friend, Anne (middle mgr) 709115
Hextall, Nigel (middle mgr) 476461
Morelli, Massimo (middle mgr) 476461
Geraghty, Dominic 709111
Henderson, Richard 476461
Knell, Tim (pda) 476461
Adley, Pat 709110
Carey-Higgs, Janice 476461
Evans, Claire 709112
Marshall, Brian 476461
Miller, Robert (John) 476461
O'Gorman, Sean 709113
Smerdon, Becca 709114
Thorne, Sharon 709116
Flower, Joan (pso) 476461
Champeney, Jennifer (pso) 709122
Chant, Pete (pso) 709121
Clarke, Lisa (pso) 709103
Cox, Steve (pso) 709105
Harper, Joe (pso) 476461
Poole, John (pso) 709119
Stewart, Alison (pso) 709118

Programmes
Jerzykowski, Ernie (p, tutor) 709104
Lusty, Keith (treatment mgr) 709126
Smith, Kerren (pso) 709105

Trainees
Churchill, Richard (trainee) 476461
Denman, Rebecca (trainee) 476461
Hillier, Sara (trainee) 476461
Hutt, Andrew (trainee) 476461
Merrett, Beth (trainee) 476461

14. **Avon & Somerset Prolific Offender Scheme (ASPOS)**
e-mail Firstname.Lastname@avonandsomerset.police.uk

New Bridewell Office
7th Floor, New Bridewell Police Station, Bridewell Street, Bristol BS1 2HQ
fax 0117-945 5133

Brown, Rosemary (admin officer) (mobile 07919 697 717)
Austin, Rachel (middle mgr) 01934 623526 (mobile 07795 507 409)
Perry, Stephanie (middle mgr) 0117-945 5525 (mobile 07920 878227)
Brockbank, Lucy 0117-945 4657 (mobile 07717 868181)
Carey-Higgs, Janice 0117-945 5158 (mobile 07717 868211)
Gupta, Gurmit 01179 454551
Phillips, Emma 0117-945 5163 (mobile 07717 868211)
Bridal, Deb (pso) 0117-945 5165 (mobile 07717 700526)
Champagnie, Cynthia (pso) 0117-945 5164 (mobile 07919 628897)
Clark, Sarah (pso) 0117-945 5160 (mobile 07919 697727)

Bath Office
Bath Police Station, Manvers Street Bath BA1 1JN
fax 01225 842417

Whateley, Anna 01225 842410 (mobile 07717 700525)
Leary, Michaela 01225 842410 (mobile 07717 868191)

HMP Bristol Office
HMP Bristol, Cambridge Road, Horfield, Bristol, BS7 8PS
tel 0117-372 3383 *fax 0117-372 3153*

firstname.lastname@hmps.gsi.gov.uk
Sherwin, David (snr prison off) 07789 753627
Watkins, Robert (prison off)
Skeen, Anna (pso)

Staple Hill Office
Staple Hill Police Station, Broad Street, Staple Hill, Bristol BS16 5LX
fax 0117-945 4240

O'Hagan, Rosie (middle mgr) 07920 878228
Sole, Stuart 0117-945 4257 (mobile 07789 753628)
Parry, Enfys 0117-9454257 (mobile 07919 697720)
Smart, Charmaine (pso) 0117-945 4257 (mobile 07919 017261)

Taunton Office
Taunton Police Station, Shuttern

Taunton TA1 3QA
fax (01823) 363250

Hamilton, Katherine (dep office mgr)
Elliott, Jennifer (snr pract) (01823) 363154
(mobile 07919 697723)
Montag, Barbara (01823) 363020
(mobile 07917 883 847)
Hancock, Gillian (p, pso) (01823) 363020
(mobile 07789 753626)

Weston-Super-Mare Office
50 The Boulevard
Weston-super-Mare BS23 1NF
tel (01934) 623526 *fax (01934) 621111*
direct dial (01934) 647 + ext

Austin, Rachel (middle mgr) 413
(mobile 07795 507409)
Elliott, Jennifer (snr pract)
(01823) 363154 (mobile 07919 697723)
Slack, Dave 420
(mobile 07717 868221)
Edgell, Kerri (pso) 421
(mobile 07919 697710)
Herowych, Trina (pso) 415
(mobile 07717 700524)
Davies, Clare (admin) 414

Yeovil Office
Yeovil Police Station, Horsey Lane
Yeovil, Somerset BA20 1SN
fax (01935) 402282

Elliott, Jennifer (snr pract)
(01823) 363154 (mobile 07919 697723)
Robinson, Shirley
(01935) 402249 (mobile 07919 697730)
Higginbotham, Coral (pso)
(01935) 402249 (mobile 07795 316204)

Youth Offending Teams

15. 12 Charlotte Street
     Bath BA1 2NF
     tel (01225) 396966 *fax (01225) 396969*
     Carvalho, Paulette

16. Kenham House
     Wilder Street **Bristol** BS2 8PD
     tel 0117-903 6480 *fax 0117-903 6481*
     Williams, Llinos

17. 48-50 Elm Park
     Filton South Gloucestershire BS34 7PP
     tel (01454) 868553 *fax (01454) 868560*
     Philpott, Gayle

18. 5-7 West End
     Street BA16 0LG
     tel (01458)440820 *fax (01458)449100*
     Jones, Mark

19. 59 Oxford Street
     Weston-super-Mare
     North Somerset BS23 1TR
     tel (01275) 888360 *fax (01275) 888361*
     Robinson, Laura

20. **Reducing Reoffending Partnership
     (South West)**
     The Pithay, Bristol BS1 2NQ
     tel 0117-945 6754 mobile 07944 663069
     e-mail mark.ellery@rrpsouthwest.org.uk
     Ellery, Mark

Approved Premises (Hostels)

21. **Ashley House Probation Hostel**
     14 Somerset Street, Kingsdown
     Bristol BS2 8NB
     tel 0117-924 9697 *fax 0117-944 4290*
     Gough, Nick (apm, hostels & resettlement)

22. **Bridge House Approved Premises**
     78 Filton Road, Bristol BS7 0PD
     tel 0117-969 3123 *fax 0117-931 2167*

     Ashby, Richard (middle mgr)
     Romain, Deane (asst mgr)
     Stirling, Malcolm (asst mgr)
     Walker, Robert (asst mgr)
     Gilroy, Alistair (apa)
     Mockridge, Leigh (apa)
     Graham, Jill (admin officer)

23. **6 Brigstocke Road Approved Premises**
     Bristol BS2 8UB
     tel 0117-942 5851 *fax 0117-944 5945*

     Jacobs, Gillian (admin mgr app premises)
     Parsons, Stephen (middle mgr)
     Jefferies Julie (asst mgr)
     Lake, Catherine (asst mgr)
     Orchard, Patrick (asst mgr)
     Richardson, Des (asst mgr)
     Warren, Martin (asst mgr)
     Bates, Alan (apa)
     Excell, Sean (apa)
     Graham, Jon (apa)
     Baker, Antony (ops mgr)

24. **Glogan House**
     59 Taunton Road, Bridgwater TA6 3LP
     tel (01278) 424165 *fax (01278) 44605*

Kelly, Phil (middle mgr)
Andrews, Wayne (asst mgr)
Day, Alison (asst mgr)
Foxwell, Tony (asst mgr)
Murkin, Robert (asst mgr)
Reid, Steve (asst mgr)
Bourton, Bob (apa)
McGill, Dave (apa)
Taylor, Richard (apa)

Institutions

25. H M Prison, Cambridge Road
Horfield **Bristol** BS7 8PS
tel 0117-372 3100 *fax 0117-372 3153*
probn fax 0117-372 3239

    direct dial 0117-372 + ext

    Pye, Denise (parole & ETS/Calm rsttlmnt)
    3265
    Whittaker, Nina (public protctn) 3348
    Broad, Sally (pso) 3102
    Rowe, Phillippa (pso) 3383
    Farrell, Nicky (pso, wkshp co-ord) 3355
    Frater, Natasha (pso child/public protctn)
    3017
    Jack, Ron (pso resettlement/bail) 3102
    Stevenson, Frances (pso, HDC/ROTL)
    3263

26. H M Prison **Leyhill**
Wotton-under-Edge, Falfield
Glos GL12 8DB
tel (01454) 264000 *fax (01454) 264001*
direct dial (01454) 26 + ext

    Trundley, Katy (middle mgr) 4178
    Peckham, Zoe (middle mgr) 4117
    Gartner, Kate 4089
    Hothersall, Anna (p) 4030
    Tonkinson, Clare (p) 4032
    Jones, Barbara (p) 4030
    Weatherley, Anne 4030
    Willett, Alison 4257
    Hancock, Susan (pso) 4019
    Nash, Carley (pso) 4039
    Smith, Angela (pso) 4026

27. H M Women's Remand Centre
Eastwood Park Falfield
Wotton-under-Edge, Glos GL12 8DB
tel (01454) 382100 *fax (01454) 382101*
Offender Management Unit (OMU) fax
(01454) 382092
direct dial (01454) 382 + ext

    Crallan, Katherine (middle mgr) 046
    Lambert, Pamela (p, head of OMU, middle
    mgr) 046

Garrett, Tina (snr pract/drug strategy
delivery mgr) 048
Bovill, Carolyn (accom officer) 065
Hall, Lesley (po/offender supvr) 125
Sullivan, Gina (po/offender supvr) 126
Starbuck, Kim (pso pso/offender supvr)
127
Rivers, Nicola (pso) 281

28. H M Prison & YOI **Ashfield**
Shortwood Road, Pucklechurch
Bristol BS16 0QJ
tel 0117-303 8000 *fax 0117-303 8001*
direct dial 0117-303 + ext

    Lane, Sue (snr pract) 8114
    Coleman, Justin (pso) 8114

29. H M Prison **Shepton Mallet**
Shepton Mallet BA4 5LU
tel (01749) 823300 *probation fax (01749)*
823307
direct dial (01749) 82 + ext

    probn visits booking: ext 3386/3444

    Fegredo, June (middle mgr/pub protctn)
    3407
    Hardman, Howard 3531
    Porter, Richard 3362

Local Justice Areas

2 Bath & Wansdyke
3-7 Bristol
7 North Avon
11, 12 North Somerset
8 Sedgmoor
13 South Somerset
9 Taunton Deane & West Somerset

Crown Courts

4 Bristol
10 Taunton

BEDFORDSHIRE PROBATION AREA

Victim enquiries contact number
(01234) 358978

e-mail Firstname.Surname@bedfordshire.
probation.gsi.gov.uk

1. **Head Office**
3 St Peter's Street, Bedford MK40 2PN
tel (01234) 213541 *fax (01234) 327497*

Hennigan, Linda (co)
Harding, Alison (aco, offender mngmnt)
Pace, Lis (aco, public protection)
West, Helen (head of business devpt
& aco, interventions)

Administration
Gunning, Ros (pa to co)
Jones, Sara (p, pa to board & aco om)
Chapple, Belinda (pa to aco pp & head of
bd)

Corporate Services & HR
Jennings, Sue (head of hr & corp services)
McSweeney, Barbara (p, comms mgr)
Morrison, Audrey (supt services & H&S
advr)
Wale, Richard (training mgr)
Foinette, Nicole (hr adviser)

Performance and Information Unit
Brown, Andrew (performance & info mgr)
Mainwaring, Mick (it mgr)

Finance
Marchant, Angela (head of finance)

2.   23-27 Napier Road, Luton LU1 1RF
tel (01582) 735153 *fax (01582) 451536*

Programmes
Hooper, Stephen (team mgr)
Blake, Kelly (p, snr admin)

Enhanced Supervision Team
Berg, Gill (team mgr)
Hunte, Charmaine (admin)

Healthlink
Dempsey, Ruth (snr nurse pract)

Unpaid Work Unit
Vacancy (team mgr)
Anderson, Stephen (dep team mgr)
Caveney, Marian (snr admin)

Contracted Services
Delmar, Elaine (team mgr)

3.   41 Harpur Street
Bedford MK40 1LY
tel (01234) 350401 *fax (01234) 328658*

Offender Management
Burnell, Karen (team mgr)
Green, Gabrielle (team mgr)
Blows, Dawn (p, snr admin)

Enhanced Supervision Team
Sparke, Jackie (team mgr)
Groom, Fiona (p, admin)

Healthlink
Oakham, Alan (snr nurse pract)

Trainees
Breakey, Paul (pda)

Unpaid Work Unit
Di Salvo, Carina (admin)

Programmes
Hooper, Stephen (team mgr)

Public Protection Team
Beaumont, Sue (team mgr)

Contracted Services
Delmar, Elaine (team mgr)

4.   **MAPPA/Victim Liaison Unit**
Saxon Centre, 1st Floor
230 Bedford Road, Kempston MK42 8PP
Victim unit
tel (01234) 358978 *fax (01234) 844289*
MAPPA unit
tel (01234) 844285

De Souza, Chris (mappa co-ord & mgr vlu)
Ince, Josie (mappa admin)

5.   Frank Lord House
72 Chapel Street, **Luton** LU1 5DA
tel (01582) 413172 *fax (01582) 418279*

Offender Management
Booth, Caroline (team mgr)
Burrows, Matthew (team mgr)
Harrington, Ruth (team mgr)
Belony, Wendy (p, snr admin)
Shirran, Andrea (p, snr admin)

Public Protection Team
Beaumont, Sue (team mgr)

Trainees
Eaden, Paul (pda)
Contracted Services
Delmar, Elaine (team mgr)

6.   **Luton Youth Offending Service**
16 Rothesay Road, **Luton** LU1 1QX
tel (01582) 547900 *fax (01582) 547901*
Secure email: lutonyos-general@
luton.gov.uk.cjsm.net

Briddon, Anita (head of yo service)
O'Byrne, Jon (dep head of yo service)
Collins, Dave (ops mgr)
Southwell, Verity (ops mgr)
Thompson, Jo (ops mgr)
Robinson, Steve (bail suprvn officer)
Vacancy (bail supervn officer)
Swiecicki, Noreen (admin & finance mgr)
Hutchinson, Troy (info mgr)

7. **Bedfordshire Youth Offending Service**
Unit 4 Franklyn Court, off Stannard Way
Priory Business Park, **Bedford** MK44 3JZ
tel (01234) 276400 *fax (01234) 276434*
e-mail firstname.surname@bedscc.gov.uk

Statutory and Prevention Base
Weatherall, Brian (ops mgr)
McKeown, Leemya (snr pract)
Stone, Lola (snr pract, preventions)
Vacancy (snr pract, statutory risk)
Vacancy (po)

8. **Bedfordshire Youth Offending Service**
39 Oakwood Avenue, **Dunstable** LU5 4AS
tel (01582) 524420 *fax (01582) 524421*
e-mail firstname.surname@bedscc.gov.uk

Fisk, Anne (ops mgr)
Drummond, Allan (snr pract)
Vacancy (p, po)

Court Services

9. **Magistrates' Court Liaison Office**
Shire Hall, 3 St Pauls Square, **Bedford**,
MK40 1SQ
tel (01234) 358402 *fax (01234) 358070*

Pettengell, Louise (crt supt admin)

10. **Crown Court Liaison Office**
Luton Crown Court
7-9 George Street, **Luton** LU1 2AA
tel (01582) 452079

Crown Court Switchboard
tel (01582) 452846 *fax (01582) 485529*

Cairncross, Sarah (team mgr)

11. **Magistrates' Court Liaison Office**
The Court House
Stuart Street, **Luton** LU1 5DL
tel (01582) 482710 *fax (01582) 482995*

Cairncross, Sarah (team mgr)

Approved Premises

12. **Luton Approved Premises**
36-40 Napier Road, **Luton** LU1 1RG
tel (01582) 418200 *fax (01582) 737391*

Andrews, Debra (mgr)
Vacancy (deputy mgr)

13. **Bedford Approved Premises**
80 Chaucer Road, **Bedford** MK40 2AP
tel (01234) 340501 *fax (01234) 351715*

Smith, Ali (mgr)
Nichols, Magda (deputy mgr)

Institution

14. H M Prison, St Loyes Street
Bedford, MK40 1HG
tel (01234) 373000 *fax (01234) 373568*

probn fax (01234) 373052
bail info fax (01234) 347268

Hart, Gordon (po) 01234 373058
Wilson, Fiona (admin) 01234 373059 or
373061

Local Justice Areas

3 Bedford & Mid Bedfordshire
5 Luton & South Bedfordshire

Crown Court

10 Luton

CAMBRIDGESHIRE PROBATION AREA

Out of hours emergency contact point
Approved Premises (01733) 551678

Victim enquiries contact numbers
Pamela Bogusz (01733) 348828
Margaret Pool (01223) 712271

e-mail Firstname.Surname@cambridgeshire.
probation.gsi.gov.uk

1. **Head Office**
1 Brooklands Avenue
Cambridge CB2 8BB
tel (01223) 712345 *fax (01223) 568822*

direct dial (01223) 71 + ext

James, Hilary (co) ext 2358
Lowe, Margaret (aco) ext 2350
Deller, Andrew (aco) ext 2369
Ryder, Matthew (aco) ext 2376
Seaton, Paul (treasurer) ext 2354
Chopra, Sheetal (team mgr) ext 2352

1a. **Support Services Unit**
Godwin House, George Street
Huntingdon PE29 3BD
fax (01480) 375731

direct dial (01480) 37+ ext

Harding, Mick (team mgr) ext 5776
Mackett, Chris (team mgr) ext 5792
McAngus, John (pro) ext 5779
Gooch, Baden (staff devpt mgr) ext 5783
Hayden, Alan (staff devpt off) ext 5784

Melrose, Gill (pda) ext 5749
Turvll, Rachel (pda) ext 5794
Goff, Christine (pract devpt &
assess off) ext 5775
Thompson, Kay (staff devpt
co-ord) ext 5787

Faulkner, Keith (team mgr, it) ext 5780
Price, Gareth (info off) ext 5773
Clampin, Dawn (p, intranet
pubs officer) ext 5755
Pereira, Chris (perf info officer) ext 5756
Jean Taylor (admin services mgr) ext 5790
Lloyd, Linda (pract mgr, info) ext 5782
Moore, Steve (it officer) ext 5781

Donaldson, Sherron (diversity
mgr) ext 5789
Sedzikowski, Sue (personnel mgr) ext
5707
Stackhouse, Joyce (personnel off) ext 5739
Jackson, Jackie (p, personnel secy) ext
5788
Young, Mary (p, office admin) ext 5785
Burridge, Pat (p, admin) ext 5786

1b. Multi Agency Public Protection Panel
Cambridgeshire Police HQ
Hinchingbrooke Park
Huntingdon PE29 6NP
tel (01480) 428013 *fax (01480) 428121*

Jarvis, Andy (team mgr)
Jones, Sarah (p, mappa co-ord)

2.   Warkworth Lodge, Warkworth Street
Cambridge CB1 1EG
tel (01223) 712271 *fax (01223) 712700*

Morrison, Roz (district mgr)
Waghorn, Hannah (team mgr)
O'Sullivan, Jacqueline (team mgr)
Flack, Julia (team mgr)
Baker, Geraldine
Durose, Jenny
Hawkes, Gary
Kiddle, Ruth
Lowes, Julie
Pepperell, Kelly
Shadbolt, Maureen
Speechley, Rachel (yot)
Taylor, Amanda
Younger, Steven
Warburton, Diana (info off)

Gawne, Louise (trainee)
Gooch, Emily (trainee)
Bailey, Maxine (pso)
Colomb, Stella (pso)
Eden, Janice (pso)
Flowerdew, Christopher (pso)

Patel, Rajesh (pso)
Payne, Barbara (pso)
Sharman, Lyn (p, pso)
Stewart, Zoe (pso)
Stone, Rebecca (pso)

Andrews, Bob (plcmnt mgr, unpaid wk)
de Souza, Jorge (pso, unpaid wk)
King, Tatiana (pso, unpaid wk)

Pool, Margaret (victim liaison officer)

3.   Sessions House, Lynn Road
Ely Cambridge CB6 1DA
tel (01353) 663523 *fax (01353) 669047*

Open Tues & Thurs only
all mail to office 2

3a. Cambridge Magistrates' Court
12 St Andrews Street
Cambridge
tel (01223) 377208
all mail to office 2

4.   Old County Buildings
Grammar School Walk
Huntingdon PE29 3LQ
tel (01480) 376100 *fax (01480) 376123*

Coleman, Lucy (team mgr)
Pease, Adrian (pract mgr)
Preston, Jay (pract mgr)
von Rabenau, Elisabeth (pract mgr)
Bardell, David
Eshelby, Clare
Holloway, Stephen
King, Lesley
Marsh, Linsey
Parker, Marsha
Prior, Marie
Roberts, Katie
Unsworth, Helen

Frost, Alison (trainee)
Kirk, Danielle (trainee)
Robinson, David (trainee)
Wilson, Daniel (trainee)
Campbell, Anita (p, pso)
Ferrari, Sarah (pso)
Fieldhouse, Adrian (pso)
Harris, Lisa (pso)
Jest, Anna (pso)
Ludlam, Marie (pso)
Mawditt, Marilyn (pso)
Robson, Jim (pso)
Templar, Ann (pso)

Bynoe, David (plcmnt mgr, unpaid work)
Mansfield, Keith (p, plcmnt mgr, unpaid wk)

Huntingdon Rear Building
Harris, Martin (team mgr) ext 5762

Thomas, Francella (team mgr) ext 5772
Walker, Mick (team mgr) ext 5460
Wallis, Lesley (pract mgr) ext 5771
Murphy, Tracy (accom adv
wrkr) ext 5768

5. Castle Lodge, 1 Museum Square
    Wisbech PE13 1ES
    tel (01945) 461451 *fax (01945) 476350*

    Drury, Adrienne (team mgr)
    Brickley, Stephen
    Douglas, Craig
    Kerr, Sally
    Talbot, Sophie
    Turner, Jayne
    Wardell, Linda

    Harrison, Nicola (trainee)
    Thomas, Owy (trainee)

    Calvert, Elizabeth (pso)
    Garrett, Shaun (pso)
    Humphrey, David (pso)
    Molloy, Val (p, pso)
    Paton,Colin (p, pso)
    Spruce, Jenny (pso)

5a. The Court House
    Market Place **March** PE15 9JF
    tel (01354) 657963

    all mail to office 5

6. Magistrates Court, Bridge Street
    Peterborough PE1 1ED
    tel (01733) 564367 *fax (01733) 315758*

    Hancock, Alison (p, district mgr)
    Tomlin, Laura (team mgr)
    Seddon, Graeme (team mgr)
    Anderson, Sue
    Beale,Julie
    Crowley, Julie
    Curphey, Joanne
    Drabble, Jacie
    Fisher-Leeman, Amanda
    Hoche, Anita
    Lace, Liz
    Providence, Belinda
    Savage, Chris
    Stocks, Simone
    Strowbridge, David (p, yot)
    Swain, Mark
    Walker, Chris
    Whaley, Claire

    Willis, Mel
    Lawrence, Victoria (trainee)
    Minns, Darren (trainee)

Sadler, Sian (trainee)

Bailey, Susan (pso)
Beech, Garry (pso)
Clarke, Lucy (pso)
Latham, Lynda (pso)
Munir, Mohammed (pso)
Nolan, Gary (pso)
Summers, Louise (p, pso)
Whitwell, Natalie (pso)
Williams, Christine (pso)

Crown Court
tel (01733) 352763 *fax (01733) 565284*

7. Gloucester House, 23a London Road
    Peterborough PE2 8AP
    tel (01733) 348828 *fax (01733) 313765*

    Ashford,Carol (team mgr)
    Block, Nigel
    Herron, Nicola
    Morse, Mike (p)

    Alderson, Michael (pso)
    Austin, Jo (pso)
    Bogusz, Pamela (pso)
    Cummings, Lorna (pso)
    Hughes, Donna (pso)
    Jacques, Caroline (pso)
    Miller, Clare (pso)
    Moore, Fay (pso)
    Neve, Joann (pso)
    Nutcher-Palmer, Barbara (pso)

    Pollard, Clare (mappa co-ord)

    Garratt, Steve (plcmnt mgr, unpaid wk)
    Howes, Michael (plcmnt mgr, unpaid wk)
    Moore, Alan (plcmnt mgr, unpaid wk)
    Smith, Susan (p, plcmnt mgr, unpaid wk)

Approved Premises (Hostel)

8. Approved Premises
    5 Wesleyan Road
    Peterborough PE1 3RW
    tel (01733) 551678 *fax (01733) 345161*

    Wallis, Stuart (team mgr)
    Moore,Sadie (deputy)
    Jackson, Shane (pso)
    Jenkins, Brian (pso)
    Martin-James, Penny (pso)
    Smith, Steve (pso)
    Trower, Adreana (pso)
    Woods, Paul (pso)
    Mohammed, Kamran (aps)
    Storey, Kevin (aps)
    Wright, Richard (aps)
    Wilson, Tim (aps)
    Friskey, Pamela (aps)

Lane, Sandee (admin)
Sidney, Jackie (finance)

Institutions

9. H M Prison **Littlehey**
    Perry, Huntingdon, Cambs PE18 0SR
    tel (01480) 333000 *fax (01480) 333070*

    Emma Humphrey (p, team mgr)
    Hill, Anne
    Robinson, Paula
    Sparke, Jackie
    Wood, Phil
    Martin, Donna (p, pso)

10. H M Prison **Whitemoor**
    Longhill Road, March PE15 0AF
    tel (01354) 602350 *fax (01354) 602351*

    direct dial (01354) 602 + ext

    Probn clerk ext 616
    Sentence management ext 455
    Domestic visits ext 800
    Special visits ext 472

    Dawkins, Ellwyn (pract mgr) ext 455/700
    Benn, Colin ext 796
    Fieldhouse, Nicola ext 796
    Loosley, Suzanne ext 486
    Forte, Monica (pso) ext 828
    Heighton, Tim (pso) ext 557
    Leigh,Maggie (pso) ext 831
    Lowe, Jane (pso) ext 831
    Martin, Rachael, (pso) ext 831
    Smith, Nick (pso) ext 832

11. H M Prison **Peterborough**
    Saville Road, Westfield
    Peterborough PE3 7PD
    tel (01733) 217500 *fax (01733) 217501*

    Martin, Wendy (team mgr)
    Ashton, Diane
    Szumlicki, Anna
    Beacham, James (pso)
    Lightfoot,Cheryl (pso)

Local Justice Areas

2 Cambridge
3 East Cambridgeshire
4 Huntingdon
5 Fenland
6, 7 Peterborough

Crown Courts

2 Cambridge
6 Peterborough

CHESHIRE PROBATION AREA

Out of hours emergency contact numbers
0151 357 3551 or 01270 759181

e-mail Firstname.Surname@cheshire.
probation.gsi.gov.uk

1. **Head Office**
    Beech House, Park West,
    Sealand Road, Chester CH1 4RJ
    tel (01244) 394500 *fax (01244) 394507*

    Collett, Steve (co)
    Davidson, John (aco)
    Edwards, Chris (aco)
    Evans, Christine (aco)
    Link, Sandra (aco)
    Thornden, Kim (aco)

    District Managers
    Gwenlan, Chris
    Meade, Donna
    Skyner, David

    Communications and Health & Safety
    Gaughran, Liz (corporate services mgr)
    Woods, Steve (h & s officer)

    Contracts & Partnerships
    Hulse, Steve (contracts officer)

    Diversity
    Theilade, Annemarie (mgr)

    Finance
    tel (01244) 394502
    Hughes, Derek (mgr)

    Human Resources & Staff Devpt
    tel (01244) 394503
    Collins, Michelle (mgr)

    Information Services
    tel (01244) 394501
    Vernon, Eileen (mgr)

    Performance & Quality Assurance
    McDermott, Gerry (spo)
    Smith, Tracy (mgr)

    Partnerships and Contracts
    Hulse, Steve (officer)

    Property & Security
    Iremonger, Gordon (mgr)

    Public Protection
    Smith, Ian (spo)

    Substance Misuse
    Jones, Peter (p, spo) (also at 3 & 16)

2. Jupiter House, Jupiter Drive
    Chester West Employment Park

Chester CH1 4QS
tel (01244) 665100 *fax (01244) 665101*

Cheshire West (Chester)
Offender Mgmnt Unit
Corbett, Catherine (spo)
Peters, Cherryl (spo)
Elwin, Nicola
Gilbert, Stephanie
Goulding, Alison
Gray, Nicola
Hickman, Hayley
Mansutti, Helen
Moss, David
Orr, Rose
Radcliffe, Karen
Robertson, Kerry Ann
Robson, Jacqueline
Scott, Christine
Shepherd, Cheryl
Wall, Helen
Warburton, Helen
Williams, Nicholas
Ballard-East, Caroline (pso)
Burrell, Clare (pso)
Crawford, Karen (pso)
Dentith, Karen (pso)
Hammersley, Clare (pso)
Howell, Karen (pso)
Littler, Kelly (pso)
Mahar, Dennis (pso)
Rose, Rachel (pso)
Shone, Jenny (pso)

Court Services Unit
tel (01244) 665192 *fax (01244) 665193*

Kernahan, Chris (spo)
McDonagh, Christine (spo)
O'Mahony, Cathy (spo)
Biddle, Malveen
Entwistle, Ben
Rowntree, Rosie
Sanders, Francis
Davies, Lisa (pso)
Graham, Kim (pso)
Hall, Stephanie (pso)
Head, Mavis (pso)
Powell, Claire (pso)

Boliver, Michael (pso) (3)

Cunliffe, Sally (4)
Jackson, Helen (4)
Nolan-Beatty, Cathy (4)
Johnson, Susan (pso) (4)
Mapson, Frank (pso) (4)
Phillips, Veronica (pso) (4)
Simpson, Richard (pso) (4)
Stoneley, Kay (pso) (4)

Summers, Julie Anne (pso) (4)

Anderson, Sue (pso) (5)
Hallett, Michelle (pso) (5)
Rawlinson-Doyle, Jan (pso) (5)

Esegbona, Helen (pso) (6)
Isherwood, Michael (pso) (6)
Jenkins, Lee (pso) (6)
Woby, Robert (bail info) (6)

Holmes, Bea (pso) (7)
Pearce, Tristram (pso) (7)

Unpaid Work Unit
Cringle, David (6) (also at 3 & 6)
Millington, Grenville (pso) (also at 3)

Victim Liaison Unit
tel (01244) 665111 *fax (01244) 665193*

Odeka, Fran (spo)
Gibbons, Julie (pso)
Parkinson, Sue (pso)
Ratcliffe, Karen (pso)
Stewart, Chris (pso)
Williams, Stella (pso)

3.   Marshall Memorial Hall
Woodford Lane **Winsford** CW7 2JS
tel (01606) 551166 *fax (01606) 861267*

Cheshire West (Winsford)
Offender Management Unit
Day, Julie (spo)
Jones, Peter (p, spo) (also at 1 & 16)
Aspden, Andrea
Devine, Chris
Goldthorpe, Heather
Keatley, Sarah
Long, Belynda
Pritchard, Carol
Alcock, Angela (pso)
Buckley, Gillian (pso)
Dibbert, Diane (pso)
Green, Samantha (pso)

Unpaid Work Unit
Cringle, David (practice mgr) (also 2 & 6)
Millington, Grenville (pso) (also at 2)
Scragg, Bill (pso) (also at 6)

4.   Howard House, 10a Friars Gate
Warrington WA1 2RW
tel (01925) 650613 *fax (01925) 445109*

Offender Management Unit
Mayo, Edward (spo)
Neary, Jackie (spo)
Ashraf, Farah
Barnard, Karen
Benbrook, Maureen

Burton, Rachel
Catterall, Jane
Lawlor, Jim
Mitchinson, Gail
Norman, Philip
Palin, Julie
Ward, Victoria
Woodruff, John
Zarebski, Caroline
Brown, Yasmin (pso)
Johnston, Jim (pso)
Jones, Kirsty (pso)
Lea, Sarah (pso)
Lilly, Alan (pso)
Lowe, Diane (pso)
Pownall, Andrew (pso)
Tickle, Anthony (pso)
Whitby, Nicola (pso)
Whittle, Elizabeth (pso)

Wright, Anna (pso)

Unpaid Work Unit
Crawford, Ann (spo)
McGregor, Sheila (practice mgr) (also at 5 & 7)
Burgess, Louise (pso)
Hamlett, Elaine (pso)

5.   Norton House, Crown Gate
     Runcorn WA7 2UR
     tel (01928) 713555 *fax (01928) 701985*

Halton Offender Management Unit
Taylor, Karen (spo)
Wallace, David (spo)
Balchin, Susan
Bennett, Diane
Eagles, Jackie
Johnson, Alma
Kneale, Elaine
Madoc-Jones, Vivienne
McIntyre, Kevin
Naylor, Emma
Pugh, Karen
Verney, Julie
Wyatt, Sue
Beech, Catherine (pso)
Bradley, Liz (pso)
Bradshaw, Frank (pso)
Cavallaro, Eileen (pso)
McCaskill, Jane (pso)
Ormrod, Danielle (pso)
Shearer, Sandra (pso)

Basic Skills/ETE
Bennett, Chris (spo)

Mentor Co-ordination
Odeka, Fran (spo) (2)

Maddock, Carolynne (mentor co-ord)

Trainees
Blackham, Caroline (mgr)

Unpaid Work Unit
McGregor, Sheila (practice mgr) (4 & 6)
Burgess, Louise (pso) (4)
Hamlett, Elaine (pso) (4)

6.   Cedric Fullwood House
     Gateway
     Crewe CW1 6YY
     tel (01270) 257781 *fax (01270) 251181*

Cheshire East (Crewe)
Offender Management Unit
O'Rourke, Jacqui (spo)
Pearce, Cynthia (spo)
Bradshaw, Suzanne
Esegbona, Clement
Nicholson, Paul
Owen, Mark
Pazio, John
Spanswick, Emma
Thorne, Michael
Waldron, Tracey
Whitwell, Danielle
Done, Joanne (pso)
Kusair, Pam (pso)
McGuinness, Angela (pso)
Moore, Karelyn (pso)
Tavoulari, Isobel (pso)
Vickers, Wendy (pso)

Unpaid Work Unit
Cringle, David (practice mgr) (2 & 3)
Scragg, Bill (pso) (also at 3)

7.   Bradshaw House, 45 Cumberland Street
     Macclesfield SK10 1BY
     tel (01625) 423974 *fax (01625) 421345*

Cheshire East (Macclesfield)
Offender Management Unit
King, Clare (p, spo)
Robertson, Liz (spo)
Horner, Ken
Judge, Christopher
Lane, Rebecca
Scott, Christine
Sergeant, David
Whalley, Michael
Woolley, Stephen
Brown, Charlotte (pso)
Gregory, Janet (pso)
Perez, Sarah (pso)
Winney, Emma (pso)

Unpaid Work Unit
McGregor, Sheila (practice mgr) (4 & 5)

Burgess, Louise (pso) (4)
Hamlett, Elaine (pso) (4)

8. **Area Programmes Team**
    Croft, Eve (mgr) (2)
    Jones, Sîan (mgr) (2)
    Kewley, Stephanie (mgr) (6)
    Thomas, Lydia (mgr) (5)
    Buckley, Lyndsey (2)
    Elwin, Nicola (2)
    Hudson, Steven (2)
    Humphries, Rachel (2)
    Lyden, Rosie (2)
    Holleran, Steven (pso) (2)
    Lloyd, Carol (pso) (2)
    Riccio, Marian (pso) (2)

    Snow, Heather (treatment mgr) (5)
    Couzens, Denise (prog facilitator) (5)
    Edmondson, Lorna (prog facilitator) (5)
    Sykes, Jan (prog facilitator) (5)
    Thorne, Anna (prog facilitator) (5)
    Lewis, Melissa (prog facilitator) (6)
    Barker, Val (pso) (5)
    Harvey, Ingrid (pso) (5)
    McFadden, Samantha (pso) (5)
    Prior, Gemma (pso) (5)
    Ayers, Susan (pso) (6)

9. **Drugs Intervention Programme**
    (Throughcare & Aftercare)
    Jones, Peter (p, spo) (1) (also at 3 & 16)
    Yates, Donna (mgr) (6)
    Brunton, Fiona (pso) (2)
    Jordan, Celia (pso) (2)
    Simpson, Penny (pso) (3)
    Meredith, Sandra (pso) (6)
    Hewitt, Stephen (pso) (7)

Youth Offending Team

10. **Cheshire**
    Park View, Clarke Terrace
    Byron Centre, Byron Street
    Macclesfield SK11 7QD
    tel (01625) 660500

    Jones, Brian

11. **Halton & Warrington**
    Patten Hall, Winmarleigh Street
    Warrington WA1 1NB
    tel (01925) 634981

    Griffiths, Andy
    Hilal, Nadia

Approved Premises (Hostels)

12. **Linden Bank Approved Premises**
    40 London Road

Elworth Sandbach CW11 3BD
tel (01270) 759181 *fax (01270) 759579*

Maskell, Colin (spo) (also at 13)
Peter Rowe (dep mgr)
Percival, Jane (pso)
Rozitis, Richard (pso)

13. **Bunbury House Approved Premises**
    Alnwick Drive, Stanney Grange
    Ellesmere Port CH65 9HE
    tel (0151) 357 3551 *fax (0151) 356 2102*

    Maskell, Colin (spo) (also at 12)
    Brayshaw, Alana (dep mgr)
    Jones, Ian (pso)
    Jooste, Emma (pso)
    Richardson, Colin (pso)

Institutions

14. HM Prison & Young Offender Institution
    Styal Wilmslow SK9 4HR
    tel (01625) 553000 *fax (01625) 553204*

    Butler, Peter (spo)
    Miklaszewicz, Janina (dep mgr)
    Scott, Julie
    Smith, Tom
    Atkinson, Jan (pso)
    Fox, Charlotte (pso)
    Hutt, Victoria (pso)
    Johnson, Andrew (pso)
    Smith, Emma (pso)
    Theaker, Pat (pso)
    West, Lindsey (pso)
    Whittaker, Thomas (pso)
    Wilton, David (pso)

15. H.M. Prison, Warrington Road
    Risley via Warrington WA3 6BP
    tel (01925) 733000 *fax (01925) 764103*
    probn fax (01925) 766975

    Denton, Mike (spo) (p)
    Birch, Jean
    Bray, Nicholas
    Nixon, Annette
    O'Hea, Brendan
    Marquez, Ellen-Marie
    Ramsdale, Sue
    Bywater, Mark (pso)
    Hamlett, Andrea (pso)
    Plumb, Michelle (pso)

16. H M Young Offender Institution
    Thorn Cross Appleton Thorn
    Via Warrington WA4 4RL
    tel (01925) 605100 *fax (01925) 605101*

Jones, Peter (p, spo) (also at 1 & 3)
Parkinson, Hilary
Astall, Julie (pso)
Derrig-Vanzie, Cathryn (pso)

Local Justice Areas

2 Chester, Ellesmere Port & Neston
3 Vale Royal
4 Warrington
5 Halton
6 South Cheshire
7 East Cheshire

Crown Courts

2 Chester
2 Knutsford
2 Warrington

CUMBRIA PROBATION AREA

Out of hours emergency contact point
Bowling Green Approved Premises (01228)
522360

e-mail Firstname.Surname@cumbria.probation.
gsi.gov.uk

1. Head Office
    Lime House, The Green
    Wetheral, Carlisle CA4 8EW
    tel (01228) 560057 *fax (01228) 561164*

Hennessy, Annette (chief officer)
Walker, Sara (pa)
Rhodes, Richard (chairman)
Moore, Fiona (secy to brd/solicitor)
Vacancy (aco, head of operations)
Sait, Sargon (aco, head of corp resources)
Roebuck, Duncan (business devpt mgr)
Quille, Mike (comm reintegration mgr)
Muller, Karl (unpaid wk unit mgr)
Montague, Ted (perf & qual mgr)
Marshall, Julia (dom viol business mgr)
Davidson, Chris (Scafell proj mgr)
Manson, Andrea (h&s off)
Cleminson, Christine (info mgr)
Bloomfield, Keith (finance off, corp
finance)
Williamson, Joanne (finance off, mgmnt
acc)
Livingstone, Kath (hr mgr)
Kirkwood, Christine (personnel off)
Ruddick, Maureen (training/staff devpt off)

East Division
Perry, Anna (divisional mgr)

2. Georgian House, Lowther Street,
    Carlisle CA3 8DR
    tel (01228) 522333 *fax (01228) 552179*

Carlisle Magistrates Court (01228) 590198
Carlisle Crown Court (01228) 591619

Team Ea1
Dawson, Robin (team mgr)
Stobart, Linda
Marston, Pete (p)
Paterson, Julie (p)
Doggart, Clare
Byrom, Ruth
Reynolds, Charlotte (pso)
Anderson, Annabel (pso)
Faith, Alan (pso)
Heath, Carrie (tpo)
Darling, Richard (tpo)

Team Ea2
Penton, Joanne (team mgr)
Irwin, Derek (p)
Murray, Phil
Ward, Sarah
Fisher, Jennifer
Moloney, Bill
Glaister, Rebecca (pso)
Brough, Kath (pso)
Glaister, Caroline (pso)
Keen, Nicola (pso)
Scott, Helen (tpo)
Wallace, Nicola (tpo)
Stephenson, Ben (tpo)

Team Ea3
Lear, Jon (team mgr)
Wilson (Daines), Sue
Hobbs, Kim
Gold, Rachel
Ritchie, Jane
Timperon, Jonathon
Thwaites, Ray (pso)
Deacon, Claire (pso)
McNeish, Jean (pso)
Sanders-Fox, Andrea (pso)
Edwards, Diane (tpo)

Level 4 Facilitators
Loy, Helen
Marston, Pete (p)
O'Brien, Margaret

Unpaid Work/Community Payback
Arnold, Steve (mgr)
Grey, Mike (pso, placement mgr)

Support Services
Robinson, Paul (dvnl office mgr)

3. Clint Mill, 1st Floor, Cornmarket
    Penrith Cumbria, CA11 7HW
    tel (01768) 864928 *fax (01768) 861929*

    Dawson, Robin (team mgr)
    Downie, Jack
    Lowis, Rachel (p, pso)

    Level 4 Facilitator
    Critchlow, Peggy

4. Busher Lodge, 149 Stricklandgate
    Kendal LA9 4RF
    tel (01539) 723126 *fax (01539) 720646*

    Team Ea4
    Swenson, Adrian (team mgr)
    Robinson, Jane (p)
    Carter, Roger
    Reed, Emily (p)
    Wilson, Joy (p)
    Worsley, Rob
    Hill, Diane (p)
    Davies, Patty (pso)
    Evans, Erica (p, pso)
    Dalton, Janet (tpo)

West Division
Green, Caroline (divisional mgr)

5. 10 Lawson Street
    Barrow in Furness LA14 2LW
    tel (01229) 820870 *fax (01229) 829548*

    Team We3
    Hamilton, Stuart (team mgr)
    Gallagher, Jane
    Pervez, Fiona
    Carruthers, Brian (pso)
    Rutter, Maureen (pso)
    Wilson, Claire (pso)
    Larkin-Jones, Duncan (tpo)
    Waite, Rebecca (tpo)

    Team We4
    Kelly, Tricia (team mgr)
    King, Caroline
    Cooper, Natalie
    Haslam, Jean
    Hunt, Debra
    Gregory, Gemma
    Waterston, Darren
    Childs, David (pso)
    Johnston, Philip (pso)
    Thomson, Dawn (pso)
    Jones, Sîan (tpo)

    Level 4 Facilitator
    Buttery, Rob (p)

Unpaid Work/Community Payback
Huddart, Lynn (mgr)
Birkby, Paul (pso, placement mgr)

Support Services
Martin, Julie (dvnl office mgr)
Montague, Ted (performance & qual mgr)

Partnership Workers
Bowness, Brian (CASS)

6. The Court House, Catherine Street
    Whitehaven CA28 7PA
    tel (01946) 598120 *fax (01946) 598149*

    Team We2
    MacKenzie, Barbara (team mgr)
    Hallam-Davies, Steve
    Jackson, Barbara
    Carroll, Sean
    Jackson, Lyndsay
    Pearson, Andrew (pso)
    Sewell, Eddie (pso)
    Cartner, Lee (pso)
    Coupe, Trudie (tpo)

    Unpaid Work/Community Payback
    Muller, Karl (mgr)

    Support Services
    Martin, Julie (dvnl office mgr)

    Partnership Workers
    Bowness, Brian (CASS)

7. Hall Park, Ramsay Brow
    Workington CA14 4AR
    tel (01900) 604691 *fax (01900) 603572*

    Team We1
    Watson, Richard (team mgr)
    Albon, Audrey (p)
    Bowker, Pam
    Candlish-Stuart, Patrick
    Kirkbride, Emily
    Lawson, Sarah (p)
    Williams, Sian
    Garrett, David
    Chisnall, Lindsey (pso)
    Mitchelhill, Paul (pso)
    Sewell, Wisha (pso)
    Arrowsmith, Noreen (pso)
    Sjurseth, Sharon (tpo)

    Unpaid Work/Community Payback
    Muller, Karl (mgr)
    Halder, Teresa (pso, placement mgr)

    Support Services
    Martin, Julie (dvnl office mgr)

8.   41 Curzon Street
     Maryport Cumbria, CA15 6LW
     tel (01900) 812467 *fax (01900) 815152*

     Watson, Richard (team mgr)
     Holliday, Marie (pso)
     Blythe, Margaret (pso)

     Support Services
     Martin, Julie (dvnl office mgr)

Cumbria Youth Offending Team

9.   **North Division**
     5 Brunswick Street, Carlisle CA1 1PB
     tel (01228) 607090 *fax (01228) 607094*

     Bell de Zarza, Morag

10. **West Division**
     67 Wood Street, Maryport CA15 6LD
     tel (01900) 813531 *fax (01900) 812636*

     Bushell, Lindsey

11. **South Division**
     Newbridge House
     Ewan Close, Barrow in Furness LA13 9ED
     tel (01229) 826080 *fax (01229) 824165*

     Clegg, Julie

MAPPA

12. Cumbria Constabulary HQ,
     Carleton Hall, Penrith CA10 2AU
     tel 0845 330 0247

     Richardson, Elaine (MAPPA admin)

Approved Premises (Hostel)

13. Bowling Green Approved Premises
     90 Lowther Street, Carlisle CA3 8DP
     tel (01228) 522360 *fax (01228) 590967*

     Craven, Mike (mgr)
     Miles, Clive (dep mgr)
     Allison, Dawn (pso)
     Crack, Dick (pso)
     Harrison, Stuart (pso)
     Schollick, Peter (pso)

Institution

14. H M Prison **Haverigg**
     Millom LA18 4NA
     tel (01229) 772131 *fax (01229) 770011*

     Cooper, Gill (director of prison &
     community ptnrshps, Twin Peaks proj)
     McCormick, Janet
     Wyatt, Lee

O'Brien, Di (pso)
Thorpe, Gary (pso)
Scott, Bob (pso)

Local Justice Areas

     5 Furness & District
     2 Carlisle & District
     4 South Lakeland
     3 Eden
     6 Whitehaven
     7 West Allerdale & Keswick

Crown Court

     2 Carlisle

Secondments

     NW Consortium
     Parkes, Ruth

     Scafell Project
     Davidson, Chris (mgr)
     McQuillan, Alistair
     Cullen, Marie
     Sutton-Riley, Emma
     Baker, Stephen (pso)
     Wood, Gill (pso)

     HM Inspectorate of Probation
     Hubbard, Stephen

DERBYSHIRE PROBATION AREA

Out of hours emergency contact point
Burdett Lodge, (01332) 341324

Victim enquiries contact number: (01332) 340047

e-mail Firstname.Surname@derbyshire. probation.gsi.gov.uk

1.   **Head Office**
     18 Brunswood Road
     Matlock Bath, Matlock DE4 3PA
     tel (01629) 55422 *fax (01629) 580838*

     White, Denise (co)
     Taylor, Steve (chair of board)
     Finniear, Vicky (pa to chief & chair)

     Plang, Rosemary (aco)
     O'Sullivan, David (aco)
     Allsop, John (aco)
     Corry Bond (pa/board admin secretary)
     McMahon, Louise (office mgr)
     Webster, Ian (health & safety mgr)
     Barker, Val (interim hr mgr)

Radford, Gary (finance mgr)
Brewer, Lesley (business imprvmnt mgr)
Self, Mark (partnerships mgr)
Kenny, Paul (special projects mgr)
Angrave, Richard (performance & info mgr)
Marshall, Dominic (info research evaluation off)
Parkin, Mark (info reporting supvr)
Wooliscroft, Daniel (info off)
Potter, Anji (i.t tech supt mgr)
Smith, Anna (info systems training off)
Booker, Philip (comms off)

1a. Training Unit
1 Institute Lane, Alfreton DE55 7BQ
tel (01773) 833247 *fax (01773) 831944*

Cartledge, Isobel (spo training)
Colegate, Sharon (snr training off)

Info Systems Training
tel (01773) 833074
Burton, Jennifer (snr info systems/ it training supvr)

1b. MAPPA Public Protection Unit
Derbyshire Constabulary HQ,
Butterley Hall, Ripley,
Derbyshire DE5 3RS
direct dial (01773) + number

fax (01773) 572976

Nuttall, Brian (MAPPA mgr) 573601
Paul Taylor (MAPPA co-ord) 573602
Raybould, Verity (MAPPA admin) 573634
Winnington, Nicola (MAPPA admin) 573635
Smith, Amy (MAPPA admin) 573635
Taylor, Joanne (ViSOR admin) 573632
Redfern, Joanne (ViSOR admin) 573632

2. Derby Crown Court
Derby Combined Court Centre
Morledge, Derby DE1 2XE
tel (01332) 622549 *fax (01332) 622548*

Crown Court Liaison Team
Mandair, Narinder (cclo)
Barnes, Sharon (pso)
Edwards, Shaaron (pso)

3. Southern Derbyshire Magistrates' Court
The Magistrates' Court, Shire Hall
19 St Mary's Gate **Derby** DE1 3JR
tel (01332) 293081 *fax (01332) 293082*

Southern Derbyshire Magistrates' Court Team
Robinson-Stanley, Clifton (mclo)
Rosier, Tim (mclo)
Morgan, Mikki (pso)
Dallison, Jane (pso)
Hutchinson, Karen (pso)
Doyle, Kirsty (pso)
May, Marie (pso)
Richardson, Lisa (pso)
Tutin, Doug (pso)

4. 2 Siddals Road
Derby DE1 2PB

Derby Central Reception
tel (01332) 340047 *fax (01332) 340056*

Watson, Jane (divnl office mgr)
Anderson, Sara (off mgr)
Malcolm, Robert (info off)
Masters, Sara (info off)

Offender Management Units
McLennan, Rachel (divnl mgr)

Offender Mgmnt Unit 1 (intake)
Iain MacLachlan (spo)
Brittain, Mick
Flint, Lesley
Kelly, Paula
Purser, Alison

Offender Mgmnt Unit 2
Wild, Ben (spo)
Briggs, Jo
James-Moore, Kathryn
Khalida, Tabasum
Morgan, Jon
Reid, Linda
Schofield, Bob
Diedrick, Karlana (pso)
Mather-Wood, Sara (pso)
Parker, Joanne (pso)
Small, Helena (pso)
Tomlinson, Lisa (pso)

Offender Mgmnt Unit 3
Thandi, Sandeep (spo)
Ahmed, Sofena
Ayodeji, Andrew
Curry, Laura
Higgs-Ward, Jody
Sandhu, Harjit
Tissington, Miranda
Abbott, Danielle (pso)
Ashton, Clare (pso)
Rai, Parmjit (pso)

Offender Mgmnt Unit 4
Gell, Lois (spo)

Smith, Catrin (spo)
Adler, Keren
Buxton, Helen
Dawkins, Jon
Gordon, Marlene
Johnson, Claire
Webb, Jonathan
Sheldon, Sue (pso)
Smith, Ceri (pso)
Smith, Nic (pso)
Weatherston, Andrea (pso)

Offender Mgmnt Unit 5
Gardner, Martin (spo)
Bingham, Carrie
Bouse, Martin
Gilchrist, Elizabeth
Johnson, Sally
Singh, Emma
Tugnait, Vandna
Harris, Karan (pso)
Biddick, Sharon (pso)
Kvintas, Julie (pso)

Derby Courts' Team
MacLachlan, Iain (spo)
Bailey, Vicky(breach pso)
Hawksworth, Maxine (breach pso)
Taylor, Claire (bail pso)

Employment, Training & Education
Stevens, Pete (pso)

Victim Liaison
Lyness, Fiona(spo)
Dengate, Cheryl (pso)

QPDO
McCormick, Roz (qpdo)

Trainee Probation Officers
Jennens, Joanna (trainee)

MAPPA
Shingler, Trudy (trainee forensic psy)

Community Payback Unit
Wagstaff, Neil (divnl cp mgr, S&W units)
Hough, Samantha (divnl cp off)
Adams, Lauren (cpo)
Peach, Karen (cpo)
Price, Kevin (cpo)
Tutin, Doug (cpo)
Sheldon, George (cpo)
Strong, Helen (cpo)
Woolley, Leona (cpo)
Ilic, Peter (cp placement supvr)
Pierpoint, Heather (cp supvr)
Hopkins, Peter (cp supvr)
Jones, Bob (cp supvr)
Jordan, Denise (cp supvr)

Martin, Susan (cp supvr)
Sandhu, Diljit (cp supvr)

5. **Derby Probation Centre**
    Willow House, 1a Willow Row
    Derby DE1 3NZ
    tel (01332) 361200 *fax (01332) 294011*

Lawrence, Neelum (office mgr)

Programmes
Parker, Sue (spo)
Smith, Nicola (treatment mgr)
Heini, Claire (treatment mgr)
Kean, Frances
Neville, Bill
Holmes, Lucy (pso)
Bews, Barbara (pso)
Groom, Julie (pso)
Hough, Samantha (pso)
Hosty, Gemma (pso)
Jennens, Julie (pso)
Joyce, Sarah (pso)
McArdle, Natalie (pso)
Parveen, Zureena (pso)

Substance Misuse Unit
Weetman, Ros (spo)
Brown, Steven
Fisher, Lyn
Humphrey, Sheridan
Jagpal, Nimrit
Roots, Susie
Lawton, Adele
Leak, Stewart
White, Lavina
Ashby, Jo (pso)
Gates, Daniel (pso)
Richardson, Lisa (pso)
Salmon, Robert (pso)

IAC Unit
Elliott, Gill (spo)
Coleman, Sheree
McAteer, Matt
Buckley, Wendy (pso)

Employment, Training & Education
Burgess, Sheila (ete mgr)
Todd, Emma (pso)
Whatton, Pam (pso)

Practice Development Assessors
Glanowski, Sarah (pda)

6. 3 Brimington Road
    Chesterfield S41 7UG
    tel (01246) 276171 *fax (01246) 556505*

Shinfield, Marion (divnl off mgr)
Hickey, Janet (aco interventions)

Mortimer, Andrew (info off)
Marjoram, Sandra (divnl mgr)

Offender Mgmnt Unit 1
Agnew, Kat (spo)
Small, Nikki
Massey, Mike
Taylor, Gemma
Cooper, Sarah
Pepper, Sarah (pso)
Webster, Mike (pso)
Roddis, Sarah (trainee)

Offender Mgmnt Unit 2
Agnew, Kat (spo)
Roberts, Siân
Evans, Rebecca
Bruty, Emma
Holmes, Phil (pso)
Quiqley, Hannah (pso)
Bower, Sarah (trainee)

Offender Mgmnt Unit 3
Box-Peyton, Kate (spo)
Doxey, Gemma
Hannant, Katy
Ingman, Rachel
James, Marcus
Walker, Angie
Goodall, Debbie (pso)
Northedge, June (pso)
Milner, Sarah (trainee)

Offender Mgmnt Unit 4
Box-Peyton, Kate (spo)
Schreder, Mark
Dymond, Laura
Gillott, Julia (pso)
Lawal, Chris (pso)
Barrett, Vickie (trainee)

Courts
Kenny, Danielle (spo)
Miller, Rachel (breach pso)
Self, Louise (breach pso)

Starnes, Jerry (pso)
Wallis, Helen (mclo)
Webster, Mark (pso)
Weatherall, Lindsey (pso)

Employment, Training & Education
Schofield, Paul (pso)

Victim Liaison
Sampson, Adrienne (pso)

Compliance
Jackson, Sandy (pso)
Weatherall, Lindsey (pso)

PDA/QPDO
Gandy, Zephaniah (qpdo)
Herward, Rebecca (pda)

Programmes
Parry, Chris (treatment mgr)
Trivett, Diane (treatment mgr)
Lewis, Claire
Dennis, Laura (pso)
Smedley, Emma (pso)
Wilcockson, Mark (pso)

Community Payback Unit
Clay, Stephen (divnl cp mgr)
Rowland, Viv (divnl cpo)
Ludlam, Craig (cpo)
Fury, Mike (cpo)
Hutchinson, Margaret (cpo)
Smith, Alfred (cpo)
Freeman, Gaynor (cp placement supvr)
Lennon, Bevin (cp placement supvr)
Gee, Jeff (cp supvr)
Waterfield, Charles (cp supvr)

6a. **Chesterfield Magistrates' Court**
The Court House
Tapton Lane **Chesterfield** S41 7TW
tel (01246) 278340 *fax (01246) 237582*

6b. Bayheath House, Rose Hill West,
Chesterfield S40 1JF
tel (01246) 229844 *fax (01246) 554679*

Offender Mgmnt Unit 5 (subst misuse)
Hume, Tracey (spo)
Fitton, Brian
Turner, Phillip
Anderson, Lynda
Randall, Laura
Kajla, Mandeep (pso)
McMahon, Richard (pso)
Shannon, Katie (pso)
Smith, James (pso)
Statham, Beverley (pso)

7. 1 Institute Lane **Alfreton** DE55 7BQ
tel (01773) 835536 fax (01773) 831944
part time office

8. 2d Dale Road
Matlock DE4 3LT
tel (01629) 582148 *fax (01629) 57872*
Tuesday to Friday only

Offender Mgmnt Unit
Baker, Lawrence
Chapman, Louise
Weston, Jackie (pso)

9. Chesterfield House
    24 Hardwick Street **Buxton** SK17 6DH
    tel (01298) 25558 *fax (01298) 79132*

    Clitheroe, Pat (divnl off mgr)
    Mortimer, Andrew (info off)

    Offender Mgmnt Unit
    Wray, Shelagh (spo)
    Baker, Lawrence
    Long, Jane
    Gittins, Jane
    Rogers, Jane
    Sloan, Sue
    Ardern, Cathy (pso)
    Cottrell, David (pso)
    Glover, Tony (pso)
    McNicholas, Sally (pso)
    Miller, Claire (pso)
    Weston, Jackie (pso)

    Courts
    Smith, Ellen

    Employment, Training & Education
    Cottrell, David (pso)

    Substance Misuse
    Whitlaw, Clare
    Ashwood, Rebecca (pso)

    Community Payback Unit
    Bates, Deborah (cpo)
    Fairhurst, David (cpo)
    Fox, Joy (cp placement supvr)
    Buckley, Norman (cp supvr)
    Crich, Amanda (cp supvr)

9a. 14 Ellison Street
    Glossop SK13 8BX
    tel (01457) 852546 *fax (01457) 853272*

    Monday to Thursday only

    Offender Mgmnt Unit 1
    Gittins, Jane
    Rogers, Jane
    Ardern, Cathy (pso)

10. 34 South Street
    Ilkeston DE7 5QJ
    tel 0115-930 1123 *fax 0115-930 2503*

    Nicholson, Barbara (divnl off mgr)
    Masters, Sara (info off)

    Offender Mgmnt Unit 1 (Ilkeston)
    Knowles, Kaye (spo)
    Cammack, Jane
    Gee, Di
    Vassell, Lenford
    Jackson, Ian

    Smyth, Nicola (pso)
    Don, Jennifer (trainee)
    Duncan, Samantha (trainee)

    Offender Mgmnt Unit 2 (Ilkeston)
    Beardmore, Di (spo)
    Emslie, Ann
    Gooch, Dan
    Hill, Phil
    Wharton-Howett, Mark
    Murphy, Gill (pso)
    Taylor, Claire (pso)
    Ali, Lisa (trainee)

    Offender Mgmnt Unit 3 (subst misuse)
    Dunkley, Charlotte (spo)
    Southall, Francine
    Mason, Jacqueline
    Nudd, Daniella
    Purewal, Harjit
    Wilkinson, Jennie
    Roberts, Hannah (pso)
    Wood, Graham (pso)
    Baugh, Raelene (pso)
    Kemp, Kathy (trainee)

    Offender Mgmnt Unit 4 (Alfreton)
    Knowles, Kaye (spo)
    Monck, Daniel
    Shankland, Nicola
    Wood, Rachel (pso)

    Offender Mgmnt Unit 5 (Alfreton)
    Beardmore, Di (spo)
    Blackburn, Rebecca
    Bowden, David
    Hartley, Matthew (pso)

    Offender Mgmnt Unit 6 (breach)
    Hardingham, Sally (pso)

    Employment, Training & Education
    Martinson, Daryl (pso)

    Victim Liaison
    Farry, Christine (pso)

    PDA/QPDO
    Penman, Linda (pda)
    Johnson, Claire (qpdo)

10a. **Community Payback Unit**
    Mill Lane, off Greenhill Lane
    Riddings DE55 4DB
    tel (01773) 605812 *fax (01773) 605347*

    Martin, Marjory (divnl cpo)
    Guy, Mark (cpo)
    Hilliard, Neil (cpo)
    McDonald, David (cpo)
    Thandi, Arvinder (cpo)
    Marshall, John (cp placement supvr)

Clayton, Melanie (cp supvr)
Hopkinson, Ken (cp supvr)
Meakin, Richard (cp supvr)

Seconded Staff

11. **Derby YOT**
    2nd Floor, St Peter's House
    Gower Street, Derby DE1 9BR
    tel (01332) 256820 *fax (01332) 256830*

    Channon, Jim
    Morgan, Byron

12. **Ilkeston YOT**
    Kingfisher House, Cotmanhay Road
    Ilkeston DE7 8HU
    tel (01629) 531779 *fax 0115-909 8184*

    Boyer, Sue

13. **Chesterfield YOT**
    56 Cobden Road, Chesterfield S40 4TD
    tel (01629) 537615 *fax (01246) 347651*

    Jackson, Keith

14. **Buxton YOT**
    Area Education Office
    Kents Bank Road, Buxton SK17 9HR
    tel (01629) 531085 *fax (01298) 308411*

    Markham, Simon

15. **Other Secondments**

    Criminal Justice Board
    Gurnett, Laura (derbys cjb board proj mgr)

    **Derbyshire County Council
    Community Safety Team**
    Mason, Glenn (spo)

    **Midlands Training Assessment
    & Devpt Consortium**
    Hodgson, Robert
    Ryan, Natalie

    Ministry of Justice
    Slade, Michael (aco, perf imprvmnt mgr)
    Connor, Peter (spo)
    Morrison, Caroline (spo)
    Purewal, Manjinder (aco)
    Sein, Sarah Winwin (aco)
    Woods, Joe (spo)
    Williams, Trevor (spo)

Approved Premises (Hostel)

16. **Burdett Lodge**
    6 Bass Street, Derby DE22 3BR
    tel (01332) 341324 *fax (01332) 202089*

Francis, Deanna (spo)
Kelly, Paula (dep mgr)
Woodhouse, Sharon (bursar)
Bremmer, Carol (hostel off)
Carson, Lynn (hostel off)
Gilligan, Dominic (hostel off)
Hatto, Julie (hostel off)
Griggs, Alan (hostel off)
Scrivener, David (hostel off)
Webster, Rebecca (hostel off)
Wrighte, Shelley (hostel off)
Adams, Tracey (hostel supt wrkr)
Bano, Shamshad (hostel supt wrkr)
Cleary, Cathy (hostel supt wrkr)
Gordon, Fitzroy (hostel supt wrkr)
McWilliam, Fiona (hostel supt wrkr)
Marshall, Mary (hostel supt wrkr)

Institutions

17. H M Prison **Sudbury**
    Ashbourne, Sudbury DE6 5HW
    tel (01283) 584000 *fax (01283) 584001*
    probn clerk ext 4074

    Page-Smith, Marion (spo) ext 4073
    Butler, Melanie ext 4232
    Jones, Corinne ext 4232
    Johnson, Sally ext 4074
    Needham, Carly ext 4097
    Millard, Lynne ext 4100
    Egginton, Matthew ext 4228
    Britton, Penny ext 4228
    Eames, Kerry (pso)
    Fearon-King, Lynette ext 4233 (pso)
    Wilkinson, Paul ext 4232 (pso)

18. H M Prison **Foston Hall**
    Foston, Derby DE65 5DN
    tel (01283) 584300 *fax (01283) 584301*

    Dosanjh, Michael (spo) ext 4491
    Davey, Clare ext 4482
    Gorton, Kate ext 4482
    Fitch, Adrian ext 4494
    Sansom, Michelle (pso) ext 4494
    Nuttall, Corinne (pso) ext 4378
    Leek, Rebecca (pso) ext 4418/4497

Local Justice Areas

6, 7, 8 North East Derbyshire & Dales
3, 4, 5, 10 Southern Derbyshire
9 High Peak

Crown Court

2 Derby

DEVON & CORNWALL PROBATION AREA

Out of hours emergency contact point
Lawson House (01752) 568791

Victim enquiries contact number Exeter (01392) 421122, Plymouth (01752) 827500, Torbay (01803) 213535, N Devon (01271) 321681

e-mail firstname.surname@devon-cornwall. probation.gsi.gov.uk

1. **Head Office**
    Queen's House, Little Queen Street
    Exeter EX4 3LJ
    tel (01392) 474100 *fax (01392) 413563*

    McFarlane, Mary Anne (co)
    Wooderson, Alan (chair)
    Clewlow, Ian (director of ops)
    Menary, Rob (director business services)
    Cash, Rosie (divnl business mgr) 474136
    Meaden, Graham (aco, hr) 474117
    Lambert, Maggie (hr mgr) 474114
    Addicott, Marie (hr business prtnr) 474105
    Legon-Taylor, Victoria (hr bus prtnr) 474126
    Pratt, Sheila (payroll officer) 474129
    Atherton, Sandra (training mgr) 474145
    Lamb, Carol (treasurer) 474128
    Luffman, David (finance mgr/acc) 474146
    Lloyd, Lyndsay (financial analyst) 474114
    Felix-Mitchell, Jacquie (pr & comms off) 474104
    Sussex, Trevor (ict systems mgr) 474121
    Cox, Ben (asst ict supt off) 474149
    Dickens, Matt (ict supt technician) 474140
    Donohue, Ian (ict supt & training tech) 474135
    Ambrosini, Victor (asst ict supt off) 474101
    Shergold, Katy (asst info off) 474152
    Cupit, John (info compliance off) 474108
    Mandeville Norden, Rebecca (snr research off) 474139
    Rakestrow, Janine (asst res off) 474110

N & E Division

2. 3/5 Barnfield Road
    Exeter EX1 1RD
    tel (01392) 421122 *fax (01392) 434839*

    Mitchell, Mary (aco)
    Ough, Shirley (aco pa) 455411
    Murphy, John (divnl business mgr) 455400
    Perkins, Simon (ptnrship & joint commissioning mgr) 455449
    Bailey, Rachel (p, peri po) 455432

Edmonds-Hughes, Cassandra (p, IT skills facilitator) 455580

Offender Management

Courts Services
Coker, Charlotte (p, spo) 455447
Birchnall, Olive 415361
Emmen, Peter 455464
Johnson, Tig (p) 455473
Spiller, Paul 455477
Wilson, Laura (p) 455478
Boniwell, Tracey (pso) 455428
Taylor, Carol (senior lpo) 455436

Substance Misuse
Janus-Harris, Colin (spo) 455405
Banham, Caron 455475
Davies, Mandy 455421
Haydon, Carol 455490
Furness, Des (pso) 455443
Sails, Jacci (pso) 455471
Williams, Sarah (p, pso) 455474

General Offending
Coker, Charlotte (p, spo) 455447
Tilby, Gaynor
Wood, Dani 455432

Risk of Harm
Coker, Charlotte (p, spo) 455447
Bishop, Sasha 455434
Broaders, Gabriel 455462
Lydon, Shaz 455461
Demirci, Tina 455426
Weeks, Dennis 455455
Murdock, Leah 455489
Campbell, Kate (pso) 455414
Welland, Sue (pso) 455413

Public Protection Unit
Clapinson, Colin (spo) 455452
Clarke, Dee
Rayfield, Mike 455467
Stockley, Rachel 07738503720
Savage, Viv 455492
Johnson, Tig (p) 455473
Shaljean, Rosie (vlo) 455448

Prolific & other Priority Offender Unit
Janus-Harris, Colin (spo) 455405
Davies, Diane 455486
Ballm, Carole (pso) 455450

Interventions

Programmes
Benden, Mark (spo) 455412
Munday, Sue (treatment mgr) 455493
Willett, Rachel (p, treatment mgr) 455476
Stammers, Jackie (p) 455488
Albany, Melissa (p, pso) 455482
Bennett, Neal (pso) 455466

Davis, John (pso) 455491
Greenhill, Laura (ETE pso) 455478

Unpaid Work Unit
Dan, Samantha (unit mgr) 455423
Davies, Trina (p, pso) 455417
Holland, Darren (pso) 455456
Lovell, Gemma (pso) 455402
Smith, Shirley (pso) 455419
Champion, Dawn (p, pso plcmnt supvr)
455460
Crockett, Julia (pso plcmnt supvr) 455435
Little, John (p, pso plcmnt supvr) 455435
May, Alfie (pso plcmnt supvr) 455460
Smith, Peter (pso plcmnt supvr) 455460

Practice Development Unit
Greenslade, Tim (pda) 455481
Hamilton, Mike (pda) 455487
Ross, Louise (p, pda)
Bennett, Jane (trainee) 455489
Dobel, Elizabeth (trainee)
Elek, Sophia (trainee) 455474
Fairweather, Chris (trainee)
Glide, Judith (trainee) 455425
Heywood, Hannah (trainee)
Holloway, Angela (trainee)
King, Louise (trainee)
Merryman, Naomi (trainee) 455459
Mitchell, Phillipa (trainee)
Murdock, Leah (trainee) 455489
Pope, Matthew (trainee)
Wright, Melanie (trainee) 455458

3. **East Devon Youth Offending Team**
Ivybank, 45 St David's Hill
Exeter EX4 4DN
tel (01392) 384933 *fax (01392) 384985*

Caddick, Claire (p)
Annison, Keith
Kennett, Peter

4. Kingsley House, Castle Street
Barnstaple, EX31 1DR
tel (01271) 321681 *fax (01271) 329864*
Offender Management
Integrated Case Management
McGregor, Jamie (spo) 312278
Ballam, Sue 312335
Bennett, Jane
Burgess, Linda
Coker, Julian (p) 312283
Dawson, Lesley
Fairweather, Christine
Jones, Sara 312274
Marshall, Barbara 312261
Pope, Matthew

Wilson, Anne (p)   312270
Watts, Sally 312271
Wells, Jenny 312272
Feesey, Sue (pso) 312255
Slade, Wendy (pso) 312265
Thompson, Jo (lpo/vlo) 312260

Prolific & other Priority Offender Unit
Milton, Mark 312334
Jones, Tessa (pso) 312256

Inverventions
Programmes
Dare, Catherine (p) 312284
Palmer, Jo (p) 312285
Knibbs, Elaine (pso) 312266

Unpaid Work Unit
tel (01271 312279)
Ford, Geraldine (unit mgr) 312264
Turner-Hewson, Chrissie (pso) 312267
Harber, Stephen (pso plcmnt supvr)
Johns, Pauline (pso plcmnt supvr)
Tomkinson, David (p, pso plcmnt supvr)

Practice Development Unit
Raitt, Andrew (pda) 312269

Plymouth Division

5. St Catherine's House
5 Notte Street, **Plymouth** PL1 2TS
tel (01752) 827500 *fax (01752) 267189*

Vallis, Peter (aco)
O'Sullivan, Siobhan (aco pa) 827531
Williams, Ros (divnl business mgr) 827553
Adams, Barry (area h&s advr) 827554
Vacancy (ptnrshp & joint com mgr)
Williams, Bob (p, volunteer co-ord) 827533
Willson, Greg (Skills for Life co-ord) 827584
Vacancy (p, IT skills facilitator)

Team 1
Roesner, Sue (spo) 827582
Arube, Zahra
Auty, Angela (p) 827645
Downing, Vanessa 827579
Harris, Guy (p) 827583
Hill, Joanne 827580
Jackson, Caroline
McFarlane, Andy 827581
Richards, Jane
Solomon, Gail 827590
Toms, Min (trtmnt mgr) 827578

Team 2
Clark, Brian (p, spo) 827543
Lucas, Sonia (pa)
Casey, Charlie 827552
Dent, Becky 827538
Garvey, Sarah 827535

Gerry, Jayde 827534
Henderson, Alistair (p) 827533
McGeorge, Penny 827536
Stewart, Val 827540

Team 3
Webb, Georgia (spo) 827640
Lovejoy, Vyaj (temp pa) 827600
Bishop, Gary 827594
Dickson, Michelle 827596
Hollingsworth, Nicola 827599
Lamerton, Mark 827595
Narin, Jill 827597
Smith, Marina 827641

Team 4
Squire, Lynn (spo) 827506
Hodgson, Sharon (pa) 827546
Atkinson, Michael (napo chair) 827570
Berglund, Kristina 827569
Carson, Tim 827564
Costello, Anne 827541
Davis, Simon 827561
Edgecombe, Helen 827566
Gunn, Hilary 827562
Young, Judy 827563

Court Services
Lister, Maggie 827641
Millin, Geoff (p) 827549
Ross, Bernadine (p) 673105
Wooler, Tony (p) 673105
Burns-Jones, Diane (pso) 673105
Lee, David (pso) 252419

**Interventions &
Commissioned Services**
Munn, Chris (spo) 827606
Tucker, Melanie (p, temp pa) 827607
Measures, Debbie (vlo) 827604
Lawrence, Jayne (p, mappa co-ord) 827605
Amphlett, Kirsten (p, pso) 827504
Clark, Sarah (pso) 827613
Lester, Scott (pso) 827557
Prior, Claire (p, pso) 827612
Saunders, Janis (p, pso) 827559
Tarrant, Eleanor (pso) 827558
Lawrence, Nadine (p, pso trtmnt mgr)
827614
Lord, Kelly (p, legal proc off) 827610
Rowe, Dawn (legal proc off) 827608
Sherwin, Lisa (p, legal proc off) 827609

Unpaid Work & ETE
Wakley, Richard (unit mgr, spo) 827642
Allen, Sam (case mgr) 827572
Brownlow, John (case mgr)
Cowling, Edgar (case mgr)
Dean, Darren (case mgr) 827572
Haskell, Norman (case mgr) 827575

Kelly, Mark (case mgr)
Tricker, Paul (case mgr) 827576
Eaton, Julian (ete) 827615
Hall, Claire (ete) 827602

Practice Development Unit
Lacey, Hugh (pda) 827626
Wellock, Neil (pda) 827625

Plymouth Prolific Offender Unit
Hyde Park House
Mutley Plain, **Plymouth** PL4 6LF
tel (01752) 434567 *fax (01752) 314268*

Aisbitt, Ian 434597
Cherrett, Jill 434593

6.   **Plymouth Youth Offending Team**
3rd Floor, Midland House
Notte Street, **Plymouth** PL1 2EJ
tel (01752) 306999 *fax (01752) 306998*

Oakes, Naomi

South Devon Division

7.   Thurlow House
Thurlow Road **Torquay** TQ1 3EQ
tel (01803) 213535 *fax (01803) 290871*

Proctor, Anne (aco)
Medd, Sarah (divnl business mgr) 219328
Drennan, Alex (unit mgr) 219308
Dubash, Nariman (spo) 219333
Hart, Becky (spo) 219301
Wood, Hayley (spo) 219307

Offender Management Team 1
Dubash, Nariman (spo) 219333
Jones, Alex (spo) (from 1.4.09)
Dawe, Susan (p) 219346
Gaubert, Ian
Harding, Lin 219322
Heckford, Julia 219338
Tucker-Last, Jamie 219348
Winter, Debbie (p) 219377
Britton, Colin (pso) 219323
Hughes, Chaylla (p, pso) 219304
Scattergood, Shirley (pso) 219325

Offender Management Team 2
Wood, Hayley (spo) 219307
Caulfield, Michael (pso) 219330
Ferris, Chris 219374
Fraser, James 219345
Holman, Jen 219339
Jones, Amanda
Keehner, Cindy (p) 219379
Stansbie, Sarah (p) 219303
Unwin, Martin 219337

Courts Services
Hart, Becky (spo) 219301

Cale, Pam (p) 219311
Caughey, Lois 219302
Harrison, Lyn (p)
Knowles, Veronica 219370
Moore, Polly 219334
Robinson, Derek (p) 219331
Randle, Heidi (legal proc off) 219343

Public Protection
Hart, Becky (spo) 219301
Nunn, Melanie 219316
Sharples, John 219376
Vacancy
Noble, Val (vlo) 219321

Punishment & Reparation/UPW
Drennan, Alex (unit mgr) 219308
Dark, Jacqui (pso) 219315
Hawkey, Rebecca 219349
Steer, Cheryl (pso) 219335
Bammens, Russell (plcmnt mgr/supvr)
Cloherty, Dave (plcmnt mgr/supvr)
Pitt, Barry (plcmnt mgr/supvr)

Project XL
Marder, Briony (pso) 219329
Palmer, Bev (ete, pathfinder pso) 219309
Taylor, Patricia (mentor) 219371

8.   Commerce House
97-101 Abbey Road
Torquay TQ2 5PJ
tel (01803) 408510 *fax (01803 29939)*

Jones, Alex (spo) (until 1.4.09) 408511
Dubash, Nariman (spo) (from 1.4.09)
Roberts, Ruth (prtnrshp & joint
commissioning mgr) 408520

Programmes Team
Jones, Alex (spo) (until 1.4.09) 408511
Dubash, Nariman (spo) (from 1.4.09)
Lewis, Maddi (p, pso, trtmnt mgr) 408514
Randle, Steve (pso) 408518
Swinfen, Marian (p, trtmnt mgr) 219347
Waine, Rosemary (pso) 408517
Winser, Tulane (pso) 408513

Partnerships Team
Roberts, Ruth (prtnrshp & joint
commissioning mgr) 408520
Greening, Ken (pso, housing intrvntns off)
408524
Curtis, Sarah (pso, alcohol intrvntns off)
408523

Substance Misuse
Eames, Mary (pso) 408515

Prolific & Priority Offender Unit
Gaywood, Anthony 408522

Reeby, Lorraine 408528
Trump, Simon (pso) 408521

9.   **Torbay Youth Offending Team**
Commerce House
97-101 Abbey Road, Torquay, TQ2 5PJ
tel (01803) 201655 *fax (01803) 201721*

Heather, Emily

Cornwall Division

10.   **Divisional Head Office**
Park House, Threemilestone Industrial
Estate, Truro TR4 9LD
tel (01872) 326262 *fax (01872) 326263*

Nason, Jon (aco)
Logue, Mel (aco pa) 326261
Jesson, Kathy (divnl business mgr) 326264

Business Services (Area)
tel (01872) 326 + ext

Overend, Mark (aco ict) ext 252
Wooding, Sarah (pa) ext 254
Linscott, Cris (project mgr) ext 253
Henry, Stephen (snr web devpr) ext 257
Stoddern, James (snr web devpr) ext 255
Thompson, Michael (web devpr) 01872
226283
Dutton, Michael (ict supt & training
technician) ext 265
Pierce, Jason (ict supt & training
technician) ext 258
Hanbidge, Gemma (info off) ext 256
Guy, Helen (info admin) ext 01872 226282
Orchard, Susie (financial analyst) ext 269
Emmett, Lucy (asstve solutns co-ord) ext
250

11.   Tremorvah Wood Lane
off Mitchell Hill, **Truro** TR1 1HZ
tel (01872) 261293 *fax (01872) 261311*

Vacancy (pship & joing commissioning mgr)

Integrated Case Management
McConnel, Su (p, spo)
Davies, Jenny
Lewis, Mary
Lowe, Mags
Bray, Brydie
Brown, Tony (p)
Southern, Robert
Berryman, Alison (pso)

Programmes
Gates, Liz
MacDonald, Lorna
McDonald, Joe

01209 612006

Coley, Helen (p, treatment mgr)
Bose, Julian (prog tutor)
Davies, Linda (prog tutor)
O'Hagan, Gail (p)

12. **Cornwall Youth Offending Team**
Chiltern House, City Road
Truro TR1 2JL
tel (01872) 274567 *fax (01872) 242436*

Beddow, Jon

13. Endsleigh House, Roskear
Camborne TR14 8DN
tel (01209) 612006 *fax (01209) 612551*

Fitzsimmons, Chris (p, spo)

Integrated Case Management
Godfrey, Trudi
Harris, Carly
Lanyon, Maria
Pascoe, Nigel
Parsons, Kelly
Penhaligon, Sylvia
Skinner, Julie
Williams, Richard
Collier, Maxine (p, pso)
Douglas, John (pso)
Wells, Peter (vlo)

Programmes
Lawrance, Jo (p, treatment mgr)

Public Protection
Coad, Lorna (p)
Rowe, Sarah (p)
Tregoning, Meg

Enhanced Community Punishment
Adams, Robert (plcmnt mgr/supvr)
Cotton, Steve (plcmnt mgr/supvr)
Mitchell, Ted (plcmnt mgr/supvr)

14. **W Cornwall Prolific Offender Unit**
Coach House, Tolvean, West End
Redruth TR15 2SS
tel (01209) 881944 *fax (01209) 881919*

**Cornwall CJIT Prolific
Offenders & DRRs**
Mitchell, Deborah (spo)
Edwards, Zoe
Payne, Sara
Rees, Michelle,
Canan, Serena
Robson, Phil (pso)
Vacancy (pso)

15. 1 Guildhall Road
Penzance TR18 2QJ

tel (01736) 363934 *fax (01736) 330690*

McKenzie, Anita
Skewes, Nicky (p)
Stubbings, Pauline
Gough, Brendan (pso)

16. 3 Kings Avenue
St Austell PL25 4TT
tel (01726) 72654 *fax (01726) 63553*

Offender Management
Parkinson, Ann (spo)
Arrowsmith, Paul
Element, Jane (p)
Frazer, Mark
Shirley, Ian
Thomas, Hannah (p)
Wilson, Gail
Bond, Mark (pso)
Heard, Liz (pso)
Vacancy (pso)

Court Report Writer
Malcolm, Sarah

Unpaid Work
tel (01726) 76282 *fax (01726) 76982*

Bishop, Sue (scheme mgr)
Gomersall, Anne Marie (p, case mgr)
Richards, Geoff (case mgr)
Rowe, Sandra (case mgr)
Dronfield, Adrian (plcmnt mgr/supvr)
Hill, Steve (plcmnt mgr/supvr)
Tonkin, Bob (plcmnt mgr/supvr)

ETE
Baines, Carol (ete co-ord)
Fildes, Tim (ete facilitator)

17. Culverland Road
Liskeard PL14 6RF
Resettlement tel (01579) 344299
Case Mngmnt tel (01579) 344299
fax (01579) 340277

Nason, Kerri (p, spo)
Flashman, Emma
Lynch, Gill
Swan, Mark
Ryan, Rose (pso)
Stacey, Sharon (pso)
Dale, Heather (vlo)
Gay, Peran (ca)
Wilson, Jacqueline (ca)

Projects/Secondments

18. **C.A.R.D.**
14 York Road, Exeter EX4 6BA

tel (01392) 270279

Douglas, Paul (spo)

19. **Public Protection Unit**
Devon & Cornwall Police HQ
Middlemoor, Exeter EX2 7HQ
tel (01392) 452865 *fax (01392) 452025*
e-mail nicola.whiley@
devonandcornwall.pnn.police.uk

Whiley, Nicola (mappa mgr)

Approved Premises (Hostels)

20. **Lawson House**
13/14 Paradise Place
Stoke, **Plymouth** PL1 5QE
tel (01752) 568791 *fax (01752) 606815*

Moss, Duncan (hostels mgr)
Pridmore, Giulia (deputy mgr)
Bailey, Lisa (asst mgr)
Bishop, Gerry (asst mgr)
Foster, Ashley (asst mgr)
Goodwin, Paul (asst mgr)
Reeby, Bernard (asst mgr)

21. **Meneghy House**
East Hill, Tuckingmill
Camborne TR14 8NQ
tel (01209) 715050 *fax (01209) 612595*

Cookson, Andy (hostels mgr)
Aldridge, Kevin (asst mgr)
McGoughan, Kay (asst mgr)
Spear, Ashley (asst mgr)

Institutions

22. **H M Prison Channings Wood**
Denbury, Newton Abbot TQ12 6DW
tel (01803) 814600 *fax (01803) 814601*

Bown, Gary (spo)
Hopkins, Lynne
Clark, Dee
Durie, David
Godfrey, Dick
Jones, Chris
Moore, Bernard
Turnbull, Adam (p)
Gue, Kevin (prog co-ord)
O'Toole, Patrick (prog co-ord)
Austen, Nicci (pso)

23. **H M Prison Dartmoor**
Yelverton PL20 6RR
tel (01822) 322000 fax (01822) 322001

Carey, Jack

Herron, David (p)
McFarlane, Andy
McVey, Judy (p)
Steele, Kate
Ward, Bob
Arrowsmith-Brown, Tessa (pso)
Chakrabarti, Santosh (pso)
Creasy, Pauline (pso)
Mellows, Jenny (pso)

24. **H M Prison Exeter**
New North Road, Exeter EX4 4EX
tel (01392 415650 *fax (01392) 415651)*

Burns, Melanie (pso)
English, Brent (pso)
Grummett, John (pso)
Haslam, Carl (pso)

Remand in Custody
tel (01392) 415836 *fax (01392) 415782*

Benbow, Laraine
Farrell, David
French, Gill (p)
Godfrey, John
Mannion, Christie (p)

Local Justice Areas

2 Central Devon
4 North Devon
5 Plymouth
7 South Devon
11 West Cornwall
12, 15, 16 East Cornwall

Crown Courts

2 Exeter
4 Barnstaple
5 Plymouth
11 Truro

DORSET PROBATION AREA

Out of hours emergency contact points
Weston Probation Hostel Weymouth (01305)
775742
The Pines Bail & Probation Hostel
Bournemouth (01202) 391757

e-mail Firstname.Surname@dorset.probation.
gsi.gov.uk

Performance Managers (formerly SPOs) are
responsible for specialist officers in different
offices.
Shown below is a list of teams and Performance
Managers

Offender Mgmnt (om)	Poole	
	Toni Baptiste	(7)
Offender Mgmnt (om)	Bournemouth	
	Elaine Morgan	(8)
Offndr Mgmnt (om & c&a)	Weymouth	
	Duncan Ireland	(4)
Public Protectn (pp)	East & Pines Hostel	
	Mel Gauden	(8)
Public Protectn (pp)	West & Weston Hostel	
	Denise Norton	(14)
Crt & Assessment (c&a)	Bournemouth	
	Chris Woolf (temp)	(8)
Probn Centre, Progrs	Poole	
	Alan Yelling	(7)
Community Service	Wareham	
	Mike Thomas	(6)

1. **Head Office**
    Forelle House, Marshes End
    Upton Road, Creekmoor
    Poole BH17 7AG
    tel (01202) 664060 *fax (01202) 664061*
    direct dial (01202) 66 + ext

    Wiseman, John (co) 4069
    Hutchinson, Andy (aco, director of
    commissioning & prtnrshps) 4064
    Shackleford, Murray (aco, public
    protctn & prisons) 4066
    Lane, Ben (aco finance & resources) 4063
    Drew, David (area mgr, finance &
    supt services) 4083
    Matthews, Mike (operatnl supt off) 4082
    Hallett, Peter (bus imprvmnts mgr) 4070
    Curtis, Glo (finance off) 4099
    Brittain, Gail (hr & devpt mgr) 4079
    Southam, Vanessa (hr off) 4080
    Goss, Steph (info unit mgr) 4078
    Bowers, Rick (snr IT supt off)
    Churchill, Judy (info supt asst) 4077
    Miller, Carol (MAPPA co-ord) 4085
    Sanderson, Nikki (MAPPA secy) 4086
    Douglas, Matt (business devpt mgr) 4071

    South West Training Consortium
    (Effective Practice Training)
    Cooney, Barry (effective pract training
    mgr) 4089 (mobile 07813 715 519)
    Towers, Wendy (pa) 4088

2. **Dorchester Probation Office**
    Wadham House, 50 High West Street
    Dorchester DT1 1UT
    tel (01305) 224742 *fax (01305)225122*
    direct dial (01305) 22 + ext

    Ireland, Duncan (perf mgr) (om &

    courts) 4742 (3 & 4)
    Corbett, Helen (p, c&a) 4471
    Evans, Janet (p, om) 4742
    Pursglove, Melanie (p, om) 4471
    Woolcock, Sarah (prtnrshp devpt
    officer) 4673

    Crown Court Liaison 4742

    Trainee
    Quinn, Melanie 4672

3. Law Courts, Westwey Road
    Weymouth DT4 8SU
    tel (01305) 774921 *fax (01305) 780102*
    direct dial (01305) + ext

    Ireland, Duncan (perf mgr) (om &
    crts) 752606 (4 & 2)
    Rogers, Ray (info supt asst) 752600

    Offender Management
    Pursglove, Melanie (p) 752612
    Rowe, Christine (p) 752609
    Fisher, Carol (pso)
    McGown, Sandra (pso) 752618
    Payne, Keith (pso) 752614

    Public Protection
    Dolder, John (p) 752616
    Walker, Stephanie (p) 752608

    Court & Assessment
    Goodchild, Mike (p) 752619
    Phoenix, Laura (p) 752607
    Pugh, Linda (p) 752607
    Staddon, Linda (p) 752615
    Townley-Walker, Sarah (p) 752613

    Trainees
    Doe, Martin 752611
    Hewson, Sharon 752611

4. Law Courts, Salisbury Road
    Blandford DT11 7HP
    tel (01258) 483552/438551
    fax (01258) 483550
    direct dial (01258) + ext

    Ireland, Duncan (perf mgr,
    om & c&a) (2 & 3)
    Openshaw, Heather (p) 483560
    Weston, Peter (p) 483558
    Payne, Keith (pso) 483557

5. **Community Service Office**
    Unit 19, Sandford Lane
    Wareham BH20 4JH
    tel (01929) 556513 *fax (01929) 553756*
    direct dial (01305) + ext

    Thomas, Mike (perf mgr) 557657

Hallett, Peter (deputy mgr) 557658
Hall, Karen (info supt asst) 557644
Brett, Steve (site admin/
task co-ord) 557641

Community Service Officers
Carey, Francis (cso) 557647
Hudson, Shellie (cso) 557651
Jones, Janet (cso) 557646
Jones, Julie Anne (cso) 557654
Mason, Tony (cso) 557652
Richardson, Rosemary (cso) 557649
Thomas, Diana (cso) 557648
Smyth, Deirdre (cso) 557655
Doward, Graham (wrkshp suprvr) 557656

6.   **Poole Office & Probation Centre**
63 Commercial Road, Parkstone
Poole BH14 0JB
tel (01202) 724053
fax (01202) 724023 (reception)
(01202) 724060 (om) 724040 (centre)
direct dial (01202) 72 + ext

Webber, Jan (info supt asst) 4056

Offender Management
Baptiste, Toni (perf mgr) 4001
Baker, Michelle (p) 4025
Brand, Jayne (p) 4058
Morgan, Mark (p) 4064
Oliver, Richard (p) 4030
Chiverton, Gerry (pso) 4066
Finch, Kay (pso) 4073
Reeves, Kelly (pso) 4071
Duty Officer Desk 4057

Public Protection
Woolridge, Matthew (p) 4070

Worth, Maggie (p) 4068

Trainees
Billings, Sean 4072
Hughes, Louise 4059
Peate, Martin 4059
Smith, Paul 4072

Probation Centre
Yelling, Alan (spo progs/centre mgr) 4051
Shepherd, Toni (snr pract) 4069
Counterson, Rachel (p) 4013
Rubie, Val (p) 4008
Simpson, Jackie (p) 4015
Watts, Claire (p) 4016
Cooke, Jacie (pso) 4006
Fehr, Sonya (pso) 4065
Foot, Christine (pso) 4006
Garrett, Jillian (pso) 4024
Martin, Jane (pso) 4004
McKay, Ian (pso) 4005

Shutt, Paul (pso) 4011

ETE Unit
Power, Jeanne 4067 (deputy mgr)
Lane, Terri (skills devpt off) 4002
Bascombe, Rima (ete off/pso) 4099
Cooke, Jacie (ete off/pso) 4002
Holmes, Kerry (ete off/pso) 4002
Kearey, Derek (ete off/pso) 4002
Sides, Susan (snr admin) 4098

7.   7 Madeira Road
Bournemouth BH1 1QL
tel (01202) 200200 *fax (01202) 200280*
direct dial (01202) 200 + ext

Vieira, Paulo (info supt asst) 218

Public Protection
fax 01202 200225
Gauden, Mel (perf mgr) 221
Cain, Jo (p) 254
Dixon, James (p) 211
Ennis, Joe (p) 258
Gibbs, Rupert (p) 230
Holmes, Debbie (p) 212
Middleton-Roberts (p) 259
Smith, Miranda (p) 213
McGrath, Della (vlo) 234

Court & Assessment
Woolf, Chris (perf mgr temp) 223
Goodchild, Mike (devpt mgr) 215
Denton, Kerry (p) 264
Harris, Avril (p) 264
Hussey, Caroline (p) 264
James, Denice (p) 265
Newman, Rachael (p) 266
Taylor, Anna (p) 265

Offender Management
fax 01202 200247
Morgan, Elaine (perf mgr) 245
Psaradelli, Micheal (devpt mgr) 236
Zakrzewski, Adrian (devpt mgr) 215
Fear, Laura (p) 227
Johnson, Tim (p) 260
Loynes, Amy (p) 231
Marsh, Natalie (p) 216
Martin, Alison (p)
Mathias, Kate (p) 235
Mitchell, Ann (p) 226
O'Donnell, Jocelyn (p) 214
Topliss, Oliver (p) 232
Wilkins, Charlotte (p) 202
Freemantle, Kim (pso) 262
Langley, Sue (pso) 249
Magnum, Nichola (pso) 248
O'Dell, Kirsty (pso) 250
Price, Jacqui (pso)

Pycroft, Carrie (pso) 263

Breach Unit (CAT)
Greaves, Kate (spo)
Dark, Nigel (pso, breach off) 243
Higgins, Sue (duty asst) 253
Stevens, Mel (pso) 244
Wheeler, Steve (pso, breach off) 282

Compliance Team
Greaves, Kate (spo)
Burgis, Debs (pso) 206
Richey, Adrian
Russell, Carol (pso) 253

Trainees
Zakrzewski, Adrian (devpt mgr) 215
Fuller, Lisa
Lamley, Kirstin 228
Hutchings, Juliette 267
Wade, Claire 261

Gateway Accommodation
fax 01202 200233
Lofts, David (mgr) 207
Blacoe, Nigel (proj wrkr) 269
Brown, Simon (proj wrkr) 239
Saunders, Helen (proj wrkr) 269
Webb, Joanne (snr admin) 270

8. **Magistrates' Court Liaison Office**
The Law Courts, Stafford Road
Bournemouth BH1 1LE
tel (01202) 291392 (magistrates' admin)
tel (01202) 293341 (magistrates' off)
fax (01202) 789468

9. **Crown Court Liaison Office**
The Courts of Justice
Deansleigh Road
Bournemouth BH7 7DS
tel (01202) 430565 (admin)
fax (01202) 430522

10. **Dorset Youth Offending Team**
Monkton Park, Winterborne Monkton
Dorchester DT2 9PS
tel (01305) 221400

11. **Bournemouth & Poole Youth Offending Team**
5 Hyde Road, Kinson
Bournemouth BH10 5JJ
tel (01202) 453939 *fax (01202) 453940*

Harcombe, Samantha (p)
Pilgrim, Amanda (p)

Approved Premises (Hostels)

12. **Weston Probation Hostel**
2 Westwey Road, **Weymouth** DT4 8SU

tel (01305) 775742 *fax (01305) 766510*

Norton, Denise (perf mgr)
Banks, Caroline (pso)
Crane, Louise (apa)
Heslop, Delena (apa)
Hursthouse, Natasha (apa)
Jarman-Norris, Andrew (apa)
Moverley, Patrick (apa)
Noyce, Darren (apa)
Read, Sandra (apa)
Fry, David (apa nights)
Logan, Alex (apa nights)
McGown, Chris (apa nights)
Taylor, Cheryl (oso)
Metcalfe, Jane (p, secy, Mon, Weds & Fri)

13. **The Pines Bail & Probation Hostel**
11 Cecil Road, Boscombe
Bournemouth BH5 1DU
tel (01202) 391757 *fax (01202) 391867*

Gauden, Mel (perf mgr) (7)
Morrell, Paul (oso/pso)
Welch, Susan (pso)
Azzaro, Bridget (apa)
Bedford, Martin (apa)
Collinson, Peter (apa)
Moore, Anne (apa)
Penny, Carol (apa)
Bracher-Howard, Susan (p, apa nights)
Mc Grath, Andy (p, apa nights)
O'Leary, Sue (p, apa nights)

Institutions

14. **HMP Dorchester**
7 North Square, **Dorchester** DT1 1JD
tel (01305) 714500 *fax (01305) 714501*
direct dial (01305) + 71 ext
special visits (am only) 4571

Macdonald, Jennifer (perf mgr) 4627
Phoenix, Laura (po) 4518
Baker, Nicole (pso) 4632
Dryer, Lorraine (pso) 4624
Mitchell, Tori (pso) 4632

15. **HMP The Verne**
Portland DT5 1EQ
tel (01305) 825000 fax (01305) 825001
probn fax (01305) 825028
direct dial (01305) 82 + ext

Benson, Deborah (p) 5034
Friday, Beryl (p) 5226
Moverley, Sarah (p, obp intrvntns) 5029
Pugh, Linda (p)

16. **HM Young Offender Institution**
The Grove, Easton

Portland DT5 1DL
tel (01305) 715600 *fax (01305) 715601*
direct dial (01305) 71 + ext

Russell, Kay (spo) 5748
Asker, Jane (p) 5867
Doe, Martin (p) 5911
Hamilton, Ian (pso) 5757
Maguire, Teresa (pso) 5863
Monger, Michelle (pso) 5856
Richards, Caroline (pso) 5852
Scriven, Richard (pso) 5823

17. **HMP Guys Marsh**
Shaftesbury SP7 8AH
tel (01747) 856400 *fax (01747) 850217*
spo fax (01747) 856529
direct dial (01747) 85 + ext

Ward, Martin (spo) 6409
Gaines, Fiona (p) 6634
Lewis, Samantha (pso) 6667
Moger, Barry (pso) 6633
Moon, Donna (pso) 6632
Solly, Chris (pso) 6631

Local Justice Areas

7 East Dorset
2, 4, 5 West Dorset

Crown Court

9 Bournemouth
2 Dorchester

DURHAM PROBATION AREA

Out of hours emergency contact number
(01642) 826606 or (01642) 456811 (offender
issues c/o Teesside hostels)

Victim enquiries contact number
Dawn Carter (01325) 315444

e-mail Firstname.Surname@durham.probation.
gsi.gov.uk

1. **Head Office**
Forest House
Aykley Heads Business Centre
Durham City DH1 5TS
tel 0191-383 9083 *fax 0191-383 7979*

Bruce, Russell (co)
Hine, Susan (director interventions
Co Durham & Teesside)
Carey, Carina (director offender mngmnt
Co Durham only)

Rackstraw, David (brd secy/head of
legal services, Co Durham & Teesside)
Willoughby, Hazel (director PPU
Co Durham & Teesside)
Ibbotson, Margaret (finance mgr)
Vitty, Helen (technology & info mgr)
Collins, Helen (business devpt unit mgr
Co Durham & Teesside)
Raine, Helen (pa to co/office mgr)
Burnip, Diane (pa to directors)
Woods, Rae (sec/admin asst)
Lincoln, Samantha (comms off)
Bartlett, Sandra (finance asst)
Hodgson, Joan (finance asst)
Craddock, Jonathan (TIM officer, tech)
Horner, Steven (TIM officer, tech)
Crompton, Andrew (data analyst)
Murray, Elizabeth (data analyst)
Metcalfe, Neil (data analyst)
Mitchell, Suzanne (TIM officer)
Taylor, Sheila (office co-ord)
Currie, Carol (QA co-ord)
McArthur, Clare (TIM officer qa)
Ward, Mandy (TIM officer qa)

Public Protection Unit
Storey, Hugh (middle mgr mappa)
Bagley, John (middle mgr)
Burns, Darryl
Lumley, Mari
Moss, Hayley
Reay, Gillian
Timoney, Pearl

Stringwell, Margaret (mappa admin PPU)
Steel, Valerie (case admin PPU)
Wilkinson, Wendy (case admin PPU)

Seconded
D'Souza, Nikki (middle mgr)
Ellis, Jayne (HR off, Co Durham
& Teesside)
Ashworth, Sarah
Ferry, Julie (pso)

2. Highfield House, Parliament Street
Consett DH8 5DH
tel (01207) 502821 *fax (01207) 583989*

OM Community
Ghosh, Marc (middle mgr)
Brown, Diane
Farrow, Phillippa
Key, Gareth
Somersall, Paula
Stewart, Louise
Buckingham, Jane (pso)
Carney, Liz (pso)
Cawson, Sheena (pso)

Jobling, Lynsey (pso)
Paget, Michelle (pso)
Smith, James (pso)
Waterworth, Marion (pso)

Whiteman, Carole (case admin)
Dukes, Margaret (case admin)
Johnson, Marion (case admin)
Wilson, Karen (case admin)

OM Interventions
Thomson, Keith (pso)

3. Oakdale House, Oakdale Terrace
    West Lane **Chester-le-Street** DH3 3DH
    tel 0191-388 7951 *fax 0191-388 1252*

    Askew, Sheila (asst director)
    Egglestone, David (asst director)
    Robinson, James (courier/caretaker)

    OM Community
    Barbara Passmore (middle mgr)
    Bruce, Karen (office co ord)
    Anderson, Kay
    McNiven, Helen
    Thompson, Helen
    Williams, Janette
    McHugh, Maureen (pso)
    Peacock, Mark (pso)
    Cox, Janice (case admin)
    Randell, Susan (case admin)

    OM Interventions
    Hounam, Ken (unit mgr)
    Coleman, Paul
    Forster, Norman (pso)
    Harker, Brian (pso)
    Anderson, Kay
    Parker, Fiona (pdo)
    Quinn, Stephen (pso)
    Walton, David (pso)
    Randell, Susan (case admin)

    Trainees
    Boyack, Lisa
    Clarke, Gemma
    Gray, Simon
    Navarro, Donna

4. 84 Claypath
    Durham DH1 1RG
    tel 0191-386 1265 *fax 0191-386 4668*

    OM Community
    Francis, Hannah
    Newton (née Wilson), Louise
    Gray, Eileen (pso)
    McGuire, Craig (pso)
    Appleby, Nicola (case admin)
    Caile, Carole (case admin)

Hancock, Amy (case admin)
Murphy, Sherida (case admin)

OM Interventions
Hunt, Gill (middle mgr)
Buckingham, Howard
Rohan, Julieann
Richardson (née Scott), Rachel
Cooper, Elaine (pso)
Hamilton, Diane (pso)
Hancock, Susan (pso)
Cunnigham, Martin
Herrington, Claire (pso)
Hunter, Fiona (pso)
Leigh, Fiona (pso)
Russell, Julie (pso)

5. **Durham Crown Court**
    Old Elvet, Durham DH1 3HW
    tel 0191-384 8130 *fax 0191-386 2695*

    Madgin-Ellison, Lindy (pso)

6. Durham House, 60 Yoden Way
    Peterlee SR8 1BS
    tel 0191-586 2480 *fax 0191-586 3442*

    Health & Safety
    Fox, Mavis (health & safety advr)

    OM Community
    Graham, Janet (middle mgr)
    Trotter, Jeanne (middle mgr)
    North, Saphron (acting middle mgr)
    Berry, Steven
    Cooper, Paula
    Flynn, Louise
    Griffiths, Charlotte
    Hodgson, Mel
    Richards, Paul
    McKenzie (née Robinson), Lisa
    Stoddart, Kathryn
    Watkin, Anna
    Willmore, Nichola
    Dinsdale, Brian (pso)
    Dougherty (née Johnson), Eileen (pso)
    Townshend, Jonathon (pso)
    Gibson, Tracey (pso)
    Green, Sandra (pso)
    Harland, David Ryan (pso)
    McKenzie, Aidan (pso)
    Neale, Gay (pso, EASE)
    Nichols, Melanie (pso)
    Rodgers, Gary (pso)
    Rogers, Sharon (pso)
    Stead, Brian (pso)
    Walton, Andy (pso)

    Barry, Lin (volunteer co ord)

Newell, Terry (case admin)
Riley, Chris (case admin)
Robinson, Denise (case admin)
Waters, Sarah (case admin)
Wilson, Tony (case admin)

OM Interventions
Vincent, Marie (office co ord)
Playfor, Duncan (pso)

Trainees
Leishman, John (middle mgr)
Douglas, Stewart (pda)
Howard, Rebecca
Johnson, Kelly
McShane, Julie

7. 9 Corporation Road
    Darlington DL3 6TH
    tel (01325) 486231 *fax (01325) 382760*

    OM Community
    Capstick, Anna (middle mgr)
    Lambert, Steve (middle mgr)
    Pearson, Dominic (snr psychologist)
    Sedgewick, Leila (office co ord psych)
    Cadwallader, Steve
    Clayton, Rob
    Davies, Andrea
    Davison, Ken
    Dixon, Jo
    Casswell, Glyn
    Coombs, Laurence
    Hamalainen, Kerry
    Hill, Christine
    Hood, Chris
    Hope, Victoria
    Hussain, Akram
    Iveson, Simone
    Longworth, Emma
    McAndrew, Kath
    Marr, Anne
    Scarr, Laura
    Walton, Leanne

    Ashley, Mark (pso EASE)
    Auld, Caroline (pso)
    Briggs, Maria (pso)
    Davidson (née Booth), Ingrid (pso)
    Hood, Jacqui (pso EASE)
    Hooper, Mark (pso)
    Kemp, Karen (pso)
    Kirkbride, Ruth (pso)
    Patterson (née Allison), Lisa (pso)
    Robertson, Brenda (pso)
    Sibert, Maureen (pso)
    Thresher, Kathryn (pso)

    Sedgewick, Leila (office co-ord)
    Shaw, Andrea (case admin)

Carletta, Lynne (case admin)
Carrs, Alison (case admin)
Cunningham, Jon (case admin)
Hamilton, Sunshine (case admin)
Nicholson, Jayne (case admin)
Williams, Julie (case admin)
Baker, Kelly (receptionist)

OM Interventions
Leighton, Rhonda (middle mgr)
Sinclair-Day, Julie (middle mgr)
Crosby, Helen (unit mgr)
Howard, Joe
Shah-Stroyan, Naheed
Simpson, Alison
Starkie, Erika
Byers, Karen (pso)
Denton, John (pso)
Edgar, Kevin (pso)
Kelly, Michael (pso)
Lochore, Margaret (pso)
Strike, Nigel (pso)
Popple, Nadine (office co ord)

Trainees
Place, Shirley (pda)
Abel, Claire
Anderson, Kathryn
Teggert, Melanie

8. Probation Office, Greenwell Road
    Newton Aycliffe DL5 4DH
    tel (01325) 315444 *fax (01325) 329599*

    OM Community
    Creedon, Mike (asst director)
    Blackburn, Karen (asst director)
    Anderson, Diane (middle mgr)
    Cuthbertson, Haley (vlo)
    Helmke, Sandra
    Howard, Andrew
    Johnson, Susan
    Langthorne, Chris
    McEwen, Laura
    Sygrove, Julie
    Thompson, Donna
    Zacharias, Anna
    Armstrong, Helen (pso)
    Bell, John (pso)
    Docherty, Valerie (pso)
    Eland, Maureen (pso)
    Hopson, Alison (pso)
    Jordan, Ena (pso)
    Payne, Hilary (pso)
    Wardman, Allison (pso)
    Waterworth, Marion (pso)
    McDonald, Carole (case admin)
    Hill, Lisa (case admin)
    Meale, Susan (case admin)

Palmer, Lynda (case admin)
Richardson, Jean (case admin)

OM Interventions
Bryson, Jean
Best, David (pso)
Coulson, Anthony (pso)
Jones, Stephen (pso)
Maddison (née Carter), Dawn (pso victims)
Proudlock, Susan (pso accom)

Thompson, Joan (off co-ord)
Meale, Susan (case admin)
Palmer, Lynda (case admin)

Trainees
Burnett, Karen

9. Beechburn House, 8 Kensington
Cockton Hill Road
Bishop Auckland DL14 6HX
tel (01388) 602182 *fax (01388) 458403*

OM Community
Bake, Andrew (middle mgr)
Bligh, Carolyn
Dobson, Claire
Hancox, Joanne
Knox, Amanda
Liivand, Ann
McEvoy, Siobhan
Moore, Kendra
Ridley, Karen
Watson, Jane

Alderton, Julie (pso)
Dale, Tracey (pso)
Hardy, Janice (pso)
Maddison, George (pso)
Park, Philip (pso)
Brison-Main, Thomas (case admin)
Brown, Allison (case admin)
Coulson, Lynne (case admin)
Walton, Patricia (case admin)

OM Interventions
House, Mark (pso)
Lowery Mark (pso)
McMahon, Linda (pso)

10. **Co Durham Youth Engagement
Service, East Area**
3rd Floor, Lee House, Yoden Way
Peterlee SR8 1BB
tel 0191-518 6302 *fax 0191-518 6328*

South Area
Aycliffe Young People's Centre
Newton Aycliffe DL5 6JE
tel (01325) 372808 *fax (01325) 372814*

Priestman, Elizabeth
Stokeld, Keith

North Area
Andill House, North Road
Catchgate, Stanley
Co Durham DH9 8UW
tel (01207) 291400 *fax (01207) 235483*

Darlington Youth Offending Service
Central House, Gladstone Street
Darlington DL3 6JX
tel (01325) 346267 *fax (01325) 346846*

Joyce, Ian

Institutions

11. H M Prison, Old Elvet
Durham DH1 3HU
tel 0191-386 2621 *fax 0191-386 2524*

Thomas, Neil (middle mgr)
Bell, George
Irving, Derrick
Vallente, Claire
Harrison, Linda
Banham, Stephen (pso)
Cook, Susan (pso)
Duncan, Lynn (pso)
Evans, Harvey (pso)
Lewis, David (pso)
Lopez-Real, Annie (pso)
Merrick, Janet (pso)
Mulligan, Mike (pso)
O'Neill, Fiona (pso)

12. H M Prison **Frankland**
Finchale Avenue, Brasside
Durham DH1 5YD
tel 0191-332 3000 *fax 0191-332 3001*

Furniss, Paul
Hancock, Derek
Hodgson, Jean
Penzer, Anne
O'Keeffe, Peter
O'Sullivan, Claire
Todd, Jayne
Copeland, Ena (pso)

13. H M Remand Centre **Low Newton**
Brasside, Durham DH1 5SE
tel 0191-376 4000 *fax 0191-376 4001*

Murphy, Anne
Thompson, Sarah
Hind, Linda (pso)
Pape, Yvonne (pso)
Pears, Derek (pso)

14. H M Young Offender Institution
Deerbolt Bowes Road
Barnard Castle DL12 9BG
tel (01833) 633200 *fax (01833) 633201*

Auckland, Mary
Thomas, Jenny
Ware, Bruce
Begg, Maureen (pso)
Snowball, Sharon (pso)

Local Justice Areas

2, 3, 4, 6 North Durham
7, 8, 9 South Durham

Crown Court

5 Durham

ESSEX PROBATION AREA

Central Bail Referral telephone number
(01268) 557550

Out of hours emergency contact point
Basildon Hostel (01268) 557550

Victim enquiries contact number (01268)
412241

e-mail Firstname.Surname@essex.probation.
gsi.gov.uk

1. **Head Office** Cullen Mill
49 Braintree Road, Witham CM8 2DD
tel (01376) 501626 *fax (01376) 501174*
aco's fax (01376) 519955

Archer, Mary (co)
Ayree, Eric (aco)
Bamber, Alex (aco)
Hirst, Gill (aco)
Kennerson, Shirley (aco)
Jones, Peter (aco)
Mangan, Pete (aco)
Atkinson, Sue (aco human resources)
Came, Debbie (p, treasurer)

McCann, Helen (training & staff devpt
mgr)
Day, Derek (nvq proj mgr)
Payne, John (p, nvq assessor)
Rowlands, Gill (nvq assessor)

Mott, Sam (p, hr mgr)
Butt, Andrew (h&s mgr)
Pervez, Neelam (p, diversity mgr)
Moon, Garry (performance mgr)

Gorrie, Paul (finance mgr)
Moffat, Colin (supt services mgr)
Thompson, Bill (info & systems mgr)
McKay, Lynne (communications mgr)
Ward, Paula (dv co-ord)
Woollard, Peter (partnerships mgr)
Davis, Colin (contracts mgr)
Turl, Gordon, (drr mgr)
Taplin, Caroline (operational
investigations mgr)
Smith, Barry (partnerships officer)
Wood, Dee (marac mgr)

2. Carraway House, Durham Road
Laindon **Basildon** SS15 6PH
tel (01268) 412241 *fax (01268) 544241*

Castle, Katie, (spo)
Linahan, Rosan (spo)
Osler, Alex (p, spo)
Toper, Sue (p, spo)
Connolly, Terence
Curtin, Rich
Colnbrook, Lee
Gidden, Amy
Harbon, Jacqui
Robertson, Karen
Rowe, Christopher
Bearman, Fiona (om)
Bird, Lindsay (om)
Comish, David (om)
Elliot, Laura (om)
Fisher, Marion (om)
Jones, Rhys (om)
Karby, Leigh (om)
Keevil, Claire (p, om)
Kreyling, Joseph (om)
Parker, Liz (om)
Price, Sue (om)
Smith, David (om)
Taiani, Heidi (om)
Turner, Diane (p, om)
Virtcheva Gana, Eleonora, (p, om)
Webster, Maggie (om)

Courts
Clark, Dawn (pso)
Gardiner, Claire (pso)
Sheed, Fran (pso)
Waterfield, Kathleen (pso)

Programmes
Routh, Jo (spo)
Dowden, Clive
Davison, Natalie (p, treatment mgr)
McGregor, Tim (treatment mgr)
Norman, Stacey (treatment mgr)
Baker, Steve (pso)
Dzambo, Ruth (pso)

Ford, Elaine (pso)

Women's Safety Officers
Bulman, Wendy (wso)
Hubbard, Carol (wso)
Jackson, Tricia (wso)

Victim Unit
Dewitt, Jane (spo)
Anderson, Debbie (pso)
Clark, Roland (pso)
Levy, Marion (pso)

Unpaid Work
Watson, Chris (supt mgr, also 7)
Parratt, Margaret (supt services mgr)
Fallon, Carol (pso, basic skills)
Felice, Paul (pso accom)

3.   **Basildon Crown Court**
     The Gore, Basildon SS14 2EU
     tel (01268) 458118 *fax (01268) 458116*

     Cadzow, Anna (pso)
     Turner, Janet (pso)

4.   4th Floor, Ashby House, Brook Street
     Chelmsford CM1 1UH
     tel (01245) 287154 *fax (01245) 491321*

     Auguste, Pauline (pso)
     Lewis, Florence (spo)
     Messam, David (spo)

     Hards, Joanne, (report writer)
     Kelly, Susan (ric sdr writer)
     Bigg, Melaine
     Walters, Neil
     Cornwell, Hazel, (p)
     Mead, Gemma
     Teather, Carole
     Windus, Charlotte

     Austin-Carroll, Sarah (om)
     Chapple, Melanie (om)
     Cooper, Lucy (om)
     Dow, Maggie (om)
     Exley, Tim (om)
     Glass-Hirse, Caroline (om)
     Grant, Hayley (om)
     Hegarty, Sarah (om)
     Kettle, Alison (p, om)
     Migliorini, Kayleigh (om)
     Murphy, Michelle (p, om)
     Prince, Melissa (om)
     Sadler, Mark (om)
     Sapwell, Steve (om)

     Courts
     Aston, Mike (pso)
     Clarke, Jeanette (pso)

Programmes
Brown, Katherine (p, mgr)
Boutel, Helen
Chatten, Chris
Childs, Ben (treatment mgr)
Fernandez, Sara (p, treatment mgr)
Griffin, Sarah (treatment mgr)
Saward, Adrian (treatment mgr)
Catto, Mark (pso)
Harris, Kerry (pso)
Kennedy, Greg (pso)

Unpaid Work
Richardson, Jill (sup mgr)
Haworth, Vanessa (supt services mgr)
Perrott, Claire (pso accom)
Pond, Catherine (p, pso basic skills)
Wardrop, Avril (p, pso basic skills)

5.   Ryegate House, 23 St Peter's Street
     Colchester CO1 1HL
     tel (01206) 768342 *fax (01206) 768348*

     Chapman, Liz (p, spo)
     Charlton, Douglas (spo)
     Hargrave, Sally (p, spo)
     Haxton, Liz (spo)
     Bell, Doiminic
     Coward, Wendy (p)
     Doy, Natalie
     Evans, Anne-Marie
     Fitzpatrick, John
     Hogg, Jenni
     Huard, Mike (p)
     McPhillips, Anthony
     Meadows, Max
     Pryke, Steven

     Ainsworth, Tony (om)
     Atkinson, Caroline (om)
     Baldwin, Iris (om)
     Bond, Lucy (om)
     Campbell, Carol (om)
     Cassidy, Elisabeth (om)
     Cock, James (om)
     Coker, Steven (om)
     Gibson, Jenny (om)
     Grover, Paul (om)
     Haggerty, Sheila (p, om)
     Hardstaff, Sharon (om)
     Leader, Lisa (om)
     Litton, Victoria (om)
     McQuoid, Lisa (om)
     Paige, Catherine (om)
     Wheeler, Claire (p, om)
     Wright, Sue (om)

     Courts
     Double, Linda (pso)

Esposito, Kathleen (pso)
Snowling, Elana (pso)
Vasquez-Walters, Elisa (pso)

Programmes
Rodway, Debbie (p, spo)
Ross, David
Mateer, Beau (treatment mgr)
McGregor, Tim (treatment mgr)
James, Hayley (treatment mgr)
Bennett, Alan (pso)
Morris, Karen (pso)
Speed, Joanne (pso)
Stokes, Ruth (pso)

Unpaid Work
Minns, John (sup mgr)
Woodhouse, Karen (supt services mgr)
Clarke, Anne (pso basic skills)

6. **Crown Court Liaison Office**
Crown Court, New Street
Chelmsford CM1 1EL
tel (01245) 358833 *fax (01245) 258136*

Franklin, Arlita (p, spo, North)
Hepworth, Fay (p, spo, North)
Alun Gower, (spo, South)
Auguste, Andre (pso)
Jarman, Gail (pso)

7. Five Wells, West Street
Grays Thurrock RM17 6XR
tel (01375) 382285 *fax (01375) 394715*

Hooper, Terry (p, spo)
Parker, Carol (spo)
Pearson, Chris (p, spo)

Budd, Louise (ric sdr writer)
Doney, Lisa
Fasulo, Selina
Hogben, Sarah
Legg, Pat (p)
Redgwell, Tracey
Rossi, Bill
Callender, Claire (p, om)
Cuthbert, Julia (p, om)
Franklin, Keri (om)
Hubbard, Carol (om)
Knight, Stephen (om)
Mohamed, Sam (om)
Prosser, Tim (om)
Scott, Jan (om)
Sturman, Thomas (om)

Courts
Lester, Emma (pso)
Morgan, Rachel (pso)

Programmes
Powers, Martin (spo)
Gurnett, Graham (treatment mgr)
Bryant, Jack (pso)
Cherifi, Sindy (pso)
Coleman, Liz (pso)

Unpaid Work
Ofeke, Ann (supt services mgr)
Gray, Trevor (pso basic skills)
Reynolds, James (pso accom)

8. Centenary House, 4 Mitre Buildings
Kitson Way **Harlow** CM20 1BL
tel (01279) 410692 *fax (01279) 454116*

Bishop, Neeve (spo)
Mason, Frances (spo)
Toper, Sue (p, spo)

Brunton, Jason
Hughes, Gerry
Lock, Sarah
Martin, Nicola
Sampson, Carol
Beveridge, Caroline (om)
Clarke, Lorraine (om)
D'Silva, John (om)
Grace, Caroline (om)
Hawkins, John (om)
Jones, Sandra (om)
Jones, Michael (om)
Marshall, Isabel (om)
Matthews, David (om)
Morgan, Martina (om)
Peck, Andrew (om)
Perry, Kathy (om)
White, Rowena (om)

Courts
Hallesy, Teresa, (pso)
Wenzel, Karen (pso)

Programmes
Stiles, Min (spo)
Coombes, Paul (treatment mgr)
Dedman, Colette (pso)
Nethercoat, Pat (pso)
Poole, Claire (pso)

Unpaid Work
Hill, Adele (sup mgr)
Wallace, Caroline (p, supt services mgr)
Woolf, Denise (p, supt services mgr)
Neill, Lorraine (pda)
Simon, Jennet (pso basic skills)

9. Blue Heights, 45 Victoria Avenue
Southend-on-Sea SS2 6BA
tel (01702) 337998 *fax (01702) 333630*
Crown Court enquiries to office 6

Butlin, Carolyn (spo)
Dent, Julie (p, spo)
Mozzanica, Louise (spo)
Turner, Hilary (spo)

Brenkley, Sam, (p)
Couch, Keelan
Edosomwan, Jonathan
Frost, Michelle
Grant, James
Griffiths, Clare
Hamilton, Zoe (p)
Jess, Michael
Moore, Bruce (p)
Pocock, Rebecca
Roberts, Dawn
Stack, Anne
Wright, Joanne

Atkins, Sarah (om)
Bolton, Christine (om)
Carbutt, Carol (om)
Cook, Jacqui (om)
Dawson, Anne (om)
Eve, Rebecca, (om)
Farrey, Larissa (om)
Gunn, Ted (om)
Hobart, Toni (p, om)
Jones, Tony (om)
Karby, Leigh (om)
Kinder, Keith (om)
Manton, Jackie (om)
Nicola, Careena (om)
O'Leary, Leigh (om)
Palmer, Jane (om)
Penton, Kelly (om)
Penton, Sue (om)
Pickford, Pauline (om)
Smith, Tina (om)
Spencer, Richard (om)
Summerhayes, Lesley (p, om)

Courts
Chamberlain, Lucy (pso)
Champ, Joanne (pso)
Murray, Allen (pso)

Programmes
Frost, Russell (p, spo)
Burr, Stephen
Johnson, Susan (p)
Smith, Pat
Merenda, Natalie (p, pso)
Parkes, Ernie (pso)

Unpaid Work
Meads, Richard (interventions mgr)
Owens, Jan (sup mgr)
Sales, Debra (p, supt services mgr)

Brown, Paul (pso accom)
Scott, Emma (p, pda)

Youth Offending Services

10. **Essex Youth Offending Service**
    Head Office
    Suite 4, Empire House,
    Victoria Road, Chelmsford CM1 1PE
    tel (01245) 265151 *fax (01245) 346396*

a. **Mid Essex YOT**
    Suite 2 Empire House
    Victoria Road **Chelmsford** CM11PE
    tel (01245) 358092 *fax (01245) 358337*

    Mead, Gemma

b. **North Essex YOT**
    Stanwell House, Stanwell Street
    Colchester CO2 7DL
    tel (01206) 573188 *fax (01206) 564660*

    Finch, Martine

c. **West Essex YOT**
    Suite 3 - 5, Level 10, Terminus House
    The High **Harlow** CM20 1XA
    tel (01279) 427495 *fax (01279) 436494*

    Fairchild, Christine

d. **South Essex YOT**
    31 Battleswick
    Basildon SS14 3LA
    tel (01268) 520612 *fax (01268) 270924*

    Baker, Karen

11. **Thurrock Youth Offending Service**
    Five Wells, West Street
    Grays RM17 6SX
    tel (01375) 413900 *fax (01375) 413901*

    Kay, Peter (mgr)
    Hossack, Roy (team ldr)
    Grant, Katherine

12. **Southend Youth Offending Service**
    4th Floor, Queensway House, Essex St
    Southend-on-Sea SS1 2NY
    tel (01702) 534300 *fax (01702) 534301*

    Hogben, Nick

Approved Premises (Hostel)

13. Basildon Bail Hostel
    1 Felmores, Basildon SS13 1RN
    tel (01268) 557550/557600
    fax (01268) 558661

Werry, Malcolm (mgr)
Kay, Michael (dep hostel mgr)
Amobi, Chris (hostel off)
Falayi, Olayemi (hostel off)
Gibson, Andrew (hostel off)
Jamieson, Kathy (p, hostel off)
Kreyling, Annette (hostel off)
Laycock, Terry (hostel off)
Nestor, Paulette (hostel off)
Nichol, Roland (hostel off)
Olusina, Louis (hostel off)
Strong, Brenda (p, hostel off)
Sturch, Anthony (p, hostel off)
Wood, Anne (p, finance asst)

Institutions

14. H M YOI & Prison
    Bullwood Hall
    High Road, Hockley SS5 4TE
    tel (01702) 562800 *fax (01702) 207464*

    Ward, Gill (snr pract)
    Jones, Barbara (pso)

15. H M Prison, Springfield Road
    Chelmsford CM2 6LQ
    tel (01245) 272000 *fax (01245) 272001*
    probn fax (01245) 272074

    Juniper, Laurel (spo)
    Allison, Sue
    Madden, Vicky
    Oviatt, Leigh
    Rockenbach, Chloe
    Gallant, Jane (p, om)
    Ling, Kevin (om)
    Redman, Debbie (p, om)
    Turnbull, Kathryn (om)
    Vale, Luke (om)
    Williams, Jon (om)

Local Justice Areas

5 North-East Essex
4 Mid-North Essex
8 North-West Essex
9 South-East Essex
2 Mid-South Essex
7 South-West Essex

Crown Courts

6 Basildon
6 Chelmsford
6 Southend

GLOUCESTERSHIRE PROBATION AREA

Out of hours emergency contact point
Ryecroft Hostel (01452) 380268

Victim enquiries contact number (01242) 534546

e-mail Firstname.Surname@gloucestershire. probation.gsi.gov.uk

abbreviation cmo: case management officer

1. **Head Office**
   Bewick House, 1 Denmark Road
   Gloucester GL1 3HW
   tel (01452) 389200 *fax (01452) 541155*

   Ball, Yvette (co)
   Cryer, Naomi (aco)
   Holden, Garry (aco)
   Baker, Charlie (aco)
   Bennett Darrill (aco)
   Bensted John (aco)
   Kerr-Rettie, Kathy (staff devt mgr)
   Fogarty, Tim (business syst & info mgr)
   Allen, Brian (it officer)
   Perratt, Alan (information officer)
   Bircher, Jane (it training officer)
   Boggon, Campbell (information officer)
   Schoen Lynne (hr manager)
   Leese, Ann (hr adviser)
   Taylor, Lesley (hr adviser)
   Maloney, Debra (finance mgr)
   Longbotham, Rachel (finance off)
   Westhead, Chris (facilities mgr, h&s adviser)

   Support Staff
   Boseley, Sophie
   Darlow, Sharon
   Jones, Sue
   Richards, Jackie
   Riches-Jones, Liz
   Salcombe, Karen

Cheltenham and Tewkesbury (CAT)

2. County Offices, St George's Road
   Cheltenham GL50 3QF
   tel (01242) 532500 *fax (01242) 534590*

   Scully, Mark (area mgr)
   Smeaton, Christine (service supt mgr)
   Buxton, Sally (performance mgr)

   Donald, Nick (resettlement)
   Ilsley, Vicky (cmo, resettlement)

   Belshaw, Lisa (pda)

Adlard, Steve
Clayton, Sharon
Coulson, Elaine
Donnelly, Laura
Hall, Anita
Hughes, Dan
Hughes, Joanna
Jones, Carolyn
Mills, Lisa
Nunn, Elizabeth
Pearson, Pauline
Read, Matthew

Cowmeadow, Hillary (cmo)
Cudmore, Jean (cmo)
Havard, Pat (cmo)
McNeill, Kevin (cmo)
Walker, Lisa (cmo)
White, Lynda (cmo)
Garrington, Ann (accom off)

Court Cluster
Johnson, Ann (cmo)

Trainees
Mercouris, Paula (pda)
Bombera, Isoline
Nelmes, Kayleigh
Simson, Kate
Wessex, Mark

ETE Team
Lear, Margaret (ete off)
Jones, Gillian (ete wrkr)

Support Staff
Gleed, Sian (saso)
Allison Mark
Frazier, Lesley
Hewitt, Neil
Hughes, Kerry
Keeling, Angela
Middlecote, Lesley
Spashett, Louise
Stanley, Rosamund

Stroud and Cotswolds (SAC)

3.   118 Cainscross Road
     Stroud GL5 4HN
     tel (01453) 760100 *fax (01453) 760107*

     Offender Management
     Knott, Jane (performance mgr)
     Pritchard, Clive
     Spouse, Mike
     Taylor, Sue
     Williams, Jan
     Johnson, Leanne (cmo)
     Leibbrandt, Stephanie (cmo)
     Phelps, Tanya (cmo)

Wilkinson, Erik (ete mgr)

Hirst, Ronnie (ete off)

Support Staff
Ellis, Lisa
Maquire Patricia
Powell, Susan
Ward, Sue

Gloucester (GLO)

4.   Barbican House, 31 Barbican Road
     Gloucester GL1 2JF
     tel (01452) 872800 *fax (01452) 872890*
     Court Fax (01452) 872891

     Offender Management Team
     McBride, Stephanie (area mgr)
     Dennison, Alex (performance mgr)
     Knight, Tony (performance mgr)
     Allen, David
     Bennett, Catherine
     Cooper, Lesley
     Cort, John
     Cousins, Terry
     Leishman, Angela
     Powell, Val
     Rea, Mary
     Sims, Clare
     Slack, Sue
     Smith, Kim
     Waldron, Amanda
     Walford, Verity
     Boughton, Angie (cmo)
     Butcher, Sue (cmo)
     Chapple, Andrew (cmo)
     Clee, Mark (cmo)
     Jones, Paula (cmo)
     Palmer, Mavis (cmo)
     Rennabach, Rachel (cmo)
     Taylor, Beverley (cmo)
     Tracy, Patrick (cmo)
     Worrall, Sîan (crt team)

     Support Staff
     Moss, Elizabeth (saso)
     Butt, Jean
     Edwards, Peter
     Hill, Kay
     Morgan, Deborah
     Morris, Clare
     Powick, Carolyn
     Smith, Val
     Taylor, Sharon

     Trainees
     Wilson, Julie (pda)
     Bray, Richard
     Broderick, Tessa

Hogg, Vicky
Kitchener, Dionne
Sonnichsen, Kirsten

Forest and Sex Offenders (FAS)

5. **Coleford Probation Office**
The Court House
Gloucester Road **Coleford** GL16 8BL
tel (01594) 837090 *fax (01594) 837256*

Offender Management
Coombs, Sue
Sims, Clare
Smith, Stephen (cmo)

Support Staff
Tooze, Gillian

6. **Oakes House, 55-57 London Road**
Gloucester GL1 3HF
tel (01452) 551200 *fax (01452) 522181*

Programmes Team
Temple, Richard (prog mgr)
James, Shirley (treatment supvr)
Matchett, Chris (treatment supvr)
Purcell, Angie (treatment supvr)
Hill, Eddie
Carter, Sarah (prog wrkr)
Jones, Karen (prog wrkr)
Brooks, Sue (prog wrkr)
Cassidy, John (prog wrkr)
Hudson, Julie (prog wrkr)
Patterson, Chris (prog wrkr)
McRoberts, Vicky (prog wrkr)

ETE Team
Buchanan, Robin (ete wrkr)
Ayling, Carol (ete wrkr)
Trigg, Lilian (ete wrkr)

Support Mgrs
Herniman, Sally (area business
process devpt & imp mgr)

Support Staff
Symons, Nicola (saso)
Baldwin, Julie
Barlow, Kerry
Daws, Monique
Head, Zoe
Keable, Sheena
McClay Eve-Louise
Merry, Jan

DIP Team
Yates, Ted (DIP mgr)

7. **Crown Court** Longsmith Street
Gloucester GL1 2TS

tel (01452) 420101 *fax (01452) 381292*

Worrall, Sîan (pso)

Support Staff
Turner, Gill

8. **Community Payback Unit**
Bewick House, 1 Denmark Road
Gloucester GL1 3HW
tel (01452) 389227 *fax (01452) 541155*

Thompson, Allan (cp mgr)
Grant-Jones, Pauline (qual assur/allocn
mgr)
Hanson, Steve (cp co-ord)
Allan, Daryl (supvr)
Greenshields, Jim (supvr)
Hills, David (supvr)
Joseph, Sam (supvr)
Knibbs, Clive (supvr)
Smith, Steve (supvr)
Tocknell, Richard (supvr)

Support Staff
Moat, Mandy
Timur, Judith

9. **Youth Offending Team**
48 London Road **Gloucester** GL1 3NZ
tel (01452) 547540 *fax (014520) 551114*

Gough, Will

10. **Drug Intervention Programme**
4 Whitfield Road, Gloucester, GL1 3DP
tel (01452) 545769

Fletcher, James (pso)
Hall, Tracy (pso)

11. **MAPPA**
Public Protection Office
County Police HQ
No 1 Waterwells, Waterwells Drive
Quedgeley GL2 2AN
tel (01452) 752203 *fax (01452) 725731*

Reynolds, Kate (MAPPA co-ord)
Rousseau, Pauline (Dep MAPPA mgr)
Bailey, Maxine (admin)
McDonald-Bell Kirsty (admin)

Approved Premise (Hostel)

12. **Ryecroft Approved Premises**
78 Ryecroft Street, Tredworth
Gloucester GL1 4LY
tel (01452) 380268 *fax (01452) 302969*

Berry, Dave (hostel mgr)
Dower, Kevin (deputy mgr)

Jukes, Gary (asst mgr)
Cottrell, Susan (asst mgr)
Bees, Harry (hostel sup)
Morgan, Greg (hostel sup)
Pellent, Chris (hostel sup)
Taylor, Steve (hostel sup)

Support Staff
Corrigan, Emma (admin)

Institution

13.   HM Prison, Barrack Square
Gloucester GL1 1JN
tel (01452) 453000 *fax (01452) 453001*

Cooper, Andrew
Farr, Derek (pso)
Gough, Petra (pso)
Hall, Joanne
Keith, Emma
Wright, Julian (pso)

Support Staff
Baker, Jacqui (visitor centre mgr)
Lovell, Jane (visitor centre supt wrkr)

Local Justice Areas

2 Cheltenham
5 Coleford
4 Gloucester
3 Stroud

Crown Court

7 Gloucester

HAMPSHIRE PROBATION AREA

Out of hours contact point
The Grange Probation Hostel 023-9236 3474

Victim enquiries contact number 0845 6040150

e-mail firstname.surname@hampshire. probation.gsi.gov.uk

1.   Head Office
Friary House, Middle Brook Street
Winchester SO23 8DQ
tel (01962) 842202 *fax (01962) 865278*
direct dial (01962) 842 + ext

Crook, Barrie (co) ext 203
Mitchell, Chris (dir offender mgmnt) ext 207
Bailey, Sharon (dir finance & resources)

ext 206
Beattie, Sarah (dir ops [intrvntns]) ext 210
Straw, Christine (dir of hr) ext 208
Carruthers, George (area mgr courts-martial report service, yots) ext 206
Kiely, Dave (asst dir offender mgmnt) ext 207
Renouf David (asst dir for bus devpt) ext 210
Bahaj, Julia (diversity advr)
(mobile 07974 971896)
Crowther, Teresa (hr servs mgr) ext 202
Charlton, Maggie (hr adv) ext 202
King, Emma (hr adv) ext 202
Howson, Monica (payroll off) ext 202
Rooke, Ginette (personnel asst, recruitment) ext 202
Turtle, Steve (perf imprvmnt mgr) ext 202
Rolley, Rhiannon (perf analyst) ext 202
Davies, Jonathan (perf analyst) ext 202
Hacker, John (info systems mgr) ext 202
Collins, Nicki (it tech & supp mgr) ext 202
Judd, Peter (it ntwk supt off) ext 202
Abraham, Rebecca (it devpt supt off) ext 202
Jones, Rachael (finance mgr) ext 202
Scott, Barry (finance technician) ext 202
Bacciarelli, Harry (finance off) ext 202
Stranks, Helen (p, finance off) ext 202
Hatch, Belinda (pa) ext 203
Gray, Rachel (p, pa) ext 208
Gaster, Sue (pa) ext 207
Josling, Sarah (pa) ext 210
Welsh, Chris (pa) ext 206
Townsend-Brown, Angela (bus supt mgr) ext 202

IT Helpdesk (01962) 842043
Bhangal, Harj

2.   Imperial House, 2 Grosvenor Road
Aldershot GU11 1DP
tel (01252) 324288 *fax (01252) 329515*

Hall, Jackie (area mgr north) (4, 6, 10)
Baker, Sheila (spo) (4, 10)
Morgan, Catherine (p, spo, mappa) (4)
Barber, Rachael
Despicht, Kathy
Dodson, Rachel
Eames, Laura
Etherington, Kate (p, drr)
Ferris, Kresta
Vacancy
Hutton, Suzanne (court off)
James Gavin
Nunn, Irene (court off)
Phillips, Natasha

Roomes, Mel (drr)
Vacancy (pso)
Burrell, Elaine, (om admin)
Fowler, Carolyn (om admin drr)
Freeland, Julie (om admin)
Johnson, Maureen (court admin) (4, 10)
Wyatt, Leona (upw off)
Haxby, Jo (asst res mgr) (4, 10)

3. Alresford Police Station
   Station Road
   Alresford SO24 9JG
   tel (01962) 734109 fax (01962) 871143

   Visor Team
   Dixon, Tom (visor & e-oasys cpc,
   risk mgmnt co-ord)
   Locke, Nicola (visor admin)
   Radford, Mike (visor admin)

4. 25 Normandy Street
   Alton GU34 1DQ
   tel (01420) 84155/88134 *fax (01420)
   542375*

   Hall, Jackie (area mgr north) (4, 6, 10)
   Morgan, Catherine (p, spo) (2)
   Cooper, Tony (resource mgr) (2, 6, 10)
   Evans, Lynda (pda)
   Shearing, Hazel
   Wade Peter (pso)
   Haxby, Jo (asst resource mgr) (2,10)
   Gedge, Nikki (om/mappa admin)

   Interventions Unpaid Work (N Region)
   Robertson, Paula (placement mgr)
   Heskith, Terry (placement mgr)

5. The Court House
   West Street **Andover** SP10 1QP
   tel (01264) 364411 *fax (01264) 335457*

   Holmes, Sue (spo) (12, 14)
   Appleby, Allan
   Dicker, Richard
   Thomas, Jeremy
   James, Michelle (pso)
   Morse, Barry (pso) (14)
   Vacancy (ete off)
   Bridgeman, Jo (om admin)
   Crannaford, June (om admin)
   Gray, Liz (om admin)
   Priestley-Cooper, Jenny (om admin)
   Jones, Lesley (asst resource mgr) (12, 14)

6. Level Two, St Clement House
   1-3 Alençon Link
   Basingstoke RG21 7SB
   tel (01256) 464272 *fax (01256) 812374*

Probation
Hall, Jackie (area mgr north) (2, 4, 11)
Cluff, Jeff (spo)
Gray, Caroline (spo)
Alderton, Judith
Boules, Lewis
Browning, Tom (crts)
Burley, Emma
Davies, Nicola
Gaster, Rachel
Griffiths, Ceri
Keevash, David
Stace, Andrea
Steed, Julie
Tomkins, Peter
Boyes, Julie (pso)
Finch, Jane (pso, ppo co-ord)
Irving, Pauline (pso)
Mills, Nathan (pso)
Neale, Chris (pso)
Souter, Lynda (pso)
Glen, Ray (off mgr oper mgr)
Hills, Eric (breach prosection off)
Saunders, Cara (breach prosecution off)
Brown, Helen (asst resource mgr)
Hocking, Angela (ete off)
Berrecloth, Jane (om admin)
Doublet, Sue (om admin breach)
Day, Susan (om admin)
Froud, Carol (om admin crts)
Hughes, Jane (om admin)
Sadler, Nicola (om admin)
Wingrave, Felicity (om admin)

Reducing Custody Project
tel (01256) 464272 *fax (01256) 812374*

Fry, Chris (area mgr) (mobile 07813 152
110)
Ager, Jackie (spo, based at 22)
Mellish, Louise
Grantham, Rebecca (pso)
Daouti, Popi (eng off)
Coloza-Aleria, Donna (om admin)

7. Level 1, St Clement House
   1-3 Alençon Link
   Basingstoke RG21 7SB
   tel (01256) 464272 *fax (01256) 357292*

   Programmes
   Vacancy (spo, idap)
   Kirstine Hall (resource mgr)
   Hall, Louise (p, progs mgr)
   George, Amy (treatment mgr)
   Levett, Richard (treatment mgr, idap)
   Whitefield Sarah (p, treatment mgr) (16,
   21)

Tiffin, Hannah (sogp facilitator)
Innes, Nicky (progs off)
Mills, Christina (prog off)
Hayes, Emma (prog off)
Larkins, Toni (p, prog off idap)
Small, Rebecca (progs off)
Smith, Julia (progs off)
Standing, Paula (progs off idap)
Storey, Alison (prog off, idap)
Underwood, Alan (progs off)
Hocking, Angela (ete off)
Kelley, Emma (psy off)
Jordan, Gerri (p, women's safety wrkr)
Fender, Louise (women's safety wrkr)
Grimston, Alison (progs admin)

8. Barclays House
   20-24 Upper Market Street
   Eastleigh SO50 9FD

   3rd Floor
   Programmes & Hostels Team
   tel 023-8064 7441 *fax 023-8064 7445*

   Barrett, Niki (area mgr progs &
   ap) (7, 16, 20, 33-35)
   Hall, Kirstine (resource mgr progs
   & ap) (7, 16, 20, 33-35)
   Blackman, Jo (p, asst resource mgr, progs)
   Weston, Natalie (p, asst resource mgr, progs)

   2nd Floor
   Programmes Administration
   tel 023-8064 7441 *fax 023-8064-7446*

   Taylor, Deborah (progs admin)
   Harrison, Carol (progs admin)

   2nd Floor
   Training, Health & Safety Unit
   tel 023-8064 7443 *fax 023-8064 7447*

   McMullan, Pearl (org devpt & change mgr)
   Keysell, Ben (training officer)
   Witt, Margaret (training administrator)
   Sitaram, Shashi (it trainer)
   Allen, Rob (health & safety adviser) (based
   at 11)

   2nd Floor
   Essential Skills & ETE Team
   tel 023-8064 7442 *fax 023-8064 7446*

   Waldman, Keith (ptnrshp mgr)
   Cavanagh, Mary (ete mgr)
   Hyde, Cindy (essential skills admin)
   Tuck, Trudi (ete off for women offenders)
   Vacancy (ete admin)

9. 20 High Street
   Fareham PO16 7AF

tel (01329) 235888 *fax (01329) 825023*

Skinner, Corinne (spo)
Hatton, Dean (spo)
Caswell, Paul
Crooks, Avril
Croset, Paula
Davies, Susan
Haynes, Claire (p)
Herbert, Lorraine (p)
Manuel, Rachel
Marshall, Richard
Pagett, David
Paradise, Erika
Pencavel, Katie
Talbot, Polly
Winkworth, Jane
Young, Heather (p)
Burns, Jill (pso)
Chuter, Sam (p, pso)
Vacancy (pso)
Hartman, Jenny (p, pso)
Hawkes, Abi (pso, ppo co-ord)
Podmore, Ann (p, pso)
Smith, David (pso)
Smith, Penny (pso)
Starr, Brian (pso)
Wyeth, Les (pso)
Pickering, Debbie (p, ete off)
Collins, Debbie (p, asst resource mgr)

10. 46-48 Victoria Road
    Farnborough GU14 7PG
    tel (01252) 513020 *fax (01252) 370246*

    Hall, Jackie (area mgr north) (2, 4, 11)
    Baker, Sheila (spo) (2, 4)
    Briggs, Sue
    Gallichan, Gail
    Tickner, Christy
    Buckle, Gill (pso)
    Cordery, Louise (pso)
    Boon, Linda (om admin)
    Joce, Barbara (om admin)
    Haxby, Jo (asst resource mgr) (2, 4)

11. Elmleigh Road
    Havant PO9 2AS
    tel 023-9247 3011 *fax 023-9249 8275*

    Hyslop, Alex (spo)
    Pearce, Melanie (p, spo)
    Wells, Andy (pda)
    Bottomley, Joanna
    Crawford, Colin
    Emmonds, Ginette
    Hayward, Tanith
    Keys, Carly

Lawrence, Nicola
Meads, Genevieve (p)
McDuff, Helen
Taylor, Susannah
Tomlinson, Chris
Edwards, Paul (pso)
Logan, Sue (pso)
Palmer, Victoria (pso)
Spencer, Patrick (pso)
Taylor, Danielle (pso)
Blight, Alaina (oma, mappa co-ord)
Butler, Gill (oma)
Hobbs, Rosemary (oma)
McCourt, Judy (oma)
Charles, Carrol (crt admin)
Cafferky, Janet (recept/oma)
Ross, Jean (upw off)
Henderson, Yvonne (ete off)
Allen, Rob (corp servs/health &safety mgr)
Shaw, Karen (p, js, pm asst resource mgr)
Blake, Lisa (p, js, asst resource mgr &
p, oma, mappa)

12. West Shore House
     West Street **Hythe** SO45 6AA
     tel 023-8084 3684 *fax 023-8084 2354*

     Holmes, Sue (spo) (5, 14)
     Youl, Jonathan
     Pearce, Elaine (pso)
     Jones, Lesley (asst resource mgr) (5, 14)
     Reilly, Sharon (om admin)
     Taylor, Kerry (p, om admin)

13. 8 Sea Street, Newport
     Isle of Wight PO30 5BN
     tel (01983) 523265 *fax (01983) 528994*

     Burgess, Heather (spo)
     Fitch, Sarah (spo)
     Evans, Trish (pda)
     Ambrose, Pete
     Grimes, John
     Lester, Annette
     Milford, Amy
     Osborn, Estelle
     Sanders, Donna
     Shardlow, Rob
     Smith, Sam
     Tate-Beasley, Angela
     Bacon, Justine (pso)
     Kennedy, Jo (pso)
     Leighton, Jenny (pso)
     Lewis, Amanda (pso)
     Savege, Vicky (pso ppo)
     Yates, Rebecca (pso)
     Banks, Clare (pso)
     Fisher, Peter (pso)

Ward, Ian (pso)
Fran Newnham (p, women's safety wrkr
SE/SW)
Gulliver, Pauline (ete off)
Campbell, Anne (asst resource mgr) (16,
17)

Interventions Unpaid Work
Steed, Darren (placement mgr)

14. Island House, Priestlands Place
     Lymington SO41 9GA
     tel (01590) 673107 *fax (01590) 671521*

     Holmes, Sue (spo) (5, 12)
     Orman, Lin (p, perf devpt mgr)
     Edom, Matthew (mappa)
     Jones, Lesley (asst resource mgr) (5, 12)
     Morse, Barry (pso) (5)
     Shergold, Aggie (pso)
     Charton, Kathy (om admin)
     Martin, Holly (om admin)
     Piper, Ceri (om admin)
     Pontin, Amanda (om admin)
     Sparks, Debbie (om admin)
     Taylor, Kerry (p, om admin)

     Unpaid Work (Forest) Offender Mgmnt
     tel (01590) 675359 *fax (01590) 671521*

     Emans, Trevor (upw off)
     Smith, Brian (upw off)

15. Newforest Magistrates' Court
     The Court House, Pikes Hill
     Lyndhurst SO43 7NR
     tel (02380) 283189

     Nicholas, Wendy (pso)

16. Portsmouth Probation Office
     PO Box 703 **Portsmouth** PO1 2WZ
     tel 023-9272 8300 *fax 023-9285 1618*

     Floor 5
     Shave, Nikki (area mgr) (13, 17)
     Bridden, Dave (spo)
     Christie, Steve (spo)
     Marsh, Rob (spo, drr team)
     Welch, Yasmin (spo)
     Shawl, Richard (legal services mgr)
     Goodbody, Tony (resource mgr) (13, 17)
     Campbell, Anne (asst resource mgr) (js)
     (13)
     Tatlow, Roy (ete off)
     Moloney, Mike (asst resource mgr) (js)
     (17)
     McDermott, Michelle (p, pda) (18)

     MAPPA
     tel 023-9272 8330

Austerberry, Anne
Bowes, Tom
Doran, Anna
Harvey, Matt
Judd, Estelle
Peckham, Jennifer

**Community Supervision &
Resettlement**
Team 1
tel 023-9272 8360
Bizley, Jane
Clemson, Kim
Courtney, Ben
Frampton, Pat
Postin, Laura
Purewal, Savita
Arnold, Denise (pso)
Barnard, Dennis (pso)
Borg, Marc (pso)
Gough, Kelly (pso)
Greenhalgh, Barry (pso)
Larter, Sharon (pso)

Team 2
tel 023-9272 8340
Connolly, Ellie
Jones, Alison
Joslin, Susie
Vosper, Jo
Babbington, John (pso)
Dumper, Dave (pso)

DRR/PPO
tel 023-9272 8392
Gray, Rebecca
Gaites, Tim
McKeown, Cora
Punton, Bridget
Sorrell, Katie

Floor 6
**Interventions Unpaid Work (SE
Region)**
tel 023-9272 8400 *fax 023-9287 1183*

Davies, John (area mgr, unpaid wk, ete
& essential skills) (14, 22, 24)
Skinner, Alan (op mgr int/upw N and IoW)
Chambers, Steph (op.mgr int/upw SW)
Leigh, Brian (health trainer project mgr)
Richards, Teresa (upw resource mgr) (14,
22, 24)
Stedman, Ros (asst resource mgr) (14, 22,
24)
Harris, Jeff (placement mgr)
Pervin, Eddie (placement mgr)

Portsmouth Programmes Unit
6th floor, Enterprise House

Isambard Brunel Road
Portsmouth PO1 2RX
tel 023-9272 8470 *fax 023-9282 7841*
Black, Tracy (spo)
Barrrett, Sally (progs mgr)
Connell, Soozin (p, treatment mgr) (21)
Janvrin, Jane (treatment mgr)
Hewitt, Mary (treatment mgr)
Whitefield, Sarah (p, treatment mgr) (7,
21)
Bassford, Clair (prog off)
Coomber, Carianne (prog off)
Cowles, Hannah (prog off)
Dyke, Matthew (prog off)
Eckersley, Louise (prog off)
Heptner, Nina (prog off)
Koffeman, Nelianne (prog off)
Lewis, Sarah (prog off)
Van Beek, Frankie (prog off)
Welfare, Natalie (prog off)
Tilford, Richard (facilitator)
Warburton, Jane (psy admin)
Whitelock, Kate (psy admin)
Adkins, Anna (p, progs admin) (8)
Correa, Helen (prog admin)
Terracciano, Sarah (prog admin)

SOGP Team
Vacancy (prog mgr)
Haynes, Sarah (prog off)
Webb, Dawn (facilitator)

IDAP team
Simpson, Sandra (p, spo idap) (42)
Vigar-Taylor, Sue (prog off)
Bennett, Alison (women's safety wrkr)
White, Sandra (prog off)
Damani, Ishret (p, prog off) (42)

17. **52,Isambard Brunel Road**
Portsmouth PO1 2BD
tel 023-9283 9800 *fax 023-9273 5192*

Court Unit
tel 023-9272 8940 *fax 023-9275 5663*

Lightburn, Marilyn (spo, crts)
Clarke, George
Devereux, Jan
Eden, Julie
Hahn, Colin
Wilkinson, Caroline (p) (40)
Ball, Jackie (pso)
Edwards, Sam (pso)
West, Lynn (pso)

Breach Unit
tel 023-9272 8930 *fax 023-9273 5192*

Stubbs, Lisa (pso, bpo)

Green, Lisa (pso, bpo)
Newman, Roger (pso, bpo)
Richards, Ian (pso, bpo)

ETE
tel 023-9272 8937 *fax 023-9287 7340*

Wishart, Corinne (ete off)

18. 70 London Road
Southampton S015 2AJ
tel 023-8063 5011 fax 023-8023 1801

MAPPA Unit
O'Driscoll, Paul (spo)
Alford, Alison (acting spo crts) (19, 23)
Edom, Matt
Evans, Lisa
Humphray, Jennifer
Lidstone, Fiona
May, Simon
McDermott, Michelle (p)(16)
Rogers, Fiona
Smith, Angela
Thwaites, Natasha
Watt, Sue
Winter, Emma Jane
Sherwood, Alex (pso)
Bulpitt, Carol (admin)
Horswell, Janette (om admin)
Mitchener, Lisa (om admin)
Reilly, Lynn (om admin)
Wright, Samantha (om admin)

**Young Adult Offender Team
& OM Unpaid Work**
Turkington, Robbie (spo)
Ball, Liz
Brown, Marsha (pso)
Collins, Yvonne
Gladdis, Jayne (pso)
Gunn, Mark
Leeds, Kelly Ann (pso)
Palmer, Donna (pso)
Skinner, Joanne (pso ppoc)
Cowley, Anthony (ete off)
Barnes, Clare (om admin)
Donovan, Leanne (om admin)
Webb, Rebecca (om admin)
Emery, Dennis (upw off)
Keites, Hayley (upw off)
Sutton, Gill (upw off)
Kitson, Nicola (om admin)
Adams, Tracy (asst resource mgr)

Reducing Custody Project
Fry, Chris (area mgr) (mobile 07813 152
110)
Ager, Jackie (spo, based at 22)

Bottomley, Jo
Lewis, Zara
Bland, Bernadette (pso)
Eason, Jessica (pso)
Loader, Sam (eng off)
Harrison, Carol (om admin)

19. **Southampton Magistrates' Court**
100 The Avenue, Southampton SO17 0EY
tel 023-8033 6113 *fax 023-8033 6122*

Alford, Alison (acting spo crts) (18, 23)
Bridger, Jane
Glew, David
Johnson, Don
Paul, Debbie
Woodham, Sue
Arnold, Andrea (pso)
Mullen, Lisa (pso)
Forte, Donna (asst resource mgr) (15, 20,
22, 23)
Swatton, Di (om admin)
Widlake, Kris (om admin)

20. **Southampton Crown Court**
The Courts of Justice
London Road, Southampton SO15 2AA
tel 023-8023 2642 *fax 023-8023 5929*

Gladwin, Peter (pso)

21. 7 Town Quay House, Town Quay
Southampton SO14 2PT
tel (02380) 831300 *fax (02380) 831333*

Svendsen, Jo Inge (area mgr) (5, 12, 14,
18, 23)
Rutherford, Alison (resource mgr) (5, 12,
14, 18, 23)
Shone, Lynne (p, asst resource mgr)
Pilkington, Michelle (p, asst resource mgr)

**CRO/CPRO Supervision Team &
Resettlement Cluster**
Lawrence, Jill (spo, drr)
Morris, Pete (spo)
Bainbridge, Adam
Bell, Amanda
Bone, Rebecca
Brider, Heather
Broughton, Steve (drr)
Cato, Len
Christopher, Rosie (drr)
Ducommun, Yvonne
French, Daniella
Hearn, Jenny
Remnant, Tracy (drr)
Rogers, Kirsty
Rushforth, Rachel

Russell, Claire
Sharratt, Matthew
Williams, Tina (drr)
Butt, Lauren (pso, drr)
Cleeve, Kate (p, pso)
Cupid, Kenny (pso, drr)
Evans, Heather (pso)
Goodchild, Nicky (p, pso)
Goodeve, Jayne (pso)
Hopper, Sarah (pso)
Kennelly, Gerry (pso)
James, Nigel (scheme mgr upw)
Crouch, Liz (pso, upw)
Parker, Bill (pso,upw)
Smythe, Pat (pso, upw)
O'Connor, Lou (ete)

Programmes Unit
Sealy, Judi (spo)
Green, Libby (idap treatment mgr)
Whitefield, Sarah (treatment mgr) (7, 16)
Bennett, Keith (prog off)
Cleal, Davina (prog off)
Connell, Soozin (p, prog off) (16)
George, Amy (prog off)
Nugent, Vanessa (prog off)
Storey, Alison (prog off)
White, Dominic (prog off)
Selvage, Michele (psychometrics off)
Green, Libby (idap treatment mgr)
Gover, Tanya (prog off idap)
Kirkpatrick, Sara (prog off idap)
Vacancy (prog off idap)
Waddington, Sue (prog off idap)
Miles, Nikki (p, women's safety wrkr)
Newnham, Fran (p, women' safety wrkr)
Easterby, Elaine (prog admin)
Gatt, Jan (prog admin)
Garnham, Joy (prog admin)

TV-CSOP Team
Black, Tracey (progs magr)
Metcalfe, Suzie (sogp treatment mgr)
Emery, Jane (sogp facilitator)
Hendricks, Caroline (sogp facilitator)
Saunders, Clare (sogp facilitator)

22. Old Bank House, 66-68 London Road
Southampton S015 2AJ
tel 023-8033 9992 *fax 023-8023 5778*

SW Breach Team
Hill, Jo (bpo)
Hall, Leo (bpo)
Thorndyke, Mel (pso, union & h&s rep.)
Darlington, Joanne (breach admin)
Farthing, Debbie (breach admin)
Swatton, Di (om admin)
Widlake, Kris (om admin)

Forte, Donna (asst resource mgr) (16, 20,
21, 23, 24)

SW Region Interventions Unpaid Work
Taggart, Kelly (op mgr int/upw SE)
Annell, Sharon (placement mgr)
Challender, Wayne (placement mgr)

23. 9 Testwood Lane **Totton**
Southampton S040 3BT
tel 023-8086 2287 *fax 023-8066 0314*

Alford, Alison (spo crts) (18, 19)
McAllen, Marie
McVeigh, Carol
Ryder, Zoe
Black, Janet (pso) (12, 14)
Forte, Donna (asst resource mgr)
Tilley, Wendy (om admin)
Wilde, Natalie (om admin)

24. 3rd Floor, Cromwell House
Andover Road **Winchester** S023 7EZ
tel (01962) 842662 *fax (01962) 866228*

Roscoe, Martin (area mgr) (8, 9, 11,
25, 27, 36-40)
Dunne, Margaret (spo) (25, 27)
Hardy, Susan (pda)
Moore, Sarah (act resource mgr 8, 9,
11, 25, 27, 36-40)
Boddy, Pat
Dealey, Jill
Kavanagh, Lewis
Stainton, Kate
Abbott, Heidi
Bland, Bernadette (pso)
Howell, Steve (pso, ppoc)
Stroud, Sarah (pso)
James, Marion (resource mgr) (25)
Barclay, Michelle (om admin)
Nayyar, Sarah (om admin) (25)
Rothery, Dianne (om admin)
Orchard, Frances (om admin)

25. **Winchester Combined Court Centre**
The Law Courts **Winchester** SO23 9EL
tel (01962) 849256 *fax (01962) 870405*

Dunne, Margaret (spo) (24, 27)
Nayyar, Sarah (admin) (24)

26. **Victim Contact Unit**
3rd Floor, Cromwell House
Andover Road **Winchester** SO23 7EZ
tel 0845 6040 150 *fax (01962) 844983*

Dunne, Margaret (spo) (24, 25)
Ball, Liz
Turner, Kirsty

Rooney, Debi
Smith, Victoria (om admin)

Youth Offending Teams

27 **Wessex Youth Offending Team**
85 High Street, Winchester SO23 9AE
tel (01962) 876100 *fax (01962) 876109*

Crocker, Steve (hd of youth offending svces)
Owen, Mark (perf, info & training mgr)

28. **Wessex YOT (NE & NW)**
180 Culver Road, Basingstoke RG21 3NL
tel (01256) 464034 *fax (01256) 327210*

Humphrey, Jean (area mgr)

29. **Wessex YOT (SE & Portsmouth City)**
Darby House, Skye Close
Cosham, Portsmouth PO6 3LU
tel 023-9237 0013 *fax 023-9220 0374*

Wade, Sue (area mgr)

30. **Wessex YOT (SW & Southampton City)**
33 Selbourne Avenue
Harefield, Southampton SO18 5DZ
tel 023-8046 3336 *fax 023-8047 0060*

Morse, Sue (area mgr)

31. **Wessex YOT (Isle of Wight)**
62 Crocker Street, Newport
Isle of Wight PO30 5DA
tel (01983) 522799 *fax (01983) 523175*

Abbott, Meg (area mgr)

32. **Wessex YOT (Intensive Supervision & Surveillance Programme)**
2nd Floor Ashville House 260-262
Havant Road, Drayton, Portsmouth PO6 1PA
tel 023-9228 3900 *fax 023-9238 1318*

Ballard, Jeff (area mgr)

Approved Premises (Hostels)

33. **Dickson House Approved Premises**
77 Trinity Street, Fareham PO16 7SL
tel (01329) 234531 *fax (01329) 284523*

Newman, Mark (spo)
Brockwell, Pam (support services off)
Binfield, Iris (res services off)
Dobson, Gemma (res services off)
Kitching, Peter (res services off)

Wheeler, Philip (res service off)
Vigar-Taylor, Sue (res services off)
Knott, Patricia (res adm sup off)
Nomuoja, Benjamin (night wk supvr)
Muzivani, Norman (night wk supvr)

34. **The Grange Approved Premises**
145 Stakes Road, Purbrook PO7 5PL
tel 023-9236 3474 *fax 023-9236 3481*

Wensley-Smith, Sonia (spo)
Mazzetelli, Dianne (supt services off)
Clark, Michelle (res service off)
Brown, Neil (res service off)
Maidment, Hayley (res service off)
Smith, Elaine (res services off)
Pack, Steve (night wk supvr)
Rogers, Mary (night wk supvr)
Robbins, Erin (res admin supt)

35. **Landguard Road Approved Premises**
32 Landguard Road, Shirley
Southampton SO15 5DJ
tel 023-8033 6287 *fax 023-8033 6290*

McKie Jenny (spo)
Davis, Kate (support services off)
Collins, Paul (res services off)
Williamson, Paul (res services off)
Pittila, Kayleigh (res services off)
Pickering, Darren (res services off)
Bone, Darren (night wk supv)
Carrington, Jackie (night wk supvr)
Davidson, Donna (res admin supt)

Institutions

36. H M Prison **Albany**
Newport, Isle of Wight PO30 5RS
tel (01983) 556300 *fax (01983) 556362*

Direct dial (01983) 556 + ext
Probn Clerk ext 465

Vacancy (spo) ext 467
Clarke, David ext 469
Snell, Patricia (pso) ext 466
Jenkins, Susan (pso) ext 470
Vacancy ext 462

37. H M Prison **Camp Hill**
Newport, Isle of Wight PO30 5PB
tel (01983) 554600 *fax (01983) 554799*

Direct dial (01983) 55 + ext

Vacancy (spo) ext 4806
Pennell, Stephen ext 4634
Pond, Dawn (pso housing) ext 4655
Simon, Pauline (pso housing) ext 4655

38. **H M Prison Parkhurst**
Newport, Isle of Wight PO30 5NX
tel (01983) 554000 *fax (01983) 554001*

Direct dial (01983) 55 + ext
Probn Clerk ext 360

King, Andrea (spo) ext 4119
Ellis, Michelle ext 4155
Holland, Mary ext 4235
Owen, Bryony ext 4081
Vacancy ext
Blackwell, Sheila ext 4282

39. **H M Prison Kingston**
122 Milton Road, Portsmouth PO3 6AS
tel 023-9295 3100 *fax 023-9295 3181*

Direct dial 023-92953 + ext
Admin & answerphone ext 216

Clist, Terry (spo) ext 217
Coffey, Mick ext 236
Markie, Jacqueline ext 218
Storey, Estelle ext 218
Wilkinson, Caroline (p) ext 236 (15)

40. **H M Prison Winchester**
Romsey Road, Winchester SO22 5DF
tel (01962) 723000 *fax (01962) 723001*
probn fax (01962) 723008

Direct dial (01962) 723 + ext

Neary, Paul (spo) ext 161
Murray, Andrea ext 160)
Rynne, Martin 160
Walden, Amy ext 180
Topping, Graham (pso) ext 157
Carter, Judith (pso bail info) ext 036
Beatson, Jennifer (pso bail info) ext 036
Kowalska-Brona, Marcelina (pso) ext 160
(pso, accom) ext 078

Local Justice Areas

15, 23 New Forest
2, 4 NE Hampshire
5, 6 NW Hampshire
11, 16 SE Hampshire
8, 9 S Hampshire
18 Southampton
13 Isle of Wight

Crown Courts

13 Newport
17 Portsmouth
21 Southampton
26 Winchester

HERTFORDSHIRE PROBATION AREA

Victim enquiries contact number (01727) 792709

e-mail Firstname.Surname@hertfordshire.probation.gsi.gov.uk

1. **Head Office**
Graham House, Yeoman's House
Ware Road, Hertford SG13 7HJ
tel (01992) 504444 *fax (01992) 504544*

Webb, Tessa (cpo)
Frayne, Jon (aco,om/interventions)
Hughes, John (aco,operations)
Johnson-Proctor, Steve (aco, offender mngmnt & crt)
Riccardi, Lisa (aco supt services)
Pattman, Laura (aco of finance)
Ball, Rosie (training mgr)
McSweeney, Barbara (p, press & pub)
Moses, Sandra (h.r. mgr)
Scully, Sonia (centre mgr)
Spencer, Lucy (perf improvement mgr)
Vacancy (h&s officer)
Parkin, Bob (unpaid work mgr)

East Herts Probation Centre
fax (01992 516900)
Vacancy (spo)
Weston, Jackie (spo)
Crawford, Anthony (pda)
Dowling, Jackie,
Bruno, Tina
Gordon, Shanti (p)
Jervis, Andrea
Kinsey, Ian
Kusevra, Ozen
Smith, Nicola
St Luce, Cheryl

Trainees
Doole, Katherine
Ling, Darren
Turner, Sarah

PSOs
Ferguson, Sarah (court)
Johnson, Di (court)
Price, Amanda (court)

Champion, Zoe (gen)
Durrant, Sarah (gen)
Ganatra, Anjana (gen)
Insaf, Ayse (gen)
Smith, Christine (gen)
Toofail, Jackie (gen)
Winter, Hazel (gen)

Black, Lorraine (gpwk)
Holmes, Min (gpwk)
Williams, Di (gpwk)

Taylor, Diane (ETE)
Lally, Dawn (project supervisor)

2. **Mid Herts Probation Centre**
62-72 Victoria Street
St Albans AL1 3XH
tel (01727) 847787 *fax (01727) 792700*

List, Terry (spo)
Leng, Sally (spo)
McConnell, Elaine (p, spo)
Holloway, Tony (p, pda)
Glasscock, Jo (p, pda)
Martindale, Vicky (pda)
Vacancy (treatment mgr)
Adams, Katie (p)
Vacancy
Bond, Nicola
Bucknor, Carlene
Ewington, Mark
Flower, Melanie
Golding, Victoria
Goodall, Anika
Joseph, Jenny (p)
Kozlowska, Beata
Larkin, John
Duncan, Jacqueline
Murphy, John
Willis, David

Trainees
Ferguson, Dave
Onione, Anna
Pole, Charlotte
Whyman, Robert

PSOs
Ashard, Laura (p, court)
Berardi, Patrizia (court)
Davis, Lynda (p, court)
Harrison, Nicola (court)
O'Neil, Desmond (court)
Runham, Jennifer (court)

Foster, Margaret (gen)
McGovern, Maureen (gen)
Hillhouse, Lyne (gen)
Pledge, Nicola (gen)
McKenna, Natalie (gen)
Parris, Mervyn (gen)
Bousefield, Chris (gen)
Cracknell, Matthew (gen)
Ivey, Linda (gen)
Johnson, Monique (gen)
Terrywall, Naznean (gen)

Appleyard, Phil (gpwk)
Finch, Marion (p, gpwk)
Marino, Collette (gpwk)
Wright, Lex (gpwk)

Vacancy (ETE)

Hook, Doug (prtnshp commissioning mgr)
Evans-Hughes, Julie (partnership mgr)
Bouma, Esther (prolific offender)
Maurice, Jane (choices & consequences proj)

McConnell (C2, p spo)
Amos, Jo (C2) (p)

Monery, Peter (placement off)
Brasset, John (project supvr)
Brazil, Diana (project supvr)

Victim Unit
tel (01727) 792709 *fax (01727) 792706*

Hornsey, Sue (victim devpt mgr)
Radcliffe, Frank (victim contact)
Ford, Donna (victim contact)
Bouma, Esther (prolific offender)
Mayles, Shelley (centre mgr)

3. **North Herts Probation Centre**
Argyle House, Argyle Way
Stevenage SG1 2AD
tel (01438) 747074 *fax (01438) 765206*

Martindale, Clare (spo)
Spencer, Maureen (spo)
Tassell, Sue (MAPPA mgr)
Wain, Lynda (spo)
Kate Harvey (court mgr)
Holmes, Alex (prog mgr)
Brooks, Dawn (treament mgr)
Rea, Emma (pda)
Bibi, Majabin
Bolton, May
Downes, Tom
Fawcett, Kelly
Jones, Victoria
Keyte, Bernie
Lachford, Michelle (p)
Moss, Nik (dtto)
Oliver-Blais, Merle
Raynor, Catherine
Tooley, Neil

Sex Offender Specialists
Jarvis, Phil (regnl sex offndr specialist)
Lawrance, Alison
Roderick, Liz (p)
Shirley, Matthew
Gurr, Lydia
Shults, Peter (pso)

Trainees
Cox, Sarah
Davis, Matthew
Hudson, Rebecca

PSOs
Pearson, Tony (crt)
Pratt, John (crt)
Roskilly, Caitrin (p, crt)
Winter, Louise (crt)

Clay, Natalie (gen)
Cliffe, Helen (gen)
Cotton, Janette (gen)
Cross, Samantha (gen)
Ebeling-Jones, Cheryl (p, gen)
Hood, Alison (gen)
Johnston, Anne (p, gen)
Parker, Heather (gen)
Stewart, Cindy (gen)

Graham, Rose (gpwk)
Sheedy, June (gpwk)
Mulqueen, Clare (gpwk)
White, Catherine (gpwk)
Woolmer, Paul (grpwk)

Morris, Emma (ETE)
Harding, Karen (project mgr)
Croft, Kay (centre manager)

4. **South & West Herts Probn Centre**
16-22 King Street **Watford** WD1 8BP
tel (01923) 240144 *fax (01923) 699195*

Cowen, Jon (spo)
Johnson, Morris (spo)
Mentern, Hannah (spo)
Hughes, Will (pda)
Ostrowski, Liz (treatment mgr)
Boorman, Laura
Carrol, Joannne
Harwood, Sarah
Hopkins, Alison
Hughes, Sarah
Hylton, Gary
McFarlane, Julia (p)
Marco, Francesca
Mikk, Jaanus
Pinder, Julie
Ross, Sarah-Jane
Thompson, Tanya
Urwin, Sue
Wojdyla-St.James, Barbara
Wyper, Fiona

Trainees
Adams, Samatha
Farrance, Denese
Kielthy, Bridgit

Russell, Sheila
Smallman, Gary
Stark, Laura

PSOs
Che, Simon (crt)
Brooks, Michaela (crt)
Gilbride, Aiden (crt)
Penn, Rebecca (crt)

Almond, Dawn (p, gen)
Crook, Janet (gen)
Egglesfield, John (gen)
Flaherty, Mary (gen)
Foley, Louise (gen)
Graham, Sarah (p, gen)
Hughes, James (gen)
Isherwood, David (gen)
Kropidlowska, Emilia (gen)
O'Donnell, Carole (gen)

Bruce, Sarah (gpwk)
Clarke, Sue (p, gpwk)
Isaacs, Susan (gpwk)
Mullings, Sonia (gpwk)
Richardson, Fiona (gpwk)
Warrington, Claire (p, gpwk)

Spencer, Jeff (project supervisor)
Vacancy (ETE)
De Castro, Eunice (centre manager)

5. **Crown Court Probation Office**
Bricket Road **St Albans** AL1 3JW
tel (01727) 753290 *fax (01727) 868276*

6. **Youth Offending Team**
S&W, Watford
tel (01923) 229012
Baker, Jill
N Herts, Stevenage
tel (01438) 219420
Jeffery, Peter

S&W, Hemel Hempstead
tel (01442) 388755
Tiernan, Janet

E Herts, Hatfield
tel (01707) 897440
Perkins, David

Institution

7. H M Prison **The Mount**
Molyneaux Avenue, Bovingdon
Hemel Hempstead HP3 0NZ
tel (01442) 836300 *fax (01442) 836301*

Gherundi, Ioan
Webster, Steve

Vacancy
Borg, Michelle (pso)
Kane, Lauren, (pso)
Carter, Richard (pso)
Munna, Jebeda (pso)

Local Justice Areas

1 East Hertfordshire
2 Central Hertfordshire
3 North Hertfordshire
4 West Hertfordshire

Crown Court

5 St Albans

HUMBERSIDE PROBATION AREA

e-mail: Firstname.Surname@humberside.probation.gsi.gov.uk

1. **Head Office**
   21 Flemingate **Beverley**
   E Yorks HU17 0NP
   tel (01482) 867271 *fax (01482) 864928*

   Hemming, Steve (ceo)
   Alexander, Voni (aco om)
   Fridlington, Kevan (aco prisons)
   Razzell, Ian (aco it)
   Robinson, Janet (aco, hr)
   Wright, Peter (aco interventions)
   Montgomery, Angela (solicitor)
   Siddy, Brian (aco corporate services)
   Munson, Kate (area mgr om)
   Ware, Ian (area mgr om)
   Redfern, Kate (area mgr int)
   Clarke, Mike (area mgr int)
   Tallant, Chris (spo nvq co-ord)
   Rhodes, Sharon (hr mgr)
   Goodrick, Steve (contracts mgr)
   Scott, Jayne (finance mgr)
   Archer, Kevin (health & safety advisor)
   Birt, Janet (pa to ceo)

   East Riding MAPPA Team
   Razzell, Gillian (pso)

   Victims Team
   Brookes, Chris (spo safeguarding children)
   Dent, Pamela (victim mgr)

   PPO Unit
   Galloway, Brenda (spo)

1a. **East Riding PPO Unit**
    Hornsea Police Station
    Hornsea HU18 1HP
    tel (01964) 550312

    Lee, Stephen
    Akrill, Angela (pso)

2. 4 St Johns Avenue
   Bridlington E Yorks YO16 4NG
   tel (01262) 672512 *fax (01262) 400336*

   Hodcroft, Felix (spo)
   Brookes, Mike
   Everitt, Heidi
   Hall, Rachel
   Prout, Lisa
   Walmsley, David
   Wilson, Jennifer
   Boxhall, Lesley (pso)
   Duncan, Maggie (pso)
   Stephenson, Ms Lesley J (pso)
   Wild, Jonathon (pso)
   Franks, Terry (case admin)

3. Greenawn, 1 Airmyn Road
   Goole E Yorks DN14 6XA
   tel (01405) 767177 *fax (01405) 720983*

   Mellor, Adrian (spo)
   Bates, Elizabeth
   Gaunt, Christine
   Lowden, Peter
   Jubb, Louise (pso)
   Throssel, Sara (p, pso)
   Wilson, Sally (pso)
   Patterson, Helen (ca)

4. **Hull Office**
   Liberty House, Liberty Lane
   Kingston upon Hull HU1 1RS
   tel (01482) 480000 *fax (01482) 480003*

   Neale, Marie (diversity mgr)
   Ellis, Jean (training mgr)
   Walster, John (IT mgr)
   Lloyd, Matt (quality imprvmnt mgr)

   Hull Offender Management
   Forton, Alison (sao OM)
   Pullan, Wendy (sao PPO, DRR)

   Hull Offender Mngmnt Unit 1
   Elmugadem, Mohamed (spo)
   Armstrong, Rob
   Clare, Hannah
   Cormack, Shona (p)
   Fishwick, Rachel (p)
   Goldring, Dave (p)
   Harris, Brian

Kelly, Paul
Street, Catherine
Sugden, Matthew
Wilson, Lee
Carr, Alex (pso)
Lee, Diane (p, pso)
Mansson, Magnus (pso)
Marrino, Donna (p, pso)
Pickering, Lisa (p, pso)
Timmings, Dawn (pso)
Beadle, Caron (ca)
Sargerson, Karen, (ca)

Hull Offender Mngmnt Unit 2
Scargill, Vicki (spo)
Birkett, Lynne
Griffiths, Eleanor (p)
Hall, Sally (p)
Hancock, Jane
Heald, Fliss (p)
Henderson, Peter
Jackson, Caroline
Phillips, Sarah
Robb, Haydn
Sutton, Emma
Westmoreland, Chris
Chamba, Ravinder (pso)
Lupkin, Cynthia (pso)
Tennison, Leanne (p, pso)
Ward, Niki (p, pso)
Adams, Judith (p, ca)
Bramley, Sam (ca)

Hull Offender Mngmnt Unit 3
Baker, Sue (spo)
Bate, Liz
Brown, Kathryn
Goforth, Kate
Hookem, Michelle
Morrell, David
Peck, Julie (p)
Swales, Liza
Watts, Sally
Wells Gareth
Chamba, Ravinder (pso)
Dent, Jane (pso)
McAllister, Carmel (p, pso)
White, Steve (pso)
Adamson, Sue (p, ca)
Haldenby, Angie (p, ca)
Hartley, Christine (ca)

Hull Offender Mngmnt Unit 4
Cook, Darran (spo)
Chung, David (p)
Cripps, Rosie
Hamilton-Rudd, Nick
Hardy, Rebecca (p)
Hastings, Joanne (p)

Sage, Clare
Thornton, Jade
Warner, Ian
Wright, Lizzie
Burton, Helen (pso)
Taylor, Zoe (pso)
Timperley, Mary (pso)
Trowell, Paula (pso)
Heath, Sue (ca)
Longhorn, Mandy (ca)

Hull Offender Mngmnt Unit 5
Wright, John (spo)
Baldwin, Suzanne
Carter, Tony (p)
Catterson, Neil
Donachie, John
Hamson, Louise (p)
Harrison, Catherine
Kiddle, Jo (p)
Langdon, Jonathon
Leighton, Katie
Priestley, Ray
Stonehouse, Vicky
Bahn, Steve (pso)
Proctor, Tracey (pso)
Rymer, Jayne (p pso)
Fox, Sarah (ca)
Fussey, Diane (ca)

DRR
Atkin, Sarah (p, spo)
Boyne, Linda
Frank, Joy
Harrison, Rebecca
McIntyre, Michelle
Guy, Elaine (pso)
Kirkpatrick, Joe (pso)
Pullen, Wendy (sao)
Brooks, Carol (ca)

PPO
Adegmembo, Sally (p, spo)
Hall, Dr Mariam
James, John
Kiney, Brighid
Mitchell, Nick
Wilkinson, Andrea
Atkinson, Eve (pso) (p)
Dhamrait, Jazz (pso)
Pullen, Wendy (ca)

Court Services
Harvatt, Diana (spo)
Naylor, Leroy
Shaddick, Brian
Wadforth, Neil (prosecutions officer)
Allen, Elaine (pso)
Billam, Lynne (pso)

Dee, Catherine (pso)
Dhamrait, Neelam (pso)
Eyles, Linda (pso)
Green, Sharon (pso)
Harding, Mike (pso)
Jarvis, Tina (pso)
Rookyard, Tracey (pso)
Sleight, Maxine (pso)
Arnett, Elaine (sao, all Humberside)

Victims Team
Cross, Jackie (wsw/vlo)
Stevens, Ellen (wsw/vlo)
Gowland, Paul (vlo)

Interventions Team
Sellors, Rupert (spo, all Humberside)
Campbell, Tara (spo, all Humberside)
Taylor, Donna (spo, all Humberside)
Baker, Glynis
Hurst, Phil
Oliver, Anita (p)
Sambrook, Mark

Adamson. Liz (pso)
Billam, Lesley (pso)
Clark, Jamie (pso)
Clark, Mike (pso)
Eyles, Stuart (pso)
Kimenia, Macharia (pso)
Matthews, Claire (pso)
Mounce, Pauline (pso)
Oyston, Sam (pso)
Robinson, Andy (pso)
Rollinson, Sonja (pso)
Simpson, Karen (pso)
Styche, Helen (p, pso)
Walkington, James (pso)
Wong, Jimmy (pso)
Wright, Ruth (pso)
Young, Pete (pso)

Cunningham, Mo (ao)

UPW Unit
Morton, Dave (upw unit mgr)
Merritt, Simon (upw pso)
Williams, Gwendoline (upw pso)

NVQ/PDA Unit
Dawson, Pat
McCartney, Sarah (p)
Parrott, Andrea (p)
Winters, Chris

5. **Hull MAPPA Team**
c/o Pearson Park LPT
Priory Road, Kingston upon Hull HU5 5SF
tel (01482) 334835 *fax (01482) 334850*

Zobkiw, Ivan (spo)

Smith, Mark
Wood, Lorraine (pso)

6. **Hull DIPT**
Suite J, Conifer Rooms
Shirethorne Centre
37-43 Prospect Street
Hull HU2 2PR
tel (01482) 620013 *fax (01482) 210084*

7. **Crown Court Liaison Office**
Hull Combined Courts Centre
Lowgate, Hull HU1 2EZ
tel (01482) 585044 *fax (01482) 581120*

8. Queen Street
Grimsby NE Lincs DN31 1QG
tel (01472) 357454 *fax (01472) 355572*

Court Services Team
Coleman, Sarah (spo)
Jackson, Robert
Marshall, Graham
Busby, Emma (pso)
Fairbank, Martin (pso)
Hookham, Di (pso)
O'Hanlon, Graeme (pso)
Riley, Marie (pso)
Matson, Mary (prosecution off)
Arnett, Elaine (sao)

Grimsby Offender Management
Oxborough, Sue (sao)

Grimsby Offender Mngmnt Unit 1
Bolton, Wendy (spo)
Cowper, Sophie
Lowery, Kirsten
Lynn, Phil
Parnell, Diane
Sanghera, Peramjit
Shepherd, John
Cassidy, Joanne (pso)
Frith, Linda (pso)
Hoyle, Sarah (pso)
Huxford, Karen (pso & mappa)
Humphries, Helen (ca)

Grimsby Offender Mngmnt Unit 2
Leake, Sonia (spo)
Adams, Michelle
Bailey, Becky
Binns, Alison (p)
Cotterill, Alan
Ford, Jo
Martin, Julia
Blow, Nichola (pso)
Glendenning, Dawn (pso)
Hazzard, Laura (pso)
Seward, Katie (ca)

Grimsby Offender Mngmnt Unit 3
Gilbert, Amy (spo)
Chung, Emma
Gillender, Clare
Harrison, Sonja
Thomas, Lorraine
Phillips, Kerry (p)
Lynn, Kerry-Jo
Sprakes, Marie
Duffield, Paul (pso)
Kirby, Jihan (p, pso)
Peart, Rachel (pso)
Nurse, Caroline (ca)

Victims' Team
Rix, Phil (pso, vlo)
Whitehand, Donna (wsw, mappa)

Practice Development Assessors
Martland, Arthur
Ratcliffe-Cooper, Enid

DRR/DIP/PPO
Houghton, Ian (spo)
Watson, Alexa
Woods, Heather
Austwick, Rachel (pso)
Chadli, Allel (pso)
Iggo, Amanda (pso)
Jackson, Linda (pso)
Stephen, Alan (pso)
Suiter, John (pso)
Whittingham, Lisa (p, pso)
Pullen, Wendy (sao)
Stratford, Emma (ca)

Interventions
McGrath, Anne-Marie
Hughes, Catherine
Doherty, Carole (pso)
Duffield, Kate (pso)
Kong, Alison (pso)

UPW Unit
Blythin, Lynette (upw pso)
Thorpe, Paul (proj mgr)

Grimsby Crown Court
tel (01472) 357454

9. 1 Park Square
    Scunthorpe N Lincs DN15 6JH
    tel (01724) 861222 *fax (01724) 289343*

    Barker, Sam (sao site supt Humberside)

Court Services Team
Coleman, Sarah (spo)
Taylor, Rachael (p)
Ellse, Linda (p, pso)
Harding, Keith (pso)

Henry, Sue (p, pso)
Arnett, Elaine (sao)

Scunthorpe Offender Management
Oxborough, Sue (sao)

Scunthorpe Offender Mngmnt 1
Robothom, Delyse (spo)
Anderson, Shaun
Green, Jackie
Joyce, Debbie
Ross, Di
Smith, Nicola
Sutton, Lucie
Thrower, Keith
Bonner, Caroline (pso)
Exton, Zoe (p, pso)
Robinson, Trudi (pso)
Elliot, Lynn (ca)
Westfield, Helen (ca)

Scunthorpe Offender Mngmnt 2
Evans, Adrian (spo)
Bell, Angi
Firth, Rebecca
Hemmings, Jennifer
Newton, Becky
Rawson, Amanda
Curtis, Debbie (pso)
Gunn, Helen (pso)
Kirby, Laura (pso)
Clayborough, Dawn (ca)
Holland, Claire (ca)

DRR/PPO
Corkhill, Kirsty (spo)
Butterworth, Alison
Emerson, Julie
Cochrane, Hayley (pso)
Jacomb, Donna (pso)
Sivorn, Tony (pso)
Pullen, Wendy (sao)
Wood, Jackie (ca)

DIP
Devine, Jessica (p)
Walker, Terry (pso)

Victims Team
Whitehand, Donna (mappa/vlo)

Interventions
Campbell, Tara (spo)
Taylor, Donna (spo)
Jones, PeterAtherton, Gary (pso)
Franklin, Lyndsay (pso)
Howe, Miranda (pso)
Permaine, Erica (pso)
Perry, Emma (pso)

UPW Unit
Postill, Bill (upw unit mgr)
Wilson, Ann (qa upw mgr)
Adams, Liz (upw pso)
Blythin, Lynette (upw pso)

Victims' Team
Bearne, Ann (wsw)

10. **Hull Youth Offending Team**
Myton Centre
Porter Street, Hull HU1 2RE
tel (01482) 609991

Porteous, Mandylee
Harwood, Lara (pso)

11. **East Yorkshire YOT**
Council Offices, Main Road
Skirlaugh, Nr Hull HU11 5HN
tel (01482) 396623

12. **North Lincolnshire YOT**
55-57 Oswald Road
Scunthorpe DN15 7PE
tel (01724) 858864

Gordon, Les

13. **NE Lincolnshire YOT**
44 Heneage Road
Grimsby DN23 9ES
tel (01472) 325252

Gibson, Steve

Approved Premises (Hostels)

14. **Hull Approved Premises**
41 Queens Road
Kingston upon Hull HU5 2QW
tel (01482) 446284 *fax (01482) 470704*

Lloyd, Pat (spo)
Baker, Paul (asst warden)
Dixon, Marilyn (asst warden,
Higginbottom, Chris (asst warden)
Scarah, Dawn (asst warden)
Tongrack, Joanne (asst warden)
Wells, Carol (ao)

15. **Scunthorpe Approved Premises**
Victoria House, 31 Normanby Road
Scunthorpe DN15 6AS
tel (01724) 289124 *fax (01724) 289126*

Godley, John (spo)
Spindley, Roy (pso)
Adams, John (asst warden)
Corbett, Diane (asst warden)
Cottingham, Caroline (asst warden)

Hayes, David (asst warden)
Ives, Dean (asst warden)
Yorke, Karen (asst warden)
Shipley, Barrie (ao)

Institutions

16. H M Prison **Hull**, Hedon Road
Kingston upon Hull
E Yorks HU9 5LS
tel (01482) 282200 *fax (01482) 282400*

Probn clerk ext 301
Special visits ext 284

Vacancy (spo)
Boyd, Christine
Jackson, David (p)
Sefton, Wendy
Birt, Chris (pso)
Burnett, Sarah (pso)
Gibson, Claire (pso)
Hines, Cher (pso)
Rees, Andrew (pso)
Riby, Sam (pso)
Stainforth, Wendy (pso)
Waddy, Rachel (pso)

17. H M Prison, Moor Lane
Full Sutton York YO41 1PS
tel (01759) 475100 *fax (01759) 371206*

McNicol, Ian (spo)
Baldwin, Moira
Barnes, Alison
Collins, Susan
Garrett, Tony
MacKenzie, Michelle (p)
Gawtry, Kerry (pso)
Hutchinson, Joe (pso)
Longstaff, Rebecca (pso)
Ward, Jenny (pso)

18. H M Prison
Everthorpe Brough
East Yorkshire HU15 1RB
tel (01430) 426500 *fax (01430) 426501*

Pearson, Rob (spo)
Bissenden, Dave
Flynn, John
Haynes, David
Hockney, Gary
Hill, Katrina
Gill, David (pso)
Rowe, Debbie (pso)
Rowley, David (pso)
Wilkinson, Sue (pso)

19. H M Prison **Wolds**
Everthorpe, Brough
East Yorkshire HU15 2JZ

tel (01430) 428000 *fax (01430) 428001*

Mellor, Adrian (spo)
Elkomi, Gamal
Fraser, Robert
Futter, Suzanne (p, pso)

Local Justice Areas

2 Bridlington
4 Beverley & The Wolds
8 Grimsby & Cleethorpes
3 Goole & Howdenshire
4 Hull & Holderness
9 North Lincolnshire

Crown Courts

7 Kingston upon Hull
8 Great Grimsby

KENT PROBATION AREA

Out of hours emergency contact point
Fleming House (01622) 755918

Victim enquiries contact number
Maidstone (01622) 202120

e-mail: Firstname.Surname@kent.probation.
gsi.gov.uk

Kent has the following specialised posts

(bus mgr)	business manager
(cp mgr)	community payback manager
(cp devt mgr)	community payback development manager
(cp qa)	community payback quality assurance
(cpo int)	community payback officer, intervention
(cp om)	community payback officer, offender management
(dist bus mgr)	district business manager
(gpwrkr)	groupworker
(probn crt rep)	probation court representative
(vlo)	victim liaison officer
(wsw)	Womens' Safety Worker

1. **Area Office**
   Chaucer House, 25 Knightrider Street
   Maidstone ME15 6ND
   tel (01622) 350820 *fax (01622) 350853*

   Billiald, Sarah (co) ext 822
   Hazell, Sandy (p, pa to co & board sec solicitor) ext 839
   Baillieu, Adrian (dir, finance, perf & standards) ext 830

Dowie, Alan (dir, offender mngmnt) ext 825
Last Lynne (dir, hr) ext 829
Verity, Robert (dir, interventions & business devpt) ext 828
Clark, Robert (area mgr, business devpt) ext 824
Vacancy (area mgr, perf & standards) ext 826
Hockley, Rita (p, process mgr) ext 831
Hook, Heather (p) (executive off) ext 844
O'Reilly, Maurice (area mgr progs) ext 827
Collins, Pauline (finance mgr) ext 846
Brown, Alison (financial accountant) ext 849
Dowarris, Colin (p, diversity mgr) ext 823
Lampert, Neil (comms mgr) ext 840
Boulden, Michell (comms off) ext 858
McCarthy, Anne (area bus mgr) ext 832
Simpson, Liz (bus mgr) ext 833
Davis, Caroline (hr mgr) ext 841
Jones, Laura (hr officer) ext 843
Newberry, Elaine (p, hr officer) ext 857
Morton, Katherine (p, hr officer) ext 857
Harley, Elaine (p, hr admin) ext 842
Burkin, Sara (hr assist) ext 856
Wilson, David (h&s officer) based at Sheerness
tel (01795) 423321 *fax (01795) 663240*

2. **Training Unit**
   24 Maynard Road, Wincheap Estate,
   Canterbury CT1 3RH
   tel (01227) 769345 *fax (01227) 764339*
   Doherty, Sean (training mgr)
   direct dial tel (01227) 866630 Fax (01227) 785946

   James, Nick (spo pract devpt)
   Wilding, Rebecca (training admin)
   Lowry, Caroline (asst training admin)

   Practice Development Assessors
   Coley, David (based at Maidstone)
   Crabb, Deborah (p) (based at Sittingbourne)
   Wright, Pam (p, based at Thanet)
   Peall, Jeanne (based at Gravesend)
   Puce, Eriks (based at Ashford)

Offender Management
Dowie, Alan (director) (01622) 350825
*Covering Courts, East Kent, Mid Kent &
North Kent offender management teams*

3. **Court Services Team**
   Probation Office, Maidstone Crown Court
   The Law Courts, Barker Road

Maidstone ME16 8EQ
tel (01622) 202121 *fax (01622) 677312*

King, Barney
Smedley, Georgina (pso)
Stevens, Julie (probn crt rep)
Strydom, Angela (pso)
Wilson, Susan (probn crt rep)

3a. **Canterbury Crown Court**
Liaison Probation Office, The Law Courts
Chaucer Road, Canterbury CT1 1ZA
tel (01227) 819299/819301 *fax (01227)
764961*

Williams, Susan-Anne
Lindsay, Brenda (probn crt rep)
Sookun, Prakash (pso/probn crt rep)
Watson, Valerie (probn crt rep)

3b. **Magistrates' Court Staff**

Canterbury
Tel/fax (01227) 766254
Mantle, Caroline (pso/probn crt rep)

Thanet
Tel/fax (01843 223297)
Hunt, Lynne (probn crt rep)
Nicolaou, Sophie (probn crt rep)

Ashford
tel (01303) 852004
Morris, Wendy (p, pso/probn crt rep)
Neve, Susan (probn crt rep)
Rickwood, Helen (probn crt rep)
Williams, David (probn crt rep) (01233)
650637

Gravesend
tel (01474 569546)
Louch, Deborah
Low, John (probn crt rep)
Roe, Julie (probn crt rep)

Maidstone/Sevenoaks
based at Maidstone
tel (01622) 687521
Smith, Angela (p, probn crt rep)

Tunbridge Wells
tel (01892) 559350
Taft Morris, Lesley (probn crt rep)

Medway
tel (01634 849284)
Samuda, Evonne
Waters, Trevor (probn crt rep)
Ravate, Dawn (probn crt rep)

Swale
tel (01795 423321)
Foreman, Josie (pso)

East Kent
Allen, Cynthia (district mgr East Kent)
Redman, Julia (dist bus mgr)
Spence, Joy (p, pa/sec to dis mgr)
based at Canterbury (01227) 769345
fax (01227) 785946
*Covering Canterbury, Folkestone, Dover, Ashford
and Thanet.*

4. **Canterbury Unit**
24 Maynard Road
Wincheap Estate,
Canterbury CT1 3RH
tel (01227) 769345 *fax (01227) 764339*

Morton, Susie (spo)
James, Nick (spo pract devpt)
Rootes, Ros (spo/mgr domestic abuse & vl)
Sahagian, Karen (p) (bus mgr)
Bassett, Linda
Coleman, Deborah
Fyles, Susan (sort)
Gillon, Anne (p, term time)
Goddard, Rebecca (programmes)
Hammond, Claire (sort)
Harris, Rachel
Hollins, Sue (p, treatment mgr, idap)
Mathews, Daphne (programmes)
Moore, William
Walczak, Rebecca
Williams, Sue

Crealock, Carol (treatment mgr)
Curteis, Michael (pso)
Groves, Val (pso)
Hawksworth, Jeremy (pso prog, idap)
Mason, Alison (pso)
Reeves, Tania (p, pso)
Rutland, Emily (pso, prog facilitator)
Scott, Gary (pso)

Saxby, Lynn (ete off)
Doherty, Fiona (treatment mgr)
Holloway, Suzanne (wsw)
Andrews, Lesley (sub misuse mgr)

Gatward, Clair (kcjb ppo co-ord)

5. **Folkestone Unit**
The Law Courts, Castle Hill Avenue
Folkestone CT20 2DH
tel (01303) 851140 *fax (01303)
248379/221277*

Barry, John (spo)
Tinkler, Phyl (bus mgr)
Bayley, Sara
Bywater, Elizabeth (sort)
Callister, Andy (p)
Ivory, Tessa

Jarvis, Collette (p)
Jones, Claire
Stockle, Anthony
Thomson, Helen

Allen, Gillian (pso)
Foster, Gary (pso)
Hayward, Anna (pso)
Lavelle, Jeanette (p, pso)
Sprinks, Jill (p, pso)

Hyden, Heather (gpwrkr)

5a. **Dover Unit**
Ground Floor, Maybrook House
York Street **Dover** CT17 9AJ
tel (01304) 244700 *fax (01304) 215561*

Mackey, Heather (spo)
Davies, David
Mitchell, Rebecca
Raeburn, Stephen (p)
Squire, Stephen
Wright, Stanley

Evenden, Colin (pso)
Graham, Robert (pso)
Lavelle, Jeanette (p, pso)
Stabler, Jim (pso)

5b. **Ashford Unit**
Elwick House, Elwick Road
Ashford TN23 1NR
tel (01233) 656500 *fax (01233) 647459*

Kenny, Joanne (spo)
Hadden, Richard
Mowbray, David
Moyse, Susan
Udale, Lisa

Puce, Eriks (pda)

Gough, Carly (pso)
Grace, Headley (pso)
Jones, Romi (pso)
Keeler, Simon (pso)
Rasmussen, Nichola (p, pso)

6. **Thanet Unit**
38/40 Grosvenor Place
Margate CT9 1UW
tel (01843) 228727 *fax (01843) 291527*

Johnston, Mark (spo)
Mackey, Heather (p, spo)
Sahagian, Karen (bus mgr)
Borda, Julie (p)
Cesbron, Ben
Cox, Deborah
Goulbourne, Theresa (sort, trtmnt mgr)

Lawrence, Carmen
Lister, Jane
Lovell, ChristineRees, Abbie
Ryder, Anne
Stevens, Candice
Townsend, Sîan
Wildman, Jennifer

Wright, Pam (p, pda)
Boarder, Ellie (trainee)
Hinge, Sarah (trainee)
Reader, Sally (trainee)
Squires, Clifford (trainee)

Clarke, Terri (vlo)
Brackley, Amanda (wsw)
Cossell, Susan (pso)
Jeacock, Linda (pso)
Jones, Sarah (pso)
Lewis, Janette (pso)
Smith, Julie (p, pso)
Tyrell-Smith, Matt (pso)

Jefferies, John (ete team leader)
Kane, Sarah (ete officer)

Mid Kent
Kadir, Tracey (district mgr mid kent)
Homewood, Cindy (dist bus mgr)
McGhie, Yvonne (pa sec)
based at Maidstone (01622) 687521
*Covering Maidstone, Tunbridge Wells,
& Swale*

7. **Maidstone Unit**
56 College Road
Maidstone ME15 6SJ
tel (01622) 687521 *fax (01622) 661653*

White, Nick (spo) (also covering crts)
Tancred, Tania (snr psychologist)
Smith, Jan (bus mgr)
Balsamo, Delaine
Bratton, Jane
Callar, Brian
Chandler, Peter (p)
Greenhalgh, Julie
Hambly, Gemma
Hay, Jenny (sort, treatment mgr)
Hook, Heather (p)
Houghton, Lynda
Norman, Joanne

Smith, Tracy
Soloman, Laura

Coley, David (pda)
Dove, Neil (trainee)
Godmon, Karen (trainee)

Davis, Kevin (pso)
Greenaway, Rose (pso)
Ludlow, Jacqueline (pso)
Marriott, Andrew (pso)
Marsh, Yvonne (pso)
Robinson, Carol (p, pso)
Smith, Robin (pso)
Vardy, Ashley (pso)

8. **Tunbridge Wells Unit**
    17 Garden Road,
    Tunbridge Wells TN1 2XP
    tel (01892) 559350 *fax (01892) 534728*

    White, Nick (spo) (also covering Crts)
    Collison, Mark
    Griffiths, Paul
    Henderson, Kathryn (p)
    Hogg, Joanna (p)
    Hooper, Laura
    Kimber, Kevin
    Lumsden, Nadine
    Mason, Denise
    Tomlinson, Rachel
    Wood, Richard

    Gosling, Rebecca (trainee)
    Lane, Jane (trainee)

    Baker, Alison (p, pso)
    Dicks, Jacqueline (pso)
    Lindeman, Anna (pso)
    Paterson, Tami (cpo pm)

9. **Swale Unit**
    *Sittingbourne & Sheerness are
    amalgamated.
    All admin based at Sittingbourne. All phone
    calls and faxes to the Admin at
    Sittingbourne.*

    Thames House, Roman Square
    Sittingbourne ME10 4BJ
    tel (01795) 423321 *fax (01795) 474251*

    46 High Street
    Sheerness ME12 1NL
    fax (01795) 663240

    McGarry, Kevin (spo)
    Sewell, Anne-Marie (p, bus mgr)
    Houghton, Lynda
    Kirk, Johanna (p)
    Port, Jane
    Tindall, Pam
    Whittall, Andrea

    Williams, Debra
    Willis, Sue (p)
    Wood, Andrew (p)

Crabb, Deborah (p, pda)
Berry, Timothy (trainee)
Strong, Thomas (tranee)

Berry, Karen (p, vlo)
Baldock, Jayne (pso)
Dummott, Karen (p, pso)
Humphrey, Diana (pso)
Goodwin, Jayne (pso)
Marchant, Clive (pso)
Moat, Tina (pso)
Shaw, Liz (p, pso)

North Kent
Edgar, Jeanette (district mgr N Kent) (01634
887462)
Wickens, Tina (dist bus mgr) (01634 887453)
Roberts, Diane (pa/sec to dist mgr) (01634
887454)
based at Medway (01634) 849284
Covering Medway/Chatham & Gravesend.

10. **Medway Unit**
    27-35 New Road, **Chatham** ME4 4QQ
    tel (01634) 849284 *fax (01634) 812331*

    Callingham, Debbie (spo)
    Skinner, Fran (spo)
    Knight, Jane (spo mappa)
    Thorne, Tracy (spo prog mgr)
    Mason, Toni (bus mgr)
    Akers, Joanne
    Campbell, Valerie
    Faturoti, Laura
    Graham, Trudie
    Harvey, Nick
    Hughes, Pauline (p)
    Leek, Katherine
    MacDonald, Iris
    Plank, Sally
    Price, Anna
    Rawlings, Kelly
    Russell, Ishbel
    Thomson, Kelly (p, treatment mgr)
    Tupper, Kelly

    Crocker, Alan (po, prog facilitator)
    Nettleton, Terry (po prog facilitator)
    Thompson, Allison (po prog facilitator)
    Vecchiolla, Emma (po prog facilitator)
    Maurice, Carol (accred prog co-ord)
    Jagger, Marie (accred prog co-ord)
    Wheal, Sarah (prog facilitator)

    Conelly, Tracey (vlo)
    Baker, Katie (p, pso)
    Eva, Diane (pso)
    Hammond, Tim (pso)
    Hayes, Simon (pso)
    Keable, Angela (pso)

Laverie, Deborah (pso)
McDermott, Sally (pso)
Sanders, Jodie (pso)
Silvey, Sonja (p, pso)
Tremain, Julie (pso)
Flood, Trish (ete off)

Cass, Hazel (syso)

11. **Gravesend Unit**
Joynes House, New Road
Gravesend DA11 0AT
tel (01474) 569546 *fax (01474) 563103*

Hardy, Ruth (spo)
Imison, Carol (bus mgr)
Harris, Sonia (diver mgr)
Alderson-Rice, Nick
Bloomfield, Jenny
Campbell, Henry (sort)
Dorrell, Karen (p)
Logan, Sue
Morris, James
Sanders, Ron
Smith, Laura
Young, Pam

Crocker, Alan (p, pda)
Peall, Jeanne (pda)
Donovan, Kevin (trainee)
Harris, James (trainee)
Smith, Amanda (trainee)
Watson, Stephen (trainee)
Watson, Stewart (trainee)

Bennett, Justin (ete off)
Cowell, Ernie (p, vlo)
Burns, Kim (pso)
Dodd, Steve (pso)
Gould, Caroline (pso)
Manktelow, Mel (p, pso)
Sharp, Carole (pso)
Sutherland, Alison (pso)

Community Payback & YOTs
Adelsberg, Sarah (area mgr, interventions)

12. **Management Office**
118A West Street
Faversham, ME13 7JB
tel (01795) 532587 *fax (01795) 530454*

Adelsberg, Sarah (area mgr, intrvntns)
Lee, Carol (cp resource mgr)
Hockley, Rita (p, cp operations mgr)

Vacancy (admin asst)

East Kent District
Salisbury, Tim (cp mgr)

tel (01303) 851140
(covering Folkestone, Canterbury, Thanet & Dover)

Folkestone
tel (01303) 852007
Foster, Gary J (cpo)
Wilkinson, Jane (cpo)
Medlock, Pam (cpo qa)

Canterbury
tel (01227) 769345
Gregory, Hazel (cpo)
Howes, Winston (cpo qa)

Thanet
tel (01843) 228727
Craig, Ian (cpo)

Mid Kent District
Majuqwana, Alison (cp mgr)
Tel (01622) 687521
(covering Ashford, Maidstone & Tunbridge Wells)

Ashford
tel (01303) 656500
Gooding, Michelle (cpo)

Maidstone
tel (01622) 687521
Hlwatika, Alison (cp mgr)
Jenkinson, Linda (cp qa)
Walmsley, Chris (cp qa)
McLaren, Kenneth (cpo int)
Wellman, Kelly (cpo int)

North Kent District
Cullen, Stuart (cp mgr)
Tel (01634) 849284
(covering Medway, Gravesend & Swale)

Medway
tel (01634) 849284
Cullen, Stuart (cp mgr)
Crealock, Nick (cpo int)
Kirby, Kevin (cpo int)
Gravesend
tel (01474) 569546
Legg, Pat (cp qa)
Pluck, Steve (cpo int)

Swale
tel (01795) 423321
Woolley, Alan (cpo int)

13. **Youth Offending Teams**

13a. **East Kent**
Apollo House, Chapel Place
Ramsgate CT11 9SA

tel (01843) 587976 *fax (01843) 590009*

Cox, Martin

13b. Avenue of Remembrance
Sittingbourne ME10 4DD
tel (01795) 473333 *fax (01795) 420016*

Bennett, Peter

13c. **Mid Kent**
Bishops Terrace, Bishops Way
Maidstone ME14 1LA
tel (01622) 691640 *fax (01622) 663928*

Vacancy

13d. Queen's House, Guildhall Street
Folkestone CT20 1DX
tel (01303) 253476 *fax (01303) 224329*

Goldspring, Joanne

13e. **West Kent**
Joynes House, New Road
Gravesend DA11 0AT
tel (01474) 544366 *fax (01474) 544569*

Plaiche, Aline

13f. Social Services Dept,
Croft House, East Street
Tonbridge TN9 1HP
tel (01732) 362442 *fax (01732) 352733*

Vacancy

13g. **Medway Area**
The Family and Adolescent Centre
67 Balfour Rd **Chatham** ME4 6QU
tel (01634) 818753 *fax (01634) 849660*

Kramer, Julie (p) (pso)
Laws, Jackie (pso)

Interventions & Business Development
Verity, Rob (director) (01622) 350828
*Public Protection, MAPPPA, Sex Offender
Resource Team, victims & Hostel*

Performance & Standards
Vacancy (area mgr)
based at Chaucer House (01622) 350826
*Covering Info Systems, DAT/DTTO,
Research & Devpt and Communications*

14. **Information Systems Unit (ISU)**
58 College Road **Maidstone** ME15 6SJ
tel (01622) 687521 *fax (01622) 688004*
e-mail: is.unit@kent.probation.gsi.gov.uk

Webb, Peter (ISU mgr)
direct dial (01622) 697128)

Wickens, Julie (database mgr)
Wright, Julie (it mgr)
Craker, Vicky (ict training off)
Mattison, David (info sys developer)
Wickens, Adam (application devpt)
Bamblett, Peter (syso) Maidstone
Burgess, Marcus (syso) Gravesend
Cass, Hazel (syso) Medway
Jacques, Robert (syso) Maidstone
Maynard, Sarah (syso) Folkestone
Roberts, Sarah (syso) Maidstone
Sanders, Steven (syso) Thanet
Silveston, Ali (p, syso) Swale

DAT & DTTO
tel (01227) 769345
Based at Canterbury
Andrews, Lesley (subst misuse mgr)

Research & Development
Based at Maidstone (01622) 687521
Brewer, John (performance analyst)
Vacancy (p, info asst)

Communications
tel (01622) 350840
Based @ Chaucer House
Lampert, Neil (com mgr)
Boulden, Michelle (coms officer)
Mattison, David (p, sys developer)

Programmes & Victims
O'Reilly, Maurice (area mgr, programmes)
based at Chaucer House, Maidstone (01622)
350827
*covering Sex Offender Resource Team (SORT),
Victim Liaison Services & Fleming
House Probation & Bail Hostel.*

15. **MAPPPA Joint Co-ordination Team**
Kent Police HQ
Sutton Rd **Maidstone** ME15 9BZ
tel (01622) 650459 *fax (01622) 654679*

Knight, Jane (spo mappa co-ord)
Gain, Tracy (mapppa co-ord)
Brooks, Fiona (visor admin)
Jezusek, Teresa (p, visor admin)

16. **Sex Offender Resource Team (SORT)**
58 College Road
Maidstone, ME15 6SJ
tel (01622) 687521 *fax (01622) 697101*

O'Hagan, Melanie (p) (spo, high risk
off/sort pub prot)
Ling, Sarah (admin)
Bywater, Elizabeth (SE Kent) (Folkestone)
Campbell, Henry (Gravesend)
Fyles, Susan (Canterbury)

Goulbourne, Theresa (Thanet)
Hammond, Claire (Canterbury)
Hay, Jenny (Maidstone)

16a. **General Offender Behaviour Programmes**
Thorne, Tracy (spo prog mgr, Medway)
Crocker, Alan (po prog facilitator, Medway)
Goddard, Rebecca (po prog facilitator, Canterbury)
Mathews, Daphne (p, po prog facilitator, Canterbury)
Thompson, Allison (po prog facilitator, Medway)
Rutland, Emily (pso, prog facilitator, Canterbury)
Wheal, Sarah (pso, prog facilitator, Medway)
Crealock, Carol (treatment mgr, Medway)
Doherty, Fiona (treatment mgr, Canterbury)
Thomson, Kelly (treatment mgr, Medway)
Hyden, Heather (gpwrkr, Folkestone)
Jagger, Maria (accred prog co-ord, Medway)

17. **Victim Liaison Service**
Ralphs Unit, 24 Maynard Rd
Wincheap Estate,
Canterbury CT1 3RH
tel (01227) 769345 *fax (01227) 785946*

Rootes, Ros (spo/mgr domestic Abuse & vl) (based at Canterbury)
King, Joanna (admin, victim liaison & idap) (01227) 866644)
Berry, Karen (p, vlo) (Sheerness)
Brackley, Amanda (wsw, Thanet)
Clarke, Terri (vlo) (Thanet)
Holloway, Suzanne (wsw, Canterbury)
Conelly, Tracey (vlo) (Medway)
Cowell, Ernie (p, vlo) (Gravesend)
Barber, Sharon (p, vlo) (Maidstone crown crt)

Approved Premises (Hostel)

18. **Fleming House Probation & Bail Hostel**
32 Tonbridge Road
Maidstone ME16 8SH
tel (01622) 755918 *fax (01622) 674809*
e-mail unit mail box: Fleming House

Hughes, Tina (a.p. mgr)
Hall, Julie (dep. mgr)
Curtis, Joanne (p, off supvr)
McGrath, Richard (off supvr)

McVeigh, Vanessa (off supvr)
Dhami, Kirinjit (pso)
Linton, Donna (pso)

Lawrence, Sharon (ca)
Bildstein, Theresa (finance admin)

Prisons & Business Development
Clark, Robert (area mgr, business development)
based at Chaucer House (01622) 350824
*Covering ETE Team, Basic Skills,
Commissioning Service, and Institutions.*

19. **Emplt, Training & Educn Team (ETE)**
58 College Road
Maidstone ME15 6SJ
tel (01622) 687521 *fax (01622) 688004*
e-mail unit mail box: ETE Team

Leigh, Donna (ete commissioning mgr)
ext 133
Jefferies, John (ete team leader based at Thanet 01843 228727)
Hammond, Jodie (p, ete county admin)

Employment Training & Education Officers
Austen, Louise (Folkestone) (01303) 851140
Bennett, Justin (Gravesend) (01474) 569546
Burls, Glynis (Sheerness) (01795) 662543
Flood, Trish (Medway) (01634) 849284
Gooderham, Katie (Sittingbourne) (01795) 423321
Haddon, Sally (Maidstone) (01622) 687521
Kane, Sarah (p) (Thanet) (01843) 227479
Macey, Gemma (Sittingbourne) (01795) 662543
Saxby, Lynn (p) (Canterbury) (01227) 769345
Treharne, Janet (Ashford) (01233) 656500

ETE Groupwork Tutors
Langridge, Claire
HMP Area Rochester (01634) 202500

Skills for Life Team
Leigh, Donna (ete commissioning mgr)
ext 134
Mepham, Pamela (skills for life devpt mgr)
vacancy (bus admin)

20. Commissioning Services
24 Maynard Rd, Wincheap Estate,
Canterbury CT1 3RH
tel (01227) 769345 *fax (01227) 764339*

Cohn, Howard (comm serv mgr)

Partnerships
Cohn, Howard (comm serv mgr)

Mentor Unit
Greenway, Margaret (comm serv
unit resource mgr)

Accom Strategy and Devpt
Ford, Malcolm (accom off)

Drink Drive Rehab Unit
Gibson, Catherine (p, admin)

Institutions

21. HM Young Offender Institution
    1 Fort Road
    Rochester ME1 3QS
    tel (01634) 803100 *fax (01634) 803101*
    direct dial 80 + ext

    parole clerk (01634) 803163
    Discipline (01634) 803211
    Special visits (01634) 803163

    Gorringe, Radley (hd of public
    protectn) ext 3120
    Kempster, Leanne ext 3213
    Brown, Deborah (pso) ext 3299
    Moss, Cheryl (pso) ext 3099
    Willoughby, Emma (pso) ext 3248

22. **Sheppey Prison Cluster
    Probation Team**

22a. HM Prison **Standford Hill**
    Church Road, Eastchurch
    Sheerness ME12 4AA
    tel (01795) 884500 *fax (01795) 880041*
    Direct dial (01795) 88+ ext
    OMU ext 4777

    Ratledge, Paula (spo, hd of public
    protectn based at 22b)
    Sennett, Paul ext 4780
    Brown, Janet (pso) ext 4780

22b. HM Prison **Swaleside**
    Brabazon Road, Eastchurch,
    Sheerness ME12 4AX
    tel (01795) 804100 *fax (01795) 804200*
    probn fax (01795) 804128
    Direct dial (01795) 80+ ext

    OMU ext 4025
    Lifer Clerks ext 4166
    Special visits ext 4177 or 4187
    or visitsbookingsswaleside@hmps.gsi.gov.uk

    Ratledge, Paula (spo, hd of public
    protectn) ext 4102
    Dold, Gavin ext 4137

Pellatt, Katherine
Willans, Jessica ext 4103
Allison, Marie (p, pso) ext 4128

22c. HM Prison **Elmley**
    Church Road, Eastchurch
    Isle of Sheppey ME12 4AY
    tel (01795) 882000 *fax (01795) 882001*
    *or phone direct to staff member by
    dialing (01795) 88 followed by the ext
    number*

    OMU Boosey, Karen ext 2242
    Tumber, Carol (Sheppey cluster public
    protectn co-ord) ext 2154
    Legal visits (01795) 882327

    Ratledge, Paula (spo, hd of public
    protectn based at 22b) ext 4102
    Green, Joseph ext 2065
    Gurr, Michaela ext 2065
    Nicolaides, Michael (dspo,dept hd of
    public protectn) ext 2074
    Varker, Annette ext 2053
    Bunn, Sandra (pso) ext 2053
    Ince, Donna (bail info off) ext 2288
    bail info tel (01795) 882288
    bail info fax (01795) 880140

23. HM Prison, County Road
    Maidstone ME14 1UZ
    tel (01622) 775300 *fax (01622) 775475*
    Probation clerk 5380

    Peel, Steve (spo) ext 5394
    Boddington, Anita ext 5477
    Emes, Jenny ext 5382
    Gardner, David (p) ext 5477
    Longley, Lorraine (p)
    Andreou, Theo (pso) ext 5356

24. HM Prison & Young Offenders' Institution
    East Sutton Park
    Sutton Valence
    Maidstone ME17 3DF
    tel (01622) 845000 *fax (01622) 845001*
    Direct dial (01622) 845 + ext

    Probn clerk ext 5030

    Gorringe, Rad (p, spo based at
    HM YOI Rochester) ext 5036
    Wall, Delia (p, pso)

25. HM Prison
    46 Longport **Canterbury** CT1 1PJ
    tel (01227) 862800 *fax (01227) 862801*
    Please note: there are no probation staff
    presence in HMP Canterbury as the
    population are foreign nationals.

26. HM Prison **Blantyre House**
Goudhurst, Cranbrook TN17 2NH
tel (01580) 213200 *fax (01580) 211060*

Gorringe, Rad (p, spo based at HM YOI
Rochester)
King, Patricia

Local Justice Areas

Central Kent	Maidstone (7)
	Tunbridge Wells (8)
	Swale (9)
East Kent	Canterbury (4)
	Folkestone, Dover &
	Ashford (5)
	Thanet (6)
North Kent	Medway (10)
	Gravesend (11)

Crown Courts

3a Canterbury
3 Maidstone

LANCASHIRE PROBATION AREA

Out of hours emergency contact point:
(01254) 395997

Central Bail Referral no: (01254) 832299

e-mail: Firstname.Surname@lancashire.
probation.gsi.gov.uk

1. **Head Office**
99-101 Garstang Road
Preston PR1 1LD
tel (01772) 201209 *fax (01772) 884399*

Mathers, Robert (co)
Dearden, Colin (dco)
Mattinson, Louise (treasurer, hd of finance)
McKevitt, Kerry (aco, h.r.)

Thomas, Janet (aco, offender mngmnt,
crown court)
Phillips, Ian (aco, prisons, approved prem)
Bennett, Andrea (aco, commisioning &
prtnrshps)

Oakes, Debbie (corp services admin mgr)
Allsop, Mark (info service mgr)
Pourmahak, Mahmood (systems admin)
Brooks, Paul (applications developer)
Spink, Kerry (communications mgr)

Milroy, Stephen (senior finance officer)
Simons, Gaynor (senior finance officer)
Douglas, Rachel (payroll officer)
Ollerton, Julie (district admin mgr,
interventions)
Blackburn, Dawn (acting district admin
mgr)
Gibson, Victoria (research & evaluation
off)
Johnson, Kimberley (info & statistics off)
Mayo, Anne (secretary to board)

2. **Human Resources Team & Staff
Development Unit**
Unit 1, Block B, Albert Edward House
The Pavilions, Preston, PR2 2YB
tel (01772) 256630 *fax (01772) 208540*

Hall, Susan (hr & training mgr)
Oram, Kerry (hr officer)
Cooper, Andrew (hr officer)
Mason, Andrea (hr asst)
Kirkby, Maureen (hr asst)
Ahmed, Bilal (hr asst, stats & monitoring)
Ferguson, Diane (pract developer)
Giddings, Melanie (training off)
Chati, Imran (senior training admin)
Dyer, Rachel (business excellence mgr)
Booth, Lynda (comm re-integration mgr)
Greenwood, Nicola (partnerships &
contracts mgr)
Buchanan, Wendy (employer engagement
mgr)
Costello, Margaret (accom officer)

Equality & Diversity
O'Neil, Brigid (equality & diversity mgr)

Health and Safety
Natalie Corry (h&s advisor)

Performance Quality Standards Unit
Beddow, David (pqsu mgr)
Morgan, Richard (pqsu po)
Bannister, Sally (pqsu po)
Johnson, Lisa (pqsu po)
Ahmed, Tahir (pqsu pso)

**NW Training Consortium
Regional Devpt & Assessment Centre**
Whittaker, Pam (pda, prog co-ord)
Peel, Roger (pda)

East District

3. 84 Burnley Road
Accrington BB5 1AF
tel (01254) 232516 *fax (01254) 396160*

Offender Management
Moorhouse, Beverley (spo)

McCloy, Kirsten (spo)
Chiappi, Daniela
Crawshaw, Christine
Hopewell, Keith
Johnson, Emma
Kimberly, Gayle
Murphy, Gayle
Kay, Jonathan
Musker, Heidi
Parkinson, Christopher
Przybysz, Linda
Ralph, Clare

McEwan, Linda (pso)
Dan, Molloy (pso)
Shouib, Kanwal (pso)
Treitl, Linda (pso)

Interventions/Unpaid Work
Baxter, Stephanie (practice mgr)
Lynne Nolan (placement co-ord)
Roberts, Paul (proj supvr)
Anthony Woodhall (proj supvr)
Pattison, Mark (proj supvr)

4. Sumner House
40b Preston New Road
Blackburn BB2 6AH
tel (01254 265221 *fax (01254) 685385*

Offender Management
Lee, Paul (district manager)

Business & Change Manager
Shinks, Elaine

Interventions/Unpaid Work
Baxter, Stephanie (qam)

Information Systems
Daud, Mohammed (dist info systems off)

5. 13/15 Wellington Street
St Johns **Blackburn** BB1 8AF
tel (01254) 265221 *fax (01254) 697852*

Offender Management
Drummond, Shona (spo)
Flynn, Jeanette (spo)
Banks, Bernadette
Bridgeman, Paul
Canning, Helen
Chadderton, Sheila
Cooper, Steven
Davies, Mary
Eccleston, Victoria
Emmot, Pauline
Endicott, Coleen
Fielding, Ashley
Johnson, Wendy
Kett, Alison

Mackley, Alison
Rosthorn, Lisa
Singleton, Janette
Stone, Sharon
Scott, Ian
Wilson, Carlene
Wilson, John

Albers, Michelle (pso)
Crook, Christine (pso)
Desai, Rukshana (pso)
Geough, Kay (pso)
Hurst, Kevin (pso)
Maden, Helen (pso)
Nyland, Patricia (pso)
O'Hanlon, Sharon (pso)
O'Sulivan, Alma (pso)
Ramsden, Joanne (pso)
Solkar, Akeela (pso)

Trainees
Barrow, Irene
Mack, Liam

Interventions/Unpaid Work
Johnson, Cathy (placement co-ord)
Beck, Andrew (proj supvr)
Gardner, Frank (proj supvr)
Luke, David (proj supvr)
McGuire, Scott (p, proj supvr)

Interventions/Victims
Lawton, Victoria (pso,vlo)
Lee, Kirsty (pso,vlo)

6. **Probation Centre**
55 Preston New Road
Blackburn BB2 6AY
tel (01254) 261764 *fax (01254) 53603*

Interventions/Programmes
Bedford, Ruth (treatment mgr)
Bentley, Stephen (pso, prog tutor)
Dinsdale, Kate (pso, prog tutor)
Dixon, Joanne (pso, prog tutor)
Nicholls, Caroline (pso, prog tutor)
Phillips, Owen (pso, prog tutor)
Pollard, Wendy (pso, prog tutor)
Smith, Louise (pso, prog tutor)
Williams, Victoria (pso, prog tutor)
Winter, Diane (pso, prog tutor)

7. **Crown Court**
Hamerton Street **Burnley** BB11 1XD
tel (01282) 457443 *fax (01282) 455211*

Waide, Walter
Bromley, Shirley (pso)

8. 1st Floor, Stephen House
    Bethesda Street **Burnley** BB11 1QW
    tel (01282) 425854 *fax (01282) 838947*

    Offender Management
    Strachan, Ian (spo)
    Willetts, Rachel (spo)
    Watson, Pauline (spo)

    Ashraf, Farzana
    Cridford, Stephen
    Dowbakin, Bernadette
    Genders, Bob
    Hartwell, Susan
    Johnson, Christine
    Orwin, Alex
    Pilling, Nick
    Shackleton, Barry
    Smith, Ray
    Storer, Georgina
    Uttley, Catherine
    Waterworth, John
    Warburton, Natalie
    White, Catherine

    Bentley, Richard (pso)
    Brierley, Christine (pso)
    Greenwood, Nicola (pso)
    Parker, Elaine (pso)
    Pollard, Barbara (pso)
    Smith, Lynne (pso)
    Mcgrow, Margaret (pso)
    Tomlinson, Lindsey (pso)

    Interventions/Unpaid Work
    Slater, Lorraine (qam)
    Sheikh, Asad (placement co-ord)
    Fort, Barry (p, proj supvr)
    Penny, Chris (p, proj supvr)
    Stanworth, Peter (proj supvr)
    Wilson, Bryan (p, proj supvr)
    Zia, Majid (p, proj supvr)

    Interventions/Programmes
    Fletcher, Peter (treatment mgr)
    Caddy, Sara (pso, prog tutor)
    Cox, John (pso, prog tutor)
    Evans, Justine (pso, prog tutor)
    Harrison, Phillipa (pso, prog tutor)
    Jones, Hannah (pso, prog tutor)
    Musso, Kathryn (pso, prog tutor)
    Sharples, Jeremy (pso, prog tutor)

    Admin
    Richardson, Pauline (office mgr)

    Trainees
    Campbell, Colin
    Hall, Elizabeth
    McCarthy, Jessica
    Pacey, Lydia

    Rudkin, Elise
    Taylor, Michael
    Spokes, Craig

9. 25 Manchester Road
    Nelson BB9 9YB
    tel (01282) 615155 *fax (01282) 619693*

    Offender Management
    Munro, Anne (spo)
    Barker, Elizabeth
    Cullis, Kate
    Ford, Terry
    Kiernan, Michael
    Matson, David
    Powell, Nicholas
    Roberts, Marie
    Stacey, Emma
    Thomas, Karen
    Drabble, Jackie (pso)
    Eatough, Geoffrey (pso)
    Gildea, Peter (pso)

    Interventions/Unpaid Work
    Blezard, Paul (project supervisor)
    Johnson, David (project supervisor)
    Sargeant, Michael (proj supvr)

    Information Systems
    Linda Mulrooney (dist info systems off)

Central District

10. **The Crown Court**
    The Law Courts
    Ring Way **Preston** PR1 2LL
    tel (01772) 844799 *fax (01772) 844788*

    Kenny, Mick (spo) 01772 844797
    Buckley, Brian 01772 844792
    Jones, Simon 01772 844793
    Robinson, Janet 01772 844795
    Calvert, Barbara (pso) 01772 844794
    Wilkinson, Niomi (pso) 01772 844791

11. 50 Avenham Street
    Preston PR1 3BN
    tel (01772) 552700 *fax (01772) 552701*

    Offender Management
    Lock, Linda (district mgr)
    Galligan, Hazel (district admin mgr,
    offender management)
    Harker, Jane (spo)
    Patel, Ami (spo)
    Whitehouse, Martin (spo)
    Booth, Sophie
    Brooks, Patricia
    Caine, Carol
    Carr, Susan

Chester, Eve
Howard, Lawrence
Johnrose, Peter
Lindow, Bill
Mayren, Scott
McBride, Kieran
McCarthy, John
Micallef, Linda
Pilkington, Arlene
Rea, Alison
Richardson, Claire
Roberts, Alex
Rollit, Steve
Rust, Luke
Sherdley, Victoria
Bradley, Janet (pso)
Burke, Louise (pso)
Griffiths, Alincia (pso)
Pace, Lynne (pso)
Richardson, Zoe (pso)
Roberts, Graham (pso)
Rocks, Helen (pso)
Sweeney, Sharon (pso)

Trainees
Barker, Alexandra
Mounsey, Claire

Interventions/Unpaid Work
Wilson, Sandra (practice mgr)
Tune, Linda (placement co-ord)
Bradley, Richard (proj supvr)
Bradshaw, Colin (proj supvr)
Eccles, Paul (proj supvr)
Hamer, Colin (proj supvr)
Young, Terry (proj supvr)

Interventions/Programmes
Ashley, Sammy (treatment mgr)
Connor, Victoria (pso, prog tutor)
Cookson, Bill (pso, prog tutor)
Lamb, Ben (pso, prog tutor)
Qureshi, Fawad (pso, prog tutor)
Twist, Jonathan (pso, prog tutor)

Admin
Foster, Sue (office mgr)

12. Leigh Street
 Chorley PR7 3DJ
 tel (01257) 260493 *fax (01257) 233177*

Offender Management
Dann, Joanne (spo)
Ward, Chris (spo)
Brooker, Martin
Horsefall, Jane
Seed, Elaine
Staniforth, Gillian
Jordan, Joanne

Ledgard, Joy
Lloyd, Tracy
Jones, Michelle (pso)
Melling, Ruth (pso)
Unsworth, Claire (pso)

Interventions/Unpaid Work
Shouib, Humayun (placement co-ord)
Williams, Gary (proj supvr)

Admin
Ramsbotham, Maureen (office mgr)

13. 107 Towngate
 Leyland Preston PR25 2LQ
 tel (01772) 621043 *fax (01772) 435090*

Offender Management
Fisher, Louise (spo)
Burton, Gemma
Finch, Janet
Gilmore, Rachel
Leach, Marilyn
Shaw, Allan
Maudsley, Thomas (pso)
Smith, Elizabeth (pso)

Trainees
Burns, Vicki
Dryden-Bircher, Danielle
Little, Stephanie

Interventions/Unpaid Work
Freeman, Bill (cs proj supvr)

Interventions/Victims
Nelson, Michelle (pso, vlo)

Information Systems
Massam, Daniel (dist info systems off)

14. Probation Office, High Street
 Skelmersdale WN8 8AP
 tel (01695) 720248 *fax (01695) 556579*

Offender Management
Shields, Dorothy (spo)
Choraffa, Lynne
Edwards, Jacqueline
McGuire, Annette
Kerrigan, Emmy
Albers, Michelle (pso)
Holden, Elizabeth (pso)
Westcott, Vivian (pso)

Trainees
Carroll, Stephen
Sansbury, Joanne

West District

15.　384 Talbot Road
　　Blackpool FY3 7AT
　　tel (01253) 394031 *fax (01253) 305039*

Offender Management
Lock, Mike (district mgr)
Dacre, Michele (spo)
Harrison, Dave (spo)
Poole, Sue (spo)
Turner, Chris (spo)

Ashcroft, Janine
Aspin, Julie
Barrass, Sherry
Baldwin, Shaun
Calvert, Sarah
Cottingham, Matthew
Dean, John
Dixon, Jacqui
Entwistle, Steven
Etherington, Darren
Fish, Lesley
Graydon, Lindsey
Hamnett, Dawn
Heslop, Robert
Keighley, Lydia
Miller, Chris
Morton, Sharon
Naden, Emma
Padley, Pam
Sorsky, Lucinda
Storey, Mary
Threlfall, Paul
Trout, Adrian
Whiteley, Annette

Brookes, Neal (pso)
Ementon, Helen (pso)
Gradwell, Rachel (pso)
Grundy, Karen (pso)
Guthrie, Kirsty (pso)
Hardisty, Carole (pso)
Liversidge, Lesley (pso)
Moran, Peter (pso)
Nisbet-Gorman, Alison (pso)
Tetlow, Lisa (pso)
Todd, Zoe (pso)

Trainees
Daglish, Nicoll
Ali, Shah
Ivett, Nicola

Interventions/Unpaid Work
Barlow, Julie (practice mgr)
Andrews, Tracey (placement co-ord)
Al-Tamimi, Tamim (cs proj supvr)
Burke, Tony (cs proj supvr)

Chambers, Richard (cs proj supvr)
Halstead, Shaun (cs proj supvr)
Spiers, John (cs proj supvr)

Interventions/Victims
Brownwood, John (pso, vlo)
Johnson, Debbie (pso, vlo)

Admin
Cree, Chris (office mgr)
Information Systems
St John-Foti, Diane (dist info systems off)

16.　9 The Esplanade
　　Fleetwood FY7 6UW
　　tel (01253) 874369/879500 *fax (01253) 776581*
　　direct dial (01253) 879 + ext

Offender Management
Rigg, Judy (spo)
Foster, Jane
Bailey, Su
Brooks, Karen
James, Caroline
Joynes, Nicola
Webb, Clare
Connelly, Sharon (pso)
Howard, Lesley (pso)
Wood, Mary (pso)

Interventions/Unpaid Work
Brown, Iain (placement co-ord)
Taylor, Richard (proj supvr)

17.　41 West Road
　　Lancaster LA1 5NU
　　tel (01524) 63537 *fax (01524) 848519*

Offender Management
Jolly, Allan (spo)
Turner, Sonia (spo)
Bruno, Maggie
Frankland, Roger
Parkin, Susan
Quraishi, Fariha
Ralston, Cath
Thompson, Donna
Thomson, Rebecca
Williams, Joanne
Hall, Becky (pso)
Housley, Liz (pso)
McGarry, Samantha (pso)
Smith, Amber (pso)
Wood, Mary (pso)

Trainees
Burnyeat, Kate
Porter, Mark
Seath, Stephanie

Interventions/Unpaid Work
Greenwood, Chris (placement co-ord)
Green, Barry (proj supvr)
Blezard, Paul (proj supvr)
Scanlon, Roger (project supervisor)

Interventions/Community Re-integration
Cushen, Frank (pso, basic skills)

Admin
Watson, Jane (office mgr)

18. 2 Kensington Road
Morecambe LA4 5LX
tel (01524) 416171 *fax (01524) 832154*

Offender Management
Preston, Roger (spo)
Barrow, Margaret
Clough, Michelle
Johnson, Helen
Prior, Ralph
Robinson, Bryan
Smith, Doug
Carr, Vicky
Cullen, Larraine (pso)
Thompson, Lisa (pso)

Trainees
Baxendale, Neil

19. 2 Avroe Crescent
Blackpool Business Park
Blackpool FY4 2DP
tel (01253) 685050 *fax (01253) 349759*

Interventions/Programmes
O'Donnell, Phil (district manager)
Javed, Anna (spo)
Sargaent, Adam (treatment mgr)
Buckley, Shaun (treatment mgr)
Gawthrope, Jane (treatment mgr)
Holder, Cathy (treatment mgr)

Bartley, Michael (po, prog tutor)
Bentley, Glenys (po, prog tutor)
Bretherton, Gaynor (po, prog tutor)
Boyle, Wendy (po, prog tutor)
Johal, Gurjit (po, prog tutor)
Koowaroo, Natasha (po, prog tutor)
Leeming, Jackie (po, prog tutor)
McHugh, James (po, prog tutor)
Maister, Jane (pso, prog tutor)
Nagy, Shiela (po, prog tutor)
Poulter, Fiona (po, prog tutor)
Rees, Sharon (po, prog tutor)
Ross, Roderick (po, prog tutor)
Whitehouse, Paul (po, prog tutor)

Bullough, Louise (pso, prog tutor)

Cushen, Hilary (pso, prog tutor)
Gaughan, Stephen (pso, prog tutor)
Hallett, Heather (pso, prog tutor)
Haworth, Melanie (pso, prog tutor)
Hill, Doug (pso, prog tutor)
Stringfellow, Gemma (pso, prog tutor)
Suleman, Rehana (pso, prog tutor)
Townsley, Jacqueline (pso, prog tutor)
Walmsley, Hayley (pso, prog tutor)
Yates, Louise (pso, prog tutor)

Interventions/Victims
Martin, Geraldine (spo)
Moulds, Charmain (women's safety wrkr)
Winterbottom, Barbara (women's safety wrkr)

Interventions/Unpaid Work
Booth, Robert (unpaid work scheme mgr)

Admin
Ali, Rifat (office mgr)

Youth Offending Teams

20a. Blake Street
Accrington BB5 1RE
tel (01254) 389456 *fax (01254) 872614*

(inc Hyndburn, Rossendale, Clitheroe, Ribble Valley)
Susan Rodgers

b. Exchange Building
Ainsworth St
Blackburn BB1 8AF
tel (01254) 666995 *fax (01254) 666652*

Lambert, Jeremy

c. Stanley Buildings
1-3 Caunce Street
Blackpool FY1 3DN
tel (01253) 478686 *fax (01253) 478687*

d. Rokeby Centre, 316 Colne Road
Burnley BB10 1XJ
tel (01282) 456620 *fax (01282) 459706*

Green, Julie
Murray, Martin

e. Halliwell House, 15/17 Halliwell Street
Chorley PR7 2AL
tel (01257) 516051 *fax (01257) 516053*

(inc Skelmersdale)
Collum, Seamus

f. 15 North Albert Street
Fleetwood FY7 6DW
tel (01253) 772761 *fax (01253) 771328*

g.   108 St Leonardsgate
     Lancaster LA1 1NN
     tel (01524) 384780 *fax (01524) 842467*

     Loxley, Sarah

h.   143-161 Corporation Street
     Preston PR1 2UG
     tel (01772) 532047 *fax (01772) 532130*

     Fox, Teresa
     Hesketh, Phiona

Approved Premises (Hostels)

21. **Highfield House Probation Hostel**
     Lydia Street, Wood Nook
     Accrington BB5 0PX
     tel (01254) 395997 *fax (01254) 398536*

     Marsh, Anne (asst mgr)
     Mayers, Jane (asst mgr)
     Passmore, Ken (asst mgr)
     Sullivan, Barry (asst mgr)
     Scott, Sean (hostel supvr)
     McCarthy, Tony (hostel supvr)
     Mclean, Yvette (hostel supvr)
     Taylor, Charlene (hostel supvr)

22. **Haworth House**
     St Peters Street
     Blackburn BB2 2HL
     tel (01254) 59060 *fax (01254) 672062*

     Dewhurst, John (mgr)
     Lawson, Amanda (dep mgr)
     Hallett, Peter (asst mgr)
     Gee, Wendy (asst mgr)
     Marsden, John (asst mgr)
     O'Connor, Alan (asst mgr)
     Shingleton, Iain (asst mgr)
     Bird, Gillian (hostel supvr)
     Dennett, Terence (hostel supvr)
     Marshall, Anthony (hostel supvr)

Institutions

23. H M Prison **Garth**
     Ulnes Walton Lane
     Leyland, Preston PR26 8NE
     tel (01772) 443300 *fax (01772) 443301*

     Probn general office ext 3383

     Bailey, Graham (spo)
     Bent, Sarah
     Bewley, Caroline
     Hill, Christopher
     Warbrick, Kevin

24. H M Prison **Kirkham**
     Preston PR4 2RN
     tel (01772) 675400 *fax (01772) 675401*

Probn clerk/special visits ext 5614
ROTL Clerk ext 5612
HDC Clerk ext 5613
Prison admin/temp release enquiries ext 5472

Westrop, Wendy (spo)
Christian, Diana
Greatorex, Pam
Harrington, Stephen
Lamba, Manjeet
Murphy, Gayle
Edmondson, Gabrielle (pso)
Fisher, Joanne (pso)
Webster, David (pso)

Intermittent Custody Project
ext 5711/2
Edmondson, Gabrielle (cso)
Webster, Dave (cso)

25. H M Prison
     The Castle **Lancaster** LA1 1YJ
     tel (01524) 385100 *fax (01524) 385101*
     direct dial (01524) 385 + ext

     hdc/probn fax (01524) 385233

     Probn clerk ext 235
     Special visits ext 218
     Parole clerk ext 229
     A wing ext 240
     B wing ext 244
     C wing ext 243

     Graham, Jed (spo)
     McGauran, Andra
     Fairclough, Emma
     Housley, Elizabeth (pso)
     Levey, Lynne (pso)
     Vidyacitta (pso)

26. H M Young Offenders' Institution
     Lancaster Farms
     Stone Row Head, off Quernmore Road
     Lancaster LA1 3QZ
     tel (01524) 563450 *fax (01524) 563451*
     bail info (01524) 563820
     bail info/HDC fax (01524) 563833

     Special visits 563542

     Sunderland, Marcus (spo)
     Atkinson, Gwen
     Smith, Anthony
     Edwards, Julie (pso, bail info)

     Visitors' Centre
     Brew, Pat (pso)
     Dixon, Pauline (pso)
     Edwards, Julie (pso)
     McClelland, Barbara (pso)

27. H M Prison
2 Ribbleton Lane **Preston** PR1 5AB
tel (01772) 444550 *fax (01772) 444551*

Special visits (01772) 444715
bail info (01772) 444587
bail info fax (01772)444553
reception fax (01772) 444563
healthcare fax (01772) 444554

Probn clerk (01772) 444899

Boydell-Cupitt, Susan (spo)
Boothman, Barbara (ets rsttlmnt mgr)
Boothman, Phil
Da Costa, Louise
McClements, Julia
Weigh, Stephen
Clough, Steven (pso)
Greaves, Jane (pso)
Law-Riding, Beverley (pso)
Nyland, Patricia (pso)
Ralley, Stuart (pso)
Ward, Ann Marie (pso)
Charlton, Phil (pso-ets tutor)

28. H M Prison **Wymott**
Ulnes Walton Lane
Leyland PR26 8LW
tel (01772) 444000 *fax (01772) 444001*

Thompson, Robin (spo)
Chadwick, Roy
Deasha, Greg
Dornan, Elizabeth
McClean, Janice
Whittaker, Lesley
Wilson, Sarah (pso, ets tutor)

Local Justice Areas

4, 5, 6 Blackburn, Darwen & Ribble Valley
8, 9 Burnley, Pendle & Rossendale
12 Chorley
15, 16, 18, 19 Fylde Coast
3 Hyndburn
17 Lancaster
14 Ormskirk
11 Preston
13 South Ribble

Crown Courts

7 Burnley
10 Lancaster
10 Preston

LEICESTERSHIRE & RUTLAND PROBATION TRUST

Out of hours contact nos: Kirk Lodge
0116-244 8028, Howard House 0116-254 9059

Victim enquiries contact number
0116-253 6331

Central Hostels referral no: 0116-244 8028
fax 0116-244 8696

e-mail Firstname.Surname@leicestershire.
probation.gsi.gov.uk

Offices

1. **Head Office**
2 St John Street, Leicester LE1 3WL
tel 0116-251 6008 *fax 0116-242 3250*
direct dial 0116-242+ext
e-mail LRPA@dial.pipex.com

Munro, Heather (chief exec) ext 3200
Curran, Martin (aco) ext 3205
Harnwell, Miriam (aco) ext 3215
Kennedy, Paul (aco) ext 3203
Pollard, Karen (aco) ext 3206
Reynolds, Sean (aco) ext 3204
Worsfold, Trevor (aco) ext 3202
Vacancy (p, spo area training) ext 3263
Naylor, Camille (spo perf/risk) ext 3270
Owens, Marilyn (po area training) ext 3260
Akers, Linda (HR) ext 3225
Irwin, Gaynor (IT) ext 3258
Rose, Sue (finance) ext 3251
Stretton, Caroline (finance) ext 3252
Thomas, Mandy (premises) ext 3221

Trainee Probation Officer Team
Vacancy (p, spo)
Gray, Chrissie (p, pda)
Henry, Jenny (pda)
Simpson, Chris (pda)

Offender Management Teams

2. 38 Friar Lane
Leicester LE1 5RA
tel 0116-253 6331 *fax 0116-242 4511*

Leicester 1 Offender Mngmnt Team
Wynter, Colin (spo)
Bradley, Stephen (pdm)
Ford, Mark
Gardner, Mark (p)
Gregory, Mark
Haque, Dot
Hodgins, Ellen (p)
Illston, Suzanne
Neale, Rachel

Patton, Julie
Paul, Ellis
Reynolds, Cherilee
Singh Hayre, Jasdeep
Turner, Beverley
Turner, Carly
Williams, Gemma
Briers, Zoe (p, pso)
Broad, Kim (pso)
Crocker, Alison
Jones, Kim (pso)
Sharma, Prembala (pso)

MAPPOM (Multi Agency Prolific &
Priority Offender Management)
fax 0116-242 4519

Scotson, Tim (strategic mgr)
Strong, Grace (p, spo)
Li, Joseph (pdm)
Cousins, Nicola
Griffiths, Richard (p)
Langridge, Tony
Mason, Claire
Prideaux, Katrina (p)
Sherry, Christie
Wright, Nicola
Foreman, James (pso)
Kedie, Oliver (pso)
McGinley, Luke (pso)
Schilling, Tim (pso)
Vadher, Jig (pso)

Psychology Team
McClymont, Kirsten (snr psychologist)
Baguley, Steve
Castledine, Sue
Gardner, Mark (p, po)
Henfrey, Sarah (trainee psychologist)

Accom & Supported Housing Team
tel 0116-242 4532 *fax 0116-2424535*
Mattson, Neil
Dublin, Andrew (p, pso)
Straw, Trisha (pso)
Thomas, Suzanne (p, pso)

3. **Probation Centre**
    2 Cobden Street **Leicester** LE1 2LB
    tel 0116-262 0400 *fax 0116-253 0819*

Leicester 2 Offender Mngmnt Team
Bob Bearne, (spo)
Bellingham, David (pdm)
Alabi, Stella
Aston, Laura
Doughty, Victoria
Gill, Jasvir
Holland, Nicola
Kassam, Shiraz

Keysell, Elspeth
Pearce, Jo (p)
Watson, Emma
Wilkinson, Ruth
Cawston, Martin (pso)
Clarke, Anthony (pso)
Griffin, Christopher (pso)
Lad, Anjna (pso)
Okan, Olive (p, pso)
Parmar, Nalini (pso)
Reece, Neil (pso)
Shuttlewood, Laura (pso)
Wagstaff, Stephen (pso)

Leicester 3 Offender Mngmnt Team
Wisniewska, Dreda (spo)
Chadwick, Liz (p, pdm)
Allard, Natalie (p)
Boddington, Katy
Duckham, Selena
Hadley, Jennie
Hermiston, Johnnie
Hubbard, Joanne
Megennis, Helen
Price, Amy
Shah, Beena
Tilley, Hannah
Bhavsar, Anjuna (pso)
Hodson, Karen (p, pso)
Newbrooks, Clare (p, pso)
Pilkington, Alex (p, pso)
Spencer, Shona (pso)
Sullivan, Liam (pso)
Wilton, Katie (p, pso)

4. 27 London Road
    Coalville LE67 3JB
    tel (01530) 836688 *fax (01530) 834136*

Smith, Jeanne (p, spo)
Johnston, Lee (p, pdm)
Ball, Margaret
Bonner, Joanne
Meakin, Tarnya
Williams, Sarah
Barney, Christopher (pso)
Barney, Fran (p, pso)
Bonser, Paul (p, pso)
Hextall, Sylvia (pso)

5. 35 Station Road
    Hinckley LE10 1AP
    tel (01455) 615645 *fax (01455) 891147*

Smith, Jeanne (p, spo)
Johnston, Lee (p, pdm)
Costello, Maxine
Hinson, Kristina

Martin, Iain
O'Mahony, Marie
Kitching, Suzanne (p, pso)
Waite, Anthony (pso)
Wheeler, Helen (pso)

6. 12 Southfield Road
    Loughborough LE11 2UZ
    tel (01509) 212904 *fax (01509) 218954*

    Cripps, Ian (p, spo)
    Holland, Richard (pdm)
    Brown, Jenny
    Kotey, Amon (p)
    Matthews, Annette
    Morfett, Richard
    Mouland, Janet
    Warmington, Christine (p)

    Hallam, Claire (pso)
    Luik, Naomi (p, pso)
    Neale-Badcock, Stephen (pso)
    Weaver, Sarah (pso)
    Williams, Dawn (pso)

7. County Council Area Office
    Leicester Road
    Melton Mowbray LE13 0DA
    tel (01664) 410410 *fax (01664) 412771*

    Cripps, Ian (p, spo)
    Holland, Richard (pdm)
    Appleton, Jane (p)
    Cusack, Steve
    Plenn, Rene (p)
    Price, Arlene (p)
    Thompson, Michelle (p)
    Vega, Jane (p)
    Chenery, Margaret (pso)
    Howarth, Diana (pso)

8. 28 Station Road
    Wigston Leicester LE18 2DH
    tel 0116-257 3800 *fax 0116-257 0240*

    Leicester South
    Hulait, Jaspal (spo)
    Boonham, Ellie
    Bowers, Sonia
    Gravestock, Lisa
    Jones, Martin (p)
    Kotecha, Rahul
    Leyland, Keeley
    Wiltshire, Jeanette
    Browne, Marc (p, pso)
    Cuke, Charlene (pso)
    Hewitt, Julie (pso)

Interventions

9. **Probation Centre**
    2 Cobden Street **Leicester** LE1 2LB
    tel 0116-262 0400 *fax 0116-253 0819*

    Programme Provision
    Chivers, Andy (spo)
    Charlton, David
    Elsmore, Jennifer
    Statham, Sarah
    Ross-Myring, Laura (pso, trtmnt mgr)
    Saunt, Shelley-Anne (p, pso, trtmnt mgr)
    Brighty, Stacey (pso)
    Collins, Judith (pso)
    Davis, Emma (pso)
    Evill, Anthony (pso)
    Granger, Louise (pso)
    Paige, Oliver (pso)
    Spicer, Catherine (pso)

    Domestic Violence
    Wain, Stuart (treatment mgr)
    Seniuk, Stefan (pso)

    Sex Offender Unit
    Scott, Eric (treatment mgr)
    Lawler, Linda
    Modi, Panna
    Smillie, Phil
    Yorke, Tina

    Employability Team
    Doran, Simon (spo)
    Parle, Greg
    Attewell, Tony (pso)
    Devshi, Sajan (pso)
    Edan, Peter (pso)
    Fegan, Yvonne (p, pso)
    Gamage, Greg (pso)
    Smith, Kathy (skills devpt co-ord)
    Turley, Adele (pso)

    Unpaid Work Unit
    tel 0116-262 2245 *fax 0116-248 0563*

    Middleton, Glynis (spo)
    Pearce, Alison (treatment mgr)
    Cave, John (pso)
    Godfrey, Graham (pso)
    Holmes, Richard (pso)
    Killick, Peter (p, wkshp mgr)
    Mann, Elayne (pso)
    Staszak, Irek (pso)
    Theobald, Roger (pso)
    Turnock, Paula (pso)

10. **High Risk Support Workers (SHARP)**
    137a Narborough Road,
    Leicester LE3 0PB
    tel 0116-275 8777 *fax 0116-275 7775*

Crawford, Helena (p, pso)
Dublin, Andrew (p, pso)
Cole, Rachel (pso)
Lockwood-Jones, David (pso)
McIntyre, Mark (pso)

Approved Premise (Hostel)

11. **Howard House Hostel**
    71 Regent Road, Leicester LE1 6YF
    tel 0116-254 9059 *fax 0116-254 0303*

    Kirk Lodge
    322 London Road, Leicester LE2 2PJ
    tel 0116-270 8327 *fax 0116-244 8696*

    central referral point
    tel 0116-244 8028 *fax 0116-244 8696*
    central administration
    tel 0116-270 6681 *fax 0116-244 8696*
    Zaccarelli, Beverley (p, admin mgr)

    Hostel team members work from either hostel

    Marriage, Ghislaine (spo mgr)
    Hopkinson, Michael (po deputy)
    Singh Here, Dalminder (po deputy)
    Aouni, Karen (pso)
    Berry, Donna (pso)
    Bone, Sudeep (pso)
    Churchill, Marcella (pso)
    Gundry, Kelly (pso)
    Higham, Andy (pso)
    Jeggo, Steve (pso)
    Jones, Sarah (pso)
    Lay, Matthew (p, pso)
    Leech, Phil (pso)
    MacQuillan, Andy (pso)
    Maselino, Celestine (pso)
    Monk, Mary (pso)
    Patel, Dipika (pso)
    Randhawa, Manjit (pso)
    Singh, Jayshree (pso)
    Wright, Denise (pso)

Other Teams

12. 38 Friar Lane, Leicester LE1 5RA
    tel 0116-253 6331 *fax 0116-242 4511*

    Victim Contact Team
    direct line 0116-242 8407

    Gray, Alan (p, spo)
    Payne, Claire (p)
    Whitford, Penny (p)
    Chiavolini, Alessandra (pso)
    Whelan, Claire (pso)
    Heath, Linda (women's safety wrkr)
    Hunt, Suzanne (women's safety wrkr)

    Offender Mgmnt Drugs Team
    Robbins, Rena (spo)

Jones, Sian (pdm)
Courtney, Nigel
Foreman, Danielle
Goodliffe, Andy
Grieves, Sarah
Maguire, Helen
McGrath, Frances
Sayer, Beverley
Wissett, Andrea
Griffin, Daniel (pso)
Robson, Tony (pso)

13. **Courts Team**
    Members of the Courts Team work from both Courts

    Leicester Crown Court
    90 Wellington Street
    Leicester LE1 6HG
    tel 0116-204 4990 *fax 0116-254 1437*

    Leicester Magistrates' Court
    Pocklington Walk
    Leicester LE1 9BE
    tel 0116-255 3799 & 0116-254 2693
    fax 0116-255 3805

    Jordan, Sue (spo)
    Cotterill, Amelia
    Frazer, Rachael
    Houghton, Paul (p)
    Piper, David
    Pugh, John
    Yates, Paul (p)
    Acton, Susan (pso)
    Garvey, Amanda (pso)
    Patel, Jaimy (pso)
    Reed, Janet (pso)
    Savage, John (pso)
    Smith, Anita (pso)

14. **Multi Agency Public Protectn Panel**
    c/o Leicestershire Constabulary HQ
    St John's, Enderby
    Leics LE19 2BX
    tel 0116-248 5293 *fax 0116-248 5297*

    Petrie, Bob (mgr)
    Gullick, Andy (spo)

15. **Youth Offending Teams**

a. Eagle House, 11 Greyfriars
    Leicester LE1 5QN
    tel 0116-299 5830 *fax 0116-233 6003*

    Dhokia, Anita
    Hughes, Tanya
    Rawle, Paul,
    Foster, Rachel (p, pso)
    Lail, Andeep (pso)

b. 674 Melton Road
Thurmaston LE4 8BB
tel 0116-260 6000

James, Linda
Muskwe, Chester (pso)

c. 4 Druid Street
Hinckley LE10 1QH
tel (01455) 636068 *fax (01455) 613129*

Thompson, Sara
Walker, Katie (pso)

16. **Criminal Justice Drugs Team**
Castle House, 6-8 Nelson Street
Leicester LE1 7BA
tel 0116-257 5700 *fax 0116-257 5749*
duty desk 0800 7311 118

Wale, Carrie (spo)
Randon, Melvyn (data mgr)
Radford, Jan (p)
Talbott, Charlotte (clinical trtmnt mgr)
Galway, Kayley (drug counsellor)
Duncan, Jude (snr casewrkr)
Hanley, Lianne (snr casewrkr)
O'Callaghan, Joe (snr casewrkr)
Thoor, Inderjit (snr casewrkr)
Wilton, Lindsey (helpline mgr)
Allan, Lorraine (case wrkr)
Benstead, Diane (case wrkr)
Benvenuto, Celine (case wrkr)
Brockie, Sarah (case wrkr)
Cave, Joanne (case wrkr)
Champaneria, Ketna (case wrkr)
Chapman, Nicola (case wrkr)
Chavda, Raj (case wrkr)
Harrison, Emma (p, case wrkr)
Hobster, Mark (case wrkr)
Jackson, Selena (case wrkr)
Jagger, Dean (case wrkr)
Jeahes, Eleanor (case wrkr)
Johal, Vicky (p,case wrkr)
Kaur, Manjit (p,case wrkr)
Mason, Kerry (case wrkr)
Millington, Rhiann (case wrkr)
Moore, Trish (p, case wrkr)
Neal, Viv (case wrkr)
Niland, Grania (case wrkr)
Page, Nicola (case wrkr)
Pattni, Sheetal (p, case wrkr)
Purewal, Sukhvinder (case wrkr)
Reece, Charlotte (case wrkr)
Ruprai, Mandeep (case wrkr)
Sohal, Amandeep (case wrkr)
Takhar, Jaskaren (case wrkr)
Walker, Martin (case wrkr)
Wren, Alison (p, case wrkr)

Bulsara, Hina (pso treatment mgr)
Baxter, Sue (pso)
Berridge, Jane (p, pso)
Francis, Dulcie (p, pso)
Jones, Mo (p, pso)
Kilpatrick, Andy (pso)
Newton, Neil (pso)
Noble, Laura (p, pso)
Tansey, Joanne (p, pso)
Wan, Sui (pso)
Wynter, Idona (pso)

Institutions

17. H M Prison **Ashwell**
Oakham, Rutland LE15 7LF
tel (01572) 884100 *fax (01572) 884101*
direct dial (01572) 88 + ext

Lake, Nicola (spo)
Evens, Sally
Fish, Mike
Ludlam, Melanie (p)
McCarthy, Danielle
Bailey, Anne (p, pso)
Cassidy, Jane (pso)
Clegg, Ann (pso)
Ingram, Maxine (pso)
Mitchell, Paul (pso)

18. H M Prison **Gartree**
Gallowfield Road
Market Harborough LE16 7RP
tel (01858) 436600 *fax (01858) 436601*

Brotherton, Christine ext 6681
Clayton, Rebecca ext 6617
Fowler, Joanne ext 6654
Lawson, Susan (p) ext 6653
Marshall, Pete ext 6668
Panter, Lesley (p) ext 6617
Roskell, Sharon ext 6653
Statham, Sarah-Jane ext 6786
Stone, Jeff (p) ext 6795
Walworth, John (p) ext 6676
Weaver, Lestroy ext 6653
Ardley, Karen (pso) ext 6864
Brooker, Olivia (pso) ext 6617
Cameron, Natalie (pso) ext 6669
Flannagan, Lucy (pso) ext 6744
O'Callaghan, Steve (pso) ext 6656
Whiteley, Hannah (pso) ext 6858

19. H M Prison, 116 Welford Road
Leicester LE2 7AJ
tel 0116-228 3000 *fax 0116-228 3001*

direct dial 0116-228+ext
probn fax 0116-228 3112

Parker-Leehane, Freda (p, spo) ext 3036

Duncan, Nicky ext 3158
Evens, Sally (p) ext 3167
Dorrington, Samantha (pso) ext 3167
Hallissey, Michael (pso) 3138
Oldham, Esther (pso) ext 3059
Pipes, Ian (pso) ext 3059
Winfield, John (probn clerk) ext 3075

20. **H M Young Offender Institution**
Glen Parva Saffron Road
Wigston LE18 4TN
tel 0116-228 4100 *fax 0116-228 4262*

direct dial 0116-228 + ext
Probn clerk ext 4320
Special visits ext 4260

Pearce, Jan (spo) ext 4336
Kirby, Arlene ext 4321
Maxwell, Margaret ext 4211
Cross, Lisa (pso) ext 4281
Gargan, Gill (p, pso) ext 4231
McArdle, Fiona (pso) ext 4317
Neckles, Julian (pso) ext 4318
Penney, Kevin (p, pso)ext 4337
Wood, Debbie (pso) ext 4286

21. **H M Prison Stocken**
Stocken Hall Road, Stretton
Nr Oakham LE15 7RD
tel (01780) 795100 *fax (01780) 410767*
direct dial (01780) 79 + ext

Coles, Nicola
Evans, Graham
Gardiner, Pauline (p)
Green, Tom
Breslin, Constance (pso)
Drinkwater, Rebecca (pso)
Spence, Becky (p, pso)

Local Justice Areas

2, 3, 9 Leicester
4 Ashby-de-la-Zouch
5 Market Bosworth
6 Loughborough
7 Melton, Belvoir & Rutland
8 Market Harborough & Lutterworth

Crown Court

13 Leicester

LINCOLNSHIRE PROBATION AREA

Out of hours emergency contact point
Wordsworth House (01522) 528520

Victim enquiries contact number
Lincoln (01522) 510011, Skegness (01754)
763906, Grantham (01476) 583131
e-mail: Firstname.Surname@lincolnshire.
probation.gsi.gov.uk

1. **Head Office**
7 Lindum Terrace
Lincoln LN2 5RP
tel (01522) 520776 *fax (01522)
527685/580469*

Nicholls, Graham (co)
Adey-Johnson, Pete (aco)
Gregory, Melanie (aco, hr)
Oliver, Joanne (aco)
Rushby, Pete (aco, finance/info)
Bateman, Andy (middle mgr, finance)
Burke, Tony (middle mgr, info systems)
Crook, David (middle mgr, om project)
Hough, Quin (h&s off)
Martel, Rachel (middle mgr, comms)
Pollard, Simon (middle mgr, trg & staff devpt)
Smith, Nigel (middle mgr, perf & exc)
Starkie, Jayne (p, middle mgr, hr)

2. **8 Corporation Street**
Lincoln LN2 1HN
tel (01522) 510011 *fax (01522) 514369*

Offender Management
Hawley, Sarah (middle mgr)
Mountain, Angela (middle mgr, compliance)
McMahon, Paul (middle mgr)
Newborn, Clare (middle mgr)
Bennett, Tracey
Byrne, Clare
Collett, Becky (p)
Gibbs, Leanne
Gooderson, Steve
Loffhagen, Jane
Melling, Caragh
Morrissey, Matthew
Sackfield, Helen
Smith, Jacqui
Smith, Paul
Taylor, Katy (p)
Walters, Zoe
Welsh, Sara
Allnutt, Steve (pso)
Atkinson, Leanne (pso)
Barwise, Steph (pso)
Birks, Rachel (pso)
Gostelow, Elaine (pso)
Holmes, Wendy (pso)

King, Nigel (pso)
Maddocks, Darren (pso)
O'Rourke, Diane (pso)
Simpson, Nicci (p, pso)
Smith, Laura (pso)
Thompson, Shahara (pso)

High Risk
Kavanagh, Jo (p, middle mgr) (14)
Norton, Nicole (middle mgr) (14)
Connelly, Gabi (7)
Cook, Andrew
Croft, Nicole
Evans, Tracey
Hobill, Fiona (9)
Jackson, Angela
Storey, Tammy (p)
Wilson, Angela (7)

Victims
Kavanagh, Jo (p, middle mgr) (14)
Murphy, Lindsay (p, vco)

Interventions

Offenders' Healthy Living Project
Hoole, Lisa (middle mgr)
Miechowski, Helen (pso)

Unpaid Work
Connell, Tony (middle mgr) (7a)
Byrne, Mick (quality ass mgr)
Jutsum, Sue (pso)
Merrix, Joanne (p, pso)
Williams, Sarah (pso)
Wright, Richard (pso, placements)

Programmes
Reed, Sarah (middle mgr)
Baker, Graham
de Vries, Aggie
Smith, Janet
Walker, Janet
Banks, Janice (pso)
Cochrane, Nicolette (pso)
Edwards, Fiona (pso)
Smith, Karen (pso)

Employment, Training and Education
O'Meara, Tricia (middle mgr)

Corporate Services

Training & Staff Devpt Unit
Pollard, Simon (middle mgr) (1)
Plant, Kim (p, pda)
Rose, Sue (pda)
Bradley, Louise (trainee) (9)
Edmondson, Sarah (trainee) (9)
Hadjigeorgiou, Georgina (trainee)
Jones-Lobley, Bobbi (trainee)
Main, Darryl (trainee) (7)
Marshall, Danielle (trainee)
Phillips, Neil (trainee) (7)
Strevens, Anna-Verity (trainee)

Wilks, Helena (trainee)

Business Supt
Goude, Tony (middle mgr) (3-9)
Gentry, Judith (business supt off)

3. Lincoln Magistrates' Court Office
    The Courthouse, High Street
    Lincoln LN5 7QA
    tel (01522) 533352/560063 *fax (01522) 546332*

Offender Management
Hawley, Sarah (middle mgr) (2)
Davies, Mark (fdr writer) (5)
Vaughan, Tammy
Dunkling, Marilynne (crt service off)
French, Jolyon (crt service off)
Shaw, Maureen (crt service off)

3a. **Lincoln Crown Court**
    The Castle, Castle Hill
    Lincoln LN1 3AA
    tel (01522) 526767 *fax (01522) 528779*

Offender Management
Hawley, Sarah (middle mgr) (2)
Smith, Sue (p)
Phillips, Martin (p,crt service off)
Gibson-Tomkins, Linda (p, snr admin)

4. Police Station, Morton Road
    Gainsborough DN21 2SY
    tel (01427) 612260 *fax (01427) 612975*

Offender Management
Hawley, Sarah (middle mgr) (2)
Page, Dan
Wood, Janine (p)
Nolan, Linda (pso)
Wild, Layla (p, pso)

Corporate Services, Business Supt
Gentry, Judith (business supt off) (2)

5. The Town Hall, North Parade
    Skegness PE25 1DA
    tel (01754) 763906 *fax (01754) 760202*

Offender Management
Lynch, Andrew (middle mgr)
Peacock, Jean
Read, Camilla
Sarin, Raish (p)
Clarke, Alan (pso)
Hoffman, Kathryn (p, pso)
Hoy, Caroline (p, pso)
Jennings, Nicola (pso)
Murray, Wayne (pso)
Williams, Marie (p, pso)

Victims
Kavanagh, Jo (p, middle mgr) (14)
Nicholls, Alan (p, vco)

Courts
Lynch, Andrew (middle mgr)
Davies, Mark (fdr writer)
Marshall, John (crt service off)

Corporate Services, Business Supt
Johnson, Gary, (business supt off) (7)

6. Police Station, Eastfield Road
    Louth LN11 7AN
    tel (01507) 604427 *fax (01507) 608642*

    Offender Management
    Lynch, Andrew (middle mgr) (5)
    Sumner, Katie
    Maddison, Mercedes (pso)

    Corporate Services, Business Supt
    Johnson, Gary (business supt off) (7)

7. The Annexe, The County Hall
    Boston PE21 6DY
    tel (01205) day 316300 *fax (01205) 316301*
    evening 310245/310246

    Offender Management
    Aylward, Ali (middle mgr)
    Hutchinson, Sandie
    Jones, Angela (p)
    Lawson, Amy
    Roberts, Angie
    Waller, Stacey
    Blackman, Paul (pso)
    Lee, Kathy (pso)
    Lyon, Michelle (pso)
    Ogilvie, Esther (pso)
    Weston, Sara (pso)

    Courts
    Aylward, Ali (middle mgr)
    Davies, Mark (fdr writer) (5)
    Downs, Tony (p, crt service off)
    Hartley, Barbara (p, crt service off)

    High Risk
    Kavanagh, Jo (p, middle mgr) (14)
    Connelly, Gabi
    Norton, Nicole (middle mgr) (14)
    Wilson, Angela

    Corporate Services, Business Supt
    Johnson, Gary (business supt off)

    Training & Staff Development
    Pollard, Simon (middle mgr) (1)
    Main, Darryl (trainee)
    Phillips, Neil (trainee)

7a. Probation Centre
    The Old School, Carlton Road
    Boston PE21 8LN
    tel (01205) 316350 *fax (01205) 316351*
    Interventions
    Programmes
    Reed, Sarah (middle mgr) (2)

Butterfield, Karen
Briggs, Mel
Hancock, Paul (pso)
Hodgson, John (pso)
Scott-Smith, Tuula (pso)
Waplington, Claire (pso)

Unpaid Work
Connell, Tony (middle mgr) (2)
Martin, Kristy (qa mgr)
Rate, Rebecca (qa mgr)
Cooke, John (pso placements)
Ford, Peter (pso)
Harris, Nigel (pso)
Wattam, Robin (p, pso)

Corporate Services, Business Supt
Johnson, Gary (business supt off) (7)

8. Broadgate House, Westlode Street
    Spalding PE11 2AD
    tel (01775) 722078/767708
    fax (01775) 713936

    Aylward, Alison (middle mgr) (7)
    Eveleigh, Carol
    Hutchinson, Sandie
    Hopkins, Cheri (p, pso)
    Day, Jenny (pso)
    Stacey, Krystyna (p, pso)

    Corporate Services, Business Supt
    Johnson, Gary (business supt off) (7)

9. Grange House, 46 Union Street
    Grantham NG31 6NZ
    tel (01476) 583131 *fax (01476) 583130*

    Lillyman, Rebecca (middle mgr)
    Gray, Holly
    Izard, Verity
    Leachman, Beccy
    Medhurst, Debbie
    Michelson, Sally
    Conlin, Emma (pso)
    Dearden, Francesca (pso)
    Hamblett, Chris (pso)
    Lee, Rebecca (pso)
    Leivers, Bev (p, pso)
    Saunderson, Debbie (p, pso)

    Courts
    Lillyman, Rebecca (middle mgr)
    Davies, Mark (fdr writer) (5)
    Patel, Kiran (crt service off)
    Woodhouse, Sandra (p, crt service off)

    High Risk
    Kavanagh, Jo (p, middle mgr) (14)
    Norton, Nicole (middle mgr) (14)
    Hobill, Fiona

    Victims
    Kavanagh, Jo (p, middle mgr) (14)
    Keller (p, vco)

Interventions

Programmes
Smith, Annette (women's safety wrkr)

Corporate Services, Business Supt
Payne, Chris (business supt off)

Training & Staff Development
Pollard, Simon (middle mgr) (1)
Bradley, Louise (trainee)
Edmondson, Sarah (trainee)

Contracts
Callery, Bev (p, middle mgr)

Offender Management

10. **Multi Agency Public Protection Panel**
Lincolnshire Police HQ
PO Box 999 **Lincoln** LN5 7PH
tel (01522) 558255 *fax (01522) 548800*

Cooke, Amanda (middle mgr)

11. **Youth Offending Service (East)**
The Old Courthouse, North Street
Horncastle LN9 5EA
tel (01507) 528250 *fax (01507) 528251*

Garnett, Hilary

12. **Youth Offending Service (South)**
The Old Barracks, Sandon Road
Grantham NG31 9AS
tel (01476) 591522 *fax (01476) 569166*

Reeds, Elaine

13. **Youth Offending Service (West)**
8 The Avenue, Lincoln LN1 1PB
tel (01522) 554550 *fax (01522) 553563*

Nisbet, Steve

Interventions

Approved Premise (Hostel)

14. **Wordsworth House**
205 Yarborough Road
Lincoln LN1 3NQ
tel (01522) 528520 *fax (01522) 526077*

Laughton, Keith (middle mgr)
Bhatti, Cherie (pso)
Greasley, Allan (app premises supt wrkr)
Page, Ashleigh (app premises supt wrkr)
Wilson, Bill (app premises supt wrkr)
Young, Sally (app premises supt wrkr)
Roberts, Chris (app premises supv)
Earl, John (app premises supv)
Paynter, Malcolm (app premises supv)
Pell, David (p, app premises supv)
Smith, Rebecca (p, app premises supv)
Taylor, Roly (p, app premises supv)

Offender Management

Institutions

15. **H M Prison**, Greetwell Road
Lincoln LN2 4BD
tel (01522) 663000 *fax (01522) 663001*
probn fax (01522) 663001

Probn clerk ext 3062
Legal visits ext 3154
Discipline/Offender administration ext 3075
Doyle, Denise (p, middle mgr)
Morris, Andrew
Virr, Lesley
Armstrong, Phil (pso)
Broughton, Lesley (pso)
Dean, Jackie (pso)
O'Rourke, Diane (pso)

16. **H M Prison Morton Hall**
Nr Swinderby LN6 9PS
tel (01522) 666700 *fax (01522) 666775*
Probn direct line (01522) 666847 / 666730

Parole clerk ext 6706
HDC clerk 6728
Discipline ext 6707
Visits booking line ext 6760

Eyres, Tony (p, middle mgr)
Reddish, Michael
Flewers, Lee-Anne (pso)

17. **H M Prison North Sea Camp**
Frieston, Boston PE22 0QX
tel (01205) 769300 *fax (01205) 769301*
probn fax (01205) 760098

Gilbert, Mike (middle mgr)
Booth, Chris
Steel, Linda (p)
Templeton, Donna (pso)

Local Justice Areas

7 Boston
9, 11 Bourne
4 Caistor
8 Elloe East
8 Elloe West
4 Gainsborough
9 Grantham
5, 6 Horncastle
2 Lincoln County
6 Louth
4 Market Rasen
9 Sleaford
5 Skegness & Spilsby
9 Stamford

Crown Court

3a Lincoln

LONDON PROBATION

1 Hammersmith
2 Kensington & Chelsea
3 Westminster
4 Islington
5 City
6 Southwark
7 Lambeth

BUC Business Unit Co-ordinator
BUA Business Unit Administrator
BSU Business Support Unit
EA Executive Assistant
PQM Performance & Quality Manager

London Probation has offices in every London borough and is organised on a borough and functional basis.

London Postcodes by Borough

Barking & Dagenham
IG11, RM6, RM7 (part), RM8, RM9, RM10

Barnet
N2, N3, N10, N11 (part), N12, N14 (part), N20, N22, NW2, NW4, NW7, NW9, NW11, EN5

Bexley (with Beckenham)
SE2 (part), SE9 (part), SE28 (part), DA1 (part), DA5, DA6, DA7, DA8 (part), DA14, DA15, DA16, DA17 (part), DA18 (part)

Brent
NW6 (part), NW10, HA0, HA9

Bromley
SE20, SE26 (part), BR1 (part), BR2, BR3, BR4 (part), BR5, BR6, BR7, TN16 (part)

Camden
EC1 (part), N7, N19, NW1 (part), NW2 (part), NW3, NW5, NW6 (part), NW8, WC1, WC2 (part)

City of London & Tower Hamlets
EC1 (part), EC2 (part), EC3, EC4, E1, E3, E14

Croydon
SE19, SE25, SW16, CR0, CR2, CR3, CR5, CR6, CR7, CR8

Ealing
W3, W4, W5, W7, W13, UB1, UB2, UB4 (part), UB5, UB6

Enfield
N9, N11 (part), N13, N14 (part), N18, N21, EN1, EN2, EN3, EN4,

Greenwich
SE3, SE7, SE8, SE10, SE18

Hackney
EC1 (part), EC2 (part), E2, E5, E8, E9, N1 (part), N4, N16

Hammersmith & Fulham
SW6, W6, W12, W14

Haringey
N4 (part), N6, N8, N11 (part), N15, N17, N22

Harrow
HA1, HA2, HA3, HA4 (part), HA5, HA7, HA8

Havering
RM1, RM2, RM3, RM4, RM7 (part), RM11, RM12, RM13, RM14

Hillingdon
HA4 (part), HA6, UB3, UB4 (part), UB7, UB8, UB9, UB10

Hounslow
TW3, TW4, TW5, TW6, TW7, TW8, TW9, TW13, TW14

Islington
WC1 (part), EC1 (part), EC2 (part), N1 (part), N4 (part), N5 (part), N7 (part), N16 (part), N19

Kensington & Chelsea
SW1 (part), SW3, SW5, SW7, SW10, W2, W8, W11

Kingston-upon-Thames
SW19, SW20 (part), KT1, KT2, KT3, KT4 (part), KT5, KT9

Lambeth
SE5, SE11, SE21, SE24, SE27, SW2, SW4, SW8, SW9, SW12

Lewisham
SE4, SE6, SE8, SE12, SE13, SE14, SE23, SE26 (part)

Merton
SW17 (part), SW19, SW20, SM4, CR4

Newham
E6, E7, E12, E13, E16

Redbridge & Waltham Forest
E4, E10, E11, E15, E17, E18, IG2, IG3, IG4, IG5, IG6, IG7, IG8, IG10

Richmond-upon-Thames
SW13, SW14, TW1, TW2, TW9, TW10, TW11, TW12

Southwark
SE1, SE5, SE11, SE15, SE16, SE17, SE21 (part), SE22, SE23 (part), SE24 (part), SE26 (part)

Sutton
SM1, SM2, SM3, SM5, SM6

Wandsworth
SW4 (part), SW8 (part), SW11, SW12 (part), SW15, SW16 (part), SW17 (part), SW18, SW19 (part)

Westminster
W1, W2, W9, W10, W11, W12, NW1 (part), WC2 (part)

e-mail: Firstname.Surname@london.probation.gsi.gov.uk

1. **Head Office**
    71-73 Great Peter Street
    London SW1P 2BN
    tel 020-7222 5656 (switchboard)
    fax 020-7960 1188 (reception)

    direct dial (unless otherwise indicated)
    020-7960 + ext

    Chief's Office
    Scott, David (co)
    Grant, Pam (ea to co) ext 1006

    Gavin, Geraldine (chief operations off)
    Dormer, Kim (ea) ext 1878

    Board Chair
    Dent, Julie (board chair) ext 1006
    Davies, Paul (board secretary) ext 1191
    Rae, Rebecca (board services
    officer) ext 1698

    Directors
    fax 020-7960 1114

    Jenkin, Malcolm (director, London North, public protectn & resttlmnt) ext 1656
    Deane, Cheryl (pqm) ext 1065
    Rodrigues, Cheryl (bua) ext 1653

    Responsible for clusters
    Hackney, Tower Hamlets, Barking
    Dagenham/Havering, Newham
    Haringey, Waltham Forest/Redbridge
    Barnet/Enfield, Camden/Islington
    Ealing, Harrow/Hillingdon

    McFeely, Mary (director London South, London CJ Board, Crts & OASys) ext 1846
    Picard, Roger (pqm) ext 1838
    Rodrigues, Cheryl (ea) ext 1653

    Responsible for clusters
    Hounslow, Kingston/Richmond
    Hammersmith/Fulham, Kensington/
    Chelsea, Westminster, Merton/

Sutton, Wandsworth, Lambeth,
Southwark, Greenwich/Lewisham
Bexley/Bromley, Croydon

Harwood, Hilary (director
interventions) ext 1099
Edgington, Ben (bua) ext 1121
Vinci, Angelo (pqm) ext 1009
Pinkerton, Nina (buc) ext 1063

Responsible for
Approved Premises, Prisons, UPW,
Community Payback, Offending Behaviour
Programmes, Partnerships, Housing,
Mental Health, Victims, Substance Misuse,
Enforcement.

Karvé, Chitra (director of equality &
diversity) ext 1186
McCabe, Cynthia (ea) ext 1815

Functions
Advice/support to Board & Directors
on diversity issues, partnerships
with external stakeholders,
Implementation of Diversity Strategy,
Management of Diversity Team

Swash-Wallbank, Pauline (director
of finance, facilities & information
technology) ext 1199
Almeida, Verna (ea) ext 1844

Functions
Finance, Information Communications
Technology, Facilities Management,
Central Services

Drury, Phil (director of HR) ext 1658
Mohiuddin, Naseem (ea) ext 1140

Functions
Human Resource Management, Human
Resource Devpt, Health & Safety

Moran, Stephen (director of business
solutions) ext 1650
Mohiuddin, Naseem (ea) ext 1140
Roberts, Derryn (relationship mgr,
business solutions) ext 1816

Functions
Resource Development, Corporate
Procurement, Marketing &
Communications,
Quality Standards, Web Services &
Innovation

**Corporate Governance & Legal
Services**
Davies, Paul (head) ext 1191
Thernstrom, Helena (legal asst) ext 1007

Management Information
Simmonds, Steve (head of unit) ext 1676
Elkington, Rob (ea to unit) ext 1694
Durrance, Pauline (snr research off) ext
1124
Stone, Chris (perf info mgr) ext 1134
Butler, Malvia (bus mgr) ext 1059
Walters, Mark (nsmart mgr) ext 1127
Russell, Shirley (research off) ext 1125

Inspection & Standards Unit
Smith, Adrian (head of unit)
Day, Rosanna (ea & SFO admin) ext 1820
Mackenzie, Yannik (aco)
Thompson, Ruby (ea to aco) ext 1824
Farren, Niamh (spo) ext 1161
O'Brien, Gillian (spo) ext 1061
Barnish, Mary (spo) ext 1057
Spring, Pamela (spo) ext 1105
Heerah, Mari (spo) ext 1104

at Mitre House
Owens, Jacqueline (spo)
Beck, Amy Mitre (snr forensic psy)
at 4 Birkbeck Road
Cook Lisa (trainee forensic psy)
at 39 Greenwich High Road
Delaney, Monica (spo ViSOR)
Buchanan, Lee (case admin)
Woodhall, Howard (case admin)
at Olympic House
Basith, Shah (case admin)
Tewari, Priya (case admin)

Equality & Diversity Directorate
Karvé, Chitra (director) ext 1186
McCabe, Cynthia (ea) ext 1815
Weston, Alan (equal, diversity, confidence
& European projects mgr) ext 1693

Akram, Abida (E&D mgr) ext 1005
Abernethy, Rosemary (E&D off) ext 1834
Carr, Des (E&D off) ext 1836
Dixon, Liz (hate crime co-ord) ext 1862
Duff, Delphine (E&D off) ext 1167
Hammond, Nick (E&D off) ext 1821
Rafiq, Saima (E&D off) ext 1835
Kapoor, Kalpana (diversity &
communities off) ext 1864

Finance & Facilities
Swash-Wallbank, Pauline (director of
finance, facilities & info tech) ext 1199
Almeida, Verna (ea) ext 1844

Finance
Lee, Geoff (chief accountant) ext 1179
Dungan, Greg (financial accounting
mgr) ext 1675

Cummins, Robert (3rd party proj off) ext 1669
Donohue, Robert (sys rec & bank mgr) ext 1677
Edwards, Sharon (processing off) ext 1039
Tarrant, Ray (payroll mgr) ext 1026
Gerza, Nicola (processing mgr) ext 1025

Facilities & Central Services
Piddington, Glen (head of unit) ext 1066
Tabraham, Joan (buc) ext 1668
Green, Leslie (cs mgr) ext 1070
Findlay, Sue (cs off)
Dunford, Jo (conf service mgr) ext 1095
Karnilajevaite, Ernesta (asst conf service mgr) ext 1095
at Crosby House
Engleman, Phil (snr facilities mgr)
at Mitre House
Moore, Patricia (building mgr)
Wright, Noah (asst building mgr)

Information Communications Technology
Pengelly, Mary (head of unit) ext 1878
Piercey, Anne (IT service desk mgr) ext 1019
Russell, Colin (IT problem mgr) ext 1022
Hague, John (assistive technology mgr) ext 1144
Oguntala, Ben (information & IT security advr) ext 1839

Business Solutions Directorate
Moran, Stephen (director) ext 1650
Mohiuddin, Naseem (ea) ext 1140
Roberts, Derryn (relationship mgr, business solutns) ext 1816

Marketing and Communications
George, Elizabeth (head of unit) ext 1137
Stone, Sally (marketing mgr) ext 1021
Alexander, Cornelius (media relations mgr) ext 1151
Prager, Alison (media relations off) ext 1863
Ellis, Leona (marketing & admin off) ext 1136
Fazan-Clarke, Georgia (events off) ext 1015
Elles, Katie (marketing off) ext 1654

Resource Development Unit
Pick, Tricia (head of unit) ext 1163
Cooke, Diane (ea) ext 1668
Craigie, Clare (employment resource devpt mgr) ext 1830
Field, Lyn (project mgr) ext 1819
O'Brien, Jan (project mgr) ext 1040
Long, Alan (project devpt mgr) ext 1810

Stocker, Fil (devpt mgr) ext 1086
Lake, Stuart (project co-ord) ext 1877
Patel, Sunita (project co-ord) ext 1661

Corporate Procurement & Commercial Devpt
Blake, Martin (head) ext 1055
Steite, Katharina (procurement mgr) ext 1172

Web Services & Innovation
Fawzi, Fawzi (mgr) ext 1017
Liu, Holly (web devpt mgr) ext 1085
Tudor, Steven (web devpt mgr) ext 1012

Quality & Standards Manager
Asamoah, Audrey ext 1128

Human Resources Directorate
Drury, Phil (director) ext 1658
Mohiuddin, Naseem (ea) ext 1140

Human Resources Management
Danvers, Hope (head of unit) ext 1044
Bennett, Nicole (ea) ext 1058
Arthur, Janet (hr mgr) ext 1689
Ayton, John (hr mgr) ext 1050
Fassari, Daniel (hr mgr) ext 1832
McFarland, Marrianne (hr mgr) ext 1681
Collier, Louise (snr recruitment advr) ext 1138
Mitchell, Jenny (hr recruitment advr) ext 1686

Human Resources Development
Mitre House, 223-237 Borough High St, London SE1 1JD
tel 020-7740 8500

Pagan, Tim (head of unit) ext 8513
Coleman, Judy (ea) ext 8505
Carcavella, Susan (snr hrd admin) ext 8547
Bixby, Kay (hrd mgr admin) ext 8506
Jones, Michael (hrd mgr) ext 8533
Anderson, Delise (hrd mgr) ext 8512
Duke, Michaela (hrd mgr) ext 8588
Kelly, Andrea (hrd mgr) ext 8565
Idusohan, Victoria (hrd mgr) ext 8527
Forbes, David (OASys training mgr) ext 8542
Crews, Raymond (OASys trainer) ext 8554
Koch, Shula (learning & devpt advr) ext 8511
Wheeler, Graham (learning & devpt advr) ext 8521
Pilinski, Krystyna (pda mgr) ext 8545
Smith, Keith (pda mgr) ext 8553

IT Training
Kelly, Andrea (mgr) ext 8565

Kalembo, Masote (trainer) ext 1873
Morris, Geoff (trainer) ext 1874

Health & Safety Department
at Mitre House
Ash, Colan (head of H&S) ext 8587
McGrory, Chris (H&S advr) ext 8544
Lander, Ian (H&S advr) ext 8559
Walton, Ian (H&S advr) ext 8583
at Crosby House
Miller, Beverley (occupational health mgr)
020-8290 2125

Interventions
Harwood, Hilary (director) ext 1099
Edgington, Ben (bua) ext 1121
Vinci, Angelo (perf & qual mgr) ext 1009
Pinkerton, Nina (buc) ext 1063
Austen, Nigel (aco upw South) ext 1089
Hillas, Andrew (aco upw North) ext 1169
Davies, Ilid (aco approved premises
& prisons) ext 1185
Gilbert, Kate (aco prtnrshps, housing,
mental health, victims, subst
misuse) ext 1142
Hayward Charles (aco obp North) ext 1102
Sandhu Kuljit (aco obp South) ext 1850
Clarke Robert (enforcement imp
project mgr) ext 1875
Hosking Nigel (proj mgr, structured
supervision) ext 1135
Marshall Imogen (bua, upw) ext 1054
at Mitre House
Dennis, Dezlee (drug & alc devpt
mgr) ext 8550
Latimer, Robin (drug & alc devpt
mgr) ext 8518
Cameron, Angus (mental health
advr) ext 8517
Mellish, Paul (housing devpt
mgr) ext 8560
Mensah, Emmanuel (emplt devpt
mgr) ext 8566

Special Functions
Robinson Sara (aco crts & OASys) ext
1098
Costello Peter (aco special projs) ext 1078
Craddock Jaquilline (buc crts, OASys &
special projs) ext 1687

Other Main London Region Offices
Olympic House
28/42 Clements Road, Ilford IG1 1BA
tel 020-8514 5353 *fax 020-8478 4450*

Crosby House
9/13 Elmfield Road, Bromley BR1 1LT
tel 020-8464 3430 *fax 020-8466 1571*

45 High Street
Kingston upon Thames, Surrey KT1 1LQ
tel 020-8939 4130 *fax 020-8549 7626*

Mitre House
223-237 Borough High Street, London
SE1 1JD
tel 020-7740 8500 *fax 020-7740 8448*

LONDON NORTH

London North Cluster 1
Hackney & Tower Hamlets

2. **Olympic House**
    28/42 Clements Road
    Ilford, Essex IG1 1BA
    tel 020-8514 5353 *fax 020-8478 4450*

    Atherton, Gary (aco)
    020-8514 9208
    Brooker, Marlene (buc)
    020-8514 9226
    Worley, Jill (bua)
    020-8514 9204
    Browne, Jomo (bsu spo)

3. **34 Englefield Road**
    Hackney, London N1 4EZ
    tel 020-7241 9900 *fax 020-7241 9901*

    Hackney Offender Mgmnt Unit 2
    Howitt, Michael (spo)

    Substance Misuse Unit
    Stewart-Fraser, Laverne (acting spo)

4. **Reed House**
    1-4 Rectory Road, London N16 7QS
    tel 020-7923 4656 *fax 020-7923 4084*

    Public Protection Unit
    Green, Charles (spo)

    Prolific & Priority Offenders
    Lewis, John (spo)

5. **50 Mornington Grove**
    Bow, E3 4NS
    tel 020-8980 1818 *fax 020-8983 0020*

    Court Duty Unit
    Tuitt, Eunice (spo)

    Public Protection Unit
    Rose, Anthony (spo)

6. **377 Cambridge Heath Road**
    Bethnal Green, London E2 9RD
    tel 020-7739 7931 *fax 020-7729 8600*

Tower Hamlets Offender Mgmnt
Unit 2
Drayton, Eddie (spo)

Substance Misuse Unit
Ferguson, Kathleen

7. **Hackney YOT**
55 Daubeney Road
Hackney, London E5 0EE
tel 020-8356 1090 *fax 020-8356 1091*

8. **Tower Hamlets YOT**
4th Floor, Mulberry Place
5 Clove Crescent
London E14 2BG
tel 020-7364 1144 *fax 020-8983 9911*

9. **City of London Magistrates' Court**
Probation Liaison Department
Old Bailey, London, EC4M 7EH
tel 020-7248 3277 *fax 020-7236 6692*

Yasmin Lakhi (spo)

London North Cluster 2
Barking, Dagenham & Havering, Newham
High, Linda (bua)
tel 020 8514 9202

10. 4th Floor, **Olympic House**
28/42 Clements Road, Ilford IG1 1BA
tel 020-8514 5353 *fax 020-8478 4450*

Heckroodt, Carina (aco)
tel 020 8514 9205
Parmar, Rita (buc)
tel 020 8514 9213
Blight, Andrew (bsu spo)

11. **Havering Probation Office**
1 Regarth Avenue
Romford RM1 1TP
tel (01708) 742453 *fax (01708) 753353*

Public Protection Unit
Howell-Ives, Nick (spo)

Prolific & Priority Offenders
Grant- Williams, Anita (spo)

Havering Offender Mgmnt Unit
Willemse, Sharifa (spo)

Court Team
Serugo-Lugo, Sarah (spo)

12. **Barking & Dagenham Court Team**
Barking & Dagenham Magistrates' Court
Probation Suite, The Courthouse
East Street, Barking IG1 8EW

tel 020-8507 2115 *fax 020-8262 4200*
Serugo-Lugo, Sarah (spo) (based at 12)

13. **Havering Court Team**
Havering Magistrates' Court
Probation Suite, The Courthouse
Main Road, Romford RM1 3BH
tel (01708) 502501 *fax (01708) 736533*

Serugo-Lugo, Sarah (spo) (based at 12)

14. 29/33 Victoria Road
Romford RM1 2JT
tel (01708) 753555 *fax (01708) 752096*

Barking & Dagenham OMU
Lucas, Jerome (spo)

15. 20 Romford Road
Stratford E15 4BZ
tel 020-8534 5656 *fax 020-8534 8285*

Newham SMU/DRR Unit
Akram, Sandra (spo)

Newham Offender Mgmnt Unit 1
Scheepers, Ursula (spo)

Newham Offender Mgmnt Unit 2
Clarke, Barbara (spo)

Court Team
Vacancy (spo)

16. **Plaistow Police Station**
444 Barking Rd, London E13 8HJ
tel 020-7275 5803 *fax 020-7275 5807*

Public Protection Unit
Austin, Richard (spo)

17. **Stratford Magistrates' Court**
389-397 High Street
Stratford E15 4SB
tel 020-8522 5000 *fax 020-8534 7356*

Vacancy (spo) (based at 16)

18. **Newham YOT**
192 Cumberland Road
Plaistow, London E13 8LT
tel 020-8430 2361 *fax 020-8430 2299*

London North Cluster 3
Haringey, Redbridge, Waltham Forest

19. **Olympic House**
28/42 Clements Road
Ilford, Essex IG1 1BA
tel 020-8514 5353 *fax 020-8478 4450*

Pilgrim, Mary (aco)

020-8514 9206
Cramer, Tina (buc)
020-8514 9275
Henton, Sandra (bua)
020-8514 9276
Woolaston, Patsy (bsu spo)
020-8514 9207
Glennie, Katrina (spo, victims)

20. **Telfer House**
Church Road, Highgate, London N6 4QJ
tel 020-8341 9060 *fax 020-8341 4260*

Substance Misuse Unit & PPO
Rambarath, Joseph (spo)

Public Protection & Resettlement
Tsioupra, Fotini (spo)

Highgate Magistrates Court
Edwards, David (spo)

21. **Wood Green Crown Court Team**
Woodall House, Lordship Lane
Wood Green, London N22 5LF
tel 020-8826 4100 *fax 020-881 2665*

Edwards, David (spo)

22. **9 Bruce Grove**
London N17 6RA
tel 020-8885 0683 *fax 020-8365 1372*

Substance Misuse & PPO
Rambarath, Joseph (spo)

23. **71 Lordship Lane**
Tottenham, London N17 6RS
tel 020-8808 4522 *fax 020-8885 5946*

Offender Management Unit 1
Cooke, Pamela (spo)

Offender Management Unit 2
Thomas, Richard (spo)

Offender Management Unit 3
Vacancy (spo)

24. **Haringey YOT**
476 High Road, Tottenham N17 9JF
tel 020-8489 1508 *fax 020-8489 1588*

25. **Ilford Probation Centre**
277-289 High Road
Ilford, Essex IG1 1QQ
tel 020-8478 8500 *fax 020-8478 8518*

**Redbridge & Waltham Forest
Offender Mgmnt Unit 1**
Hull, Robert (spo)

**Redbridge & Waltham Forest
Offender Mgmnt Unit 3**
Walbank, Sarah

Substance Misuse Unit/PPO
Jolly, Melanie (spo)
Boyde, Pamela (spo)

26. 1b Farnan Avenue
Walthamstow London E17 4TT
tel 020-8531 3311 *fax 020-8531 1319*

**Redbridge & Waltham Forest
Offender Mgmnt Unit 2**
Carew, Rosaline (spo)

**Redbridge & Waltham Forest
Offender Mgmnt Unit 4**
McGeehan, Georgina

Public Protection Unit
Turner, Haley (spo)

**London North Cluster 4
Brent, Barnet & Enfield**

27. **Hendon Probation Office**
Allied House (1st Floor)
3 Burnt Oak Broadway
Edgware, Middx HA8 5LT
tel 020-8205 2561 *fax 020-8205 5462*

Charles Vincent, Donna (aco)
tel 020-8205 1885
Martin-Ross, Elizabeth (bua)
tel 020-8205 1885
Sydney, Elliot (buc)

Barnet/Enfield Offender Mgmnt Unit 1
Parr, Roger (spo)

Barnet/Enfield Offender Mgmnt Unit 2
Moore, Brigid (spo)

28. The Old Court House, Windmill Hill
Enfield Middx EN2 6SA
tel 020-8366 6376 *fax 020-8367 1624*

Barnet/Enfield Offender Mgmnt Unit 1
Williams, David (spo)

Public Protection Unit
Dervish, Jill (spo)

Barnet/Enfield Offender Mgmnt Unit 2
Rosengard, Sam (spo)

Business Support Unit
Ferguson, Carl (spo)

Enfield Magistrates Court
Williams, David (spo)

29. **Substance Misuse Unit**
The Centre, 12a Centre Way
Claverings Industrial Estate
Montagu Road **Edmonton**
London N9 OAH
tel 020 8379 6970

Cassius, Jeffrey (po)
Matthews, Harry (po)

30. **Substance Misuse Unit**
The Grove, 6-8 Alexandra Grove
Finchley London N12 8NU
tel 020 8492 2523

Russell, Diane (spo)

31. **Barnet YOT**
3rd Floor, Barnet House
1255 High Road, Whetstone
London N20 0EJ
tel 020-8359 5535 *fax 020-8359 5530*

32. 440 High Road
Willesden London NW10 2DW
tel 020-8451 6212 *fax 020-8451 3467*

Public Protection Unit
Hopwood, Joe (spo)

Offender Management Unit 3
Stevenson, Doug (spo)

Offender Management Unit 2
Valero, Brigitte (spo)

33. 402-408 High Road
Wembley HA9 6AL
tel 020-8903 4921 *fax 020-8795 0472*

Offender Management Unit 1
Benjamin, Carlene (spo)

Substance Misuse Unit
McDonald, Linda (spo)

34. **Brent YOT**
Chesterfield House,
9 Park Lane
Wembley, Middlesex HA9 7RH
tel 020-8937 3810 *fax 020-8937 3811*

London North Cluster 5
Camden & Islington

35. **53 Holloway Road**
London N7 8JD
tel 020-7609 0913 *fax 020-7700 2553*

Kerr, Adam (aco)
020-7619 1460
Davis, Sean (buc)

020-7619 1473
Parker, Fiona (bu spo)

Substance Misuse Unit
Baker, John (spo)

Prolific & Priority Offenders
Keever, Lourdes (spo)

Highbury Corner Magistrates Crt
Gardener, Aveen (spo)

36. **401 St John Street**
London EC1V 4RW
tel 020-7014 9800 *fax 020-7014 9801*

**Camden/Islington Offender Mgmnt
Unit 1**
Everitt-Story, Denise (spo)

**Camden/Islington Offender Mgmnt
Unit 2**
Foy, Anthony (spo)

**Camden/Islington Offender Mgmnt
Unit 3**
White, Joanne (spo)

Camden Public Protection Unit
Smith, Kate (spo)

Islington Public Protection Unit
Lecky, Mac (spo)

37. **Camden YOT**
218-220 Eversholt Street
London NW1 1BD
tel 020-7974 6181 *fax 020-7974 4163*

38. **Islington YOT**
27 Dingley Place, London EC1V 8BR
tel 020-7527 7050 *fax 020-7527 7066*

London North Cluster 6
Hillingdon, Harrow & Ealing

39. **Ealing Probation Office**
Leeland House, Leeland Road,
London W13 9HH
tel 020-8840 6464 *fax 020-8579 8165*

Whyte, Marcia (aco)
020-8799 2650
Hashmi, Shadab (buc)
020-8799 2649
Roberts, Michael (bsu spo)
020-8799 2663

note BSU moving to Harrow Office

Ealing Offender Mgmnt Unit 1
Kahn, Marc (spo)

Ealing Offender Mgmnt Unit 2
Antoine-Joseph, Mary (spo)

Substance Misuse Unit
Robertson, Neil (spo)

40. **The Court House, Harefield Road**
Uxbridge UB8 1PQ
tel (01895) 231972 *fax (01895) 257972*

Hillingdon Offender Mgmnt Unit 1
Wood, Andrew (spo)

Hillingdon Offender Mgmnt Unit 2
McLeod, Sonya (spo)

Public Protection Unit
Jeffcott, Alison (spo)

41. Rosslyn Crescent
Harrow Middx HA1 2SR
tel 020-8427 7246 *fax 020-8424 2101*

Harrow Offender Mgmnt Unit 1
Gallagher, Joanna (spo)

Harrow Offender Mgmnt Unit 2
Bone, Jennifer (spo)

42. **Harrow Crown Court**
Hailsham Drive, Harrow
Middx HA1 4TU
tel 020-8424 2294 *fax 020-8424 9346*

Browne, Eithne (spo)

43. 4 Birkbeck Road
Acton London W3 6BE
tel 020-8992 5863 *fax 020-8993 5942*

Ealing & Acton PPU
Scullard, Paula (spo)

44. **Ealing Youth Offending Team**
2 Cheltenham Place, Acton W3 8JS
tel 020-8993 9555

LONDON SOUTH

London South Cluster 7
Hounslow, Kingston & Richmond

45. 45 High Street
Kingston upon Thames
Surrey KT1 1LQ
tel 020-8939 4130 *fax 020-8549 7626*

Galovics, Maria (aco)
020-8939 4100
Afolabi, Folasade (buc)
020-8939 4104
Dunstan, Lisa (bua)
020-8939 4106
Linkin, Anna (bsu spo)

SMU/PPO/OMU
Godfrey, Sue (spo)

Public Protection Unit/OMU
Jarrett, Jean S (spo)

46. **Banklabs House**
41a Cross Lances Road
Hounslow Middx TW3 2AD
tel 020-8570 0626 *fax 020-8814 1238*

Nelson, Sylvia (bsu, bua)
020-8814 8250

Hounslow Offender Mgmnt Unit
Palmer, Steve (spo)

SMU/PPO/OMU
Singh, Amrita (spo)

Public Protection Unit/OMU
Sajero, Rose (spo)

47. **Feltham Magistrates' Court**
Hanworth Road
Feltham, Middx TW13 5AF
tel 020-8890 8747 *fax 020-8893 2368*

48. **Isleworth Crown Court**
36 Ridgeway Road
Isleworth, Middx. TW7 5LP
tel 020-8380 4500 *fax 020-8758 9650*

Turley, Kevin (spo)

49. **Hounslow YOT**
Redlees Centre, Redlees Park
Twickenham Road
Isleworth TW7 7EU
tel 020-8583 6363 *fax 020-8847 9418*

50. **Kingston Crown Court**
6/8 Penrhyn Road
Kingston upon Thames KT1 2BB
tel 020-8240 2551 *fax 020-8240 2555*

Nelson, Andy (spo)

51. **Kingston YOT**
Eagle Chambers
18 Eden Steet, Kingston
Surrey KT1 1BB
tel 020-8547 6920 *fax 020-8547 6920*

Maccines, Caroline

52. **Richmond YOT**
Strathmore Centre
65 Strathmore Road
Teddington, Middx TW11 8AU
tel 020-8943 3353 *fax 020-8843 3240*

Lambert, Clare (mgr)

London South Cluster 8
Hammersmith & Fulham,
Kensington & Chelsea, Westminster

53. **1-5 Dorset Close**
Marylebone, London NW1 5AN
tel 020-7563 3600 *fax 020-7560 3601*

Jones, Will (aco)
Tofts, Sue (buc)
020-7563 3602
Joels, Jonathan (spo, bsu)
020-7563 3631
Erskine, Alex (bua)
020-7563 3626

H'smith & Fulham Offender Mgmnt
Unit 1
Wood, Alastair (spo)

Kens'ton & Chelsea & Westminster
Offender Management Unit 3
Harambee, Sharon (spo)

54. **Southwark Crown Court**
1 English Grounds, Battle Bridge Lane
London, SE1 2HU
tel 020-7403 1045 *fax 020-7403 8602*

Hearne, Tony (spo)

55. **191A Askew Road**
London W12 9AX
tel 020-8811 2000 *fax 020-8811 2001*

Offender Management Unit 1
Hunt, Kathryn (spo)

Prolific & Priority Offenders
Webber, Stuart (acting spo)

Public Protection Unit
Wood, Alastair (spo)

Substance Misuse Unit
Miller, Heather (spo)

Drink Drive Rehabilitation
Kirk, Sharon (spo)

56. **West London Magistrates' Court**
181 Talgarth Road
Hammersmith W6 8DN
tel 020-8700 9351 *fax 020-8700 9494*

Hearne, Tony (spo) (based at 54)

57. **Hammersmith & Fulham YOT**
Cobbs Hall, Fulham Palace Road
Fulham, London SW6 6LL
tel 020-8753 6200 *fax 020-8753 6242*

58. **75 Marsham Street**
London SW1P 3DX
tel 020-7222 0331 *fax 020-7233 2807*

Offender Management Unit 2
Roome, Sian (spo)

Public Protection Unit
Harrington, Lily (spo)

Court Team
Hinkley, Bridget (spo)

59. **143 Notting Hill Gate**
London W11 3LE
tel 020-7908 1500 *fax 020-7221 4954*

Prolific & Priority Offenders
Benmore, Joe (spo)

60. **Kensington & Chelsea YOT**
36 Oxford Gardens
London W10 5UG
tel 020-7598 4705 *fax 020-7598 4715*

61. **Westminster YOT**
6a Crompton Street
London W2 1ND
tel 020-7641 5422 *fax 020-7641 5311*

London South Cluster 9
Merton & Sutton, Wandsworth

62. **217a Balham High Road, -** ~~Contact~~
Balham, London SW17 7BQ ~~East Hill~~
tel ~~020-8672 2682 fax 020-8682 3093~~ ~~No. 63~~

Terry, Michael (aco)
020-8682 7586
Douglas, Rita (buc)
020-8682 7587
Lewis, Ingrid (bua)
020-8682 7585
Orrin, Richard (bsu, spo)

OMU 3/Public Protection Unit
Vacancy (spo)

63. **79 East Hill**
London SW18 2QE
tel 020-8704 0200 *fax 020-8704 0201*

OMU 1/Court
Head, Sarah (spo)

Substance Misuse Unit/PPO
Reed, Thomas (spo)

64. **South Western Magistrates' Court**
176a Lavender Hill
London SW11 1JU
tel 020-72289047 *fax 020-792 4775*

65. **Wandsworth YOT**
177 Blackshaw Road
Tooting, London SW17 0DJ
tel 020-8672 1664/7074 *fax 020-8682 4255*

66. **Probation Resource Centre**
Martin Harknett House
27 High Path **Wimbledon** SW19 2JI
tel 020-8545 8500 *fax 020-8543 1178*

Merton Offender Management Unit
Omorogbe, Mark (spo)

67. 103 Westmead Road
Sutton SM1 4JD
tel 020-8652 9670 *fax 020-8770 3592*

Public Protection Unit
Nolan, Gerard (spo)

Sutton Offender Management Unit
Austen, Andrew (spo)

Merton & Sutton SMU/PPO
Clarke, Sharon (spo)

London South Cluster 10
Lambeth & Southwark

68. **Mitre House**
223-237 Borough High Street
London SE1 1JD
tel 020-7740 8522 *fax 020-7740 8447*

Wright, Hermione (aco)
Kedge, Robert (bua)
tel 020-7740 8482
Haastrup, Michael (buc)
tel 020-7740 8481
Johnson, Prue (bsu spo)
tel 020 7740 8483
Larmond, Valecia (buc)
tel 020-7326 7704

69. **117 Stockwell Road**
London, SW9 9TN
tel 020-7326-7700 *fax 020-7326-7701*

Lambeth Offender Mgmnt Unit 1
Spring, Pamela (spo)

Lambeth Offender Mgmnt Unit 2
Montgomery, Dave (spo)

Lambeth Substance Misuse Unit
Prolific & Priority Offenders
Cinamon, Kate (spo)

70. **Harpenden House**
248-250 Norwood Road
London, SE27 9AJ
tel 020-8766 5700 *fax 020-8766 5746*

Lambeth Offender Mgmnt Unit 4
Dalrymple, Melodie-Ann (spo)

Lambeth Offender Mgmnt Unit 3
Riley, Debbie (spo)

Lambeth Public Protection Unit
Josling, Anthony (spo)

71. **2 Great Dover Street**
London SE1 4XW
tel 020-7740 8400 *fax 020-7740 8449*

Southwark Offender Mgmnt Unit 1
Callum, Gordon (spo)

Southwark Public Protection Unit
Askew, Catherine (spo)

72. **2 Kimpton Road**
London SE5 7UW
tel 020-7703 0822 *fax 020-7703 8319*

Southwark Offender Mgmnt Unit 2
Harris, Angela (spo)
Logie, Koreen (spo)

Southwark Offender Mgmnt Unit 3
Banton-Douglas, Glasmine (spo)

Southwark Substance Misuse Unit
Prolific & Priority Offenders
Clare Ansdell (spo)

73. **Inner London Crown Court**
21 Harper Road, London SE1 6AW
tel 020-7407 7333 *fax 020-7403 8637*

Crown Court Team
Mavunga, Peter (spo)

London South Cluster 11
Greenwich and Lewisham

74. **39 Greenwich High Road**
London SE10 8JL
tel 020-8465 6000 *fax 020-8469 1994*

Walker, Sean (aco)
tel 020-8465 6009
Ramdheen, Marion (buc)
020-8465 6013
Johnstone, Mark (bsu spo)
020-8465 6012
Gray, Janet (bua)
020-8465 6009
Buchanan, Lee (bua)
020-8465 6024
Woodall, Howard (bua)
020-8465 6026

based at 4th Floor, Olympic House
Tewari, Priya

020-8514 9203
Basith, Shah
020-8514 9225

Greenwich Court Office
Rhone, Avis (spo)

Visor
Delaney, Monica (spo)

75. **Greenwich Probation Office**
Riverside House
Beresford Street
Woolwich, SE18 6DH
tel 020-8855 5691 *fax 020-8855 6147*

Offender Management Unit 1
Ashby, Jackie (spo)

Offender Management Unit 2
Roberts-Waldron, Kim (spo)

Public Protection Unit
Allman, Sam (spo)

Substance Misuse Unit
Benamaisia, Stephen (spo)

76. **Greenwich YOT**
Young Peoples' Support Centre
New Haven Gardens
Eltham, SE9 6HQ
tel 020-8859 4492 *fax 020-8859 2706*

Williams, Jennifer (mgr)

77. **Woolwich Crown Court**
2 Belmarsh Road,
Woolwich SE28 0EY
tel 020-8312 7000 *fax 020-8317 1605*

Rhone, Avis (spo)

78. **208 Lewisham High Street**
Lewisham SE13 6JP
tel 020-8297 7300 *fax 020-8297 7301*

Offender Management Unit 1
Ashley, Val (spo)

Offender Management Unit 2
Warnock, Mauricia (spo)

Offender Management Unit 3
Rhone, Avis (spo)

Public Protection Unit
Catnick-Phillips, Ambrozine (spo)

Substance Misuse Unit
Evans, Leighton (spo)

Trainee Unit
Martin Rouse (pda)

79. **Lewisham YOT**
23 Mercia Grove
Lewisham SE13 6BJ
tel 020-8314 7474 *fax 020-8314 3177*

McDermott, Ann (mgr)

London South Cluster 12
Bexley & Bromley, Croydon

80. **Crosby House**
9-13 Elmfield Road
Bromley, Kent BR1 1LT
tel 020-8464 3430 *fax 020-8466 1571*

Brown, Janett (aco)
Williams, Sheila (bua)
020-8290 2120

Fathers, Barbara (buc)
020-8290 2157
Grandison, Selene (bu spo)
020-8290 2148

81. **Bexley Magistrates' Court**
Norwich Place
Bexleyheath, Kent DA6 7NB
tel 020-8466 7391 *fax 020-8466 6217*

82. Norwich Place
Bexleyheath Kent DA6 7ND
tel 020-8304 5521 *fax 020-8301 5737*

PPO/Substance Misuse Unit
Forsyth, Ian (spo)

Offender Management Unit 1
Ambrose, Lizette (spo)

83. **Bexley YOT**
2 Nuxley Road
Belvedere, Kent DA17 5JF
tel 020-8284 5555 *fax 020-8284 5560*

Eastham, James

84. 6 Church Hill
Orpington Kent BR6 0HE
tel (01689) 831616 *fax (01689) 875253*

Offender Management Unit 1
Jacobs, Stanley (spo)

Public Protection Unit
Roberts, Claire (spo)

85. **Bromley Magistrates' Court**
1 London Road
Bromley BR1 1RA
tel 020-8466 7391 *fax 020-8466 5217*

Studd, Peter (spo)

86. **Bromley YOT**
    8 Masons Hill, Bromley BR2 9EY
    tel 020-8466 3080 *fax 020-8466 3099*

    Vacancy

87. **Church House**
    Old Palace Road
    Croydon Surrey CR0 1AX
    tel 020-8686 6551 *fax 020-8688 4190*

    Offender Management Unit 1
    Moore, Lissa (spo)

    Offender Management Unit 2
    Nowell, Elisabeth (spo)

    Offender Management Unit 3
    Forbes, Michelle (spo)

    Public Protection Unit
    Mead, Hannah (spo)

    Special Projects
    Grindley, Tina (spo)

88. **Croydon Crown Court**
    The Law Courts
    Altyre Road, Croydon CR9 5AB
    tel 020-8681-5039 *fax 020-8681 6604*

    Glaister, Alice (spo)

89. **Croydon Magistrates' Court**
    Barclay Road, Croydon CR9 3NG
    tel 020-8688 0739 *fax 020-8681 7325*
    tel 020-8688 0611 (breach)

    Glaister, Alice (spo)

90. **Substance Misuse & PPO Unit**
    51 Wandle Road
    Croydon, Surrey CR0 1DF
    tel 020-8686 4441 *fax 020-8686 4442*

    Shipley, Diane (spo)

INTERVENTIONS

Approved Premises

91. 1st Floor, 71-73 Great Peter Street
    London SW1P 2BN
    tel 020-7960 1043 *fax 020-7960 1116*

    Davies, Ilid (aco)
    Wintersgill, Jack (bua)
    tel 020-7970 1185

92. **Central Referral Scheme**
    Mitre House
    223-237 Borough High Street
    London SE1 1JD

tel 020-7407 7293 *fax 020-7357 7140*

Ray, Jessica (snr referrals officer/mgr)
Barron, Clive (referral officer)
Philbert, Tunde (referral officer)
Raison, Peter (referral officer/seconded)
Skinner, Madeleine (referral officer)
Pearson, John (admin)

93. **Seafield Lodge Approved Premises**
    71/73 Shoot Up Hill
    London NW2 3PS
    tel 020-8452 4209 *fax 020-8450 2037*

    Wisdom, Andrew (manager)
    Farmer, Brendan (dep mgr)

94. **Camden House Approved Premises**
    199 Arlington Road
    London NW1 7HA
    tel 020-7482 4288 *fax 020-7284 3391*

    Hutt, Robert (spo/mgr)
    Foot, David (dep mgr)

95. **Westbourne House Approved Premises**
    199 Romford Road
    Forest Gate
    London E7 9HL
    tel 020-8534 0673 *fax 020-8534 8286*

    Thomas, Barbara (spo mgr)
    Jackson, Gary, (dep mgr)
    Matondo, Panaka (dep mgr)

96. **Beckenham Approved Premises**
    4 Beckenham Road
    Beckenham, Kent BR3 4LR
    tel 020-8658 3515 *fax 020-8663 6244*

    Marshall, Trevor (spo mgr)
    Roye, Andrea (dep mgr)

97. **Tulse Hill Approved Premises**
    147 Tulse Hill
    London SW2 2QD
    tel 020-8671 4086 *fax 020-8671 8546*

    Harris, Grace (spo mgr)
    Orlebar, Diane (dep mgr)

98. **Canadian Avenue Approved Premises**
    7 Canadian Avenue
    London SE6 3AU
    tel 020-8690 3234 *fax 020-8314 0650*

    Morgan, Rhys (spo mgr)
    Hayward, Lynda (dep mgr)

99. **Ellison House Approved Premises**
    370 Albany Road

London SE5 OAJ
tel 020-7703 3332 *fax 020-7525 6327*

Clarke, Angela (spo mgr)
Gardener, Michael (dep mgr)

100. **Ealing Approved Premises**
2 Corfton Road
London W5 2HS
tel 020-8997 7127 *fax 020-8810 6213*

Holland, Alan (spo mgr)
Royle, Jennifer (dep mgr)

101. **Kew Approved Premises**
96 North Road, Richmond upon Thames
Surrey TW9 4HQ
tel 020-8876 6303 *fax 020-8876 7402*

Weijman, Hans (spo mgr)
Hill, Jean (dep mgr)

Voluntary Approved Premises

102. **Katherine Price Hughes Hostel**
28 Highbury Grove
London N5 2EA
tel 020-7226 2190 *fax 020-7354 3221*

Owen, Ted (mgr)

103. **Kelley House**
18-20 Royal College Street
London NW1 OTH
tel 388 3945 *fax 020-7383 7211*

Roch, Davina (acting mgr)

104. **Hestia Streatham**
298 Leigham Court Road
London SW16 2QP
tel 020-8769 8096 *fax 020-8664 7392*

McGuinness, Elaine (mgr)
Goede, Teresa (dep mgr)

105. **Hestia Battersea**
9 Cologne Road
London SW11 2AH
tel 020-7223 3006 fax 020-7924 2156

Saunders, Lee (mgr)
Green, Shirley (dep mgr)

Offending Behaviour Programmes

106. 1st Floor, 71-73 Great Peter Street
London SW1P 2BN
tel 020-7960 1043 *fax 020-7960 1116*

Hayward, Charles (aco, obps London N)
tel 020-7960 1102

Sandhu, Kuljit (aco, obps London S)
tel 020-7960 1850
Redwood, Colleen (bua)
tel 020-7960 1851

107. **191A Askew Road**
London W12 9AX
tel 020 8811 2000 *fax 020-8811 2001*

OBPs
Smith, Annell (prog mgr)
CSOG
Cover, Gwen (treatment mgr)

108. **Crosby House**
9-13 Elmfield Road
Bromley Kent BR1 1LT
tel 020 8464 3433 *fax 020-8460 9990*

Johnson, Georgia (spo, csog)
Noon Christine (spo)
Satchell-Day, Lucy (prog mgr, csog)
Bowie, Eleanor (treatment mgr, idap)
Waters, Jill (women's safety officer mgr)

109. **Camden House** 199 Arlington Road
London NW1 7HA
tel 020-7428 8430 *fax 020-7428 1967*

Watson, Katharine (treatment mgr)
Margai, Nichola (treatment mgr)
Harrod, Claire (treatment mgr)
Yaiche, Susan (prog mgr)
Brown, Sunshine (women's safety mgr)

110. 1st Floor, King's House
The Green, **Southall**
Middlesex UB2 4QQ
tel 020-8574 9951 *fax* 020-8813 9124

Sawyer, Malcolm (spo, upw)

111. **Ilford Probation Centre**
277 High Road
Ilford, Essex IG1 1QQ
tel 020-8478 8500 *fax 020-8911 4169*

Osborne, Soroya (spo)
Rose, Yvonne (trmt mgr, csog)
Knight, Deborah (treatment mgr)

112. **75 Marsham Street**
London SW1P 3DX
tel 020-7222 0331 *fax 020-7233 2807*

Norman, Adrian (prog mgr)
Cook, David (treatment mgr)
Norman, Adrian (treatment mgr)
Vanbemmel, Nikolas (trtmnt mgr)

113. Probation Resource Centre
Martin Harknett House
27 High Path **Wimbledon** SW19 2JL
tel 020-8545 8500 *fax* 020-8543 1178

Brady, Dermot (prog mgr, IDAP)
Buckley, Philippa (trtmnt mgr, obp)
Oyerinde, Remi (trtmnt mgr, obp)

114. Norwich Place
Bexleyheath Kent DA6 7ND
tel 020-8304 7203 *fax 020-8301 5737*

Leighton, Michele (trtmnt mgr, art)

115. **143 Notting Hill Gate**
London W11 3LE
tel 020-7908 1527 *fax 020-7221 4954*

Lad, Sunil (treatment mgr)

116. **Reed House**
1-4 Rectory Road, London N16 7QS
tel 020-7923 4656 *fax 020-7923 4084*

Sowoolu, Adetokundo (trtmnt mgr, obp)
Osbourne, Emma (prog mgr, obp)

117. **2 Great Dover Street**
London SE1 4XW
tel 020-7740 8415 *fax 020-7740 8449*

Osborne Emma (prog mgr)

118. **208 Lewisham High Street**
London SE13 6JL
tel 020-8297 7300 *fax 020-8297 7301*

Coker, Eve (programme mgr)

119. **401 St John Street**
London EC1V 4RW
tel 020-7014 9863 *fax 020-7014 9801*

Barker-Semple, Sharon (treatment mgr)

120. **90 Lansdowne Road**
London N17 9XX
tel 020-8808 4849 *fax 020-8365 0981*

Bunker, Nick (treatment mgr)

Unpaid Work

Hillas, Andrew (aco, London North)
tel 020-7960 1169
Austen, Nigel (aco, London South)
tel 020-960 1089
Marshall, Imogen (ea)
tel 020-7960 1054

London North

121. **90 Landsdowne Road**
London N17 9XX
tel 020-8808 4849 *fax* 020-8365 0981

*Boroughs: Enfield, Haringey, Barnet
Camden, Islington*

Odogwu, Rosemary (buc)
Clarke, Anastasia (scheme mgr)
Carroll, James (qa mgr)
Chaplin, Matthew (qa mgr)
Spyrou, Yvonne (qa mgr)
Anderson, Lois (workshop manager)

122. Rosslyn Crescent
Harrow Middlesex HA1 2SR
tel 020-8427 7246 *fax* 020-8424 2101

Boroughs: Harrow, Hillingdon, Brent

Cassidy, Mark (scheme mgr)
Thakur, Shaila (buc)
Gibbs, Alton (qa mgr)
Ford, Dominique (qa mgr)

123. 29-33 Victoria Road
Romford Essex RM1 2JT
tel (01708) 753555 *fax (01708) 752096*

*Boroughs: Redbridge, Havering, Barking
& Dagenham, Waltham Forest*

Parkin, Elaine (scheme mgr)
Padden, Eddy (qa mgr)
Hewitt, Gary (qa mgr)
Kendell, Paul (workshop mgr)
Cook, Nichola (buc)

124. 15 Belton Road
Forest Gate London E7 9PF
tel 020-8472 5412 *fax* 020-8471 6673

*Boroughs: Newham, Tower Hamlets,
Hackney*

Francis, Viv (scheme mgr)
Ali, Sarfraz (qa mgr)
Flower, Rob (qa mgr)
Yarde, Trevor (qa mgr)
Wallace, Toni (buc)

London South

125. **Harpenden House**
248-250 Norwood Road
London SE27 9AJ
tel 020-8766 5700 *fax* 020-8766 5772

Boroughs: Lambeth, Southwark

White, Jacqueline (scheme mgr)

Gordon, Annette (qa mgr)
Parker, Yvonne (qa mgr)
Turner, Lesley (qa mgr)
Johnson, Michael (workshop mgr)

126. 6 Beckenham Road
Beckenham Kent BR3 4LR
tel 020-8658 3511 *fax 020-8658 8678*

Jenkins, Tracy (bu co-ord)
Olaeye, Dolly (bua)

Boroughs: Croydon, Bexley, Bromley,
Lewisham & Greenwich

Spooner, Pamela (scheme mgr)
Bishop, Karen (qa mgr)
Driver, Carol (qa mgr)
House, Peter (qa mgr)
Johnson, Debbie (qa mgr)

127. Martin Harknett House
27 High Path
Wimbledon London SW19 2JL
tel 020-8545 8500 *fax 020-8543 1178*

Boroughs: Merton & Sutton, Richmond,
Kingston, Wandsworth

Kumey, Adelaide (bua)
Martin, Rosie (scheme mgr)
DeAntiquis, David (qa mgr)
Smith, Davina (qa mgr)
Astbury, Fred (workshop mgr)

128. 1st Floor, King's House
The Green, **Southall**
Middlesex UB2 4QQ
tel 020-8574 1071 *fax 020-8813 9124*

Boroughs: Ealing & Hounslow,
Hammersmith & Fulham, Westminster,
Kensington & Chelsea

Houslin, Lisa (acting scheme mgr)
Bagot, Michael (qa mgr)
Lamont, Angela (qa mgr)
Copeland, Robert (acting qa mgr)
Davis, Ian (acting qa mgr)
Young, Beverley (buc)

Victim Liaison Units

All London cases should be referred to
Central Admin at Acton

129. 71-73 Great Peter St
London, SW1P 2BN
020-222 5656 *fax 020-7960 1116*

Gilbert Kate (aco)

130. **London North**
a. **Ilford Victim Liaison Unit**
4th Floor, Olympic House
28-42 Clements Road
Ilford IG1 1BA
tel 020-8514 5353 *fax 020-8220 2356*

Glennie, Katrina (spo) (130 a, b, c)

covers London boroughs of Barking, City
Dagenham, Enfield, Hackney,
Havering, Newham, Tower Hamlets
& Waltham Forest

b. **Camden House Victim Liaison Unit**
199 Arlington Road
London NW1 7HA
tel 020-7428 8474 *fax 020-7428 8431*

covers London boroughs of Barnet, Camden,
Haringey, Harrow, Hillingdon, Islington

c. **Acton Victim Liaison Unit**
4 Birbeck Road
Acton London W3 6BE
tel 020-8993 0934 *fax 020-8992 7408*

covers London boroughs of Ealing
Hammersmith & Fulham, Hounslow
Kensington & Chelsea, Merton
Richmond, Wandsworth, Westminster

131. **London South**
a. **Bromley Victim Liaison Unit**
Crosby House
9/13 Elmfield Road
Bromley BR1 1LT
tel 020-8290 2158 fax 020 8313 1621

Johnson, Georgia (spo) (131 a, b)

covers London boroughs of Croydon,
Greenwich, Lewisham, Bexley &
Bromley, Hounslow

b. **Kingston Victim Liaison Unit**
45 Unit Street
Kingston upon Thames KT1 1LQ
tel 020-8939 4120/4127 *fax 020-8549 8900*

covers London boroughs of Hammersmith
& Fulham, Wandsworth, Merton & Sutton,
Kingston & Richmond, Hounslow

PARTNERSHIP UNIT

132. **Mitre House**
223-237 Borough High Street
London SE1 1JD
tel 020-7740 8500 (switchboard)
fax 020-7740 8447

Kate Gilbert (aco for Partnerships inc
Substance Misuse, Mental Health,
Housing Victim Liaison Service)
based at Great Peter Street
tel 020-222-5656

Cameron, Angus (spo, mental health advr)
020-7740 8517
Latimer, Robin (subst misuse devpt mgr)
020-7740 8518
Vacancy (spo, prolific & priority
offenders devpt mgr)
020-7740 8500 (managed
by Maria Galovics aco)
Dennis, Dezlee (subst misuse
devpt mgr)
020-7740 8523
Kirk, Sharon (ddr project mgr)
Seabrook, Kevin (data analyst)
020-7740 8519

Housing
Tooth, Amanda (housing devpt mgr)
020-7740 8514
Mellish, Paul (housing devpt mgr)
020-7740 8560
Downie, Fergus (housing devpt off)
020-7740 8532

COURTS & OASys TEAMS

133. **71-73 Great Peter Street**
London SW1P 2BN
tel 020-7960 1098
Robinson, Sara (aco)
020-7960 1098
Craddock, Jacqueline (buc crts & OASys)
020-7960 1687

Crown Courts in the London Area	Borough in which Situated
Blackfriars Crown Court	Southwark
Central Criminal Court	City of London
Croydon Crown Court	Croydon
Harrow Crown Court	Harrow
Inner London Crown Court	Southwark
Isleworth Crown Court	Middlesex
Kingston Crown Court	Kingston-upon-Thames
Middlesex Guildhall Crown Court	Westminster
Royal Courts of Justice (Criminal Division, Court of Appeal)	Westminster
Snaresbrook Crown Court	Waltham Forest
Southwark Crown Court	Southwark
Wood Green Crown Court	Haringey
Woolwich Crown Court	Greenwich

134. **Central Criminal Court**
Old Bailey, London EC4M 7EH
tel 020-7192 2227 fax 020-7236 6692

Lakhi, Yasmin (spo)

135. **Court of Appeal**
Room E303 Royal Courts of Justice
London WC2A 2LL
tel 020-7947 6066 *fax 020-7947 6704*

Lakhi, Yasmin (spo)

136. **Southwark Crown Court**
1 English Grounds, Battle Bridge Lane
London SE1 2HU
tel 020-7940 8149 *fax 020-7403 8602*

Hearne, Tony (spo)

137. **Inner London Crown Court**
21 Harper Road, London SE1 6AW
tel 020-7940 6173 *fax 020-7403 8637*

Mavunga, Peter (spo)

138. **Blackfriars Crown Court**   0207
1-15 Pocock Street, London SE1 0BT 02 1
tel 020-7940 8149 *fax 020-7403 8602* 07 69

Hearne Tony (spo)

139. **Wood Green Crown Court Team**
Woodall House, Lordship Lane
Wood Green, London N22 5LF
tel 020-8826 4100 *fax 020-881 2665*

Edwards, David (spo)

140. **Harrow Crown Court**
Hailsham Drive, Harrow
Middx HA1 4TU
tel 020-8424 2294 *fax 020-8424 9346*

Browne, Eithne (spo)

141. **Snaresbrook Crown Court**
Crown Court, Hollybush Hill
Snaresbrook, London E11 1QW
tel 020-8530 1725 *fax 020-8530 1399*

Elliott, Martyn (spo)

142. **Croydon Crown Court**
The Law Courts
Altyre Road, Croydon CR9 5AB
tel 0208-681 5039 *fax 0208-681 6604*

Glaister, Alice (spo)

143. **Isleworth Crown Court**
36 Ridgeway Road

Isleworth, Middx. TW7 5LP
tel 020-8380 4500 *fax 020-8758 9650*

Turley, Kevin (spo)

144. **Kingston Crown Court**
6/8 Penrhyn Road
Kingston upon Thames KT1 2BB
tel 020-8240 2551 *fax 020-8240 2555*

Nelson, Andy (spo)

145. **Woolwich Crown Court**
2 Belmarsh Road
London SE28 0EY
tel 020-8312 7001 *fax 020-8317 1605*

Rhone, Avis (spo)

LOCAL JUSTICE AREAS

for fines enquiries for all Central and NE Area Courts plus Camden & Islington, Greenwich & Lewisham, Woolwich, Lambet & Southwark, Tower Bridge, West London and Wandsworth Magistrates' Courts: Central Accounting Office 0845 940 0111

Central Area

City of London LJA
City of London Magistrates' Court
City of Westminster LJA
Bow Street Magistrates' Court
Horseferry Road Magistrates' Court
Marylebone Magistrates' Court

North East Area

Barking LJA
Barking Magistrates' Court
Hackney & Tower Hamlets LJA
Thames Magistrates' Court
Havering LJA
Havering Magistrates' Court
Newham LJA
Stratford Magistrates' Court
Redbridge LJA
Redbridge Magistrates' Court
Waltham Forest LJA
Waltham Forest Magistrates' Court

North West Area

Barnet LJA
Barnet Magistrates' Court
Hendon Magistrates' Court (closed for rebuilding)
Brent LJA
Brent Magistrates' Court
Camden & Islington LJA
Highbury Corner Magistrates' Court

Enfield LJA
Enfield Magistrates' Court
Haringey LJA
Haringey Magistrates' Court
Harrow LJA
Harrow Magistrates' Court
Hillingdon LJA
Uxbridge Magistrates' Court

South East Area

Bexley LJA
Bexley Magistrates' Court
Bromley LJA
Bromley Magistrates' Court
Croydon LJA
Croydon Magistrates' Court
Greenwich & Lewisham LJA
Greenwich Magistrates' Court
Woolwich Magistrates' Court
Lambeth & Southwark LJA
Camberwell Green Magistrates' Court
Tower Bridge Magistrates' Court
Sutton LJA
Sutton Magistrates' Court

South West Area

Ealing LJA
Ealing Magistrates' Court
Acton Magistrates' Court
Hounslow LJA
Brentford Magistrates' Court
Feltham Magistrates' Court
Hammersmith & Fulham and Kensington & Chelsea LJA
West London Magistrates' Court
Kingston upon Thames LJA
Kingston upon Thames Magistrates' Court
Merton LJA
Wimbledon Magistrates' Court
Richmond upon Thames Magistrates' Court
Wandsworth LJA
South Western Magistrates' Court

Youth Courts by Region

See table over page.

YOUTH COURTS BY REGION

Youth Court	London Borough in which Court situated	London Area(s) covered by Youth Court
Acton	Ealing	
Balham	Wandsworth	Wandsworth, Lambeth
Barking	Barking	Barking & Dagenham
Barnet	Barnet	
Bexley	Bexley	
Brent	Brent	
Brentford	Hounslow	
Bromley	Bromley	
Camberwell (Divnl Youth Court)	Southwark	Southwark, Greenwich, Lewisham
Croydon	Croydon	
Enfield	Enfield	
Haringey	Haringey	
Harrow	Harrow	
Havering	Romford	
Kingston	Kingston	
Redbridge	Ilford	
Richmond	Richmond	
Stratford	Newham	
Sutton	Sutton	Wallington
Tower Hamlets	Tower Hamlets	Tower Hamlets, Hackney, Camden, Islington
Uxbridge	Hillingdon	
Walthamstow	Waltham Forest	
West London (Divnl Youth Court)	Hammersmith	Hammersmith & Fulham, Kensington & Chelsea, Westminster
Wimbledon	Merton	

PRISONS

146. **71/73 Great Peter Street**
London SW1 2BN
tel 020-7960 1185 *fax 020-7960 1116*

Davies, Ilid (aco prisons)
Weintersgill, Jack (bua)
tel 020-7960 1043

147. HMP **Brixton**
Jebb Avenue, London SW2 5XF
tel 020-8588 6000 *fax 020-8588 6283*
direct dial 020-8588 + ext

probn clerk 020-8588 6062
probn fax 020-8588 6342

Lowe-Thompson, Yvonne (spo) ext 6339

148. HMP **Belmarsh**
Western Way, Thamesmead
Woolwich, London SE28 OEB
tel 020-8331 4400 *fax 020-8331 4401*
direct dial 020-8331 + ext

fax (probn) 020-8317 8719
discipline ext 300/301/313

Lauchlan, Neil (acting spo) ext 4713

149. HMP **Holloway**
Parkhurst Road, London N7 ONU
tel 020-7979 4400 *fax 020-7979 4401*
direct dial 020-7979 + ext

probn fax 020-7979 4763

professional & legal visits

tel 020-7979 4763/4478
Herson, Karen (spo) ext 4486

150. HMP **Pentonville**
Caledonian Road, London N7 8TT
tel 020-7023 7000 *fax 020-7023 7250*
direct dial 020-7023 + ext
Vacancy (spo) ext 7174

151. HMP **Wandsworth**
Heathfield Road
London SW18 3HS
tel 020-8588 4000 *fax 020-8588 4001*
direct dial 020-8588 + ext

probn fax 020-8588 4011
Professional & Legal visits
020-8588 4176
e-mail legalvisitswandsworth@hmps.gsi.
gov.uk
Probation admin/duty
020-8588 4229
Probation HDC Clerks
020-8588 4125

Jolley, James (spo) ext 4300

152. HMP **Wormwood Scrubs**
Du Cane Road, London W12 0AE
tel 020-8588 3200 *fax 020-8588 3201*
probn office 020-8588 3238
probn fax 020-8588 3549

*healthcare fax (suicide alerts) 020-8588
3554*
legal visits fax 020-8588 3563
(all Legal Visits booked by fax)

Fearnley, Janet (spo) ext 3237

153. HMP **Latchmere House**
Church Road, Ham Common
Richmond upon Thames TW10 5HH
tel 020-8588 6650 *fax 020-8588 6698*
direct dial 020-8588 + ext
probation fax 020-8588 6667

Convisser, Sharon (spo) ext 6665

GREATER MANCHESTER PROBATION AREA

Out of hours emergency contact point
tel 0161-226 1179

e-mail Firstname.Surname@manchester.
probation.gsi.gov.uk

1. **Head Office**
6th floor, Oakland House
Talbot Road, Manchester M16 0PQ
tel 0161-872 4802 *fax 0161-872 3483*

Crawforth, John (co)
Noah, Chris (dir intrvntns & supt services)
Hamilton, Roz (dir offender mgmnt)
Jones, Penny (aco)
Groves, Nigel (aco)
Seale, Manjit (aco)
Bate, Barbara (aco)
Barnes, Richard (aco)
Bristow, Owen (head of i.t.)
Carman, Andrew (business &
commissioning mgr)
Greenhalgh, Judith (director of finance)
Jiacoumi, Maria (diversity mgr)

Jackson, Graham (sec/solicitor)
Kettle, Melanie (hd of pr & comms)
Thornley, Lucy (head of h.r.)
Kelly, Phil (practice mngr, sfo)
Woods, Jane (pa to co)
Parris, Helen (librarian/info officer)

2. **Manchester Crown Court**
Crown Court Buildings, Crown Square
Manchester M3 3FL
tel 0161-954 1750/3 *fax 0161-839 3856*

Minshull Street Crown Court
Courts of Justice, Minshull Street
Manchester M1 3FS
tel 0161-954 7654 & 7661/2 *fax 0161-954
7664*

Smith, Celia (spo)
Baggoley, Martin
Campbell, Mark
Edwards, Les
Ledder, Jacqueline
McClintock, Tania
Blomeley, Helen (pso)
Carlon, Joanne (pso)
Clarke, Wendy (pso)
Clarke, Fiona (pso)
Hollinworth, April (pso)
Lyzniak, Adam (pso)

Percival, Matthew (pso)
Ward, Stephen (pso)
Worsley, Andrew (pso)
Xavier, Anthony (pso)

3. **Bolton Crown Court**
   Liaison Office, Black Horse Street,
   Bolton BL1 1SU
   tel (01204) 372119 *fax (01204) 380963*

4. **Magistrates Court Building**
   Probation Dept, 2nd Floor
   Quay House, Quay Street
   Manchester M3 3JE
   tel 0161-830 2250 *fax 0161-834 3064*

   Keane, Ruth (spo)
   Bell, Abigail
   Davies, Howard
   Dutton, Ben
   Entwistle, Karen
   Evans, Marie
   McNorton, Barry
   Stavrinides, Philip
   Treherne, Nikki

   Brownjohn, Julie (pso)
   Hilton, Louise (pso)
   McDermott, Wendy (pso)
   Nelson, Tania (pso)
   Raggatt, Doris (pso)
   Simpson, Pamela (pso)
   Taylor, Rebecca (pso)

Offender Management

Bolton

5. St Helena Mill
   St Helena Road, **Bolton** BL1 2JS
   tel (01204) 387699 *fax (01204) 382372*

   Brimley, John (dist mgr)
   Berry, Susan (spo)
   Elliott, Nigel (spo)
   Hunt, Sean (spo)
   Riley, Kath (spo)
   Taylor, Phil (spo)

   Andrew, Dominic
   Bannister, Sue
   Butler, Gaynor
   Copeland, Susan
   Corr, Martin
   Cotterill, Gemma
   Donlon, Mike
   Dunn, Lisa
   Earnshaw, Suzanne
   Eniola, Yinka
   France, Janice

Gregory, Alison
Hargreaves, Julia
Johnston, Ted
Lashimba, Suzanne
Lipman, Marcelle
Maddix, Leonie
Marland, Toni
Maurizi, John
McGuinness, Sam
Murphy, Diane
Oakes, Christine
Redfern, Mandy
Rigby, Ben
Scott, Gillian
Shearman, Catherine
Sheerin, Karen
Stevenson, Chris
Tinsley, Claire
Warburton, Bernie
Warburton, Emma
Wake, Rob
Waterhouse, Mandy

Ankers, Dave (pso)
Bailey, Linda (pso)
Barlow, Jill (pso)
Davies, Ellen (pso)
Downes, Shirley (pso)
Edwards, Chris (pso)
Grundy, Joanne (pso)
Hardman, Jim (pso)
Hinchcliffe, Allan (pso)
Holmes, Val (pso)
Homewood, Chris (pso)
Jones, Karen (pso)
Joynson, Gail (pso)
Knight, Phil (pso)
McDonald, Sue (pso)
Moffatt, Steve (pso)
Nikrafter, Tish (pso)
Roberts, Nadine (pso)
Sullivan, Jim (pso)
Warburton, Mark (pso)
West, Marie (pso)

Hopkinson, Stuart (vlo)
Unsworth, Cathy (vlo)

Bury

6. Argyle House, Castlecroft Court
   Castlecroft Road **Bury** BL9 0LN
   tel 0161-764 9514 *fax 0161-761 2638*

   Farooq, Mohammed (dist mgr)
   Perry, Hellen (spo)
   Yunus, Mohammed (spo)
   Davies, Claire (spo)
   Booth, Celina

Deegan, Karen
Fairclough, Justine
Harrison, Alan
Iqbal, Zahida
Kayley, Marie
Knowles, Leah
Litherland, Sue
McGill, Justine
Mill, Christine
Murray, Daniel
Prince, Andy
Riches, Iris
Straughn, Kenrick
Staines, Tracey
Stefanuto, Lisa
Taylor, Sarah
Whittam, Jen
Wright, Wayne

Birtles, Rod (pso)
Breen, Paul (pso)
Connell, Avis (pso)
Dawson, Emma (pso)
Hamilton-Coles, Lisa (pso)
Hill, Tracy (pso)
Jones, Francine (pso)
Keenan, Linda (pso)
Noble, Vicky (pso)
Sherlock, Rachel (pso)

Manchester

7. **Manchester City Mgmnt Unit**
    Victoria Park, Laindon Road
    Longsight, Manchester M14 5YJ
    tel 0161-224 0231 *fax 0161-248 6953*

    Ross, Enda (dist mgr)
    Kyle, Tim (dist mgr)
    Bellamy, Clare (spo risk)
    Coles, Sarah (spo)
    Poulson, Amy (spo)
    Otto, Clare (pso/vlo)
    Sharples, Margaret (pso/vlo)
    Knight, Lisa (pso, ppo)
    Archer, Carol (dist admin mgr)
    Gates, Pam (dist admin mgr)
    Shepherd, Andrea (dist admin mgr)
    Wild, Andrea (dist admin mgr)

8. 20 Humphrey Streeet
    Cheetham Hill Manchester M8 7JR
    tel 0161-795 1777 *fax 0161-720 6707*

    Murphy, Barbara (spo)
    Wood, Nick (spo)
    Black, Mike
    Blair, Del
    Donovan, William

Lashimba, Des
Latham, Helen
Mears, Val
Metcalf, Malcolm
Murphy, Aine
Phillips, Lynne
Raoof, Farha
Rawlinson, Laura
Reast, Carrie
Saunders, Barry
Cunningham, Virginia (pso)
Davies, Cathy (pso)
Egan, Kim (pso)
Francis, Janet (pso)
Goodhall, Christine (pso)
Jones, Rachel (pso)
McLoughlan, Margaret (pso)
Orwin, Chris (pso)
Read, Tracey (pso)
Vassell, Janice (pso)
Whelan, Ann (pso)

9. **Longsight District Centre**
    521 Stockport Road
    Manchester M12 4NE
    tel 0161-248 6273 *fax 0161-248 8679*

    Ward, John (spo)
    Campbell, Fran (spo)
    Bancroft, Sarah
    Conte, Lara
    Coughlan, Patricia
    Edwards, Samantha
    Goodfellow, Jonathan
    Hale, Pamela
    Howarth, Paul
    Hughes, Andrea
    Mitchell, Jane
    Newton, Amy
    Rose, Juliet
    Totten, John
    Atcha, Saeed (pso)
    Ellis, Andrew (pso)
    McGrady, Siobhan (pso)
    Walker, Joanne (pso)
    Yates-Rogers, Ziggi (pso)
    Zaman, Jessica (pso)

10. 87 Moss Lane West
    Moss Side Manchester M15 5PE
    tel 0161-226 3515 *fax 0161-232 0649*

    Kyle, Tim (Dist mngr)
    Orr, Cranmer (spo)
    Wright, Debbie (spo)
    Bell, Mike
    Cassidy, Ann
    Christopher, Ossie

Diamond, Daniel
Dowling, Jo
Ghuffar, Anneella
Greenwood, Jillian
Nicholls, Carol
Reynolds, Tim
Roberts, Priscilla
Robertson, Shelley
Sharpe, Julian
Stapleton, Samantha
Baldwin, Carole (pso)
Bradley, Sarah
Emery, Mark (pso)
Hart, Jaki (pso)
Kiernan, Luke (pso)
Nield, Michelle (pso)
Parker, Sharon (pso)
Topping, Cheryl (pso)

11. **Varley Street**
Miles Platting, Manchester M10 8EE
tel 0161-205 7444 *fax 0161-205 7563*

Metcalf, Ian (spo)
Shah, Assia (spo)
Bolger, Paula
Botterill, Claire
Bowker, Debbie
Carton, Kathleen
Hanley, Paulette
Higgins, Jayne
Hill, Raph
Kopcic, Amela
Martin, Chris
Merchant, Marcia
Ali, Salma
Baker, Susan (pso)
Brown, Karen (pso)
Hossner, Angela (pso)
Simister, Carl (pso)
Williams, Chantelle (pso)

12. 2 Candleford Road
Withington, Manchester
tel 0161-434 3039 *fax 0161-448 7529*

Kaczynska, Nina (spo)
Bamber, Khaldip
Casey, Sue
Grant, Monica
Hawthorne, Elaine
Hayward, Claire
Potter, Claire
Jackson, Sarah (pso)
Moore, Tim (pso)
Owen Jones, John (pso)
Roberts, Mo (pso)
Slobodian, Andrij (pso)

Intensive Contact Team
Bendon, Kerri (spo)
Balkwill, Alison
Oliver, Lisa-Jo
Wickstead, Lorna
Burney, Karen (pso)
Frain, Rebecca (pso)
Gordon, Julien (pso)

13. 258 Brownley Road
Wythenshawe Manchester M22 5EB
tel 0161-436 1919 *fax 0161-498 8304*

Scanlon, Dave (spo)
Tasker, Stuart (spo)
Ankers, Sally
Briggs, Carolyn
Hamilton, Alex
James, Caroline
Lambert, Jayne
Lee-Kilgariff, Mark
Morrison, Angela
Seymour, Brian
Simpson, Craig
Walley, Michael

Clarke, Hugh (pso)
Daniels, Maxine (pso)
Donnelly, Lorraine (pso)
Germain, Hilary (pso)
Sanderson, Kirsty (pso)

Oldham

14. 128 Rochdale Road
Oldham OL1 2JG
tel 0161-620 4421 *fax 0161-628 2011*

Cavanagh, Paul (dist mgr)
Araya, Christina (dist admin mgr)

Offender Mgmnt Unit 1
Saunders, Phil (spo)
Belfield, Helen
Doherty, Kerry
Litherland, Sue
Smith, Amanda
Smith, Lisa
Burton, Fred (pso)
Edwardson, Pam (pso)
Taylor, Janet (pso)
Edge, Margaret (vlo)

Offender Mgmnt Unit 2
Chadwick, Wendy (spo)
Adams, Steve
Clarke, Dionne
Pollard, Leanne
Purslow, Kelly
Rogers, Marilyn

Travis, Simon
Jarvis, Squire (pso)
Kershaw, Gill (pso)
Warburton, Sheena (pso)

Court Assessment Team
Scott, Faith
Singh, Dal
Lovell, Polly (pso)
Ward-Hilton, Sandra (pso)

15. 64 Bridge Street
Oldham OL1 1ED
tel 0161-620 4421 *fax 0161-628 2011*

Offender Mgmnt Unit 3
Bibi, Imraz
Clarke, Margaret (spo)
Cuddy, Louise
Heap, John
O'Brien, Maureen
Patterson, Phillippa
Pitchford, Jordanna
Brookes, Dave (pso)
Ford, Liz (pso)
Haywood, Jennifer (pso)

Rochdale

16. **Rochdale District Admin Office**
151 Green Lane, Heywood
Manchester OL10 2EW
tel (01706) 620702 *fax (01706) 368951*

McGinn, Des (dist mgr)
Hampson, Joan (dist admin mgr)

17. 193/195 Drake Street
Rochdale OL11 1EF
tel (01706) 653411 *fax* (01706) 713524

Offender Mgmnt Unit 1
Murphy, Alison (spo)
Cunningham, Gary
Hay, Dan
Heyes, Rosemary
King, Jonathon
Samuels, Michaela
Whelan, Natasha
Briddon, Janine (pso)
McCorriston, Paula (pso)
Sidderley, Colin (pso)

Offender Mgmnt Unit 2
Thomas, Angela (spo)
Greenhalgh, Lynne
Hoyle, Jayne
Jackson, David
Kelly, Peter
Khan, Nazeem

McGee, Dave
Willis, Neil
Carney, Auriol (pso)
Fletcher, Ray (pso)
Gisbourne, Tracey (pso)
Howarth, Mike (pso)
Taylor, Milka (pso)

18. Middleton Office
St Michael's House
Oldham Road
Middleton M24 2LH
tel 0161-643 0826 *fax* 0161-643 2414

Offender Mgmnt Unit 3
Williams, Carolyn (spo)
Coore, Debra
Coulton, Martin
Gratton, Fiona
Robb-Elliott, Mike
Rothwell, Jenny
Strang, Dannielle (pso)
Ward, Pauline (pso)
Worrall, Sue (pso)
Burton, Roy (vlo)

Offender Mgmnt Unit 4
Albuquerque-Neale, Maria (spo)
Bryan, Ryan
King, Jonathan
Oakley, Angela
Rothwell, Jenny
Ahmed, Sophie (pso)
Mistry, Natalie (pso)
Neville, Lorna (pso)
Robinson, Dionne (pso)

Salford

19. 2 Redwood Street
Pendleton **Salford M6 6PF**
tel 0161-736 6441 *fax 0161-736 6620*

Buckley, Angela (dist mgr)
Jones, Debra (dist admin mgr)

Offender Mgmnt Unit 1
Ventris, Michael (spo)
Assinder, Clare
Campion, Sophie
Jones, Adrian
Callaghan, Danny (pso)
Crook, Tina (pso)
Williams, Pamela (pso)

Offender Mgmnt Unit 2
Phillips, Mandy (spo)
Brayshaw, Elizabeth
Ledger, Jackie
Murray, Jim

Prokofiev, Anastasia
Stafford, Zoe
Thompson, Hilary
Todd, Liane
Ashton, Chris (pso)
Mitchell, Anna (pso)
Pope, Robert (pso)
Thompson, Claire (pso)

Offender Mgmnt Unit 3
Burton-Francis, Sheron (spo)
Barton, Gemma
Brearley, Heather
Buckley, Sarah
Cogan, Beverley
Loney, Juliette
O'Kane, Seamus
Thomson, Neil
Busby, Michelle, (pso/vlo)
Byers, Joanne (pso/vlo)
McKenna, Claire (pso)
Reed, Laura (pso)

Offender Mgmnt Unit 4
Hill, Joanne (spo)
Badachha, Simi
Bowes, Simon
Bullough, Ruth
Davies, Stephen
Fitzpatrick, Sandra
Hart, Kirsty
Howe, Joanne
Wroe, Julia
Clarke, Joan (pso)
Dawson, Louise
Dormer, Joanne (pso)
Grayson, Joanne (pso)

Court Team
Brown, Trudie (spo)
Jenks, Amanda
Morley, John
Awwad, Anne (pso)
Kaylor, Leanne (pso)
Sackfield, Jayne (pso)

Stockport

20.   19/37 High Street
Stockport SK1 1EG
tel 0161-429 0010 *fax 0161-476 2709*

Meakin, Marion (dist mgr)
Cavanagh, Deborah (dist admin mgr)
McDonagh, Mary (spo)
Nicholls, Steve (spo)
Ross, Jean (spo)

Andrew, Christine
Armitage, Catherine

Barker, Sara
Dooley, Gavin
Finn, Siobhan
Grafton, Fiona
Griffiths, Rhian
Coulson, Jim
Horton, Joanne
Howarth, Elaine
Jackson, Georgine
Kennington, Tom
Machin, Mark
McLean, Hannah
Penny, Diane
Ravenscroft, Chloe
Ritchie, Angela
Santinelli, Enza
Saxon, Cheree
Shallcross, Maggie
Thornton, Lisa
Wright, Sarah

Boyle, Linda (pso)
Corlett, Kevin (pso)
Dawson, Judith (pso)
Evans, June (pso)
George, Katie (pso)
Jones, Les (pso)
Marsden, Anna (pso)
McCall, Christine (pso)
Mushtaq, Noreen (pso)
Ritson, Paul (pso)
Roberts, Helen (pso)
Smith, Diane (pso)
Tooth, Simon (pso)
Truby, Michelle (pso)
Wakefield, Judith (pso)

Tameside

21.   Francis Thompson Drive
off Water Street
Ashton-under-Lyne OL6 7AJ
tel 0161-330 3695 *fax 0161-343 7475*

Smith, Carolyn (dist mgr)
Johnson, Julie (dist admin mgr)

Offender Mgmnt Unit 3
Mitchell, Jacqui (spo)
Carter, Diane
McCormick, Kirsty
March, Mike
Moremont, Gary
Murphy, Julie
Perris, Stephen
Steffani, Sally

Offender Mgmnt Unit 4
Martin, Patricia (spo)
Daniels, Diane

Schofield, Ceri
Whitbread, Rebecca

Court Team
Ready, Ann
Jeffers, Helen
Linguard, Jan
Hackney, Melvyn

22. **2 Simpson Street**
Hyde SK14 1BJ
tel 0161-366 7344 *fax 0161-368 6552*

Offender Mgmnt Unit 1
Armstrong-Burns, Janet (spo)
Ashworth, Chrissie
Bulmer, Lisa
Cutts, Brian
Green, Stephen
Lawrence, Beverley
Rowarth, Maria
Stott, Jenny
Daley, Sandra (pso)
Higginbotham, Jaine (pso)
Scott, Leroy (pso)
Senior, Gay (pso)
Thacker, Sarah (pso)

Offender Mgmnt Unit 2
Bulman, Kevin (spo)
Coyle, Rob
Eastwood, Dave
Kramer, Jennie
Plackett, Richard
Potts, Sarah
Self, Katherine
Worrall, Suzanne
Bradshaw, Lisa (pso/vlo)
Brown, Janet (pso)
Coppitch, Mags (pso/vlo)
Johnstone, Rose (pso)
Simpson, Jo (pso/vlo)

23. **Priority & Prolific Offenders &**
DRR Team
Tameside DIP, Good Hope Mill
98 Bentinck Street
Ashton-under-Lyne OL5 7SS
tel 0161-343 5622 *fax 0161-343 4754*

Delaney, Janice (team mgr)
Buckley, Andrew (pso)
Coldrick, Paul (pso)
Johnstone, Rose (pso)
Malone, Karen (pso)
May, Helen (pso, drr)

Trafford

24. Newton Street

Stretford Manchester M32 8LG
tel 0161-865 3255 *fax 0161-864 4791*

Davis, Paul (dist mgr)
McCusker, Michelle (dist admin mgr)
Powell, Chris (spo)

Bramwell, Angela (spo)
Burton, Shirley (spo)
Reid, Sarah (spo)
Abbass, Roland
Daye, Kevin
Doody, Olive
Evans, Amanda
Gibson, Jim
Greenstreet, Geoff
Hampson, Emma
Kay, Jonathan
Lancaster, Dave
McLaughlin, Peter
Robertson, Marianne
Singh, Chas
Sugrue, Laura
Ukwuoma, Chendi
Wastell, Liz
Williamson, Dave

Ashton, Claire (pso)
Barber, Dee (pso)
Blyth, Sam (pso)
Greaves, Stuart (pso)
Hodgkinson, Katie (pso)
Murphy, Lance (pso)
Scott, Amanda (pso)
Thompson, Veronica (pso)
Wiaktor-Urch, Stasia (pso/vlo)
Wright, Sandra (pso)

Wigan

25. **81 Gloucester Street**
Atherton M46 0JS
tel (01942) 876889 *fax (01942) 886109*

Roberts, Andrew (acting dist mgr)
Long, Debra (dist admin mgr)

Offender Mgmnt Unit 1
Williams, Caroline (spo)
Cole, Frank
Commissiong, Michael
Down, Adele
Holroyd, Gail
Miller, Anne
O'Hara, Janice (pso)
Stock, Anne (pso)
Waring, Kirsty (pso)
West, Tracy (pso)

Offender Mgmnt Unit 2
Berry, Eloise (spo)

Crye, Matthew
Hurley, Rachel
Stephenson, Alan
Stokes, Gina
Hodgson, Carrie (pso)
Simpson, Heather (pso)

Offender Mgmnt Unit 3
Williams, Hyacinth (spo)
Bancroft, Julian
Clifton, Paul
Edwards, Mary
Hollis, Vicki
McGovern, Nadira
Brooks, Jane (pso)
Cheetham, Susan (pso)
McMahon, Gordon (pso)

Offender Mgmnt Unit 4
Leslie, Nicola (spo)
Bryan-Jones, Adrian
Burke, Mike
Cunningham, Lorna
Manning, John
Owen, Sue
Parr, Hayley
Smith, Rebecca
Aviosn, Diane (pso)
Fenney, Janet (pso)
Halliwell, Susan (pso)
Harris, Margaret (pso)
Hopkins, Sarah (pso/vlo)
Horrocks, Kathleen (pso)
Jones, Elaine (pso)
Kneale-Roby, Kyra (pso/vlo)
Lohan, Irene, (pso)
Morrison, Sonny (pso)

Units

26. **MAPPA Support Unit**
c/o Sex Offender Management Unit
Grey Mare Lane Police Station
Bell Crescent, Beswick
Manchester M11 3BA
tel 0161-856 3636 *fax 0161-856 3685*

Fuller, Clare (spo)
Kenyon, Tina
Mayers, Martin
Paul, Sarah
Rawlinson, Nick
Wood, Jo (forensic psychologist)
Prunell, Neil (sgt, mappa co-ordinator)

Interventions

27. **12 Minshull Street**
Manchester M1 3FR
tel 0161-237 5173 *fax 0161-228 6745*

Probn Programmes & Devpt Unit
Robinson, Chris (area mgr)
Grundy, Peter (dist admin mgr)
Gazdecki, David (prog mgr, IDAP)
Willis, Julie (prog mgr, CALM,
DIDS, TFBA, TFW)
Aslam, Harris (treatment mgr)
Barnes, Susy (treatment mgr)
Broad, Rosemary (treatment mgr)
Dearing, Eric (treatment mgr)
Dunbar, Bev (treatment mgr)
McKenna, Clare (treatment mgr)
Rhodes, Natalie (treatment mgr)
Walker, Victoria (treatment mgr)
Adams, Vicki (pso/tutor)
Bailey, Tracey (pso/tutor)
Browning, Beverley (pso/tutor)
Cox, Marvin (pso/tutor)
Davidson, Robert (pso/tutor)
Healey, Sandra (pso/tutor)
Jordan, Irene (pso/tutor)
Kennedy, Rose (pso/tutor)
Kerr, Philip (pso/tutor)
MacLeod, Kerry (pso/tutor)
Massey, Ed (pso/tutor)
Morgan, Mike (pso/tutor)
Smith, James (pso/tutor)
Spotswood, Jayne (pso/tutor)
Towler, Paul (pso/tutor)
Walker, George (pso/tutor)

Manchester City Programmes Team
Nixon, Dave (programme mgr)
Hilton, Paul (treatment mgr)
Naylor, Laura (treatment mgr)
Stanley, Mark (treatment mgr)
Bedford, Lianne (pso/tutor)
Burton, Alice (pso/tutor)
Goddard, Katie (compliance officer)
Gwilt, Michelle (pso/tutor)
Lorimor, Alistair (pso/tutor)
McMahon, Gary (pso/tutor)
Saviotte, Ivan (psu/tutor)
Smith, Nina (pso/tutor)
Taylor, Susan (pso/tutor)

Oldham Programmes Team
Ashworth, Gary (programme mgr)
Begum, Anwara (pso/tutor)
Begum, Shazia (pso/tutor)
Bridge, Denis (pso/tutor)
Cleary, Rachel (pso/tutor)
Daybank, Ray (pso/tutor)
Derrett, Kevin (pso/tutor)
Fletcher, Christine (pso/tutor)
Khanum, Atia (pso/tutor)
Lorimer, Christine (pso/tutor)
Lovett, Carole (pso/tutor)

Nearny, Louise (pso/tutor)
Padkin, Lucy (pso/tutor)
Sullivan, Kim (pso/tutor)
White, Jane (pso/tutor)

Salford Programmes Team
Forsyth, Jane (programmes mgr)
Fraser, Nicola (treatment mgr)
Heywood, Jennifer (treatment mgr)
Dale, Rachel (pso/tutor)
Doody, Fiona (pso/tutor)
McLean, Emma (pso/tutor)
Smith, Shirley (pso/tutor)
Tunnicliffe, Helen (pso/tutor)
Welch, Julie (pso/tutor)

Wigan Programmes Team
Forsyth, Jane (treatment mgr)
Sievewight, Shirley (treatment mgr)
Ryan, Lisa (treatment mgr)
Carlon, Joanne (pso/tutor)
Dewsbury, Antonia (pso/tutor)
Hayden, Caroline (pso/tutor)
James, Martin (pso/tutor)
Just, Barry (pso/tutor)
Thomas, Camilla (pso/tutor)

28. **Probn Programmes & Devpt
Unit (SORT)** 53 Peel Street
Eccles, Manchester M30 0NG
tel 0161-789 2429 *fax 0161-707 9370*

Mackenzie, Ian (programme mgr)
Bakshi, Nisha
Clarke, Matt
Edmundson, Wendy
Foster, Susan
Graham, Peter
Hesford, Karl
Holmes, Deborah
Holton, Janet
Lee- Kilgariff, Mark
Maddox, Josie
O'Keefe, Ian
Ollerton, Lindsay
Yianni, John

29. **Unpaid Work Management Unit**
c/o Heywood Office
151 Green Lane **Heywood**
Manchester OL10 2EW
tel (01706) 620702 *fax (01706) 368951*

Brierley, Derek (area mgr)
Bywaters, Margaret (admin mgr)

30. **Bolton Unpaid Work Unit**
Unit 2, Kirkhall Industrial Estate
Bilbao Street **Bolton** BL1 4HH

tel (01204) 842509 *fax (01204) 465446*

Phillips, Beverley (upw mgr)
Abbott, Bob (upw off)
Bimpson, Bill (upw off)
Jones, Bill (upw off)
Jones, Caroline (upw off)
Newbould, Jim (upw off)

31. **Heywood Unpaid Work Unit**
151 Green Lane **Heywood**
Manchester OL10 2EW
tel (01706) 620702 *fax (01706) 368951*

Anderson, Paul (upw mgr)
Dunn, Ray (upw off)
Ellison, Colin (upw off)
Evans, Mick (upw off)
Holden, Terry (upw off)
Kennell, Elaine (upw off)
Sykes, Craig (upw off)

32. **Manchester Unpaid Work Unit**
Victoria Park, Laindon Road
Longsight Manchester, M14 5YJ
tel 0161-224 0231 *fax 0161-248 5378*

Humphreys, Malcolm (upw mgr)
Edwards, Caroline (upw mgr)
Barcoe, Seamus (upw off)
Crellin, Julie (upw off)
Conway, Tony (upw off)
Nixon, Ken (upw off)
Sefton, Diane (upw off)
Thompson, Gordon (upw off)

33. **Oldham Unpaid Work Unit**
64 Bridge Street
Oldham OL1 1ED
tel 0161-620 4421 *fax* 0161-628 2011

Buckley, Jim (upw mgr)
Gates, Darren (upw off)
Mayers, Paul (upw off)
Newton, Teresa (upw off)

34. **Salford Unpaid Work Unit**
2 Redwood Street, Pendleton
Salford M6 6PF
tel 0161-736 6441 *fax 0161-736 6620*

Johnson, Carol (upw mgr)
Oakley, Chris (upw off)
Gee, Kenneth (upw off)

35. **Stockport Unpaid Work Unit**
19/37 High Street
Stockport SK1 1EG
tel 0161-429 0010/0333 *fax 0161-476 2709*

Johnson, Sue (upw mgr)
Dipnall, Gary (upw off)
Francis, Mark (upw off)

36. **Tameside Unpaid Work Unit**
Francis Thompson Drive
Off Water Street
Ashton-under-Lyne OL6 7AJ
tel 0161-330 3695 *fax 0161-343 7475*

Buckley, Jim (upw mgr)
Upton, Carron (upw off)
Yates, Stephen (upw off)

37. **Trafford Unpaid Work Unit**
Newton Street **Stretford**
Manchester M32 8LG
tel 0161-865 3255 *fax 0161-864 4791*

Johnson, Sue (upw mgr)
Aldred, Dave (upw off)
Bennett, John (upw off)
Bowyer, Dave (upw off)

38. **Wigan Unpaid Work Unit**
Brookhouse Centre
31 Brookhouse Street
Wigan WN1 3RT
tel 01942 3227669 *fax 01942 829172*

Cooney, Martin (upw mgr)
Dodd, Trevor (upw off)
Dyson, Steve (upw off)
Frappolla, Jane (upw off)
Oliver, Geoff (upw off)

Youth Offending Services

39 **Bolton YOS**
Le Mans Crescent
Bolton BL1 1SA
tel (01204) 331263 *fax (01204) 331258*

Coleman, Mick (yos mgr)

40 **Bury YOS**
Seedfield Resouce Centre
Parkinson Street, Bury BL9 6NY
tel 0161-253 6862

Parton, Dawn (yos mgr)

41. **Manchester YOS**
c/o Crime & Disorder Group (room 9030)
Town Hall Extension
Manchester M60 2LA
tel 0161 234 4564 *fax 0161-234 4914*

Macdonald, Kate (mgr)

42. **Manchester North YOS**
Abraham Moss Centre, Crescent Road
Crumpsall, Manchester, M8 5UF
tel 0161-908 8368 *fax 0161-908 1835*

Mistry, Pam (team mgr)

43. **Manchester Central YOS**
Daisy Mill
345 Stockport Road, Longsight
Manchester M13 0LF
tel 0161-227 3430 *fax 0161-227 3460*

Lundie, Kath (team mgr)

44 **Manchester South YOS**
Greenbow Road, Newall Green
Manchester M23 2RE
tel 0161-437 3069 *fax 0161-437 3856*

Brundrett, Mark (team mgr)

45. **Oldham YOS**
Medtia Place, 80 Union Street
Oldham OL1 1DT
tel 0161-621 9500

Sharland, Penny (yos mgr)

46. **Rochdale YOS**
Townhead Offices
John Street, Rochdale OL16 1LB
tel (01706) 925353

Cross, Michael (yos mgr)

47. **Salford YOS**
Encombe House
10/12 Encombe Place, Salford M3 6FJ
tel 0161-607 1900 *fax 0161-832 4306*

Healy, Tom (yos mgr)

48. **Stockport YOS**
1st Floor, Owl House
59/61 Great Underbank
Stockport SK1 1NE
tel 0161-476 2876 *fax 0161-476 2858*

Belfield-Smith, Jacqui (yos mgr)

49. **Tameside YOS**
Frances Thompson Drive
Ashton under Lyne OL6 7AJ
tel 0161-330 3012 *fax 0161-330 3149*

Whittle, John (yos mgr)

50. **Trafford YOS**
4th Floor, Arndale House
Stretford Arndale, Chester Road

Stretford M32 9XY
tel 0161-911 8201 *fax 0161-911 8202*

McDonald, Ken (yos mgr)

51. **Wigan YOS**
93 Victoria Road
Platt Bride, Wigan WN2 5DN
tel (01942) 776886 *fax (01942) 776856*

Bond, Sharon (yos mgr)

Approved Premises (Hostels)

52. **Hostels Management Unit &
Central Admissions Unit**
64 Manley Road, Whalley Range
Manchester M16 8ND
tel 0161-227 1849 *fax 0161-227 9052*

**Central Referrals
tel 0161-226 8465** *fax 0161-227 9052*

Cope, Angela (dist mgr)
Crofts, Roger (spo central admin)
McGartland, John (admin & finance mgr)
Jackson, Louise (central referral off)

53. **Bradshaw House Approved Premises**
147/151 Walmersley Road
Bury BL9 5DE
tel 0161-761 6419 *fax 0161-763 4353*

Wright, Louise (spo mgr)
Colton, Andy (rso)
Davies, Stephen (rso)
Hamer, John (rso)
Young, Diane (rso)

54. **St Joseph's Approved Premises**
Miller Street, Patricroft, Eccles
Manchester M30 8PF
tel 0161-789 5337 *fax 0161-707 9085*

Murphy, Lindsey (spo mgr)
Freeman, Paul (po deputy)
Baylis, Paul (rso)
Horton, Mike (rso)
Jeffers, Franklyn (rso)
Nash, Ian (rso)
Schofield, Neil (rso)

55. **Withington Road Approved Premises**
172/174 Withington Road
Whalley Range, Manchester M16 8JN
tel 0161-226 1179 *fax 0161-227 8041*

Croall, David (spo mgr)
Hayworth, Ruth (po deputy)
Burkhill, Alison (rso)
Case, Steve (rso)

Christian, Lorna (rso)
Kirk, Jackie (rso)

56. **Chorlton Approved Premises**
10/12 Oswald Road
Chorlton cum Hardy
Manchester M21 1LH
tel 0161-862 9881 *fax 0161-862 9554*

Parkes, Glenn (spo mgr)
Brown, Joy (po)
Bernard, Trevor (rso)
Jackson, Les (rso)
Reid, Vernon (rso)
Sharples, Denise (rso)

57. **Hopwood House Approved Premises**
104 Manchester Street
Heywood, Lancs OL10 1DW
tel (01706) 620440 *fax (01706) 625927*

Morton, Carol (spo mgr)
Harris, Bernice (po deputy)
Bond, Sarah (rso)
Denby, Suzanne (rso)
Sykes, Debbie (rso)

58. **Wilton Place Approved Premises**
10/12 Edward Street
Werneth, Oldham OL9 7QW
tel 0161-624 3005 *fax 0161-628 6936*

Keith, Lynn (spo mgr)
Jones, Karl (po)
Appleton, Brian (rso)
Crook, Dave (rso)
Garner, Helen (rso)
Ravey, Ann (rso)

59. **Ascot House Approved Premises**
195 Wellington Road North
Heaton Norris, Stockport SK4 2PB
tel 0161-443 3400 *fax 0161-432 9739*

Williams, Robbie (spo mgr)
MacKenzie, Caroline (po)
Benjamin, Rachel (rso)
Cusick, Nicola (rso)
Gough, Trevor (rso)
Haslam, Alan (rso)

Hostels for Men

Ascot House, Stockport
Bradshaw House, Bury
Chorlton House, Manchester
St Joseph's, Salford (specialist MDO
hostel)
Wilton Place, Oldham
Withington Road, Manchester

Hostel for Women

Hopwood House, Heywood

Institutions

60. H M Prison, Southall Street
Strangeways Manchester M60 9AH
tel 0161-817 5600 *fax 0161-817 5601*

   direct dial tel 0161-817+ext
   visits tel 0161-817 5656
   probn fax 0161-817 5970

   HDC admin tel 0161-817 5653

   Johnston, Graham (dist mgr/
   head of off mgt) ext 6087
   Rothwell, Alison (spo) ext 5742
   Brown, Trudi ext 5963
   Buckley, Elsie ext 5972
   Dalby, Lisa ext 5652
   Davies, Claire ext 5682
   Holmes, Zoe ext 5952
   Kirk, Malcolm 5776
   Parkes, Nowill ext 5700
   Wilson, Jo ext 5978
   Coppitch, Mags (pso)
   Downey, Debbie (pso)
   Doyle, Lisa (pso)
   Gordon, Sacha (pso)

61. H M Young Offender Institution
Hindley Wigan WN2 5TH
tel (01942) 663100 *fax (01942) 663101*
probn fax (01942) 8855193

   Frank, Janice (spo) 663192
   Benjamin, Julie 663280
   Carpenter, Miriam 8663280
   Fletcher, Anne 663281
   France, Janice 663281
   Dunn, Terry (pso) 663281

62. H M Prison **Buckley Hall**
Buckley Hall Road
Rochdale OL12 9DP
tel (01706) 514300 *fax (01706) 711797*

   Parole clerk ext 290
   Special visits ext 312

   Hanley, Anne (spo) 514322
   Ali, Sultan
   Chaleson, Maggs
   Stefani, Sally
   Clapper, Susie (pso)
   Hilton, Mike (pso)

63. H M Prison **Forest Bank**
Agecroft Road, Pendlebury

Manchester M27 8FB
tel 0161-925 7000 *fax 0161-925 7001*
direct dial 0161-925+ext
bail info off 0161-925 7000 ext 2018
bail info fax 0161-925 7019
booking visits ext 7029/7030
Healthcare Centre ext 7065
Healthcare Centre fax 0161-925 7055

Driver, Sarah (spo) ext 7020
Driver, Sarah ext 7073
Foy, Ray ext 7069
Griffiths, Yvonne ext 7075
Noall, Mark ext 7078
Thom, Linda ext 7071

Local Justice Areas

5 Bolton
6 Bury
19 City of Salford
10-14 Manchester
18-19 Oldham
7, 8 Rochdale, Middleton & Heywood
22 Stockport
23, 24 Tameside
25 Trafford
26, 28 Wigan & Leigh

Crown Courts

2 Manchester
3 Bolton

MERSEYSIDE PROBATION AREA

Out of hours emergency contact point tel
0151-920 9201

Victim enquiry's contact number tel 0151-
281 0832 (Paul Holt aco)

e-mail Firstname.Surname@merseyside.
probation.gsi.gov.uk

1. **Head Office**
4th Floor, North Wing
Burlington House, Crosby Road North
Waterloo, Liverpool L22 0PJ
tel 0151-920 9201 *fax 0151-949 0528*

   Bloomfield, Linda (chair of board)
   Stafford, John (ceo)
   Pakula, Anne (head of operations)
   Gotts, Paul (treasurer)
   Beigan, Carla (hr manager)
   Atherton, Lynne (secy to probn board)

Felton-Aksoy, Kathy (external
relations asst)
Williams, Karen (courts commnctn off)
Thurston, David (health & safety adv)
Lea, Katherine (occupational health adv)
Steele, Rachael (snr research off)
Armstrong, Paul (progs divnl mgr)

ACO Management Unit
Brown, Sue (aco, community offender
management)
Chambers, Steve (aco, court services &
community punishment)
Holt, Paul (aco, resettlement offender
mgmnt divn & appr premises)
Kenyon, Lyn (hd of admin services)
Metherell, Dave (aco, community
offender mgmnt divn)
Murray, Peter (aco, community re-
integration & info services)
Stelman, Andy (aco, community offender
mgmnt divn, DRR/DTTO & PPO)
Chudleigh, Claire (aco, gp progs
& prtnrshps)
Chadwick, Jayne (aco, head of
HR & staff devpt)
Quick, John (aco, community offender
mgmnt divn)

Staff Development
Kelly, Mary (staff devpt mgr)
Aubrey, Catherine (snr staff devpt off)
Powell, Audrey (staff devpt off)
Blair, Jackie (trainer)
Teese, Briony (what works trainer)

**Information, Communications
& Technology (Business Devpt Unit)**
Steele, Bob (mgr)

2. **North Liverpool Probation Centre**
    Cheadle Avenue
    Old Swan, Liverpool L13 3AE
    tel 0151-254 7105 *fax 0151-220 7208*

    Accommodation
    Reddy, Sharon (housing off)
    Brennan, Nora (psa)
    Edwards, John (psa)

    Employment Team
    Christian, Dave (mgr 0151-666 0400)
    Taylor, Jeanette (operations mgr)
    Jones, Anne-Marie (operations mgr)

    Adamson, Helen (psa)
    Baglow, Kenny (psa)
    Fletcher, Barry (psa)
    McCormack, Claire (psa)
    Watson, Louise (psa)

Learning Resource Centre
tel 0151-254 7100

Aubrey, Catherine (snr staff devpt
off, based at 1)
Beggs, John (pda)

Community Punishment Division

3. **South Knowsley Probation Centre**
    597 Princess Drive
    Liverpool L14 9NE
    tel 0151-480 4544 *fax 0151-480 3618*

    Vacancy (snr ops mgr)

    Knowsley/St Helens
    Kimmance, Pat (qa mgr)
    Kavanagh, Jenny (ops mgr)
    Draper, Rebecca (cso)
    Dunn, Karen (cso)
    Fletcher, John (cso)
    Francis, Lorraine (cso)
    Sweeney, Carol (cso)

5. **North Liverpool Probation Centre**
    Cheadle Avenue
    Old Swan, Liverpool L13 3AE
    tel 0151-254 7103 *fax 0151-220 7205*

    Liverpool North
    Stamper, Lena (qa mgr)
    Donoghue, Pat (ops mrs)
    Chambers, Martin (cso)
    Hughes, Gareth (cso)
    Robinson, Eileen (cso)
    Ginley, Vicky (cso)

6. **South Liverpool Probation Centre**
    180 Falkner Street, Liverpool L8 7SX
    tel 0151-706 6644 *fax 0151-708 5044*

    Liverpool South
    Phillips, Jenny (qa mgr)
    Bromley, Rod (ops mgr)
    Ayres, Lesley (cso)
    Fullalove, Linda (cso)
    Losh, Jackie (cso)
    Marston, Paul (cso)

7. Sefton House, 1 Molyneux Way
    Old Roan, Liverpool L10 2JA
    tel 0151-531 6737 *fax 0151-527 2534*

    Sefton
    Kimmance, Pat (qam)
    Lavin, John (ops mgr)
    Barrett, Kate (cso)
    Cowley, Brian (cso)
    Morris, Di (cso)
    Parkinson, Joe (cso)

8. **Wirral Probation Centre**
40 Europa Boulevard
Birkenhead, Wirral, Merseyside CH41
4PE
tel 0151-666 0400 *fax 0151-666 0402*

Wirral
Wynn, Paul (qa mgr)
O'Keefe Gary (ops mgr)
Lennard, Jane (cso)
Loughran, Julie (cso)
O'Donnell, Gill (cso)
Williams, Joan (cso)

Community Offender Management

9. **Wirral Probation Centre**
40 Europa Boulevard
Birkenhead, Wirral CH41 4PE
tel 0151-666 0400 *fax 0151-666 0401*

Edwards, Jim (spo)
Humphreys, Barry (spo)
Stewart, Becky (spo)
Beuschlien, Barbara
Fishwick, Donna
Foster, Robert
Freeman, Susan
Hunter, Vicky
Jones, Carla
Joyce, Brian
Lloyd, Hugh
McAllister, Christine
McClelland, Fiona
Golding, Janine
Marmion, Christopher
Minhas, Amir
Osbourne, Steve
Totty, Stella
Adamson, Jo
Bygraves, Hazel
O'Donnell, Shaun
Whitfield, Darren
Patterson, Pat
Robinson, Kate
Summerton, Rhoni
Chandler, Collette (psa)
Haseldon, Tricia (psa)
Kennedy, Paul (psa)
Murphy, Angela (psa)
Morrison, Stephanie (psa)

10. 4 Trinity Road, **Bootle**
Merseyside L20 7BE
tel 0151-286 5667 *fax 0151-286 6900*

Dauphin, Colin (spo)
Conroy, Martin
DeGale, Hamilton

Duffy, Ashley
Fisher, John
Hayes, Malcolm
Henshaw, Nicci
Phillips, Hilton
Roach, Lynsey
Cummins, Pauline (psa)
Johnson, Angela (psa)
Jones, Ceri David (psa)

11. Gordon House, 3-5 Leicester Street
Southport Merseyside PR9 0ER
tel (01704) 534634 *fax (01704) 501845*

spo at 22
Brotherstone, Cathy
Hall, Rachel
McDonald, Michelle
Seel, David
Stott, Allan

12. **North Liverpool Probation Centre**
Cheadle Avenue
Old Swan, Liverpool L13 3AE
tel 0151-254 7102 *fax 0151-254 7204*

Andrews, Cath (spo)
Best, Jenny (spo)
Alexandra, Kat
Barnes, Roger
Burnell, Wendy
Cushen, David
Daelman, Louise
Dykes, Steven
Jones, Ann
Jones, Candice
Kenwright, Kathleen
Loram, Richard
Lynch, Valerie
McGrath, Alison
Rooney, Johanne
Smith, Alison
Wilson, Wayne
Lloyd, Neil (psa)
Underwood, Shanel (psa)
McKeown, Jennifer (psa)
Bradshaw, James (psa)

13. 142/148 Stanley Road
Kirkdale Liverpool L5 7QQ
tel 0151-286 6159 *fax 0151-284 7847*

Cameron, Jane (spo)
McPaul, Mark (spo)
Daley, Jeanette
Dinwoodie, Claire
Eisner, Julien
Keating, Lisa

Khazri, Sharon
Lawrence, Pauline
Montieth, Tracey
Nuttall, Leslie
Pennington, Nichola
Riley, James
Smith, Jan
Thomas, Andrea
Buoey, Carol (psa)
Gillies, Roz (psa)
O'Doherty, Barry (psa)
Teese, Paul (psa)

14. **South Liverpool Probation Centre**
180 Falkner Street Liverpool L8 7SX
tel 0151-706 6688 *fax 0151-708 5044*

Liverpool South/Central
Dean, Michelle (spo)
Woods, David (spo)
Griffiths, Christina
Bozkurt, Claire
Mohamed, Ibrahim
Munro, Sandy
Pickstock, Marie
Pope, Alan
Pritchard, George
Rogerson, James
Rolfe, Katin
Stevenson, Kerry
Tracey, Anna
Adekanmbi, Moji (psa)
Doherty, Tony (psa)
Li, Mandy (psa)

Black Mentor Scheme
Cameron, Jayne (spo, 13)
Diskaya, Mayling (psa)
Rogers, Darren (psa)

15. **South Knowsley Probation Centre**
597 Princess Drive
Liverpool L14 9NE
tel 0151-480 4544 *fax 0151-480 3618*

Hughes, Peter (spo)
Branford, Patsy
Gilbert, Nicola
Jones, Geoff
Holliday, John
Lindon-Richie, Rona
Loyden, Frank
McCully, Simon
Markland, Kate
Rainford, Jane
Williams, Ian
Williams, Sarah
Bell, Emma (psa)

Lloyd, Jan (psa)
O'Connor, Claire (psa)

16. **St Helens Probation Centre**
St Mary's House, 50 Church Street
St Helens Merseyside WA10 1AP
tel (01744) 630229 *fax (01744) 606224*

Milnes, Mike (spo)
Buchan, Elaine
Disley, Sarah
Edwards, George
Jones, Jo-Anne
Kelly, Lisa
Malone, Zara
Moy, Sally
Nowell, Clayton
O'Hara, Denise
O'Neale, Steve
Perkins, Tony
Sweeney, Michelle
James, Rozanne (psa)
Shaw, Christine (psa)
Wood, Jean (psa)

Court Services Division

17. **Crown Court**
PO Box 69, Queen Elizabeth II
Law Courts, Derby Square
Liverpool L69 2NE
tel 0151-236 5302 *fax 0151-255 0682*

Hamilton, Richard (spo)
Collins, Jim
Leonard, Jacci
Cummins, Susan (psa)
Harrison, Christine
Kirkpatrick, Hilary (psa)
Reil, Sue (psa)
Williams, Janet (psa)

18. **Wirral Probation Centre**
40 Europa Boulevard
Birkenhead, Wirral CH41 4PE
tel 0151-666 0400 *fax 0151-666 0402*

Rutherford, Cec (spo)
Taylor-Watson, Susan
Jones, Sam (psa)
McKenzie, Lisa (psa)
Phipps, Elizabeth (psa)
Purvis, Wendy (psa)
Surridge, Andrew (psa)

19. **Liverpool Magistrates' Court &
Court Services Liverpool Central**
111 Dale Street, Liverpool L2 2JQ
tel 0151-236 0603 *fax 0151-236 5417*

Hamilton, Richard (spo)
Loughran, Peter
McCullough, Jim
Aston, Barbara (psa)
Carroll, Liz (psa)
Fisher, John (psa)
Fuller, Claire (psa)
Grimes, Julie (psa)
McLean, Ian (psa)
O'Neill, Jan (psa)
Pilkington, Barbara (psa)
Turner, Emma (psa)
Wells, Emma (psa)

20. **South Knowsley Probation Centre**
597 Princess Drive, Liverpool L14 9NE
tel 0151-480 4544 *fax 0151-480 3618*

spo at 18
Mannion, Wendy
Donovan, Hayley (psa)
Hitch, Sandra (psa)
Patterson, George (psa)

21. **St Helens Probation Centre**
St Mary's House, 50 Church Street
St Helens Merseyside WA10 1AP
tel (01744) 630229 *fax (01744) 606224*

spo at 18
Carroll, June
Gryzb, Louise (psa)
Huthwaite, David (psa)
McCabe, Sylvia (psa)

22. **Gordon House, 3-5 Leicester Street**
Southport Merseyside PR9 0ER
tel (01704) 534634 *fax (01704) 501845*

Earlam, Cathy (spo)
Edward, Jane

23. **North Sefton Magistrates' Court**
The Law Courts
Albert Road, Southport PR9 0LJ
tel (01704) 544277 *fax (01704) 545840*

Jones, Pam (psa)
Reilly, Moira (psa)

24. **South Sefton Magistrates' Court**
The Court Building
29 Merton Road, Bootle L20 3BJ
tel 0151-285 6236 *fax 0151-933 8602*

Kibbey, Rosemarie
Bright, Pam (psa)
Dawber, Jacqueline (psa)
Hilton, Bernie (psa)

**Resettlement Offender Management
Division**

25. **Kirkby Probation Centre**
Oatlands Road Kirkby
Liverpool L32 4UH
tel 0151-547 3160 *fax 0151-547 2244*

Needham, Peter (spo)
Vellacott, Sheila (spo)
Bellamy, Mary
Bennett, Tony
Cleworth, Geoff
Corcoran, Angela
Gay, Martin
Heston, Debbie
Kelly, Julie
McGee, Carol
Morley, Fiona
Plews, Paula
Wallace, Claire
Graham, Nora (psa)
Myler, Sharon (psa)
Nash, Emma (psa)

26. **Liverpool North**
North Liverpool Probation Centre
Cheadle Avenue
Old Swan, Liverpool L13 3AE
tel 0151-254 7107 *fax 0151-220 7223*

Hamilton, Elaine (spo)
Kuyateh, Jeanette (spo)
Arnold, Maxine
Cookson, Renee
Murphy, Jennifer
Green, Rosie
Grunnill, Paul
Lynch, Katie
Macaulay, Bob
Martine, Karen
Parle, Lynne
Pritchard, Mair
Rugless, Tony
Smith, Mark
Basley, Jana (psa)
Byrne, Diane (psa)
Parkinson, Julie (psa)

27. **Liverpool South**
South Liverpool Probation Centre
180 Falkner Street, Liverpool L8 7SX
tel 0151-706 6666 *fax 0151-706 6694*

Morris, Judith (spo)
Kuyateh, Jeanette (spo)
Birchall, Jo
Craig, Michael
Davies, Lynne

Griffiths, Alex
Hanson, Caroline
Houghton, Nick
Lawrenson, Philip
Lowe, Helen
McIlveen, David
Oldham, Paul
Webster, Louise
Williams, Debbie
Roberts, Ricky (psa)
Rogers, Sandra (psa)

28. **Sefton**
   25 Crosby Road South
   Waterloo, Liverpool L22 1RG
   tel 0151-920 4444 *fax 0151-928 9143*

   Goodwin, Rosie (spo)
   Chadwick, Pat
   Clarke, Ruth
   Doherty, Eddie
   Mitchell, Janine
   Ormesher, David
   Penn, Mike
   Willis, Jo
   McDonald, Rebecca (psa)
   Pendleton, Christopher (psa)

29. **Wirral**
   Wirral Probation Centre
   40 Europa Boulevard
   Birkenhead, Wirral CH41 4PE
   tel 0151-666 0400 *fax 0151-666 0402*

   Lloyd, Shirley (spo)
   Dwyer, Clare
   Hamill, Una
   Mason, Steven
   O'Grady, Anne
   Roberts, Kelly
   O'Neill, Con
   McNiffe, Peter
   McNeill, Jenny (psa)
   Stafford, Jill (psa)
   McGinty, Norma (psa)

Accredited Programmes Division

30. **Merseyside Development Unit**
   6/8 Temple Court, Liverpool L2 6PY
   tel 0151-229 2000 *fax 0151-236 4265*

   Watson, Mary (treatment mgr)
   Anderson, Carole (treatment mgr)
   Bakhtiary-Nejad, Pat (facilitator)
   Cooke, Roy (facilitator)
   Dishman, Kath (facilitator)
   Gallagher, Julie (facilitator)
   Guinness, Rosie (facilitator)

Hutchinson, Ian (facilitator)
Johnson, Emma (facilitator)
Johnson, Norris (facilitator)
Lopez, Donna (facilitator)
Porter, Liz (facilitator)
Ross, Bernadette (facilitator)
Shaw, Stephanie (facilitator)
Waller, Tracey (facilitator)
Walsh, Jenny (facilitator)
Walsh, Leanne (facilitator)

31. **South Liverpool Probation Centre**
   180 Falkner Street, Liverpool L8 7SX
   tel 0151-706 6611 *fax 0151-708 9687*

   Green, Cindy (progrs team mgr)
   Mannix, Nancy (progrs team mgr)
   McCoy, Jill (progrs team mgr)
   Thomson, Angela (progrs team mgr)

   Groupwork Programmes
   Watkins, Doug (treatment mgr)
   Alex Hughes (treatment mgr)
   Bibby, Richard (prog tutor)
   Butler, Sue (prog tutor)
   Byron, Paul (prog tutor)
   Dauphin, Andre (prog tutor)
   East, Caroline (prog tutor)
   Fisher, Jo (prog tutor)
   Halpin, Dawn (prog tutor)
   Khandirmirian, Patrick (prog tutor)
   Lumsden, Ken (prog tutor)
   McBurney, Gill (prog tutor)
   McCarthy, Jacqui (prog tutor)
   MacDougal, Paula (prog tutor)
   Maher, Damien (prog tutor)
   Malone, Pat (prog tutor)
   Rotherham, Karen (prog tutor)
   Wilkins, Ian (prog tutor)

DRR Division

32. **DRR North Liverpool**
   North Liverpool Probation Centre
   Cheadle Avenue, Old Swan
   Liverpool L13 3AE
   tel 0151-254 7101 *fax 0151-220 7231*

   Rooney, Karen (spo)
   Hide, Louise
   Horrocks, Christine
   Jameson, Keith
   Williams, Lucile
   Riley, Sandra (psa)

33. **DRR South Liverpool**
   3-5 Rodney Street, Liverpool L1 9ED
   tel 0151-234 5826 *fax 0151-243 5870*

   Sofia, Nikki (spo) based at 35

Gowan, Steve
Phillips, Tony
Given, Michael (psa)
Ryan, Jennifer (psa)

34. **DRR Sefton**
Mersey View House, 18 Great Georges
Road, Waterloo, Liverpool L22 1RD
tel 0151-920 2068 *fax 0151-920 2059*

Baird, Allen (spo)
Jones, Hugh
Moorhead, Justin
Bracegirdle, Clare (psa)
Hypolite, Adissa (psa)

35. **DRR St Helens**
2nd Floor, Tontine House
24 Church Street, St Helens WA10 1BD
tel (01744) 740483 *fax (01744) 453971*

Sofia, Nikki (spo)
Curzon, Anna
Platt, Sarah
Holland, Catherine (psa)
Moran, Kelly (psa)

36. **DRR Knowsley**
25 Derby Road, Huyton, Liverpool L36
9UG
tel (01744) 630229 *fax (01744) 606224*

Rooney, Karen (spo)
Bradley, Claire
Owens, Steven
Brownrigg, Catherine (psa)

37. **DRR Wirral**
Arches Initiative, 23 Conway Street
Birkenhead, Wirral CH41 6PT
tel 0151-666 6867 *fax 0151-666 6802*

Baird, Allen (spo)
Chambers, Clare
Wright, Noel
Forshaw, Karen
Carrie, Nikki
Kinsey, Rebecca (psa)
Lucas, Ian (psa)

CJIP Teams

38. **Knowsley CJIP**
Knowsley Metropolitan Borough Council
4th Floor, Archway Road, Huyton
Liverpool L36 9YU
tel 0151-480 5398

39. **Liverpool CJIP**
Paul Thompson Centre,

83-93 Stonebridge Lane
Liverpool L11 4SJ
tel 0151-545 1852

Toole, John

40. **St Helens CJIP**
91 Corporation Street, St Helens
Merseyside WA10 1SX
tel (01744) 675816

41. **Sefton CJIP**
Sefton Social Services, 7th Floor
Merton House, Stanley Road
Bootle, Merseyside L20 3UU
tel 0151-934 3115

Smith, Jenny (pso)

42. **Wirral CJIP**
Arch Initiatives, 23 Conway Street
Birkenhead, Wirral CH41 6PT
tel 0151-666 6867

Community Justice Centre

43. N Liverpool Community Justice Centre
5 Boundary Street, Liverpool L5 2QD
tel 0151-298 3636 *fax 0151-298 3601*

McIlveen, John (spo)
Aney, Julie
Tubb, Eileen (psa)

Prolific & Other Priority Offender Teams

44. **Knowsley PPO**
Prescot Police Station, Derby Street
Prescot, Liverpool L34 2LG
tel 0151-493 2451

Keenan, Joy (spo)
Foster, Ian
Cheers, Becky (psa)

45. **Liverpool PPO**
Eaton Road Police Station, Eaton Road
Liverpool L12 3HF
tel 0151-777 4431 *fax 0151-777 4445*

Dickinson, Ann (spo)
Ashes, Ken
Orson, Christine
Hypolite, Diana
Lewis, Alan (psa)
Sinkinson, Joan (psa)
Melia, Chris (psa)

46. **St Helens PPO**
St Helens Probation Centre
St Mary's House, 50 Church Street

St Helens, Merseyside WA10 1AP
tel (01744) 630229 *fax (01744) 606224*

Keenan, Joy (spo)
Briggs, Danuta
Kent, Linda

47. **Sefton PPO**
Marsh Lane Police Station
Marsh Lane, Liverpool L20 5HJ
tel 0151 777 3077
Keenan, Joy (spo)
Pickstock, Kate
Munro, Lee

48. **Wirral PPO**
Old Court Building, Manor Road
Wallasey, Merseyside CH44 1BU
tel 0151-606 5760
Keenan, Joy (spo)
Evans, Margaret
McCabe, Phil

Youth Offending Teams

49. **YOT Court Services**
Liverpool Youth Court
Hatton Gardens, Liverpool
tel 0151-233 3382 *fax 0151-236 3263*

Harrison, Christine (psa)

50. **YOT Knowsley**
Youth Justice Section
10 Derby Street, Prescot
Liverpool L34 3LG
tel 0151-443 3079 *fax 0151-443 3086*

Kennedy, Irene

51. **YOT St Helens**
Youth Offending Team
2 Tickle Avenue, Parr
St Helens WA9 1RZ
tel (01744) 677990 *fax (01744) 677550*

Cox, Kelly

52. **YOT Liverpool**
Customer Focus Centre
80-82 Wavertree Road, Liverpool L7 1PH
tel 0151-255 8213 *fax 0151-255 8607*

Liverpool
Cooke, Elaine
Hutchinson, Amy
McAnallen, Donna
Nenna, Paul

53. **YOT Sefton**
Supervision Assessment/Court Services
Sefton Youth Offending Team
Police Station, Marsh Lane
Liverpool L20 5HJ
tel 0151-285 5127 *fax 0151-934 2779*

Baker, Fiona

54. **YOT Wirral**
Hamilton Building, Conway Street
Birkenhead, Wirral CH41 4FD
tel 0151-666 4536 *fax 0151-666 5651*

Marshall, Andrea
Forshaw, Peter (psa)

Approved Premises (Hostels)

55. **Canning House Probation Hostel**
55 Canning Street, Liverpool L8 7NN
tel 0151-709 4959 *fax 0151-707 0813*

Rose, Frances (po, deputy mgr)
Baker, Dave (probn res officer)
Freeman, John (probn res officer)
Hobbs, Len (probn res officer)
Lyon, Ruth (probn res officer)
Fitzpatrick, Shirley (hostel supervisor)
Bell, Claire (hostel supervisor)
Doran, Paul (hostel supervisor)
Glover, Bernie (hostel supervisor)
Kelly, Collette (hostel supervisor)
Ozerska, Diana (hostel supervisor)

56. **Merseybank Hostel**
26 Great Howard Street, Liverpool L3 7HS
tel 0151-255 1183 *fax 0151-236 4464*

Woodruff, Jan (spo, mgr)
Kennedy, Peter (po, dep mgr)
Hurst, Sheila (probn res officer)
Warren, Gary (probn res officer)
Wright, Gordon (probn res officer)
Birchall, Lorraine (hostel supervisor)
Deveney, Liam (hostel supervisor)
Gilling, Paul (hostel supervisor)
Harvey, Mike (hostel supervisor)
Harvey, Raoul (hostel supervisor)
Morris, Steve (hostel supervisor)

57. **Southwood Probation Hostel**
24 Southwood Road, Liverpool L17 7BQ
tel 0151-280 1833 *fax 0151-280 3027*

Aindow, Gail (spo, mgr)
Smeda, Michael (po dep mgr)
Dunleavy, John (probn res officer)
Gee, Tony (probn res officer)
Rhodes, Paul (probn res officer)

Blackwell, Tommy (hostel supervisor)
Diboe, Margo (hostel supervisor)
Edwards, John (hostel supervisor)
Glen, James (hostel supervisor)
Greene, Phil (hostel supervisor)
Kormoss, Tony (hostel supervisor)

58. **Adelaide House Probation/Bail Hostel**
115 Edge Lane, Liverpool L7 2PF
tel 0151-263 1290 *fax 0151-260 4205*

Thomas, Pat (mgr)
Edmunds, Gail (dep mgr)

Institutions

59. H M Prison **Altcourse**
Higher Lane, Fazakerley
Liverpool L9 7LH
tel 0151-522 2000 *fax 0151-522 2121*

Cunliffe, Jack (spo)
Burns, Julie
Caton, Barry
Fowlis, Naomi
McGrath, Karen
Taylor, Kate

60. H M Prison **Kennett**
Parkbourn, Maghull
Merseyside L31 1HX
tel 0151-213 3000 *fax 0151-213 3103*

Cunliffe, Jack (spo)
Gill, Helen
Holleran, John
Maguire, Jan
Morrison, Andy

61. H M Prison
Hornby Road **Liverpool** L9 3DF
tel 0151-530 4000 *fax 0151-530 4001*
probn fax 0151-524 1941

Kayani, Nick (spo) ext 4372
Brundell, Paul
Coburn, Kate
Lock, Peter
Smith, David
Walker, Paul
Webster, Debbie
Dooley, David (psa)
Gibbon, Stephanie (psa)
Hampson, Sue (psa)
McGenity, Lisa (psa)
Swan, Beverley (psa)

Local Justice Areas

4, 15, 20, 25, 36, 38, 44, 50 Knowsley
5, 6, 12-14, 19, 26, 27, 32, 33,
39, 43, 45, 49, 52 Liverpool
4, 16, 21, 25, 35, 40, 46, 51 St Helens
7, 28, 34, 41, 47, 53 Sefton
11, 22, 23 North Sefton
10, 24 South Sefton
8, 9, 18, 29, 37, 42, 48, 54 Wirral

Crown Court

17 Liverpool

NORFOLK PROBATION AREA

Out of hours emergency contact point
John Boag House (01603) 429488

Victim enquiries contact number (01553)
669000 (Jan Kerby)

e-mail Firstname.Surname@norfolk.probation.
gsi.
gov.uk

1. Centenary House, 19 Palace Street
Norwich NR3 1RT
tel (01603) 724000 *fax (01603) 664019*
direct dial (01603) 30 + ext

Corporate Services
Graham, Martin (cpo) ext 2232
Bull, Graham (chairman to board) ext 2243
Blackman, Judith (aco) ext 2233
Collyer, Hilary (aco) ext 2234
Macdonald, Stuart (aco) ext 2237
Wardley, Sarah (aco) ext 2239
Rayner, Karen (secy to board) ext 2244
Boast, Leanne (communication's officer)
ext 2242
Watchorn, Kemi (h.r. mgr) ext 2238
Herbert, Rachel (ass. h.r.mgr) ext 2235
Sendall, Robbie (occup health mgr) ext
2241
Wade, Belinda (finance mgr) ext 2230
Symonds, Robin (it mgr) ext 2200
Fullman, David (diversity mgr)
Wright, Andrew (spo info) ext 2247
Shaw, John (facilities mgr) ext 2006

Training
Wilson, Kate (training officer) ext 2222
Racher, Bev (pda)
tel (01533) 669000

Walker, Brian (pda)
tel (01603) 302246

Whitehead, Annette (pda)
tel (01493) 855525

Winchester Claire (pda)
tel (01603) 302245

MAPPA
Singleton, Joy (01603) 276321
singletonj@norfolk.pnn.police.uk

Butterworth, David (01603) 276344
butterworthd@norfolk.pnn.police.uk

Interventions - Programmes Unit
Ramshaw, Charles (prog mgr idap, tvp)
ext 2067
Hartland, Andy (prog mgr tf, oto,
csb, art, didp, osap) ext 2070
Austin, Jo (trtmnt mgr didp) ext 2041
DeVaux, Paula (trtmnt mgr idap) ext 2114
Feeney, Michael (trtmnt mgr idap) ext
2045
Peaford, Linda (trtmnt mgr oto, think 1st)
ext 2043
Pooley, Gill (trtmnt mgr tvp) ext 2051
Richards, Matt (trtmnt mgr osap) ext 2054
Cummins, John ext 2111
Gale, Marie ext 2080
Payne, Barbara ext 2076
Ryan, Liz (trtmnt mgr tvp) ext 2066
Wivell, Bill ext 2077

Bacon, Helen (pso) ext 2052
Colbourn, Lynne (pso) ext 2079
Cullum, Stuart (pso) 2064
Duvall, Jeni (pso) ext 2040
Eliot Stephanie (pso) ext 2058
Feeney, William (pso) ext 2049
Fenn, Sharon (pso)
Hampson, Nicola (pso) ext 2046
Hewitt, Steve (pso) ext 2059
Kirk, Pip (pso) ext 2055
Millbank, Lindsey (pso) ext 2053
Murphy, Amanda (pso) ext 2050
Page, Viv (pso) ext 2060
Payne, Stephen (pso) ext 2065
Smith, Micheal (pso) ext 2061

Victim Liaison
Burbidge, Kathy (pso) ext 2011
Blanchard, Victoria (wsw) ext 2013
Bliss, Kim (wsw) ext 2014

Interventions - Other
Baker, Stephen (procurement & prtnrshp
mgr) ext 2072
Westmacott, Julie (spo, pathway devpt
mgr) ext 2073
Leborgne, Claire (offender housing
strategy mgr) ext 2071
Cliff, Barbara (osm) ext 2069

Offender Management
Leaberry, David (spo) ext 2143
Murray, Kirstie (spo) ext 2141
Roper, Dan (spo) ext 2142
Greenhalgh, Karen (spo) ext 2185
Attfield, Clive (spo) ext 2186
Monk, Donna (spo) ext 2184
Anderson, June (osm) ext 2144

Black, Thomas ext 2120
Cleaver, Anne
Coman, Matthew ext 2165
Connolly, Laura
Connor, Elizabeth
Cooper, Michael ext 2113
Cullingford, Abigail
Cummins, John ext 2111
Cuthbert, Ann ext 2126
Daulby, Dee ext 2128
Day, Alyson
de Caesmaeker, Julie ext 2134
Dyde, Sally ext 2171
Good, Philippa
Hagger-Utting, Rowena ext 2170
Hopps, Caroline ext 2100
Jackson, Gareth ext 2157
Kennedy, Helen ext 2108
Loome, Alex ext 2177
Lynch, Rosanna ext 2133
McLoughlin, Leon ext 2162
Mulford, Gillian ext 2176
O'Mahony, Tracy 2121
Parr, Emily ext 2104
Pegg, Beverly ext 2154
Perrett, Andrew ext 2153
Plunkett, Carly
Reeve, Paul ext 2080
Robinson, Samantha ext 2117
Smith, Chris
Spyve, Elizabeth ext 2163
Tennant, James ext 2109
Young, Amanda ext 2152
Young, David ext 2156

Blackman, Paul (pso) ext 2167
Bruce, Scott (pso) ext 2172
Burton, Jim (pso) ext 2023
Cocker, Nicki (pso) ext 2181
Forrest, Paula (pso) ext 2115
Hanton, Matthew (pso)
Hill, Abigail (pso)
Hunt, Pippa (pso) ext 2168
Lamond, Charles (pso)
Macdonald, Stacey (pso) ext 2173
Menezes, Liz (pso)
Mitchell, Donna (pso) ext 2103
Myhill, Tracey (pso) ext 2179
Peck, Emma (pso) ext 2105

Pietocha, Mia (pso) ext 2131
Pyzer, Stephen (pso) ext 2029
Racher, Karen (pso) ext 2122
Stonebridge, Matthew (pso)
Swinger, Adrian (pso) ext 2151
Toovey, Bryan (pso) ext 2021
Wood, Tracey (pso) ext 2124
Young, Hannah (pso)

Crown Court Office
tel (01603) 728268
Orson, Emily

Magistrates Court
tel (01603) 724056/7
Bennett, Pauline (pso)
Cockrill, Alan (pso)
Riley, Nicole (pso)
Whitaker, James (pso)

Unpaid Work Unit
tel (01603) 30 + ext *fax (01603) 302297*

Griffey, Portia (unpaid wk scheme mgr)
ext 2035
Murphy, Tracey (area placmnt mgr) ext
2050
Hunter, Richard (area supvrs mgr) ext
2074
Colk, Miranda (pso)
Howard, Graham (pso)
Lewis, Phil (pso)
Chaplin, Bill (pso) ext 2020
George, Ramon (pso)
Young, Mark (pso) ext 2025

2. Rampart Road
    Great Yarmouth NR30 1QZ
    tel (01493) 855525 *fax (01493) 332769*

Offender Management
East, Paul (spo)
Cuell, David (spo)
Payne, Paul (osm)
Brogan, Rachel
Coleman, Guy
Hannant, Andrew
Maudsley, Lindsay
Monk, Ian
Parke-Chatten, Pauline
Tricker, Clive
Tricker, Linda
Wigg, Charlene
Williamson, Jodi

Burley, Peter (pso)
Craske, Sue (pso)
Foulser, Gary (pso)
Gore, Hannah (pso)
Hannant, Linda (pso)

Hewitt, Kathryn (pso)
McKinnell, Duncan (pso)
Taylor, Stuart (pso)
Williams, Linzi (pso)
Wood, Karen (pso)

Interventions
Doherty, Patricia (wsw)

3. **Unpaid Work Unit**
    18 Deneside
    Great Yarmouth NR30 3AX
    tel (01493) 844991 *fax (01493) 332670*

Noble, Philip (pso)
Hawkes, Roger (pso)
Riches, Jason (pso)
Rumble, Natalie (pso)
Scully, Eamonn (pso)
Walker, Jim (pso)

4. Purfleet Quay
    King's Lynn PE30 1HP
    tel (01553) 669000 *fax (01553) 776544*

Offender Management
Miller, Iain (spo)
Belham, Charlotte (spo)
Godbold, Sheila (osm)
Farelly, Joanne
Hunns, Johanna
Dawson, Annetta
Johnson, Richard
Kimmett, Janice
Nash, David
Wells, Judith
Wallis, Sarah

Barker, Andrew (pso)
Driver, Len (pso)
Garner, Roy (pso)
Jobsz, Tracy (pso)
Langham, Barry (pso)
Saunders, Julia (pso)
Steward, Kathryn (ppo pso)
Stoodley, Carl (pso)
Taylor, Victoria (pso)
Thompson, Rebecca (pso)
Kerby, Jan (vlo)

Interventions
Bertram, David (trtmnt mgr csb/ tf/ oto)
Cooper, Sharon (trtmnt mgr art)

Allen, Rita (pso)
Carter, Anita (pso)
Clement, Jane (pso)
Harpley, Jenny (pso)
Mahoney, Philippa (pso)

Unpaid Work Unit
Bullock, Nathalie (pso)
Britton, David (pso)
Eglen, Edward (pso)
Goldsmith, Terence (pso)
Todd, David (pso)

5. **12/14 Raymond Street**
   Thetford IP24 2EA
   tel (01842) 754071 *fax (01842) 751089*

   Offender Management
   Reporting office: Tues and Thurs only

   Unpaid Work Unit
   open Mon to Thurs, Sat & Sun
   Broom, Michael (pso)
   Lee, John (pso)
   Murphy, Fred (pso)

6. **Youth Offending Team**
   Norwich
   tel (01603) 877500

   Kemsley, Hannah

   Great Yarmouth
   tel (01493) 847400

   Vacancy

   Kings Lynn
   tel (01553) 819400

   Barnes, Amanda-Jayne

Approved Premise (Hostel)

7. **John Boag House**
   1 Drayton Road, Norwich NR3 2DF
   tel (01603) 429488 *fax (01603) 485903*

   Rymer, Julia (spo mgr)
   Medhurst, Ian (po deputy)
   Anderton. Neil (pso)
   Caron-Mattison, Joe (pso)
   Davison, Cathy (pso)
   Foster, Frank (pso)
   Harper, Louise (pso)

Institutions

8. **H M Prison & YOI**
   Knox Road **Norwich** NR1 4LU
   tel (01603) 708600 *fax (01603) 708601*
   probn fax (01603) 708619

   Discipline ext 8791

   Probn clerks
   Carpenter, Brian (hdc) ext 8759
   Evans, Nigel (programmes) ext 8822
   Moore, Andy (public protctn) ext 8753

Nichols, Sue (public protctn) ext 8803

McNelly, John (spo) ext 8802
Bayles, Ray (po offender supvr) ext 8752
Fergusson, Iain (lifers) ext 8759
Atkins, Tina (po offender supvr) ext 8786
Pyzer, Stephen (pso) BASS ext 8776
ext 8878 & 8758
Rutherford, John (pso offender
supvr) ext 8756 & 8854
Facey, Jenny (pso offender supvr)
ext 8758
Baker, Aaron (pso bail info) ext 8854

9. **H M Prison Wayland**
   Griston, Thetford IP25 6RL
   tel (01953) 804100 *fax (01953) 804220*
   direct dial (01953) 858 + ext

   Probn clerk (visits, gen enquiries) ext 073
   Probn typist (sch 1, temp release) ext 071

   Moulton, Bob (spo) ext 072
   Gibbons, Nadine
   Hardwicke, Dee
   Wales, Andy
   Brown, Zoe
   Wright, Julie
   Hussein, Steven
   Cox, Martin (pso)
   Payne, David (pso)

Local Justice Areas

   1 Norwich
   2 Great Yarmouth
   2 North Norfolk
   5 South Norfolk
   4 Central Norfolk
   4 West Norfolk

Crown Courts

   2 Norwich
   4 King's Lynn

NORTHAMPTONSHIRE PROBATION AREA

Central bail referral number
Bridgewood Hostel, tel (01604) 648704

Out of hours emergency contact point
Bridgewood Hostel, tel (01604) 648704

Victims enquiries contact number
tel (01604) 658060 or tel (01536) 526821

e-mail Firstname.Surname@northamptonshire.
probation.gsi.gov.uk

1. **Head Office**
   Walter Tull House, 43-47 Bridge Street
   Northampton NN1 1NS
   tel (01604) 658000 *fax (01604) 658004*

   Executive Management Team
   Pemberton, Andy (acting chief officer)
   Tomlinson, Emma (director responsible for
   DaRT, Bridgewood Hostel, prtnrshps,
   progrs & crts)
   King, Helen (finance director)
   Wilson, Katie (acting h.r. director)
   Goss, Chris (director responsible for,
   mappa,
   Unpaid Work, info, business devpt, HMP
   Wellingborough, HMP & YOI Onley, HMP
   Ryehill)
   Bedford, Roland (board secy)

   EMT Unit
   Cochrane, Graham (area mgr, intrvntns)
   Woodward, Jenny (area mgr,
   offender mngmnt)
   Shepherd, Jean (pa to co)
   Hannon, Dana (pa to Chris Goss)
   Sanders, Katie (pa to h.r director)
   Wakelin, Sarah (pa)
   Jackie Sampson (pa to H King, admin
   asst to Board Secretary)

   Business Devpt & Communications
   Frost, Darryn (business devpt mgr)
   Robinson, Becky (bus devpt & comms asst)

   Finance
   Hickman, Helen (finance off)
   Brown, Linda (accountant)
   Humphries, Angela (finance asst)

   Human Resources Unit
   Wilson, Katie (h.r.mgr)
   Bushby, Amy (h.r. advr)
   David Ledger (h.r & training co-ord)

   Training & Development Unit
   Jones, Sarah (training mgr)

Information Unit
IT Helpdesk tel (01604) 657090

Teanby, Gary (performance mgr)
Cornhill, Alan (info systems off)
Chandler, Tim (it supp off)
Harris, Len (performance off)
Jones, Mandie (info off)
Tebbutt, Brenice (info systems trainer)

2. Walter Tull House, 43-47 Bridge Street
   Northampton NN1 1NS
   tel (01604) 658000 *fax (01604) 658004*

   Unpaid Work
   Daft, Joh (dep mgr)
   Aworth, Caroline (placemnt devpt off)
   Teanby, Jon (placemnt devpt off)
   Bosworth, Chris (placemnt devpt off)
   Robinson, Lindsay (indctn placmnt off)
   Paul, Robert (indctn placmnt off)
   Samat, Ranjit (placement devpt off)
   Jennings, Margot (admin)
   Kinsella, Lorraine (clerical)

   County Office
   Medley, John (unit mgr)
   Bharadia, Bhavina (admin)
   New, Alison (admin)
   Ashley, Jane (clerical off)
   Davis, Sarah (clerical off)
   Dooley, Jeni (clerical off)
   Henson, Christine (clerical off)
   Sharp, Rhinna (clerical off)

   Court Team
   Johnson, Brian (unit mgr)
   Griffiths, Paul
   Donoghue, Lesley
   Bicki, Marta (pso)
   Blackshaw, Joe (pso)
   Burton, Tracy (pso)
   Leduc, Anglea (pso)
   Lishman, Stevie (pso)
   Hogarth, Jo (pso)
   Downer, Susan (admin)
   Knight, Stephanie (admin)
   Newman, Barbara (admin)
   Newman, Gemma (admin)

   DaRT
   Crutchley, Steve (pso)
   Smart, Karen (admin)

   Offender Management Unit
   Buckingham, Jess (unit mgr)
   Coleman, Lisa (unit mgr)
   Eason, Anne (unit mgr)
   Whelan, Beth (unit mgr)
   Aitken, Karen

Bampton, Lindsey
Bond, Kimberley
Burns, Gary
Cuttiford, Kelly
Donoghue, Dominic
Jones, Hannah
Jones, Matthew
Kingsbury, Prudence
McAulay, James
Martin, Lesley
Morrison, Lindsay
O'Shea Melaine
Presbury, Deborah
Walker, Ruth
Wallace, Noreen
Woodward, Teresa
Seabrook, Clare
Grant, Richard
Silcott, Chantel
Steele, Karen
Tomlinson, Leanne

Crouch, Laura (pso)
Roquecave, Debbie (pso)
Prendiville, Johnny (pso)
Kapoor, Ashok (pso)
James, Paul (pso)
Driver, Tracy (pso)
George, Jen (pso)
Greet, David (pso)
Holmes, Bekke (pso)
Marlow, Geoff (pso)
Newbold, Andy (pso)
Pearce, Emma (pso)
Robinson, Andrew (pso)
Todd, Claire (vlo)

Grice, Deborah (vlo)

McGee, Anna (admin)
Primus-Wilson, Claudette (admin)
Hewett, Shirley (admin)
Battersby, Jackie (admin)
Geary, Tricia (admin)
Dicicco, Carly (admin)
Chapman, Rachel (enforcement admin)

Partnerships
Kellock, Jim (unit mgr)
Clark, Barbara (ete advisor)
Hurling, Jo (admin)

Practice Development
Barrett, Sarah (pda)
Cooke, Linda (admin)
Hare, Nicola (trainee)
Kennedy, Jo (trainee)
Lad, Divya (trainee)
Salmon, Ginny (trainee)
Walker, Alison (trainee)

Programme Delivery Unit
Rose, Dawn
Blackshaw, Charlotte (treatment mgr)
Brul, Maria (pso)
Cantlow, Tracy (pso)
Ettinger, Simone (pso)
Sanders, Cheryl (pso)
Wigley, Glenn (pso)

3.   20 Oxford Street
Wellingborough NN8 4HY
tel (01933) 303680 *fax (01933) 303699*

County Office
Rice, Candice (admin)
Henson, Christine (clerical)
Spriggs, Teresa (clerical)

Unpaid Work
Edwards, Gary (inductn placemnt off)
Newcombe, Bob (inductn placemnt off)
Lackin, Bill (workshop supvr)

Court Team
Gabriel, Gail
Bartley, Delia (pso)
Winters, Sarah (pso)
Addis, Karen (admin)
Patel, Shila (admin)

DaRT
Whitaker, Sue (unit mgr)
Clements, Stella (pso)
Cox, Debbie (pso)
Fontana, Caterina (pso)
Williams, Christine (pso)
Bishop, Deb (admin)
Jennings, Lyn (clerical)

Offender Management Unit
Pratt, Joe (unit mgr)
Pratt, Liz (divnl admin)
Bayliss Rosie
Essam, Helen
Fielding, Lorna
Earl, Louise
Bell, Mari
Lewis, Lawrence
McIntosh, Hanif
McConnell, Helen
Griffin, John (pso)
Hartung, Dorothy (pso)
Smith, Kerry (pso)
Abraham, Natalie (admin)
Freeman, Karen (admin)

Programme Delivery Unit
Jones, Jackie (unit mgr)
Bullock, Sally (treatment mgr)
Wilson, Helen (IDAP facilitator)

Fitch, Jackie (pso)
Gibbons, Paulette (pso)
Westley, Linda (pso)
Arnold, Gary (admin)

4. **Edinburgh House, 7 Corporation Street**
Corby NN17 1NG
tel (01536) 463920 *fax (01536) 406607*

County Office
Pollock, Jade (admin)
Headland, Yvonne (clerical)

Unpaid Work
Garcha, Permjit, (unit mgr)
Docherty, Kathryn (inductn placmnt off)
Wood, John (placement devpt off)

Court Team
Gardner, Chris (pso)
Petitt, Jane (pso)
King, Helen (admin)

Offender Management Unit
Holmes, Elsa (unit mgr)
Flunder, Jennifer
Jones, Laura
Rowely, Lorna
Thurland, Vicki
Shiells, Emma
Carr, Pat (pso)
Johnson, Bridget (pso)
Carson, Lindsay (pso)
King, Marilyn (admin)

Programme Delivery Unit
Geraghty, Amanda (treatment mgr)
Harcourt, Diane (treatment mgr)
Johnson, Karen (admin)
Trafford, Angie (admin)
Goldie, Leanne (admin)

5. Unit 5, Baron Avenue
Telford Way Industrial Estate
Kettering NN16 8UW
tel (01536) 521740 *fax (01536) 524282*

Unpaid Work
Abela, Frank (dep mgr)
Cookson, Laurie (inductn placmnt off)
Allen, Simon (placement devpt off)
Wright, Malcolm (placement devpt off)
Cole, Derek (workshop supvr)

Offender Management Unit
Shorley, Cate (unit mgr)
Maguire, Sioban (unit mgr)
Hammond, Alison
Hegarty, Eamon
Mallard, Liz
Thompson, Gary

Thurland, Vicki
Hicks, Gina (pso)
Sludden Patrick (pso)
Clarke, Julie (pso)
Ingham, Debbie (admin)

Partnerships
Grimmit, Nigel (ETE advisor)

Practice Development Unit
Hancock, Robert (trainee)

6. **Crown Court**
85/87 Lady's Lane
Northampton NN1 3HQ
tel (01604) 637751 *fax (01604) 603164*

Donoghue, Lesley
Wilson, Anne (pso)

7. **Youth Offending Team South**
52-53 Billing Road
Northampton NN1 5DB
tel (01604) 602400 *fax (01604) 639231*

Osbourne, Liz
Wrighton, Sarah

8. **Youth Offending Team North**
73 London Road **Kettering NN15 7PQ**
tel (01536) 533800 *fax (01536) 312240*

Bond, Jodi
Woolley, Julie
Palmer, Jenna (pso)

Approved Premise (Hostel)

9. **Bridgewood House**
45-48 Lower Meadow Court
Northampton NN3 8AX
tel (01604) 648704 *fax (01604) 645722*

Enfield, Clare (unit mrg)
Willetts, Jan (po)
Lloyd-Williams, Debby (probn hostel off)
Mason, Michelle (probn hostel off)
Hulka, Cheryl (probn hostel off)
Stapleton, Lynn (probn hostel off)
Armitt, Kim (probn hostel off)
Knight, Bridget (waking nt supvr)
Waring, Dean (waking nt supvr)
Savage, Michael (waking nt supvr)
Thornton, Emma (waking nt supvr)
Timbrell, Pauline (admin)

Institutions

10. HMP & YOI **Onley**
Willoughby, Nr Rugby
Warwickshire CV23 8AP

tel (01788) 523400 *fax (01788) 523401*

Doran, Paul (unit mgr) ext 3595
Cooper, John ext 3584
Stephens, Chris ext 3651
Aslett, Peter (pso) ext 3646
Baker, Daniel (pso)
Brooks, Simon (pso)
Burgazzi, Elaine (pso)
Farnan, Michael (pso)

11. H M Prison **Wellingborough**
Millers Park, Doddington Road
Wellingborough, Northants NN8 2NH
tel (01933) 232700 *fax (01933) 232847*

probn clerk ext 2852
parole clerk ext 2760

Mackenzie, Rachel (unit mgr) ext 2853
Honour, Mike ext 2851
Lansberry, Denise
Heyworth, Sophie
Biddle, Graeme
Bailey, Yvonne (pso) ext 2850
Davis, Sharon (pso)
Doyle, Pippa (pso)
Green Lissa (pso)
Judge, Stephen (pso)
Knights, Jackie (pso)
Ryan, Nicola (pso)
Wczasek, Ryan (pso)

12. H M Prison **Ryehill**
Onley, Willoughby
Nr Rugby, Warwickshire CV23 8AN
tel (01788) 523300 *fax (01788) 523311*

De-St-Aubin, Doug (unit mgr)
Baggott, Martin
Dade, Emma
McCartney, Sinead
Maltman, Lesley

Local Justice Areas

4 Corby
2 Daventry
5 Kettering
2 Northampton
2 Towcester
3 Wellingborough

Crown Court

6 Northampton

NORTHUMBRIA PROBATION AREA

Out of hours emergency contact no 0191-477 5600

Victim enquiries contact number 0191-261 2541

e-mail Firstname.Surname@northumbria. probation.gsi.gov.uk

1. **Head Office**
Lifton House, Eslington Road
Jesmond, Newcastle upon Tyne NE2 4SP
tel 0191-281 5721 *fax 0191-281 3548*

direct dial 0191-240+ number

Williamson, Pauline (co, chief exec) 7361
Gardiner, David (director of ops) 7308
Robinson, Kevin (director of ops) 7312
Hall, Nick (Director of Resources) 7332
Israni, Roshan (head of people mgmnt & org devpt) 7333
McDine, Julie (h.r. mgr) 7379
Garrick, Rong-Ning (diversity mgr) 7348
Mackie, Chris (board secretary & solicitor) 7351
Taylor, Barry (head of performance, ICT & best value) 7366
Nesbit, Don (area mgr performance) 7362
Rigby, Matt (performance & information mgr) 7343
Holland, Margaret (snr pract, perf devpt) 7346
Mann, Louise (area mgr, service devpt)
Bilcliff Jackie, (head of finances & business services/treasurer) 7352
White, Sam (area mgr finance) 7326
Marshall, Deborah (head of interventions) 7376
Donkin, Julie (contracts & facilities mgr) 7339
Davison, Pat (head office mgr) 7368
Wilson, Gillian (business risk mgr) 7304
Clennell, John (health & safety) 7331
Tucker, Julie (health prom advr) ext 7389
Bone, David (ict mgr) 7345
Pearson, Sue (comms mgr) 7330

Secondments
Mackin, Phil (NPD)
Dale, Wendy (GONE)
Taylor, Richard (HO)
Hunter, Colin (St Nicholas Hosp)
Seebohm, Laura (Tyneside Cyrenians)
Parkinson, Gerry (p, Portsmouth Univ)
Ramshaw, Dawn (NOMS)

Sammut-Smith, Ian (NOMS)
Green, Alan (union pso)

2. **Training Centre**
Dene House, Durham Road
Low Fell, Gateshead
Tyne & Wear NE9 5AE
tel 0191-491 1693 *fax 0191-491 3726*

Murphy, Steve (org devpt mgr)
Walker, Sally (org devpt adviser)
Edison, Elaine (po org devpt)
McIntosh, Angus (consortium dir)
Smith, Mary (consortium training mgr)
Stephenson, Sharon (training &
staff devpt off)
Crowther, Lynn (pda)
Jacques, Denise (pda)
Miles, Susan (pda)

North of Tyne
3. **ACO Unit**
Mackintosh, Jane (head of offender
mngmnt north of tyne/courts) 7350

4. **Operations Unit**
6 Lansdowne Terrace **Gosforth**
Newcastle upon Tyne NE3 1HW
tel 0191-213 0611 *fax 0191-213 1361*
direct dial 0191-2468 + number

North of Tyne District Mgmnt
Kelly, Jan (dist mgr, nwcstle) 108
Kelly, Liz (dist mgr, northumberland) 114
Downing, Dorothy (dist mgr, n. tyneside)
Howson, Maxine (admin mgr, nwcstle) 135
O'Hara, Marcia (p, admin mgr, nnt) 136

5. **5 Lansdowne Terrace**
Gosforth
Newcastle upon Tyne NE3 1HW
tel 0191-213 1888 *fax 0191-213 1393*

North Team
McLaren, Cath (team mgr)
Baker, Mike
Clark, Malcolm
Humphries, James
Masendeke, Sally
Norwood, Tina
Reed, Paula (drr)
Robson, Janice
Rothwell, Diane (drr)
Willcock, Sarah
Attley, Paul (pso)
Bevans, Christina (pso)
Colloby, Cheryl (pso drr)
Connor, Rachel (pso drr)

Lawson, Rachel (pso)
O'Reilly, Michael (pso drr)
Trainor, Pat (pso)
Flounders, Debbie (trainee)
Quille, Judith (trainee)

6. **Persistent Offenders Team**
West Road Police Station
Westgate Road, Newcastle NE4 8RP
tel 0191-221 8313

Gilbert, Steve (team mgr)
Gartland, Elaine
Simpson, Tom
Brickland, David (pso)

7. **70-78 St James Boulevard**
Newcastle upon Tyne NE1 4BN
tel 0191-261 9091 *fax 0191-233 0758*

City Team
Heath, Deborah (team mgr)
Capper, Elaine (p)
Collins, Nicola
Fearon, Lee
Harrington, Kathryn
Lockie, Claire
Lowes, Elaine
Mynott, Cynthia
Ritchie, Heather
Scott, Mark
Sharpe, Ian
Smyth, Sue
Bateman, Gay (pso)
Wilcox, Chris (pso)
Martin, Deborah (trainee)
Pugh, Jan (trainee)

8. **717 West Road**
Newcastle upon Tyne NE15 7PS
tel 0191-274 1153 *fax 0191-275 0963*

West Team
Ineson, Lesley (team mgr)
Wilsdon, Maureen (snr pract)
Binley, Karen
Dale, Paul
Grierson-Smith, Marie (p)
Key, Helen
McKale, Jonathan
O'Farrell, Paul
Pyle, Colin
Thompson, Val
Wilks, Elizabeth (p)
Mullen, Angela (pso)

9. **4 Glendale Terrace Byker**
Newcastle upon Tyne NE6 1PB

tel 0191-276 6666 *fax 0191-224 2878*

East Team
Peaden, Kay (team mgr)
Anderson, Shirley
Burrows, Gerry
Coxon, Adrian
Gwilym, Matthew
Higgins, Rob
Hutchinson, Jenny
Ions, Kenneth
O'Kane, Kathy
Smith, Jennifer
Stafford, Sandra
Thorpe, Simon
Cardiff, Teresa (pso)
Lathbury, Simon (pso)
Robinson, Sharon (trainee)
Walker, Charlene (trainee)

10. Former Employment Exchange
South View **Ashington**
Northumberland NE63 0RY
tel (01670) 813053 *fax (01670) 814858*
County Team
Familton, Bev (team mgr)
Shiells, Jill (senior prac)
Campbell, Cathy
Dungait, Lynn
Foster, Susan
Gallagher, Paul
Kirk, Carole
Roberts, Joanne
Singer, Stephen
Tate, Eunike
Wylie, Sarah
Billington, Tracey (pso)
Warburton, Julie (pso)
Armstrong, Angela (trainee)
Falcus, Lindsay (trainee)

11. **Ashington Probation Centre**
South View, Ashington
Northumberland NE63 9AH
tel (01670) 520121 *fax (01670) 816130*

Randall, Barbara (proj lead-prtnshps
& diversity)
Randall, Ken (pda)

12. 27 Bondgate Without
Alnwick Northumberland NE66 1PR
tel (01665) 602242 *fax (01665) 605184*

Elliott, Katherine
Jaimin, David
Peacock, Graham

13. 32/34 Richard Stannard House
Bridge Street **Blyth**
Northumberland NE24 2AG
tel (01670) 352441 *fax (01670) 352921*

Turner, Margaret (team mgr)
Barnes, Matthew
Bates, Annie
Clarkson, Laura
Dent, Sharon
Elliott, Neil
Foster, Chris
Moor, Leigh
Smith, Allison
Weatherley, Marcus (drr)
Burns, Christine (pso)
Cox, John (pso)
Hadland, Simone (pso)
Knox, Claire (pso drr)
Hogg, Ben (trainee)

13a. **Blyth Police Station**
(01661) 861912
Hill, Louise (reducing re-offending mgr)
Storey, Fiona (prol off)
Harrison, Tracey (pso)

14. 4 Wentworth Place **Hexham**
Northumberland NE46 1XB
tel (01434) 602499 *fax (01434) 606195*

Ackerman, Sarah (om)
Bennett, Vanessa (p, om)

15. Lovaine House, 9 Lovaine Terrace
North Shields Tyne and Wear NE29 0HJ
tel 0191-296 2335 *fax 0191-257 6170*

Booth, Richard (reducing re-offending mgr)
Hardington, Gary (team mgr)
Bewick, Lisa
Coleman, Sarah
Currie, Ivan (po prolific offender)
Doggett, Steven
Fellows, Debra
Graham, Helen
Heron, Bill (drr)
Jones, Hannah
Nicholson, Tracey
Robson, Chantal
Rudram, Anna
Wade, Martin
Wallwork, Charlie
Barrett, Michelle (pso drr)
Kelly, Jean (pso)
Ellison, Gladys (pso, prol)
Hanson, Amy (pso)
McBeth, Pam (pso, prol)

Richardson, Clare (pso)
Stasik, Mark (pso)
Smith, Lindsey (trainee)

16. **13 Warwick Road Wallsend**
Tyne and Wear NE28 6SE
tel 0191-262 9211 *fax 0191-295 4824*

Seddon, Amanda (team mgr)
Wallace, Joanne (snr pract)
Alexander, Paul
Brent, Claire
Grant, Louise
Jones, Stephanie
Lennox, Mark
McNivern, Helen
Penfold, Keith
Pridie, Pam
Ward, Clare (p)
Wood, Lorraine
Beare, Gerry (pso)
Bowler, Howard (pso)
Hesketh, Lesley (trainee)
Southern, Elizabeth (trainee)

Area Court Services

17. **6th Floor Collingwood House**
3 Collingwood Street
Newcastle upon Tyne NE1 1JW
tel 0191-232 3368 *fax 0191-233 0760*

Clarkin, Liz (area mgr)

North of Tyne Court Services
Ford, Lucy (team mgr)
Connor, Stephen
Lloyd, Philip
Thompson, Kay
Douthwaite, Lynda (pso)
Maxwell, Sandra (pso)
Murray, Hannah (pso)
Smith, Maureen (pso)

North Tyneside Magistrates Court
tel 0191-296 4263
Badhan, Savina
Lane, Carol
Hudson, Sharon (pso)
Trainor, Mike (pso)

SE Northumberland Magistrates' Court
tel (01670) 843805 *fax (01670) 826180*

Bridgeman, Nicola
Flynn, Tony
Graham, Tanya
Lee, Vanessa
Bonham, Cheryl (pso)
Flisher, Eileen (pso)

South of Tyne Court Services
Mills, John (p, team mgr)
Murphy, Kirsty (p, team mgr)

Sunderland Magistrates' Court
tel 0191-514 8949
Speight, Lena
Zein-Elabdin, Sara
Brown, Malcolm (pso)
Minhas, Virinder (pso)
Mooney, Lynn (pso)
Richardson, Ian (pso)

Gateshead
tel 0191-477 5821 ext no 246
Simpson, Karen
Bell, Catherine (pso)
Greaves, Aly (pso)

South Shields
tel 0191-427 4482
Hardy, Peter
Davison, Susan (pso)
Gibson, Kim (p, pso)
McIntosh, Louise (pso)

18. **Victim Liaison Unit**
6th Floor, Collingwood House
3 Collingwood Street
Newcastle upon Tyne NE1 1JW
tel 0191-261 2541 *fax 0191-221 1438*

Clinton, Roy
Mantey, Jean
Bruce, Brenda (pso)
Graham, Lisa (pso)
Reid, Gloria (pso)
Riley, Gillian (pso)
Tempest, Kerry (pso)

19. **The Law Courts Quayside**
Newcastle upon Tyne NE1 2LA
tel 0191-230 1737 *fax 0191-233 0759*

Bell, Andrea
Davies, John
Conlon, Peter
Graham, Harry (p)
Brough, Anjali (pso)

South of Tyne

20. **ACO Unit**
tel 0191 240 7363
McCartney, Jeff (head of offender mngmnt south of tyne)

21. **MAPPA Unit**
Block 45, Northumbria Police HQ
North Road, Ponteland

Newcastle upon Tyne NE20 0BL
tel (01661) 868077 *fax (01661) 868497*

McLean, Wynne (area mgr, public
protectn) ext 68286
Love, Amanda (MAPPA co-ord)
Thompson, Mark (snr pract, pub protectn)
Cox, Jackie (snr pract)
Oxley, Ann (snr pract)
Visram, Anne (snr pract, public protectn)

22. **Operations Unit**
Warwick Street, Gateshead
Tyne and Wear NE8 1PZ
tel 0191-478 9978 *fax 0191-478 1197*

Gavin, Maureen (dist mgr, stag)
Stephenson, Maggie (dist mgr, south
tyneside)
Falcon, Sheila (admin mgr, stag)

Wearside

22a. **Wearside Management Unit**
John Street, Sunderland
Tyne and Wear NE8 1PZ
tel 0191-515 5190 *fax 0191-515 5191*

O'Neill, Karin (district mgr)
Fullard, Lynn (admin mgr)

23. Hylton Road **Pennywell**
Sunderland SR4 8DS
tel 0191-534 5545 *fax 0191-534 2380*

McElderry, Jim (team mgr)
Bosanko, Kay
Cliff, Marian (p)
Cockburn, Ben (snr pract)
Davison, Olwen
Main, Alex
Nairne, Finlay
Nolan, Michael
Rafiq, Mohammed
Stobbart, Susan
Harris, Sarah (pso)
Walker, Joan (pso)
Maughan, Jennifer (trainee)

24. Mainsforth Terrace West
Hendon Sunderland SR2 8JX
tel 0191-514 3093 *fax 0191-565 1625*

Solan, Catherine (team mgr)
Murray, Alison (persistent offndr team)
Cavanagh, Ian
Coombe, Jennifer
Devlin, Linda
Haran, Margaret
Locklan, Margaret

Smith, Susan
Sweeting, Tom
Giles, Julie (p, pso)
Price, Carol (pso)
Walker, Jeanette (pso)
Ferguson, Lucy (trainee)
Wright, Julie (trainee)

25. Kings Road **Southwick**
Sunderland SR5 2LS
tel 0191-548 8844 *fax 0191-548 6834*

Airey, Tony
Barnes, Helen
Bell, Joanne
Dowson, Catherine
Jones, Victoria (drr)
McQuillan, Steve
Middleton, Linda
Stafford, Keith
Stube, Lori (drr)
Hutchinson, Claire (pso drr)
Houghton, Karen (pso drr)
Manley, Lynn (pso)
Thompson, Keith (pso drr)

26. 1st Floor, Empire House
Newbottle Street **Houghton-le-Spring**
Tyne and Wear DH4 4AF
tel 0191-584 3109 *fax 0191-584 4919*

Stratford, Mary (team mgr)
Baker, Pam (p)
Cutter, Anne-Marie
Gettings, Sarah
Haberfield, Lee
Lowerson, Angela
Oyolu-Barker, Chin Chin
Pratt, Kathleen
Allison, Pam (pso)
Bower, Peter (pso)
Robertson, Tracey (pso)
Jackson, Sarah (trainee)
Sugden, Clare (trainee)

South Tyneside & Gateshead

27. Homer Villa, St John's Terrace
Jarrow Tyne and Wear NE32 3BT
tel 0191-489 7767 *fax 0191-483 3961*

Lamb, Mark (team mgr)
Atkinson, Jonelle
Brookes, Louise (p)
Franciosi, Heather
Norton, Michael
O'Connor, Alita
Robinson, Kerry
Johnston, Carole (pso)

O'Neill, Maria (pso)
Robson, Helen (pso)
O'Connor, Christopher (trainee)

28. Secretan Way, Millbank
South Shields
Tyne and Wear NE33 1RG
tel 0191-455 2294 *fax 0191-427 6919*

Harrison, Ken (team mgr)
Coulthard, Gail (reducing re-offending mgr)
Vacancy (snr pract)
Boad, Angela
Blaylock, Johanne
Dixon, Ian
Foreman, Siobhan (drr)
Hawes, Scott
Hayes, Mary
Hill, Linda
Jones, Vikki
Rose, Simon
Brown, Vicky (pso)
Cliff, Andrea (pso drr)
Grace, Paul (pso)
Hope, Kaye (pso)
Hills, Carla (trainee)
Mayers, Louise (trainee)

29. Wesley Court **Blaydon**
Tyne and Wear NE21 5BT
tel 0191-414 5626 *fax 0191-414 7809*

Bunney, Crawford (team mgr)
Saddington, Debbie (snr pract)
Armstrong, Anne (p)
Bowers, Tracey
Holcroft, Harma
Jarvis, Rob
Loughrey, Terry
McGovern, Christine
Marsh, Charlotte
Miles, Sandra
Smith, Clair
Taylor, Alison
Turner, Melanie
Ul-Haq, Ehtesham
Bleanch, Graham (pso)
Morren, Alex (pso)
Smiles, Simon (pso)

30. Warwick Street
Gateshead Tyne and Wear NE8 1PZ
tel 0191-478 2451 *fax 0191-478 1197*

Connor, Gary (team mgr)
Pooley, Geoff (ppo team mgr)
Bright, Kelly

Carson, Mandy
Campbell, Ged (drr)
Caush, Natalie
Davison, Rebecca (drr)
Edwards, Ian
Finnigan, John
Gkavogiannis, Kerry
Halpin, Aidan (prol)
Hope, Katherine
Morrison, Angela
Robson, Colin
Robson, Julie (p)
Vipond, Richard
Baker, Dawn (pso)
Carter, Alan (pso drr)
Cole, Liz (pso drr)
Middlemass, Lee (pso)
Murray, Karen (pso)
Reece, Emma (pso)
Vickers, David (pso drr)
Brown, Josephine (trainee)
Jennings, Dawn (trainee)
Sibbald, Karen (trainee)

Interventions

31. Lifton House
Eslington Road **Jesmond**
Newcastle upon Tyne NE2 4SP
tel 0191-281 5721 *fax 0191-281 3548*

Fiddes, Christine (head of prtnrshps/ community integration) (retires 31/12/08)
Marshall, Deborah (head of intrvntns)
Kingsland, Lory (admin mgr)

Unpaid Work

32. **14 Pitt Street**
Newcastle upon Tyne NE4 5SU
tel 0191-261 9515 *fax 0191 261 1548*

Vacancy (upw area mgr)
0191-261 9515

70-78 St James' Boulevard
Newcastle upon Tyne NE1 4BN
tel 0191-261 9091 *fax 0191-233 0758*

Forster, Maureen (upw scheme mgr)
Simpson, Dawn (qa mgr)
Archer, Mark (qa mgr)
Harrison, Reg (offender mgr)
Lowther, Jimmy (offender mgr)
Redford, Paul (offender mgr)
Anderson, Maxine (offender supvr)
Baker, Maureen (offender supvr)
Bass, Karen (offender supvr)
Coates, George (offender supvr)
Rice, Vincent (offender supvr)

Stephenson, John (offender supvr)
Tait, David (offender supvr)

33. 13 Warwick Road
Wallsend Tyne & Wear NE28 6SE
tel 0191-262 9211 *fax 0191-295 4824*

Gordon, Bernard (qa mgr)
Aitchison, George (offender mgr)
Harrington, Jim (offender mgr)
Broxson, John (offender supvr)
Harding, Georgina (offender supvr)
Lamb, Kevin (offender supvr)
Robinson, Jim (offender supvr)
Scott, Richard (offender supvr)

34. Former Employment Exchange
South View **Ashington**
Northumberland NE63 0RY
tel (01670) 813053 *fax (01670) 814858*

Ball, John (qa mgr)
Burt, Foster (offender mgr)
Coxon, Debbie (offender mgr)
Paterson, Bill (offender mgr)
Robinson, Tony (offender mgr/offndr
supvr)
Celino, Frank (p, offender supvr)
Holgate, Steve (offender supvr)
Lindsay, Alex (offender supvr)

35. 45 John Street **Sunderland**
Tyne and Wear SR1 1QU
tel 0191-510 2030 *fax 0191-565 7746*

Rees, David (uw scheme mgr)
O'Neill, Mick (qa mgr)
Hinder, Mick (qa mgr)
Dickinson, Kevin (offender mgr)
O'Neill, Richard (offender mgr)
Penty, Barbara (offender mgr)
Burnett, John (offender supvr)
Clark, Robert (offender supvr)
Elliott, Beverley (offender supvr)
Fascia, Paul (offender supvr)
Ferries, Amy (offender supvr)
Green, Alan (offender supvr)
Jacques, Geoff (offender supvr)

36. Warwick Street
Gateshead Tyne & Wear NE8 1PZ
tel 0191-478 2451 *fax 0191-478 1197*

Boyne, Stephanie (qa mgr)
Dingwall, Ed (offender mgr)
Glendinning, Alan (offender mgr)
Fay, Kevin (offender supvr)
Kirton, Iain (offender supvr)
Stimpson, Harry (offender supvr)

37. Secretan Way, Millbank
South Shields Tyne and Wear NE33 1HG
tel 0191-455 2294 *fax 0191-427 6919*

Cutting, Alan (qa mgr)
Williamson, George (offender mgr)
Withers, Viv (offender mgr)
Frazer, Adrian (offender supvr)
Gibson, Mark (offender supvr)
Oman, Tracy (offender supvr)

Programmes

38. 14 Pitt Street
Newcastle upon Tyne NE4 5SU
tel 0191-261 9515 *fax 0191-261 1548*

Francis, Anne (area mgr interventions)

NSOG Programme Team
Flynn, Alan (prog mgr)
Gow, Sue
Graham, Brenda
Loxley, Felicity (p)
Smart, Lindsey
Strachan, Ian
Ryland, Mark (treatment mgr)
Wallace, Stacey

39. **Sexual Behaviour Unit**
14 Pitt Street
Newcastle upon Tyne NE4 5SU
tel 0191-260 2540 *fax 0191-261 1548*

Devine, Eileen
Kennington, Roger

40. YMCA Building, Church Way
North Shields Tyne & Wear NE29 0AB
tel 0191-258 6601 *fax 0191-296 2396*

Walter, Dave (prog mgr cdvp)
Bailey, Douglas (treatment mgr cdvp)
Carr, Richard (treatment mgr cdvp)
Pollard, Caroline (treatment mgr)
Wylie, Karen (treatment mgr)
Amar, Urfan (cdvp)
Deary, Kath (p, cdvp)
Dymore, Claire (cdvp)
Heslop, Ian (cdvp)
Turner, Daphne (cdvp)
Beton, Carol (pso)
Gray Gillian (pso)
Miller, Claire (pso)
Reay, Rebecca (pso)
Sammons, Roger (pso)
Sherriff, Amanda (pso)
Tobin, Neville (pso)
Towns, Alan (pso cdvp)

41. **70-78 St James' Boulevard**
Newcastle upon Tyne NE1 4BN
tel 0191-261 9091 *fax 0191-233 0758*

Talbot, John (prog mgr)
Brunger, Sheila (treatment mgr)
Edge, Alan (treatment mgr)
Scott, Ian
Hodgson, Kath (pso)
Jones, Jane (pso)
O'Donnell, Sheree (pso)
Patterson, Liz (pso)
Smith, Anthony (pso)
Stevenson, Malcolm (pso)
Trembath, Jim (pso)

42. **45 John Street Sunderland**
Tyne and Wear SR1 1QU
tel 0191-510 2030 *fax 0191-565 7746*

Walton, Peter (prog mgr)
Aikman, Debbie (treatment mgr)
Patterson, Kerrie (treatment mgr)
Thomas, Ami (treatment mgr)
Rice, Vince
Byrne, Tonya (pso)
Fascia, Julie (pso)
Gerrard, Jason (pso)
Hirst, Eunice (pso)
Jackson, Suzanne (pso)
Lavery, Janice (pso)
McAree, Anna (pso)
McGough, Carol (pso)
Miles, Paul (pso)
Smith, Dawn (pso)
Stephens, Helen (pso)
Taieb, Messaad (pso)

**Approved Premises, Offender
Accommodation, Partnerships**

43. Lifton House, Eslington Road
Jesmond Newcastle upon Tyne NE2 4SP
tel 0191-281 5721 *fax 0191-281 3548*

direct dial 0191-240 +ext

Vacancy (head of prtnrshps/
community integration) 7372
Marshall, Deborah (head of intrvntns) 7376
Kingsland, Lory (admin mgr) 7373

44. **ETE Referral Unit**
4 Glendale Terrace
Byker, Newcastle upon Tyne NE6 1PB
tel 0191-275 5640 *fax 0191-275 5649*

Charlton, Eve (ete off)
Adams, Maggie (ete off)

Also based at ETE Referral Unit
Fiddes, Jeff (prtnrshps & accom mgr)
Dinning, Sean (mentor co-ord)

Approved Premises (Hostels)

45. **Cuthbert House Bail Hostel**
Derwentwater Road, Bensham
Gateshead NE8 2SH
tel 0191-478 5355 *fax 0191-490 0674*

Vacancy (mgr)
Douglas, Jason (hostel asst)
Clark, Paula (hostel asst)
Hannen, Heidi (hostel asst)

46. **Pennywell House Bail Hostel**
Hylton Road, Pennywell
Sunderland SR4 8DS
tel 0191-534 1544 *fax 0191-534 1049*

McKenna, Maureen (mgr)
Bosher, Shaun (hostel asst)
Murton, Mick (hostel asst)
Whillians, Christine (hostel asst)

47. **Ozanam House Probation Hostel**
79 Dunholme Road
Newcastle upon Tyne NE4 6XD
tel 0191-273 5738 fax 0191-272 2729

Gelder, Chris (mgr)
Bell, Geoff (deputy)

Central Referral Service
tel 0191-272 2626 *fax 0191-272 1126*

Nugent, Peter (central referring officer)

48. **St Christopher's House Bail Hostel**
222 Westmorland Road, Cruddas Park
Newcastle upon Tyne NE4 6QX
tel 0191-273 2381 *fax 0191-272 4241*

Faill, Peter (mgr)
Yoxall, Gail (dep mgr)

Youth Offending Teams

49. **Northumberland YOT**
The Riverside Centre
North Seaton Industrial Estate
Ashington, Northumberland NE63 0YB
tel (01670) 852225

Brabbins, Paul

50. **N Tyneside YOT**
153 Tynemouth Road
North Shields, Tyne & Wear NE30 1ED
tel 0191-200 6001

Blevins, Tracey

51. **Newcastle YOT**
Block D, 4th Floor, Jesmond Quadrant
3 Archbold Terrace, Sandyford
Newcastle upon Tyne NE2 1BZ
tel 0191-277 7377

Shenton, Nicola

52. **Gateshead YOT**
Former Felling Police Station
Sunderland Road, Felling
Gateshead, Tyne & Wear NE10 0NJ
tel 0191-440 0500

Heslop, Justine

53. **S Tyneside YOT**
30 Commercial Road
South Shields, Tyne & Wear NE33 1RW
tel 0191-427 2850

Malins, Petra

54. **Wearside YOT**
Lambton House, 145 High Street West
Sunderland, Tyne & Wear SR1 1UW
tel 0191-553 7370

Jamieson, John

Institutions

55. **H M Prison Acklington**
Nr Morpeth
Northumberland NE65 9XF
tel (01670) 762300 *fax (01670) 762301*
probn fax (01602) 762307

Direct dial (01670) 762 + ext

Probn clerk 453/446
Risk mgmnt co-ord 638
SOTP treatment mgr 458
Sentence mgmnt clerk 450
Sentence mgmnt officers 636/447

Cornick, Judith (team mgr) 452
Armstrong, Andrea 451
Candon, Christine 444
Cockburn, Fred 456
Gilmore, Maureen 457
Roberts, Amanda (pso) 614

56. H M Young Offender Institution
Castington Nr Morpeth
Northumberland NE65 9XG
tel (01670) 382100 *fax (01670) 382101*
probn fax (01670) 382034

direct dial (01670) 382 + ext

Parole clerk ext 162
HDC clerk ext 033
Discipline ext 113
Special visits ext 018

Cook, Fred (snr pract) 183
Lawrence, Bob 116
Wilkinson, Peter 159
Hall, Heather (pso) 159
Hamilton, Ann (pso) 022

57. HM Prison **Frankland**
Finchale Avenue, Brasside
Durham DH1 5YD
0191-332 3000 *fax 0191-332 3001*

Wilson, Margaret

Local Justice Areas

12 Alnwick
12 Berwick on Tweed
30 Gateshead District
14 Tynedale
24 Houghton-le-Spring
5-9 Newcastle upon Tyne
15, 16 North Tyneside
10, 13 South East Northumberland
27, 28 South Tyneside
23, 25 Sunderland

Crown Courts

19 Newcastle upon Tyne

NOTTINGHAMSHIRE PROBATION AREA

Out of hours emergency contact point:
Trent House tel 0115-841 5630

e-mail: Firstname.Surname@nottinghamshire.
probation.gsi.gov.uk

Offices

1. **Head Office**
Marina Road, Castle Marina
Nottingham NG7 1TP
tel 0115-840 6500 *fax 0115-840 6502*
direct dial 0115-840 + ext

Chief Officer Group
fax 0115-840 6453

Geraghty, Jane (co) 6463
Goldstraw, Christine (board chair) 0115 9936473

Kay, Claire (board secretary)
Wright, Sheila (dir of om / dep co) 6461
Moore, Rob (dir of corp services) 0115 9936519
Mark Taylor (dir of enterprise) 6537
Lewis, Kirsty (pa) 6462
Goode, Alan (dep dir) 0115 9151464
Hill, Nigel (dep dir) 0115 845 5220
Leigh, Julie (dep dir) (01909) 504 851
Khalil, Jawaid (asst dir corp services) 6450
Francis, Gill (asst dir ext relations) 6490
Newbold, Shirley (treasurer) 6468
Dhindsa, Hardyal (area mgr - ent) 0115-908 2172

Central Administration
general enquiries 6500

Finance & Payroll
enquiries 6464
Shelton, Barry (mgr) 6467

Human Resources Personnel
enquiries 0115 9936507
Gordon, Stuart (mgr) 6485

Staff Development
enquiries 6513
Tomlinson, Karen (mgr) 6510

Management Information & Services & Facilities & Support
enquiries 6476
Poyzer, Mike (mgr) 6478

Health & Safety
Churchill, Heather (mgr) 6451

Accommodation & Advice Unit
enquiries 6491
Buckley Michael (mgr)

Access (ETE) Team
Cooke, Steve (mgr) 6459

City Programmes
Khan, Abirjan (spo) 6384
Harrison, Sue (sao)
Goulder, Jennifer
Haq, Nasima
Jabeen, Saika
Macarthur, Ian
Marriott, Paul
Tribe, Sue
Turner, Del
Weaver, Paul
Bashir, Shareen (pso)
Maycock, Kelly (pso)
Oswald, Chalie (pso)
Rayment, Lesley (pso)
Ruston, Vickie (pso)
Smeeton, Elizabeth (pso)

Victim Contact
fax 0115-908 2971
Urquhart, Jane (spo)
Gerty, Ann
Raban, Deidre
O'Dare, Helen (pso)
Ryan, Marie (pso women's supt wrkr)
Slater, Selina (pso)
Woodhouse, Laura (pso & ca)

2. **Nottingham City**
206 Derby Road, **Nottingham**, NG7 1NQ
tel 0115-845 5100 *fax 0115-845 5101*

Towlson, Hilary (unit admin mgr)

City Central
Baumber, Luke (spo)
Hill, Kathryn (sao)
Conway, Bridgett
Evans, John
Fothergill, Trevor
Garner, Karen
Leech, Malcolm
Mulligan, Andrew
Burnett, Siân (om, pso)
Dawson, Gemma (pso)
Melhado, Diane (pso)
Preston, Julie (pso)

City West
Caesar, Beverley (spo)
Holmes, Claire (sao)
Davies, John
Fahy, Nicolette
Hardy, Graham
Malyan, Helen
Campbell, Lisa-Marie
Shaw, Jonathan
Standing, Oliver
Sutcliffe, Philip
Anderson, Martin (om, pso)
Cameron, Chelsea (om, pso)
Evans, Catherine (om, pso)
Russell, Caroline (om, pso)
Sudbury, Nicola (om, pso)
Unwin, Margaret (pso)
White, Rosie (pso)

Access (ETE) Team
Allen, Yvonne (emplt officer)
Barnden, Pete (basic skills tutor)
Jones, Maggie (emplt officer)
Maddax, David (emplt officer)
Moore, Wendy (emplt officer)
Potts, Sarah (emplt officer)
Prince, Dionne (pso ete)

PALS Team
Apiafi, Judi (proj mgr)

Archer, Cheryl (assessor)
Asbury, Carol (devpt wrkr)
Brotherhood, Lynda (basic skills tutor)
Fritscher, Deborah (esol tutor)
Hastings, Lynn (basic skills devpt wrkr)
Jenkins, Owain (basic skills tutor)
Spotswood, Maria (basic skills tutor)
Walters, Kate (basic skills tutor)

Unpaid Work Team
Burnage, Colin (spo)
Towlson, Hillary (unit admin mgr)
Morrison, Jean (sao)
Thomson, Lynn (sao)
Merriman, Anthony (sao)
Smith, Adge
Anderson, Jacqui (om, pso)
Henman, Nina (om, pso)
Horton, Sam (om, pso)
Lavelle, Lisa (om, pso)
Lewis, Sue (om, pso)
Morgan, Ruth (om, pso)
Robinson, Bianca (om, pso)
White, Jo (om, pso)
Whittaker, Audrey (om, pso)

CS Officers
Medcalf, Jackie (snr cso)
Goulder, Andy (cso)
Guthrie, Mick (cso)
Henson, Claire (cso)
Smith, Paul (cso)

3. **Nottingham City**
    Castle Quay, 9 Castle Boulevard,
    Nottingham, NG7 1FW
    tel 0115-908 2900 *fax 0115-908 2915*

Storer, Anita (unit admin mgr)

City South
Saddington, Marion (spo)
Gibson, Melanie (sao)
Faulkner, Dione
Fitzgerald, Joanne
Hodgson, Heather
Husson, Jonathan
Kennedy, Wendy
Kotey, Amon
Le Telliere, Sean
Mitchell, Rod
Morton, Cemona (om, pso)
Page, Jason (pso)
Piper, Alison (pso)
Stoddart, Lorna (om, pso)

City North
Martin, Susan (acting spo)
Newton, Marie (sao)
Butcher, Colin

Chambers, Helen
Cross-Illsley, Hannah
Hall, Nina
Lambert, Chris
Ramsey, Sally
Spall, Natalie
Thompson, Neil
Kouser, Sabreena (pso)
Roe, Julie (om, pso)
Wilson, Lee (om, pso)

City East
Mitchell-Clarke, Valari (spo)
Gibson, Melanie (sao)
Sawyers, Melanie
Haque, Rabina
Ahluwalia, Narinda
Malone, Ellen
Jones, Sarah
Kurcewicz, Anna (om, pso)
Longfellow, Rachel (om, pso)

Qualifying Training
Bernard, Juliette (pda)
Morris, Lesley (pda)
Molloy, Nicola (pda)
House, David (pda)
Walker, Ian (pda)

Public Protection
Goode, Linda (spo)
Balmer, Claire (spo)
Newton, Marie (sao)
Adas Rebecca
Cina, Eve
Flewitt, Wendy
Green, Judy
Hunt, Alison
Lowe, Elon
Maidens, Karen
Martin, Wendy
Smith, Sarah
Stafford, Linda
Boothe, Carol (pso)

City Enforcement Team
Butler, Laura (pso)
Hewitt, Jane (pso)

4. Castle Gate House, 24-30 Castle Gate
    Nottingham, NG1 7AT
    tel 0115-915 1414 *fax 0115-915 1412*
    Cooper, Janet (unit admin mgr)

Prolific Offender Unit (City)
Spencer, Derek (spo)
Saczek, Liz (sao)
Giordmaina, Claudine
Green, Heather
Martin, Wendy
Victor, Andy

Woolley, Roger
Barnes, Wendy (om, pso)
Barrett, Maxine (pso)
Brady, Margaret (pso)
Dinnall, Audrey (pso)
Firth, Vicky (om, pso)
Gregory, Sammy (om, pso)
Spivey, Kaye (pso)
Pilgrim, Karen (cjit drug worker)

Substance Misuse Team (City)
Singh, Gurdev (spo)
Wilson, Jez (practitioner mgr)
Bennett, Pam (sao)
Fryer, John
Peake, Nick
Perkins, Deborah
Rowe, Elaine
Zieba, Helena
Baxter, Matthew (pso)
Hibbert, Rachel (pso)
Iftikhar, Raja (om, pso)
Ramsey, Kelly (om, pso)
Smith, Rob (pso)
Spray, Liz (om, pso)
Taylor, Alison (pso)
Wilkins, Zena (pso)
Baker, Christopher (sm practitioner)
Berry, Paul (sm practitioner)
McLaughlin, Conor (sm practitioner)
Thorpe, Claire (sm practitioner)

Access (ETE) Team
Hartshorn, Barbara (emplt officer)
Rodgers, Ged (emplt officer)

Criminal Justice Intervention Team
Hagen, Gilly (spo)
Burley, Pam (sao)
Humphris, Aileen (team leader)
Cooney, Alison (team leader)
Bentley, Ian (team leader)
Wright, Rebecca (team leader)

Access
Blair, Karon (drug worker)
Carroll, Maria (drug worker)
Carver-Smith, Joni (drug worker)
Godfrey, James (drug worker)
Green, Jacque (drug worker)
Haflidadottir, Gudny (drug worker)
Harrison, Tracey (drug worker)
Hubbard, Chris (drug worker)
Keating, Sam (drug worker)
Sabat, Sumayya (drug worker)
Sargeant, Adam (drug worker)
Semmelroth, Jo (drug worker)

Throughcare / Aftercare
Bishop, Paula (drug worker-task)

Hagen, Steph (drug worker)
McDonald, Maureen (drug worker)
O'Love, Ruth (drug worker)
Remm, Kieron (drug worker)
Vine, Ngaire (drug worker)

ROB Team
Hand, David (drug worker)
Pilgrim, Karen (drug worker)
Rowell, Lorraine (drug worker)

Fit For Work
Hampton, Steve (health training co-ord)
Lee, Rowland (health training pso)

5. **Prolific Offender (Conurbation)**
Park House Health & Social Care Centre
61 Burton Road, Carlton
Nottingham NG3 4DQ
tel 0115 993 5627 *fax 0115 961 3268*

Murphy, Patrick
Evans, Chris (pso)
Morton, Rachel (cjit drugs worker)

6. **Magistrates' Court Liaison Team**
Carrington Street **Nottingham** NG1 2EE
tel 0115-840 6350 *fax 0115-840 6351*

Downey, Tony (spo)
Storer, Anita (uam)
Underwood, Angela (sao)
Clare, Jan
Stephens, Vicky
Dyer, Maxine (pso)
Howle, Alison (pso)
Marshall, Emma (pso)
Short, Diane (pso)

7. **Crown Court Liaison Team**
Canal Street **Nottingham** NG1 7EJ
tel 0115-910 3540 *fax 0115-958 6135*

Downey, Tony (spo)
Storer, Anita (uam)
Underwood, Angela (sao)
Ames, Steve
Green, Steve
Smillie, Rupert
Baird, Mary (pso)
Dominy, Megan (pso)
Cumberland, Yasmin (pso)
Fletcher, Janet (pso)
Kinkaid, Georgina (pso)

8. **Substance Misuse Team (County)**
Titchfield House, 96 Nottingham Road
Mansfield Nottinghamshire NG18 1BP
tel (01623) 488 470 *fax (01623) 488 471*

Williams, Anthony (spo)
Ben-Hassen, Tracey (uam)
East, Helen (sao)
Wilson, Jez (sub misuse trmt mgr)
Barling, Lisa
Hilton, Dawn
Jacobson, Steven
Deane, Michelle (pso)
Ealden, David (pso)
Guy, Ann (pso)
Richardson, Nicola (pso)
Bush, Suzanne (subst misuse pract)
Freeston, Sonya (subst misuse pract)
May, Ken (subst misuse pract)
Rowlands, Heather (subst misuse pract, alcohol)

9. 46 Nottingham Road,
    Mansfield Nottinghamshire NG18 1BL
    tel (01623) 460 800 *fax (01623) 460 801*

    McCabe, Michelle (unit admin mgr)

    PALS / ETE team
    tel ext. 8860 (general enquiries)
    Gravestock, Di (pso)
    Osborne, Selina (emplt officer)
    Thomas, Kirsty (PALS Officer)
    Wallace, Cassie (emplt officer)

    Mansfield Team 1
    Middleton, Karen (spo)
    Slaney, Carol (sao)
    Butler, Ann-Marie
    Castick, Gareth
    Gardner, Emma
    Parr, Sarah
    Rudkin, Carole
    Scott, Alex
    Bano, Raqia (om, pso)
    Pedley-Barrow, Rebecca (pso)

    Court Team
    Marley, Tamsin (spo)
    Slaney, Carol (sao)
    Hand, Jonathan
    Jeffries, Mike
    Parr, Sarah
    Dangerfield, Maggie (pso)
    Harrison, Lucy (pso)
    Nisbet, Cheryl (pso)

    Programmes Team
    Austin, Shelley (spo)
    Harrison, Sue (sao)
    Ashley, Tracey
    Barnett, Fiona (pso)
    Mugglestone, Alison (pso)
    Ranson, Nina (pso)
    Wyld, Natalie (pso)

10. Sherwood Court, Sherwood Street
    Mansfield NG18 1ER
    tel (01623) 468850 *fax (01623) 468851*

    Mansfield Team 2
    Jane Hilton (spo)
    Vernon, Louise (sao)
    Annison, Lesley
    Hand, Jonathan
    Hardy, Joanne
    Muyunda, Stella
    Harvey, Thea (om, pso)
    Hopkinson, Christine (pso)
    Tebbett, Michelle (pso)

    Mansfield Team 2
    Hilton, Jane (spo)
    Vernon, Louise (sao)
    Deakin-Cooper, Michelle
    Perrell, Caroline
    Roulstone, Jane
    Scanlon, Lib
    Sharma, Ranjna
    Walsh, Hannah
    Romanko, Helen (om, pso)
    Flint, Anne (pso)

    Public Protection Team
    Marley, Tamsin (spo)
    Slaney, Carol (sao)
    Belshaw, Kirstie
    Evans, Rebecca
    Hickinbottom, Alison
    Young, Lisa
    Ainsworth-Chester, Nicola (pso)

    Unpaid Work Team
    Middleton, Karen (spo)
    Slaney, Carol (sao)
    Nesbitt, Andrew (cso)
    Musgrove, Steve (cso)
    Boardman, Donna (pso)
    Gribbon, Tony (om, pso)
    Copley, Chris (pso)

11. 11 Appleton Gate,
    Newark NG24 1JR
    tel (01636) 652650 *fax (01636) 652651*

    Tangen, James (spo)
    Crossland, Jo (unit admin mgr)
    Lawrence, Charlotte (sao)
    Barraco, Zola
    Brown, Angela
    Codrington-Hopkins, Rachel
    McKechnie, Jenifer
    Moore, Mark
    Tocher, Marina
    Mallows, Stuart (pso)
    Orton, Anne (pso)

Palmley, Claire (om, pso)
Reilly, Lisa (om, pso)

Access (ETE)
Phillips, Deborah (emplt officer)

12. **Community Service Team**
51 Appleton Gate
Newark NG24 1LN
tel (01636) 605191

Russo, Roberto (cso)

13. 11 Newcastle Street,
Worksop S80 2AS
tel (01909) 473424 *fax (01909) 530082*

Graham, Jamie (spo)
Ben-Hassen, Tracey (unit admin mgr)
Roffey, Tim (sao)
Benjamin, Estelle
Burton, Mark
Ellis, Caroline
Henry, Tamar
Snell, Natalie
Allen, Greta (pso)
Drew, Margaret (pso)
Evers, Helen (om, pso)
Flynn, John (pso)
Goodwin, Errin (om, pso)
Haynes, Sarah (om, pso)
Smith, Patricia (pso)
Witts, Phil (pso)
Weston, Dave (cso)

Access (ETE)
Lowbridge, Deborah (emplt officer)

14. **MAPPA Manager & Co-ordinator**
Public Protection Unit
CID HQ, Holmes House, Ratcliffe Gate,
Mansfield, NG18 2JW
tel (01623) 483052 *fax (01623) 483056*

West, Sarah (spo)

15. **Prolific Offender Project**
Central Police Station, Great Central Road
Mansfield NG18 2HQ
tel (01623) 483092 *fax (01623) 483099*

Smith, Sue (spo)
Mack, Carolyn
Hand, Sonya
Kinsey, Vanessa (pso)
Tordoff, Jenny (subst misuse pract)
Morre, Doreen (accomm & devpt officer)

16. The Venture Centre
30-34 Watson Road **Worksop** S80 2BE

tel (01909) 530213 *fax (01909) 506431*

Smith, Sue (spo)
Mortimer, Susan
Szulc, Chris
Lever, Deborah (pso)
Taylor, Lynne (subst misuse pract)

17. **Youth Offending Team (City)**
2 Isabella Street
Nottingham NG1 6AT
tel 0115 915 9400 *fax 0115 915 9401*

Carter, Sheila
Duncan, Nat
Gayle, Natasha
Safavinaini, Rochelle

18. **Youth Offending Teams
(County North)** Dale Close
100 Chesterfield Road South
Mansfield NG19 7AQ
tel (01623) 433433 *fax (01623) 452145*

Maurer, Fergus

19. Ground Floor, Block B
65 Northgate
Newark, NG24 1HD
tel (01636) 479929 *fax (01636) 613972*

Simpson-White, Faye

20. **Youth Offending Team (County South)**
DBH House, Carlton Square, Carlton
Nottingham NG4 3BP
tel 0115-940 8612 *fax 0115-940 8603*

Approved Premises (Hostels)

21. **106 Raleigh Street** Nottingham NG7 4DJ
tel 0115-910 5450 *fax 0115-910 5451*

Bannister, John (spo)
Green, Chris (dep mgr)
Bennett, Marcus (apo)
Davies, Dawn (apo)
Foster, Sharon (apo)
Harris, Keith (apo)

22. **5 Astral Grove**
Hucknall, Nottingham NG15 6FY
tel 0115-840 5720 *fax 0115-840 5721*

Bannister, John (spo)
Feather, Budd (dep mgr)
Amos, Sue (apo)
MacKenzie, Chris (apo)
Palmer, Paula (apo)
Squires, Richard (apo)

23. **Trent House**
392 Woodborough Road, Nottingham NG3 4JF
tel 0115-841 5630 *fax 0115-841 5631*

Walker, Angela (spo)
Rodgers, Tony (dep mgr)
Ali, Mariam (intake off)
Jones, Marlien (apo)
Majid, Naima (apo)
Sadiq, Pervez (apo)
Squires, Richard (apo)

24. **Nacro Basford House Accommodation Project**
40-42 Isandula Road, Basford
Nottingham NG7 7ES
tel 0115-978 5851 *fax 0115-978 5851*

Johnson, Steve (mgr)

Institutions

25. HM Prison, Perry Road, Sherwood
Nottingham NG5 3AG
tel 0115-872 3000 *fax 0115-872 3005*

Morris, Sam (spo)
Dyjasek, Marysia
Menhennet, Matthew
Bal, Sita (pso)
Bostock, Angela (pso)
Gregory, Celia (pso)
Mawani, Rukshana (pso)
Melbourne, Maria (pso)

26. HM Prison **Ranby**
near Retford DN22 8EU
tel (01777) 862000 *fax (01777) 862001*

Snowdon, Ann (perf mgr/spo) 0771 4346120
Payne, Helen
Ryer, Nick
Tutt, Katie
White, Rachel
Jeal, Liz (pso)

27. HM Prison **Whatton**
Nottinghamshire NG13 9FQ
tel (01949) 803200 *fax (01949) 803201*

Metcalfe, Maggie (spo)
Moss, David (dep mgr)
Brown, Judith
Carter, Pam
Denham, Samantha
Douglas, Jane
Middleton, Patricia
Muller, Matt

Mulrenan, Jim
Roweth, Ken
Wright Peter
Eaton, Liz (pso)
Strange, Linda (pso)

28. HM Prison **Lowdham Grange**
Lowdham, Nottingham NG14 7DA
tel 0115-966 9200 *fax 0115-966 9220*

Snowdon, Ann (spo) 07714 346120
Brown, Danielle
Ethrington, Keith

Local Justice Areas

Nottingham
Mansfield
Worksop & Retford
Newark & Southwell

Crown Court

5 Nottingham

STAFFORDSHIRE PROBATION AREA

Out of hours: please note that Staffordshire Police retain a list of all manager's home telephone numbers.

Victim enquiries contact number:
(01782) 719045 *fax (01782) 799330*

e-mail Firstname.Surname@staffordshire. probation.gsi.gov.uk

1. **Head Office**
University Court
Staffordshire Technology Park
Beaconside, Stafford ST18 0GE
tel (01785) 223416 *fax (01785) 223108*

Mandley, Rob (chief officer)
Jones, Barbara (director of offender management)
Simpson, Bob (dir business resources)
Palmer, Clive (dir interventions & business devpt)
Forrester, Sandra (area mgr)
Staplehurst, Angela (area mgr)
Sutton, Heather (area mgr)
Trenery, Alison (area mgr)
Jolley, Mike (business resources mgr)
Clewlow, Linda (financial controller)
Bowden, Sandra (hr mgr)
Hewitt, Ian (business & supt mgr)

Parekh, Mohamed (computer services off)
Stanley, James (asst computer srvcs off)

Information Services Unit
tel (01785) 231727
Beckwith, John (p, info services mgr)
Massey, Phil (research off)

Resettlement
tel (01785) 231744
Darby, Paul (resettlement mgr)

Education, Training & Emplmnt
Beddow, Robert (educn off)
Cameron, Beverley (educn off) (at 14)
Hughes, Kim (skills devpt off)
Thompson, Cliff (workskills project mgr)

Training & Devpt Unit
tel (01785) 231723
Lidster, Val (learning & devpt off)
Parkes, Jonathon (practice devpt off)

Practice Devpt Assessors
tel (01785) 240402 *fax (01785) 240720*
Brereton, Simon (based at 14)
Hill, Pam (based at 1)
Towner, Claire (based at 14)

Business Development Unit
Scott, Peter (business devpt mgr)
Hay, Catherine (intensive progs co-ord)

Housing Unit - North
(based at Hanley)
tel (01782) 212608 *fax (01782) 208589*
Walton, Bernard (accom off)

Housing Unit - South
(based at Head Office)
tel (01785 231738 *fax (01785 243028)*
Griffiths, Linsey (accom off)

Drug Rehabilitation Team
2. Broom Street **Hanley**
    Stoke-on-Trent ST1 2EN
    tel (01782) 261961 *fax (01782) 287459*

    Vacancy (spo)
    Barber, Rachael
    Breen, Helen
    Vacancy
    Dean, Tracy
    Dehal, Rupinder
    Lowndes, Sandra (pso)
    Nixon, Anne-Marie (pso)

3. Caxton House, North Walls
    Stafford ST16 3AD
    tel (01785) 252503 *fax (01785) 252549*

    Goldie, Joanne (spo)

Flynn, Barry
Sourbutts, Robert
Beardmore, Paul (pso)
Davies, Martin (pso)

4. **Tamworth Probation Centre**
    Moor Street, Tamworth B79 7QS
    tel (01827) 302604 *fax (01827) 302649*

    Goldie, Joanne (spo)
    Campbell, Sakhmet
    Stephanie Harrison
    Dunkley, Dave (pso)

Programmes Teams

5. Melbourne House, Etruria Village
    Forge Lane, Festival Park
    Hanley, Stoke-on-Trent ST1 5RQ
    tel (01782) 202800 *fax (01782) 202858*

    Hodgkinson, Ian (spo, progs mgr)
    Wood, Tony (deputy mgr)
    MacKinnon, Nicola (IDAP tutor)
    Alcock, Louise (pso)
    Graham, Patrick (pso)
    Holford, Joe (pso)
    Richards, Lisa (p, pso)
    Riley, Michael (pso)
    Vernon, Darren (pso)
    Willis, Emma (treatment mgr/tutor)

Regional Sex Offender Unit
Cooper, Sally (p, mgr)
Baverstock, Laura
Daubner, Jacqui
Dwight, Ellie
Gilbride, Sue (p)
Raven, Mark

6. Dorrington Drive
    Dorrington Industrial Park
    Stafford ST16 3BF
    tel (01785) 279951 *fax (01785) 279959*

    Cooper, Sally (p, progs mgr)
    Cooper, Andrew (pso)
    Mottram, Ann (pso)
    Welch, Karen (pso)

7. Horninglow Street
    Burton on Trent DE14 1PH
    tel (01283) 565951 *fax (01283) 567978*

    Cooper, Sally (p,progs mgr) (based at 6)
    Bibi, Sophina (pso)
    Godwin, Claire (pso)
    Smith, Kelly (pso)

8. Moor Street
   Tamworth B79 7QZ
   tel (01827) 302616 *fax (01827) 302649*

   Cooper, Sally (p,progs mgr) (based at 6)
   Hall, Amanda (pso)
   Tromans, Charmain (pso)

Courts

9. **Crown & County Court**
   Bethesda Street, Hanley
   Stoke-on-Trent ST1 3BP
   tel (01782) 286831 *fax (01782) 287994*

   Gough, Mick (spo)
   Booth, Jane (p)
   Eckersley, Rod
   Scarratt, Wendy (pso)

   N Staffordshire Magistrates' Court
   tel (01782) 286169 *fax (01782) 287824*

   Gough, Mick (spo)
   all other staff based at office 9

10. **Crown & County Court**
    Victoria Square **Stafford** ST16 2QQ
    tel (01785) 223433 *fax (01785) 224156*

    Gough, Mick (spo) (9)
    Hill, Jeff
    Whitmore, Andrew (p)
    Tyler, Rachel (pso)

11. **N Staffordshire Magistrates' Court**
    Ryecroft
    Newcastle-under-Lyme ST5 2DT
    tel (01782) 286169 *fax (01782) 287824*

    SPO at office 9
    Cooper, Linda
    McLoone, Chris
    Ryan, Robert
    Archer, Suzanne (pso)
    Birt, Lynne (pso)
    Franks, Diane (p, pso)
    James-Harford, Tina (p, pso)
    Livesley, Jackie (pso)
    Vacancy

Area Offices

12. Horninglow Street
    Burton-upon-Trent DE14 1PH
    tel (01283) 564988 *fax (01283) 567978*

    Shaw, Judith (spo)
    Coates, Julie
    Chown, Nicola (p)
    Grice, Kelly
    Gibbs, Catherine

King, Elizabeth
Lindsay, Rachel (p)
Montgomery, Adele
Oatley, Diane
Lowrence, Nicola
Stretton, Daniel
Reynolds, Paula
Brotherhood, Rhiannon (pso)
Crouch, Zoe (p, pso)
Dunne, Kathryn (pso)
Palin, Rachel (pso)

13. 200a Wolverhampton Road
    Cannock WS11 1AT
    tel (01543) 506112 *fax (01543) 501029*

    Coplestone, Kathryn (spo)
    Broom, Denise
    Cantrill, Suzanne
    Davies, Paul
    Freeman, Hayley (p)
    Hakim, Lucinda
    Holsey, John
    Leake, Jason
    Littleford, Frank (p)
    Neville, Dean
    Rawling, Joanna
    Smith, Jenny
    Treble, Lesley
    Vose, Janet
    Vacancy (p)
    Burgess, Val (pso)
    Edwards, Anita (pso)
    Fraser, Geoff (pso)

14. **Melbourne House**
    Etruria Office Village, Forge Lane
    Festival Park
    Stoke-on-Trent ST1 5RQ
    tel (01782) 202800 *fax (01782) 202804*

    Cluster 1
    Lawrence, Diana (spo)
    Almond, Bob
    Burdon, Julie
    Matthews, Ruth
    Proctor, Wendy
    Williams, Debbie
    Brookes, Jacqui (pso)
    Parker, Rachel (pso)

    Cluster 2
    Lawrence, Diana (spo)
    Adams, Carl
    Finn, Gemma
    Hare, Karen
    Nixon, Sue
    Parsons, Jennifer

Evans, Mavis (pso)
Skelton, Julie (pso)

Cluster 3
West, Kim (spo)
Barlow, Claire
Dunne, Steve
Pitt, Joanna
Shaw, Kerry
Knox, Jennifer (pso)

Cluster 4
West, Kim (spo)
Grindey, Kerry (p)
Ford, Emma
Heap, Caroline (p)
Jones, Richard
Tomczak, Karen
Turner, Debra
Williams, Andrew)
Sutton, Nicholas (pso)

Cluster 5
Mason, John (spo)
Garland, Sharon
Gaze, Leanne
Holloway, Trevor
Newton, Angela
Skelton, Ken (p)
Da Silva, Karel (pso)

Cluster 6
Mason, John (spo)
Butler, Sally (p)
Hinds, Colin
Moss, Kelly
Rhodes, Shelley
Steele, Hayley
Litherland, Sylvia (p, pso)
Watkin, Michelle (p, pso)

Cluster 7
Mountford, John (spo)
Arnold, Catherine
Groombridge, Andrew
Kent, Helen (p)
Pugh, Alison
Steer, Jean
Dean, Emily (pso)

Cluster 8
Mountford, John (spo)
Burndred, Stephanie
Sadler Amy
Smith, Suzi
Terry, Lindsey
Whitmore, Andrew (p)
Brookes, Ann (p, pso)
Lowndes, Denise (pso)

15. Cross Street
Leek ST13 6BL
tel (01538) 399355 *fax (01538) 399245*

Mountford, John (spo)
Bentley, Stephanie
Pointon, Tim
Sproston, Stephanie
Woolrich, Claire
Heath, Pam (pso)

16. **Victim Liaison Unit**
Melbourne House
Etruria Office Village, Forge Lane
Festival Park
Stoke-on-Trent ST1 5RQ
tel (01782) 202841 *fax (01782) 202952*

Butler, Chris (spo)
Alexander, Barbara
Armstrong, Ann (p)

17. South Walls
Stafford ST16 3BL
tel (01785) 223415 *fax (01785) 224159*

Penton, Emma (spo)
Bonser, Jane (p)
Brookes , Kelly
Darnbrough, Philip
Elliot, Lynne
Hall, Margaret
Mills, Mike
Preston, Andrew
Robinson, Helen
Caddick, Janice (p, pso)
Chatterley, Julie (pso)
Tolley, Sarah (pso)
Watkins, Sarah (pso)

18. 200a Wolverhampton Road
Cannock WS11 1AT
tel (01543) 501034 *fax (01543) 501039*

Penton, Emma (spo)
Blakemore, Gill (p, crt liaison officer)
Howieson, Verney (p, crt liaison officer)
Hira, Herminder (pso)
Hewston, Tarnia (pso)
Perrin, Nicola (pso)

19. Moor Street
Tamworth B79 7QZ
tel (01827) 302600 *fax (01827) 302649*

Brown, Laura (spo)
Burch, Jeffrey
Burke, Richard
Dunford, Sue (p)
Hope, Victoria

Perry, Steven
Simon, Emma
Styles, Kim
Whitehouse, Katie (p)
Williamson, Jeanette
Collins, Diane (pso)
Dunne, Kathryn (pso)
Kaur, Baljeet (pso)
Kendall, Sarah (pso)
Maddox, Lynda (pso)

Unpaid Work Unit

20. Dorrington Drive
Dorrington Industrial Park
Stafford ST16 3 BF
tel (01785) 228608 *fax (01785) 228708*

Cartlidge, John (mgr) (at 1)
Roberts, Peter (qa mgr)
Pedley, Rebecca (placement mgr)
Anthony, Catherine (p, pso)
Harvey, Jeanette (p, pso)

21. Broom Street **Hanley**
Stoke-on-Trent ST1 2EN
tel (01782) 213324 *fax (01782) 286265*

Keeling, Neil (unit mgr)
Barker, Tony (placement mgr)
Lowndes, Chris (placement mgr)
Wootton, Alan (placement mgr)
Bromfield, Peter (pso)
Harrison, Gail (pso)
Lowndes, Tony (pso)

22. 200a Wolverhampton Road
Cannock WS11 1AT
tel (01543) 501003 *fax (01543) 501029*

Harthill, Bill (placement mgr)
Grice, Julie (pso)

23. Unit 1, Crossfields Industrial Estate
Lichfield WS13 6RJ
tel (01543) 263299 *fax (01543) 419360*

Pearson, Ian (unit mgr)
Bradley, Shirley (placement mgr)
Harries, Marc (p, placement mgr)
Thorndyke, John (placement mgr)
Dancer, Amy (pso)
Harries, Marc (p, pso)
Malone, Oliver (pso/placement mgr)

Specialist Units

24. **Public Protection Unit**
Police Headquarters, Baswich House
Cannock Road, Stafford ST17 0OG

tel (01785) 235170/1 *fax (01785) 235172*

White, Mark (unit mgr)
Charlesworth, Margaret (deputy mgr)

25. **Youth Offending Team**
Ringway House, Bryan Street
Hanley Stoke on Trent ST1 5AJ
tel (01782) 235858 *fax (01782) 235860*

Garner, Maureen
Rutter, Barbara (p, pso)

a. Seabridge Youth & Community Centre
Newcastle under Lyme
tel (01782) 297615 *fax (01782) 297616*

Toohey, Michael

b. Anson House, Lammascote Road
Stafford ST16 3TA
tel (01785) 277022 *fax (01785) 277032*

Atkins, Peter

c. The Old House
Eastern Avenue **Lichfield**
tel (01543) 512103 *fax (01543) 512100*

Lawton, Steve

26. **South Staffordshire**
Mentally Disordered Offenders Team
Marston House, St George's Hospital
Corporation Street, Stafford ST16 3AG
tel (01785) 221306 *fax (01785) 221371*

Molloy, Saul

27. **Mentally Disordered Offenders**
Bucknall Hospital
Eaves Lane, Bucknall
Stoke on Trent ST2 8LD
(01782) 275195 ext 2475
fax (01782) 275192

Bettany, Kevin

28. **Stoke Prolific Offenders**
Hanley Police Station
Bethesda Street
Hanley, Stoke on Trent ST1 3DR
tel (01785) 233167 *fax (01785) 233106*

Vacancy (spo)
Brough, Gordon
Malam, Janine
Stoddart, Neal (pso)

29. **The Chase Prolific Offenders Project**
Stafford Police Station

Eastgate Street, Stafford ST16 2DQ
tel (01785) 234024 *fax (01785) 234028*

Goldie, Joanne (spo)
Breeze, Stuart
Pilling, Steve

30. **Newcastle & Moorlands
Prolific Offender Project**
(based at Newcastle & Leek Probation
Offices) (15, 17)

Vacancy (spo)
Flowers, Dave
Stone, Martin

31. **Trent Valley Prolific Offender Project**
(based at Tamworth Police Station)
Spinning School Lane
Tamworth B79 7AP
tel (01782) 234600 *fax (01785) 234605*

Goldie, Joanne (spo)
Gilbert, Sylvia
Woolhouse, John (p)
Brake,Victoria (pso)

Approved Premises (Hostels)

32. **Wenger House Probation
& Bail Hostel**
21a Albert Street
Newcastle-under-Lyme ST5 1HJ
tel (01782) 717423 *fax (01782) 714332*

admin (01782) 622683

Butler, Chris (mgr)
Dalgarno, Claire (deputy mgr)
Azarpour, Reza (probn res services off)
Gordon, John (probn res services off)
Weaver, Peter (probn res services off)

33. **Staitheford House Probation
& Bail Hostel**
14 Lichfield Road, Stafford ST17 4JX
tel (01785) 223417 *fax (01785) 224153*

Yarwood, Ellen (mgr)
Downing, Sue (dep mgr)
Blakemore, Karen (probn res services off)
Butler, David (probn res services off)
Meara, Heidi (probn res services off)

34. **Wharflane House Bail Hostel**
34 Rectory Road, Shelton
Stoke on Trent ST1 4PW
tel (01782) 205554 *fax (01782) 205552*

Yarwood, Ellen (mgr)
Flannagan, Kate (deputy mgr)
Forrester, June (probn res services off)
Scarratt, Ian (probn res services off)
Walters, Sandra (probn res services off)

Institutions

35. H M Prison, 54 Gaol Road
Stafford ST16 3AW
tel (01785) 773000 *fax (01785)249591*

Darby, Paul (spo)
Cavanagh, Ian
Stockall, Steve

36. H M Prison **Dovegate**
Morton Lane, Uttoxeter ST14 8XR
tel (01283) 829400 *fax (01283)820066*

Vacancy (spo)
Boult, Chris
Cairns, Esther
Charlton, Julie
Kidd, Sharon
Robins, Jon
Wellings, Heather

37. H M Prison **Drake Hall**
Eccleshall, Nr Stafford ST21 6LQ
tel (01785) 774100 fax (01785) 774010

Large, Malcolm(p,spo)
Fieldhouse, Kath
Sgroi, Gerald

38. H M Young Offender Institution
Swinfen Hall 18 The Drive
Swinfen, Nr Lichfield
Staffordshire WS14 9QS
tel (01543) 484000 *fax (01543) 484001*

Darby, Paul (spo)
Burroughs, Tammie
Hibbert, Sharon
Powell, Eleanor

39. H M Prison, New Road
Featherstone Wolverhampton
West Midlands WV10 7PU
tel (01902) 703000 *fax (01902) 703001*

Large, Malcolm (p,spo)
Amer, Bob
Vacancy
Skelton, Ken (p)
Evans, Gavin (p,pso)
Salter, James (pso)

Local Justice Areas

17, 18 Central & SW Staffordshire
14, 15, 16 North Staffordshire
12, 19 SE Staffordshire

Crown Courts

10 Stoke-on-Trent
11 Stafford

SUFFOLK PROBATION AREA

Out of hours emergency contact point
The Cottage (01473) 408266
e-mail firstname.surname@suffolk.probation.
gsi.gov.uk

1. **Head Office**
   Peninsular House
   11-13 Lower Brook Street
   Ipswich IP4 1AQ
   tel (01473) 408130 *fax (01473) 408136*

   Budd, John (co)
   Garside, Martin (aco)
   Parker, Kelley (aco)
   Pestell, Steve (aco)
   Sharp, Julia (aco)
   Mansell, Carol (spo, training &
   diversity mgr)
   McLelland-Brown, Mark (spo, perf unit)
   Palmer, Rob (spo, partnerships
   & business improvement)
   Sykes, Tim (mappp mgr)
   Collings, Mark (info systs mgr)
   Patton, Andrew (hd of finance)
   Hornung, Ann (finance mgr)
   Lewis, Gill (hr mgr)
   Coopoosamy, Ruby (supt services mgr)
   Maxam, Juliette (p, comms off)
   Butt, Andrew (p, health & safety advr)

   Central Offender Management
   Woods, Victoria (spo)

   Ipswich Team

   Offender Management
   Abbott, Pat (spo)
   Bergdahl, Jo (spo)
   Pestell, Sari (p, spo)
   Winters, Terry (spo)

   Baldwin, Claire
   Black, Sharon
   Dance, Alison
   Devaux, Daniel
   Dickson, Sarah
   Dunn, Nicola
   Dyde, Clare (p)
   Hawkins, Vicky
   Hewitt, Joy
   Huggins, Wendy
   Lockhart, Sue
   MacDonald, Carolyn
   Mendham, Dene (p, drr)
   Murray, Karen
   Petch, Emma
   Pratt, Melvin
   Rohlfing, Kate (p)
   Scuffins, Carol

Sharpe, Don (drr)
Smith, Rachael
Staines, Leslie
Stock, Corrina
Stone, Katie (p)

Black, Jeanette (pso, drr)
Carney, Louise (pso, crt)
Crawford, Nicky (pso, accom)
Darke, Sula (pso)
De'ath, Ashleigh (pso, crt, temp)
Drew, Michael (pso, crt)
John, Shelley (pso)
Lane, Val (pso, crt
Lee, Sarah (pso)
Parcell, Jayne (pso)
Thelwell, Tom (pso)
Thompson, Liz (pso, crt/victim contact)
Wallis, Karen (pso, temp)
Westren, James (pso, temp)
Wilkins, Sarah (pso, crt/victim contact)

Trainees
Brame, Rachel (pda)
Stevens, Amber (p, pda)
Brinkley, David (p, nvq assessor)
Green, Mandy (p, nvq assessor)
Maudsley, Richard (p, nvq assessor)

Cohort 10
Betts, Alan (trainee)
Charles, Debbie (trainee)
Cossey, Alison (trainee)
Keating-Fedders, Richard (trainee)
McKenzie, Charlotte (trainee)
Pamment, Victoria (trainee)

Cohort 11
Chamberlain, Hamon (trainee)
Tuffin, Amy, (trainee)
Waters, Donna (trainee)

Interventions
Clarke, Richard (p, spo)
Heath, Richard (spo, tvp)
Gladden, Angela (p, facilitator)
Maudsley, Richard (p, trt mgr/faciltr)
Lister, Simone (p, trt mgr/facilitator)
Davis, Shayne (p, facilitator)
Morse, Allwyn (p, pso, trt mgr/tutor)
Robertson, Rachel (pso, tutor)
Smith, Julie (p, pso, tutor)

Reid, Heather (p, tvp trt mgr)
Bateman, Pete (p, tvp)
Herbert, Ann (p, tvp)
Lister, Simone (p, tvp)
Meadows, Karen (p. tvp)
Rickatson, Carmel (p, tvp)
White, Colin (p, tvp)

Other
Fox, Alastair (p, pso, basic skills/ete)
Sage, Lorri (pso women's safety wrkr)

Unpaid Work Scheme
Morrison, Kevin (qa mgr)
Daniel, Andy (p, case mgr)
John Wesley (placement mgr)
Ricketts, Karyn (case mgr)
Stroh, Jim (case mgr)

Peck, Tracy (office mgr)

2. **North Suffolk Probation Centre**
203 Whapload Road
Lowestoft NR32 1UL
tel (01502) 501800 *fax (01502) 525779*

Offender Management
Comyn, Diane (spo)
Hacon, Linda (p, spo)
Taylor, Barbara (spo)
Alden, Graham (p)
Best, Chantelle (p)
Brice, Sue (p)
Curtis, Sally
Everton, Dennis
Ford, Helen (p)
Frost, Jo
Grice, Vicki
Hannant, Maria
Joiner, Elise
Larter, Tracey
Moonoosamy, Krishna
Patel, Haroon
Peacock, Mark
Tandy, Anne (p)
Wilkinson, Emma

Ayres, Sylvia (pso)
Baldry, Maureen (p, pso)
Berry, Christina (p, pso, drr)
Evans, Rosanna (pso)
Martin, Jon (p, pso)
Scott, Jeremy (p, pso)
Vacancy (pso, crt)

Trainees
Brice, Sue (p, pda)
Bransby, Alison (trainee, cohort 11)
Campbell, John (trainee, cohort 11)

Interventions
O'Hanlon, Jane (spo)
Hipperson, Sarah (trt mgr & faciltr)
Alden, Graham (p, facilitator)
Davis, Shayne (p, facilitator)
Barrett, Sarah (p, pso tutor)
Berry, Christina (p, pso, tutor)
Chapman-Wright, Ian (p, pso)
Elvin, Lucy (p, tutor)

Martin, Jon (p, tutor)
Porter, Suzanne (p, tutor)

Other
Elvin, Lucy (p, pso ete)
Suzanne Porter (p, women's safety wrkr)

Unpaid Work Scheme
Houseago, Sally (qa mgr)
Leer, Colin (placement mgr)
Barrett, Sarah (p, placement mgr)
Baldry, Maureen (p, case mgr)
Whyte, Juliet (office mgr)

3. **West Suffolk Probation Centre**
Dettingen Way
Bury St. Edmunds IP33 3TU
tel (01284) 716600 *fax (01284) 716606*

Offender Management
Green Mandy (p, spo)
Hopwood, Andrew (spo)
McNamara, Adele (spo)
Bateman, Pete
Baxter, Kevin
Bertram, Angela
Brinkley, David (p)
Carr, Taryn
Calton, Tracey
Coleman, Sam
Dobell, Stacey
Meiklejohn, Jamie (p)
Ofverberg, Julian
Puscasu, Ioana
Shreeve, Alison
Smeeth, Sarah
Snodgrass, Andrew (p)
Stainton, Jayne
Steel, David (p)
Tattersall, Beth
Wood, Janet

Allen, Kerri (pso)
Barber, Ann (pso)
Bouyer, Herb (p, pso, temp)
Bridge, Colin (pso)
Gaskin-Barber, Aura (p, pso)
Lewis, Fran (pso)
Melvin, Peter (pso)
Moye, Pete (p, pso)
Kingfisher, Wendy (pso, temp)
Pritchard, Hayley (pso)
Roberts, Ian (pso, accom)
Scott, Jeremy (pso)

Trainees
Brinkley, David (p, pda)
Cornell, Sophie (trainee, cohort 10)
Gourlay, Rob (trainee, cohort 10)

Interventions
Foy, Rosemary (spo)

Reuben, Cathy (p, treatment mgr)
Bowman, Anna (facilitator)
Meiklejohn, Jamie (p, facilitator)
Steel, David (p, facilitator)
Beckett, Anna (p, pso, tutor)
Bluett, Marie (pso, tutor)
Chapman-Wright, Ian (p, pso, trt mgr)
Moye, Pete (pso, tutor)

Other
Wogan, Chris (pso, ete)

Unpaid Work Scheme
Key, Martyn (qa mgr)
Hobden, Richard (placement mgr)
Foster, Bryan (case mgr)

Layzell, Karen (office mgr)

Youth Offending Service

Almond, Nick (West Suffolk)
Needham, Marcus (Ipswich)
Vacant (North Suffolk)

Approved Premises (Hostels)

4. **Lightfoot House**
    37 Fuchsia Lane, Ipswich IP4 5AA
    tel (01473) 408280 *fax (01473)* 408282

    Clements, Paul (spo)
    Foden, Jackie (dep mgr)
    Amos, Tony (pso)
    Butler, Marie (pso)
    Goodwin, Denis (pso)
    Last, Paul (pso)
    Murray, Jim (pso)
    Perry, Paul (p, pso)
    Portfleet, Theresa (p, pso)
    Royal, Chris (pso)
    Smith, Jason (pso)
    Templeman, Paul (pso)

5. **The Cottage**
    795 Old Norwich Road
    Ipswich IP1 6LH
    tel (01473) 408266 *fax (01473) 408268*

    Clements, Paul (spo)
    Kersey, Michaela (dep mgr)
    Ball, Reg (pso)
    Breitsprecher, John (pso)
    Chapman, Fran (pso)
    Durrant, Bob (p, pso)
    Firman, Jean (pso)
    Foulger, Malcolm (pso)
    Pender, Lynda (pso)
    Ramshaw, Steph (pso)
    Ridley, Lesley (p, pso)
    Tooke, Sally (pso)

Institutions

6. HM Prison **Blundeston**
    Lowestoft NR32 5BG
    tel (01502) 734500 *fax (01502) 734503*
    direct dial (01502) 73 + ext
    probn clerk ext 4769

    Hacon, Linda (p spo) ext 4568
    Best, Chantelle (p) ext 4766
    Nikki Mead (p) ext 4580
    Moreno, Rene ext 4771
    Mitchell, Christine (p) ext 4768
    Steel, David (p) ext 4580
    Hathway, Taff (pso) ext 4759
    Suso, Hayley (pso) ext 4769

7. H M Prison **Highpoint**
    Stradishall, Newmarket CB8 9YG
    tel (01440) 743100 *fax (01440) 743049*
    direct dial (01440) 74 + ext
    admin clerk ext 3022

    Farrow, Bob (spo) ext 3314
    Gladden, Angela (p) ext
    Goddard, Lynne, ext 3081
    Herbert, Ann (p) ext 3128
    Stewart, Annette (p) ext 3132
    Tozer, Neil ext 3128
    Turnbull, Christine (p) ext
    White, Colin (p) ext 3022
    Case, Adrian (pso) ext 3022

8. H M Prison **Edmunds Hill**
    Stradishall, Newmarket CB8 9YN
    tel (01440) 743500 *fax (01440) 743568*
    direct dial (01440) 74 + ext
    admin clerk ext 3566

    Marshall, Christine (spo) ext 3563
    Mitchell, Anne ext 3721
    Guest, Sheridan (pso) ext 3565
    Salmons, Marie (pso) ext 3567

9. H M Prison & Young Offender Institution
    Hollesley Bay
    Hollesley, Woodbridge IP12 3JW
    tel (01394) 412400 *fax (01394) 412769*
    direct dial (01394) 41 + ext
    parole clerk ext 2500

    Shields, Sue ext 2487

Local Justice Areas

1 SE Suffolk
2 NE Suffolk
3 W Suffolk

Crown Courts

1 Ipswich
1 Bury St Edmunds

SURREY PROBATION AREA

Out of hours emergency contact point
St Catherine's Priory (01483) 571635

Victim enquiries contact number (01483) 860191

e-mail Firstname.Surname@surrey.probation.gsi.gov.uk

abbreviations
om   offender manager
pf   programme facilitator
smo   substance misuse officer

1. **Head Office**
   Bridge House, Flambard Way
   Godalming GU7 1JB
   tel (01483) 860191 *fax (01483) 860295*

   Ball, Yvette (co)
   Pollard, Trish (pa to co and chair)
   Vaughan, Madeleine (dir finance)
   O'Shea, Fiona (sec/admin)
   Hough, Faye (sec/admin)
   Jackson, Isobel (dir offender mngmnt)
   Handley, Sally (director hr)
   Jeremy Cox (dir perf/bus devpt)
   Davis, Barbara (board secy)
   Niechcial, Steve (area mgr, intrvntns)
   Pedrick, Lin (area mgr, om)
   Seagrove, Martin (interim aco)
   Powell, Grace (diversity mgr)
   Little, Ray (public protection mgr)
   Lane, Brenda (corp supt mgr)
   Eley, Hannah (perf & qual mgr)

   King, Kay (hr mgr)
   Barrett, Belinda (hr mgr)
   Filby, Lynsey (hr officer)
   Clark, Becky (temp hr officer)
   Rowley, Julie (hr administrator)
   Adams, Kylie (hr administrator)
   Thompson Carole (hr administrator)
   Russell, Pam (hr co-ord)
   Stewart, Julie (staff devpt mgr)
   Layzell, Judith (DipPS mgr/pda)
   Stolworthy, Tim (staff devpt off)
   Goff, Charlotte (training admin)

   Slee, Chris (principal IT off)
   Edwards, Phil (it off)
   Lawrence, Julie (it off)
   Newman, Richard (it off)

   Thomas, Kevin (perf & info off)
   Hooper, Rhian, (perf & qual info off)

   Lewis, Arlene (finance mgr)
   Barratt, Janet (finance technician)

Hammond, Sophie (finance technician)
Allen, Keith (health & safety off)
Gibson, Christine (VISOR admin)
Windless, Kate (corp supt admin)

2. Probation Centre, White Rose Court
   Oriental Road **Woking** GU22 7PJ
   tel (01483) 776262 *fax (01483) 727244*

   Offender Management Team
   Fletcher, Tamsin (mgr)
   Jeffries, Victoria (snr om)
   Cannon, Sarah (snr om)
   Baker, Emma
   Brandon-Trye, Charlotte
   Cameron, Vivienne
   Davies, Siân
   Day, Sarah
   Drapper, Susan
   Frith, Sarah
   Green, Andrew
   Hobson, Zoe
   Howe, Dawn
   Jacobsen, Timothy
   Potts, Darren
   Rozmanowski, Nicole
   Thomas, Adam
   Yeoman, Kevin
   Wardell, Amie

   Fern, Scott (trainee)
   Oakley, Lauren (trainee)
   Pain, Leigh (trainee)
   Hamilton, Andrihette (crt liaison off)
   Lewis, Philip (crt liaison off)
   Di Lauro, Giusj (crt liaison off)
   Tartari, Seren (crt co-ord)
   Mansfield, Diana (centre co-ord)
   Taylor, Josephine (case admin)
   Mulligan, Alison (case admin)
   Bentley, Holly (case admin)
   Bance, Jane (case admin)
   Trenchard, Susan (case admin)
   Raynor, Mandy (case admin)
   Allum, Elaine (receptionist)
   Backen, Katharina (receptionist)
   MacNeill, Joanna (receptionist)

   Programmes Team
   Porter, Louise (mgr offending behaviour)
   Clay, Maribel (trtmnt mgr, ob)
   Myers, Fran (trtmnt mgr, ob)
   Strong, Lynne (trtmnt mgr, IDAP & TVSOGP)
   Reynolds, Emma (trtmnt mgr, IDAP & facil)

   Coggan, Carol (pf)
   Conaboy, Chris (pf)

Hubner, Pauline (pf)
Moffitt, David (pf)
Winstone, Lisa (pf)
Fuller, Anne (pf)
Ballantine, J (pf, ob)
Henderson, C (pf, ob)
Parsons, Dawn (pf, ob)
Steen, Becci (pf, ob)
Todd, C (pf, ob)
Biggs, Catherine (prog co-ord)
Rees, Laureen (prog co-ord)

Substance Misuse Team
Homyer, Ros (mgr)
Hall, Carl (deputy mgr/trtmnt mgr osap)
Coulson, Louise (team co-ord)
Merricks, Rachel (team co-ord)

Unpaid Work
Whittle, James (mgr)
Westwood, Emma (qa mgr)
Howard, Malcolm (dev off)
Palmer, Michael (dev off)
Wright, Peter (project off)
Ponsford, Chris (project off)
Coles, Garry (project leader)
Ferranti-Donavellas, Teresa (project off)
Puttick, Terry (project off)
Pilsworth, Linda (placement co-ord)
Kler, Dalbir (placement co-ord)

Victim Liaison Team
Allum, Elaine (vlo)
Considine, Mary (vlo)
Clark, Lis (p, vlo & p, co-ord)

3. Probation Centre
    College House, Woodbridge Road
    Guildford GU1 4RS
    tel (01483) 534701 *fax (01483) 453702*

Offender Management Team
Jones, Simon (mgr)
Higgs, Brian (snr om)
Butt, Mark
Dennis, Mark (p)
Ferns, Glynn-Anne
Grayson, Anna
Greenhow, Nicola
Holt, Anna
McClure, Tracy (p)
Moore, Margaret
Pringle, Sally
Rosati, Jo
Sale, Heather
Silvester, Jo
Stone, Alan
Timoney, Alicia
Wilson, Joanna

Barford, Francesca (trainee)
Coutts, Natasha (trainee)
Lowe, Rachel (trainee)
Potter, Gemma (trainee)

English, Alison (assessment supt off)
Smart, Coleen, (centre co-ord)
Allen, Graham (case co-ord)
Lunnon, Sally (crt co-ord)
Broughton, Eleanor (case admin)
Percy, Lily (case admin)
Campbell, Rebecca (case admin)
Jones, Faith (temp case admin)
Hathaway, Jenny (crt liaison off)
Riordan, Julia (crt liason off)
Leach, Bernice (receptionist)
Jones, Rebecca (receptionist)
Walpole Nikki (receptionist)

Staff Development
Morrison, Rosina (pda)
Skeet, Lorraine (pda)
Sullivan, Tina (pda)

Substance Misuse Team
Heathcote, Jacquie (smo, B)
Allen, Angela (smo, B)
Bateman, Lee (smo, B)
Crowsley, Louisa (smo, B)
Singleton, Debbie (smo, A)
Paszkiewicz, Ewa (smo, A)

Housing Unit
Oakes, Nicholas, (snr housing off)

4. Probation Centre, Allonby House
    Hatchlands Road **Redhill RH1 6BN**
    tel (01737) 763241 *fax (01737) 765688*

Offender Management Team
Edwards, Charles (mgr)
Ayers, Carol (snr om)
Simpkins, Sue (snr om)
Neuert, Catherine (snr om)
Amor, Charlotte
Andrews, Emily
Armstrong, Jenny
Berry, Michelle
Botha, Kate
Cissokho, Kirsty (p)
Clark, Richard
Derbyshire, Gordon
Glenn, Nicola
Godly, Gemma
Groves, Jo
Heley, Helen
James, Caroline
Jones, Sally (p)
Kirk, Valerie
Mott, Helen (p)

Redfern, Holly
Rose, Gemma
Sullivan, Tina (p)
Sweetman, Julie
Thomas, Nicola
Westwood, Jane
Woollett, Chris

Lapsley, Kerrie (trainee)
Saunders, Katy (trainee)

Bruton, Olive (assessmnt supt off)
O'Brien, Lin (assessmnt supt off)
Freeman, David (crt liaison off)
Hounslow, David (crt liaison off)
Orton, Collette (crt liaison off)
Regan, J (crt liaison off)

McConnell, Pauline (centre co-ord)
Bergin, Kim (case admin)
Perkin Natasha (case admin)
Waghorn, Maggie (case admin)
Wilmott, Lewis (case admin)
Wilson, Peter (case admin)
Garland, Marie (case admin)
Brown, Michaela (case admin)
Clarkson, Jacqui (case admin)
Clare, Caroline (crt support off)
Coignet, Victoria (receptionist)
Frost, Shelley (receptionist)
Jeffree, Susan (receptionist)

Substance Misuse Team
Greenwood, Leah (smo, B)
Scoffham, Barbara (smo, A)
Porter, Jane (smo, A)

Unpaid Work
Ditzel, Nick (deputy mgr)
Spiller, Sue (devpt off)
Westgate, Alan (devpt off)
Evans, Les (proj leader)
Dean, Paul (proj off)
Hilliard, Brian (project off)
McIlwraith, Lee (placment coord)
Reynolds, Helen (placement co-ord)
Stubbings, Valerie (placement co-ord)

5. Probation Centre, Swan House
    Knowle Green **Staines**
    Middlesex TW18 1XS
    tel (01784) 459341 *fax (01784) 449932*

    Offender Management Team
    Evenden, Roz (mgr)
    Parsons, Jennifer (snr om)
    Burchmore, Lucy (snr om)
    Desai, Paula (snr om)
    Baker, Nicola
    Butler, Jo

Cullen, Christina
Gratien-Pillai, Michelle
Howard, Melody
McCrae, Louise
Millar, Randall
Moulinie, Delores
O'Connell, Louise
Unwin, Carly
Stocker, Cathy
White, Marc
Williams, Zoe

Davis, Jonathan (trainee)
Hillsdon, Freya (trainee)
Kerr, Helen (trainee)
Lewin, Joanna (trainee)
Miles, Paul (trainee)

Wolfe, Jacky (case admin)
Bristow, Medina (case admin)
Calvert, Ann Marie (case admin)
Theobalds, Charlotte (case co-ord)
Costello, Isobel (crt liaison off)
Mason-Thompson, Maria (crt liaison off)
Smart, James (crt liaison off)
Jennings, Jenny (crt admin)
Mookherji, Hanna (crt admin)

Pilatowicz, Lisa (centre admin)
Dell, Ashley (receptionist)
Ungless, Stacey (receptionist)

Substance Misuse Team
McAnuff, Doreen (smo, A)
Irving, Morine (smo, B)

Unpaid Work
Houghton, Angela (devpt off)
Wheeler, Keith (project off)

Housing Unit
Stocker, Cathy (housing off)

6. **The Crown Court**
    Bedford Road, Guildford GU1 4ST
    tel (01483) 568561 *fax (01483) 306724*

    West, Jan (temp mrg)
    Lane, Lynda (crown crt liaison off)
    Lawlor, Karen (crown crt liaison off)

7. **Youth Justice Service**
    Quadrant Court, 35 Guildford Road
    Woking GU22 7QQ
    tel (01483) 517000 *fax (01483) 517007*

    Wells, Toby (cty mgr)
    Hibbert, Geoff (mgr west)

7a. **Youth Justice Service**
    The Mansion, Church Street

Leatherhead KT22 8DP
tel (01372) 363655 *fax (01372) 363675*

Patchet, Mark (mgr east)
Reid, Janice (yjo)
Matt Raleigh (yjo)

Approved Premise (Hostel)

8. **St Catherine's Priory**
Ferry Lane, Portsmouth Road
Guildford GU2 4EE
tel (01483) 571635 *fax (01483) 454130*

Adams Mike (act mgr)
Brown, Jude (deputy mgr)
Doe, Robert (cmo, residential)
Stewart, Nicole (cmo, residential)
Whitelaw, Ellie, (cmo, residential)
Duncton, Adam (cmo, residential)
Lee, Adrian (cmo, residential)
Lake, Angela (cmo, residential)
Gwarisa, Bob (night supvr)
Olejnik, Sam (night supvr)

Institutions

9. H M Prison **Coldingley**
Shaftesbury Road
Bisley, Woking GU24 9EX
tel (01483) 804300 *fax (01483) 804427*

Parole Clerk ext 4366
Special visits ext 4418

Bazlington, Pepi (th'care mgr) ext 4384
Riley, Jenny (risk, resettlement off)

10. H M Prison **Send**
Ripley Road, Send
Nr Woking GU23 7LJ
tel (01483) 471000 *fax (01483) 471001*

Parole clerk/HDC Clerk 471008
Discipline 471006
Reception desk OMU 471051

Turner Lesley (mgr, omu) 471051
Braim, Ginny (offender suprvr) 471063
Frost, Lisa (offender suprvr) 471058
White, Lucy (pso, offender suprvr) 471252
Curtis, Vic (ets facil/oasys assessor) 471060
Allen, Stephanie (ets trtmnt mgr) 471050

11. H M Prison **Downview**
High Down Lane
Sutton, Surrey SM2 5PD
tel 020-8196 6300 *fax 020-8196 6301*

Probn clerk ext 389
Discipline ext 299

Special visits ext 285

Anderson, Daniel (mgr) ext 300
Fallows, Samantha (th'care off)
Petrillo, Madeleine (th'care off)
Woghiren, Sharon (th'care off)

12. H M Prison **High Down**
High Down Lane
Sutton, Surrey SM2 5PJ
tel 0207 147 6300 *fax 0207 147 6301*

Probn clerk ext 6617
Custody office ext 6309
Video link ext 6400
Special visits ext 6500

Mclean, Marion (mgr)
Be, Zanab (th'care off)
Eastham, Liz (th'care off)
Weston, Rebecca (th'care off)
Bedborough, Carole (th'care supt off)
Greener, Emily (th'care supt off)
Ramshaw, Lauren (th'care supt off)
Sterry, Gemma (th'care supt off)

13. H M Prison **Bronzefield**
Woodthorpe Road
Ashford, Middx TW15 3JZ
tel (01784) 425690 *fax (01784) 425691*

Larkins, Georgina (mgr)
Evans, Hannah (th'care off)
Barton-Crosby, Jennifer (th'care supt off)
Bheenick, Melissa (th'care supt off)
Shearer, Leon (th'care supt off)
Sturney, Simeon (th'care supt off)

Local Justice Areas

2 North West Surrey
3 South West Surrey
4 South East Surrey
5 North Surrey

Crown Court

6 Guildford

SUSSEX PROBATION AREA

Out of hours emergency contact point:
(01273) 622300

Victim enquiries contact number: (01273) 810410/1

e-mail Firstname.Surname@sussex.probation. gsi.gov.uk

1. **Head Office**
   185 Dyke Road, Hove
   Brighton BN3 1TL
   tel (01273) 227979 *fax (01273) 227972*

   Crozier, Sonia (co)
   Steele, John (board chair)
   Wells, Steve (board secy)

   Smart, Nick (aco director of operations)

   Berrill, Judith (aco h.r.)
   Browne, Jane (aco W Sussex)
   Hayde, Elspeth (aco h.r.)
   Hossain, Tareque (aco finance, & facilities)
   Saunders, Andrea (aco E Sussex)
   Wing, Arthur (aco)

   P.A. to Chief Officer
   Penfold, Imogen (mgr)

   Commissioning and Quality
   Ainscough, Valerie (commissioning and quality mgr)
   Arthur, Valerie (commissioning & quality p.o)

   Communications
   Hustwayte, Rob (comm mgr)

   Administration and Facilities
   Roycroft, Diane (p.a. to s.m.t)
   Simpson, Jan (asst corporate serv mgr)
   Taylor, Katie (admin asst)
   Rolf, Jason (receptionist)

   Training & Development
   Jones, Philip (mgr)
   Cassell, Jon (admin)

   Human Resources
   Attree, Sara (h.r. advr)
   Brigham-Wilmot, Justine (h.r. co-ord)
   Goncalves, Lynda (h.r. advr)
   Jeffries, Lizzie (h.r. ass.)
   Lucas, Tracy (h.r. advr)
   Muir, Julia (h.r. advr)

   Finance
   Savage, Lisa (mgr)
   Chauhan, Sangita (finance off)
   Goldberg, Mauricia (finance off)

   Shaddick, Angela (finance asst)

   I.T.
   Ehsan, Azeem (i.t system supt off)
   Piper, Walter (i.t. system supt off)
   Smedley, Alistare (i.t. trainer)
   Funnell, Lesley (i.t. co-ord)

   Performance & Excellence
   Gieler, Stefan (perf & excellence mgr)
   Finella, Giorgio (perf analyst)
   Murray, Laura (perf analyst)
   Snashall, Peter (data quality officer)
   Thrussell, Jackie (perf analyst)

   MAPPA
   Bamford, Mark (co-ord)
   Meyer, Victoria (ViSOR admin)

2. 47 Grand Parade
   Brighton BN2 9QA
   tel (01273) 810300 *fax (01273) 810399*

   Accommodation Services Team
   Blomfield, Sarah (housing co-ord)

   Offender Management Team
   Rogers, Leighe (spo)
   Knight, Kate (dep team mgr)
   Smithson, Paul (dep team mgr)
   Wood, Joanie (dep team mgr)

   Allcorn, Chris
   Bruton, Shane
   Coney, Yve
   Cummings, Dennis
   Dillon, Josh
   Evident, Gary
   Gerrard, Jake
   Hanmer, Poppy
   Harbane, Jean
   Hardy, Alison
   Herring, Sharon
   Lee, Adam
   Ley, Suzanne
   Reeve, Danielle
   Richards, Jonathan
   Rowlins, Stephen
   Shaw, Robert
   Smith, Marie
   Streeter, Linda
   Vickery, Tiffany
   Williams, Louise

   Carr, Sean (pso)
   Conduct, Emma (pso)
   Earney, Craig (pso)
   Eason, Catherine (pso)
   Fowler, Jennifer (pso)
   Hall, Olivia (pso)
   Hollington, Abigail (pso)

Light, Jacqui (pso)
Mclean, Janis (pso)
Smith, Naomi (pso)
Taylor, Abigail (pso)
Thomas, Anne (pso)
Thornton, Erica (pso)
Wray, Sarah (pso)

Public Protection Team
Bauermeister, Fiona (spo)
Alford, Liz
Bridger, Rick
Davis, Vivien
Gerrard, Wendy
Lambert, Anna
Masterson, Mark
Peacock, Philippa
Manning, Sue (admin)
Williams, Beth (admin)

Victim Liaison and Courts
Yvonne Bishop (spo)

Victims' Team
Lunderstedt, Max (vlo)
Bullock, Alex (admin)

Unpaid Work / community payback
Barzdo, Lara (operations mgr)
Berry, Stephen (placement sourcing off)
Bligh, Sean (placement supervising off)
Budgen, Sarah (pso)
Fox, Alex (placement co-ord off)
Green, Shane (placement co-ord off)
Hopkins, Kate (placement co-ord off
Apthorpe, Colin (placement suprvsng off)
Clements, Peter (placement suprvsng off)
Streeter, Mark (placement suprvsng off)

Administration and Facilities
Garrod, Lorraine (admin mgr)
Wood, Karen (admin mgr)
Bond, Paula (admin)
Coulson, Charlie (admin)
Dawes, Lisa (admin)
Godding, Lisa (admin)
Hewland, Teresa (admin)
Ivison, Nancy (admin)
Ivors, Cameron (admin)
Kochnari, Kate (admin)
Matthews, Nathaniel (admin)
Mearns, Lorraine (admin)
Paul, Katy (admin)
Ring, Maya (admin)
Roughly, Lucy (admin)
Soopraya, Gerard (admin)
Watts, Ann (admin)
Wheeler, Wendy (admin)

Accredited Programmes
Haynes, Andrea (spo)
Freeborn, Lance (dep team mgr)
Jarvis, Fiona (dep team mgr)
Maxwell, Leon (dep team mgr)
Cook, Steve (treatment mgr)
Charles, Maggie
Hughes, Siri
Jones, Kevin
Powley, Dean
Burt, Tim (prog tutor)
Davies, Micheal (prog tutor)
Donaldson, Linda (prog tutor)
Enzor, Suzanne (prog tutor)
Oko, Steve (prog tutor)
Stevens, Teresa (prog tutor)
Tilbury, Guy (prog tutor)
Wileman, Matilda (prog tutor)

Rudd, Wendy (snr admin)
Swift, Amy (admin)
Town, Abigail (admin)

ETE
McBean, Andrew (ete admin)
Spence, Susan (ete admin)
Breary, Andrew (basic skills trainer)
Smuts, John (basic skills tutor)
Williams, Paul (Nacro basic skills ptnrshp mgr)

Persistent OffendersTeam
Herring, Sharon (po)
Williams, Louise (po)
Eason, Catherine (pso)
Berry, Hannah (admin)

PDA Team
Marsh, Christine (pda)
Whitehead, Alison (pda)
Moors, Matthew (pda)
Cook, Jonathon (trainee)
Grifiths, Anthony (trainee)
Hunt, Jennifer (trainee)
Melrose, Rea (trainee)
Nevitt, Helen (trainee)
Robertson, Jenny
Skinner, Amy (trainee)
Rowlins, Stephen (trainee)

2a. **Youth Offending Team**
Brighton & Hove
22 Ship Street **Brighton** BN1 1AD
tel (01273) 296169

Howe, Angela

3. 8 Market Avenue
Chichester PO19 1YF
tel (01243) 787651 *fax (01243) 781151*

Offender Management
Leeming, Su (SPO)
Slatter, Kathryn (dep team mgr)
Clement, Dee
Snell, Victoria
Elphick Elyse
Trusson, Katie (pso)
Cotton, Carla (pso)
Helen McCarthy (pso)
Sally Field (pso)
Lavender, Geoff (pso)
Taylor, Stephen (pso)

Administration and Facilities
Broad, Trudy (admin mgr)
Chapman, Victoria (admin)
Bolton, Sophie (admin)
Guy, Sarah (admin)

Unpaid Work/community payback
Burden, Mark (spo)

4. The Old Glassworks
    c/o Christian Care Association
    St Cyriac's **Chichester** PO19 1AJ
    tel (01243) 775925 *fax (01243) 771914*

    Blanchflower, Colin (resettlement co-ord)
    Hipkiss, Jan (day centre mgr)
    Williams, Dominic (outreach wrkr)

5. Goffs Park House
    Old Horsham Road **Crawley**
    West Sussex RH11 8PB
    tel (01293) 525216 *fax (01293) 525215*

Offender Management Team
Fairbrother, Margaret (spo)
Arnold, Sally (dt mgr)
Youngs, Martyn (dt mgr)

Bannister, Claire
Bray, Jason
Budden, Claire
Clarke, Lesley
Dowse, Philippa
Fagan, Janet
Jenkins, Emma
Mortimer, Canan
Steele, Natalie
Wilson, Jane
Wilson, Susan
Wood, Joanne

Bradley, Jan (pso)
Foreman, Anna (pso)
Gale, Tania (pso)
Nicholas, Harvinder (pso)
Palin, Shelly (pso)
Stewart, Neil (pso)

Sweeney, Vicky (pso)
Wallis, Karen (pso)
Lees, Philip (breach off)

Foreign National Unit
Jones, Carol (pso)
Lane, Chris (admin)

Public Protection Team
Tierney, Jo (spo)
Barton, Jo
Blair, Lisa

Victims Team
Thorpe, Jennie (vlo)

Unpaid Work
Gear, Beverley (operations mgr)
Ali, Ehsan (placement co-ord off)
Benson, Paul (placement supervising off)
Cox, John (placement supervising off)
Pool, Anthony (placement supervising off)
Streeter, Stephen (placement supervising off)
Tomlinson, Rachel (placement sourcing off)
Wilkie, Christina (admin)

Accredited Programmes
Goodchild, Heather
Nicholson, Sarah (treatment mgr)
Murray, Ian (prog tutor)
Barker, Graham (prog tutor)
McKellar, Abigail (prog tutor/treatment mgr)
Pearce, Corrine (prog tutor)

PDA Team
Weir-Wilson, Maggie (pda)
Matthew Moors (pda)
Triggs, Nicola (trainee)
Knapman, Beverley (trainee)
Barnes, Simon (trainee)
Cronshaw, Lindsey (trainee)
Brown Sarah (trainee)
Brown Victoria (trainee)
Dolby Sonia (trainee)
Smith Theresa (trainee)

Persistent Offenders Team
Durrans, Elizabeth
Clay, Andy (police officer)
Sweeney, Vicky (pso)

Administration and Facilities
Townend, Peter (admin mgr)
Barnett Sylvia (admin)
Clarke, Yvonne (admin)
Eells, Christine (admin)
Holmes, Janet (admin)
Lane, Chris (admin)
Ley, Michelle (admin)

Lockett Louise (admin)
Mancey Christine (admin)
Robson, Alex (admin)
Paterson, Rose (admin)
Turley, Doreen (admin)
Wilks, Claire (admin)

6. **Youth Offending Team**
190 Three Bridges Road
Crawley RH10 1LN
tel (01293) 643450 *fax (01293) 643472*

Padfield, Joseph (spo)
Coombes, Jessica

7. 35 Old Orchard Road
Eastbourne BN21 1DD
tel (01323) 746200 *fax (01323) 439755*

Offender Management Team
Young, Keith (spo)
Edwards, Martin (dep team mgr)
Maxwell, Nicola (dep team mgr)
Adams, Trish
Clifford, Anna
Cooper, Peter
Dove, Joseph
Lang, Joanna
Potter, Jodie
Ockenden, Elly
Skipworth, Helen
Spiers, Angela
Winthe, Serge

Morgan, Bronwyn (trainee)
Patterson, Kate (trainee)

Bisby, Rachel (pso)
Collier, Jodie (pso)
Cook, Louise (pso)
Foreman, Liz (pso)
Greenstock, Gordon (pso)
Hanson, Terry (pso)
Lacey, Karen (pso)
Level, Karen (pso)
Little, Joanne (pso)
Melbert, Cathryn (pso, apt)
Perkins, Janet (pso)
Westbrook, Paul (pso)
Broom, Brenda (breach off)

Public Protection Team
Barnes, Jennifer
Lightfoot-Bennett Richie
Stevens, Tim
Parkes, Alison (pso)
Wood, Frank (pso)

Accomodation Services Team
Scott, Louise (hs co-ord)

ETE
Burgess, Louise (basic skills trainer)
MacDermott, Sandie (ete)
Ramakrishnan, Kim (ete)

Housing Co-ordinator
Wilkins, Debbie (housing off)

Prolific Offenders
Hughes, Dave (police off)

Administration and Facilities
Reed, Pat (admin mgr)
Brennan, Sarah (admin)
Bettridge, Jennifer (admin)
Kerry, Stepha (admin)
Lapins, Dan (admin)
McWall, Karen (admin)
Murphy, Cheryl (admin)
Needham, Christine (admin)
Stone, Susan (admin)
Webb, Helen (admin)

8. 1 St Leonards Road
Eastbourne BN21 3UH
tel (01323) 749555 *fax (01323) 738484*

Accredited Programmes Team
Ncube, Emmanual (treatment mgr)
Warner-Swann, Johanna (treatment mgr)
Smyth, Louise (prog tutor)
Hellier, Wendy (prog tutor)
Marshall, Vanessa (prog tutor)
Wallis, Jodie (prog tutor)

Health & Safety
Ferguson, Derek (h&s advr)

Unpaid Work
Barzdo, Lara (operation mgr)
Lennie, Gary (placment co-ord off)
Downs, Nick (placement co-ord off)
Bryant, Justine (placement supervising off)
Lanigan, Joseph (placement supervising off)
Akinwale, John (placement supervising off)
Houlten, Diane (admin)

9. Crozier House, 1A Shepherd Street
St Leonards-on-Sea TN38 0ET
tel (01424) 448600 *fax (01424) 448601/2*

Offender Management Team
Richardson, Martin (spo)
Hicks, Katy (dep team mgr)
Taylor, Malcolm (dep team mgr)
Adams, Kirsten
Batcheler, Kimberley
Bower-Feek, Veronica
Glover, Sarah
Hamberis, Emma

Platts, Chris
Satchell, David
Sawyer, Anne
Sullivan, Andrew

George, Marian (pso)
Harris, Pat (pso)
Jinks, Deans (pso)
Macnair, Maria (pso)
Madge, Noelyne (pso)
Webb, Michael (pso)
Willis, Joanne (pso)
Tipper, Tracey (breach off)

Crosby, Jane (admin)
Hitchman, Paula (admin)
Lawrence, Diana (admin)
Morris, Susan (admin)
Mosley, Lyn (admin)
Murphy, Kirstie (admin)
Nicholls, Hazel (admin)
Tanner, Tanya (admin)

PDA Team
Thomson, Clare (pda)
Warrick, Judith (pda)
Denestah, Siamack (trainee)
Fieldhouse, Jill (trainee)
Harrod, Lisa (trainee)
Lennard, Deborah (trainee)
Mayhew, Ben (trainee)
Whitmore, Lee (trainee)

Public Protection Team
Carr, Susie (spo)
Saunders, Rita
Connolly, Jenny
Batchelor, Gillian
Wells, Anne (pso)

Victims Team
Bayliss, Caroline (vlo)

Persistent Offenders Team
Lee, Cliff (police off)
Oakley, Victoria
Goddard, Nicky (pso)

Accredited Programmes
Furlong, Michaela (treatment mgr)
Coleman, Sharon (prog tutor)
Delaney, Mick (prog tutor)
Hambling, Phil (prog tutor)
Melbert, Cathryn (prog tutor)

Unpaid Work/Community Payback
Bond, Peter (placement co-ord off)
Browning, Lee (placement sourcing off)
Isted, Glen (placement sourcing off)
Terry, Robert (placement supervising off)
Wardroper, Tom (placement sourcing off)

ETE
Boden, John (basic skills trainer)
Giles, Tony (ete casewrkr)
Giles, Sue (ete casewrkr)

Administration and Facilities
Everson, Martha (admin mgr)

10. **Youth Offending Team**
East Sussex YOT
33 Cambridge Road **Hastings** TN34 1DL
tel (01424) 446396

Newing, Mike
Preston, Peter

11. The Court House
Friars Walk **Lewes** BN7 2PG
tel (01273) 477117 *fax (01273) 483843*

Thomas, Anne (pso/breach off)

Unpaid Work/Community payback
Burden, Mark (spo)
Berry, Stephen (placement sourcing off)
Crouch, Peter (placement sourcing mgr)

12. **Crown Courts**
a. The Law Courts
High Street **Lewes** BN7 1YB
tel (01273) 487608 *fax (01273) 487610*

Administration and Facilities
Garrod, Lorraine (admin mgr)
Wood, Karen (admin mgr)

b. Crown Court
Lansdowne Road **Hove** BN3 3BN
tel (01273) 778843 *fax (01273) 720532*

Blyghton, Anne
Donnelly, Sue
Muller, Lynn
Rhodes, Lawrie

Offender Management Team
Shaw Cromarty, Elizabeth (pso)
Hurworth, Clare (admin)
Murray, Stewart (admin)

13. Meadowfield House, East Street
Littlehampton BN17 6AU
tel (01903) 711500 *fax (01903) 711555*

Offender Management Team
Butler, Michelle (spo)
Bailey, Marcus (dep team mgr)
Jones, Paul (dep team mgr)
Ajaegbu, Christiana
Fagan, Janet
Fletcher, Ashley
Carter, Kay (pso)
Davies, Bridget (pso)

Stevens, Helen (pso)
Turner, Andrea (pso)
Denyer, Zoe (admin)
Turner, Andrea (breach off)
Gathercole, Christine (breach admin)
Lovely, Linda (admin)
Springett, Sally (admin)
Treharne, Owain (admin)

Public Protection
Carey, Louisa
Greene, Shelley
Mason, Janet
Tattersall, Lisa (admin)

Unpaid Work/Community payback
Gear, Beverley (operations mgr)
Heather, Bernie (plcmnt suprvsng off)
Valente, Ken (plcmnt suprvsng off)
Cairns, Rob (plcmnt co-ord off)
Fairbrother, Carl (plcmnt suprvsng off)
Unsted, Lesley (plcmnt co-ord off)
Field, Jacqueline (plcmnt suprvsng off)
Trew, Jean (admin)

Accredited Programmes
Ayliffe, Glenda (treatment mgr)
Jackson, Serena
Burns, Ray (prog tutor)
Lockwood, Richard (prog tutor)
Rogers, Siobhan (prog tutor)

PDA Team
Budge, Lucy (trainee)
Hadaway, Paul (trainee)
Walsh, Caroline (trainee)

Administration and Facilities
Porcas, Sarah (cpt srvs mgr)
Buss, Catherine (admin mgr)

13a. **Youth Offending Team**
County Buildings, East Street
Littlehampton
tel (01903) 718739

Mann, Simon

14. 4 Farncombe Road
Worthing BN11 2BE
tel (01903) 216321 *fax (01903) 204287*

Offender Management Team
Richards,Jonathon (dep team mgr)
Adams, Judith
Allnutt, Claire
Baird, Cheryl
Brownsey-Joyce, Carole
Britton, Joanna
Oldfield, Rebecca
Burt, Tim

McGuire, Kathy
Shaw, Stacey
Turner, Claire

Benham-Hernetz, David (pso)
Exton, Jackie (pso)
Goody, Jackie (pso)
Gowler, Jackie (pso)
Khamlichi, Lamya (pso)
Mustchin, Suzie (pso)
Scarletson, Gemma (pso)
Thompson, Rachel (pso)
Eaton, Barbara (breach off)

Quibell, Sarah (admin mgr)
McGowan, Laura (admin)
Borrer, Jean (admin)
Moore, Matthew (admin)
Phillips, Terry (admin)
Scott, Louise (admin)

Public Protection Team
Browne, Jane (spo)
Bains, Sam
Fletcher, Ashley
Claw, Katherine (pso)

Accredited Programmes
Gregory-Guider, Eleanor
Miles, Peter (treatment mgr)
Knight, Debbie (treatment mgr)
Leach, Sarah (prog tutor)
Miller, Peter (prog tutor)
Brown, Stephen (apt admin)

ETE Partnership
Saunders, Melanie (ete admin)
Muir, Eve (ptnrshp mgr)

Persistent Offenders Team
Exton, Jackie (pso)

Accommodation Services Team
Philip, Cathy (hsg co-ord)

PDA Team
Newton, Chris (pda)
Danvers-Wright, Kate (trainee)
Hill, Karen (trainee)
Lansdowne, Sarah (trainee)
Carr, Catherine (trainee)
Snell, Victoria (trainee)

15. Options Project, 24 Grafton Road
Worthing BN11 4QP
tel (01903) 204539 *fax (01903) 209416*

Approved Premise (Hostel)

16. Approved Premises, 162 Marine Parade
Brighton BN2 1EJ
tel (01273) 622300 *fax (01273) 623486*

Jones, Allan (spo/mgr)
Mcrae, Jenny (dept. mgr)
Bridges, Melanie (admin)
Bickerstaff, Kate (os)
Collins, Frank (os)
Dury, Min (os)
Glover, Natasha (os)
Hare, Wendy (os)
Howard, Mark (os)
McLoughlin, Nessa (os)
Croskell, Ian (night supvr)
Ndluvu, Ndaba (night supvr)

Institution

17. HM Prison Lewes
Brighton Road **Lewes** BN7 1EA
tel (01273) 785100 *fax (01273) 785101*
direct dial (01273) 78 + ext

Booth, Sally (dep team mgr)
Anderson, Max
Montero, Rosemary
Morrissey, Michael
Bescoby, Steve (pso)
Earnshaw, Claire (pso)
Gough, Amanda (pso)
Littlejohn, Emily (pso)
Teare, Andy (pso)
Wisby, Emily (pso)

18. HM Prison **Ford**
Arundel BN18 0BX
tel (01903) 663000 *fax (01903) 663001*
probn (01903) 663195/663186
probn fax (01903) 663197

Martin, Claire (spo) 663209
Hull, Terry 663237
Payne, Jill 663188
Sharples, Henry 663201
Walker, Julie 663185
Davey, Charlotte (pso) 663206

Local Justice Areas

2, 14 Sussex (Central)
7, 9 Sussex (Eastern)
3, 14, 15 Sussex (Western)
7, 11 Sussex (Northern)

Crown Court

12 Chichester
12 Lewes

TEESSIDE PROBATION AREA

Out of hours emergency number
(01642) 826606/456811

Victim enquiries contact number (01642) 247438

e-mail Firstname.surname@teesside.
probation.gsi.gov.uk

1. **Head Office**
6th Floor, Centre North East
73-75 Albert Road
Middlesbrough TS1 2RU
tel (01642) 230533 *fax (01642) 220083*

Lumley, Elaine (co)
Thomas, Brian (dir, business devpt unit, Teesside & Durham)
Saiger, Lucia (dir, offender mngmnt, Teesside only)
Holdhusen, Barbara (dir, hr, staff devpt, pract training, diversity, Teesside & Durham)
Rackstraw, David (brd secy/ head of legal services, Teesside & Durham)
Beckett, Tina (asst dir)
Portues, Russell (asst dir)
Burnett, Peter (asst dir)
Allan, Julie (asst dir)
Armstrong, Jill (staff devpt mgr, Teesside and Durham)
Harrison (née Lipthorpe), Denise (hr mgr, Teesside and Durham)
Petrie, Rod (health & safety advr)
Vitty, Helen (it & info mgr, Teesside and Durham)
Craig, Philip (dir, finance, Teesside and Durham)
Gleeson, Joanne (business devpt mgr, Teesside and Durham)
Gallant, Julie (alliances & volunteer/ mentor co-ordinator)
Coyle, Margaret (pa to co)

Teesside Interventions Clearing House
Gorbutt, Jane (clearing hse off)
Padgett, Chris (performance mgr)
Martin, Sam (dep mgr)
Hazell, Robin

2. 160 Albert Road
Middlesbrough TS1 2PZ
tel (01642) 247438 *fax (01642) 244651*

Court Liaison
Parry, Kevin (spo)
Craddy, Stuart (offender supvr)

Gill, Audrey (offender supvr)
Grey, Stuart (offender supvr)
Holmes, Jim (offender supvr)
Russell, Mike (offender supvr)
North, Gemma (offender supvr)
Mahmood, Mahmood (offender supvr)
Leech, Jennifer (offender supvr)
Smith, Val (offender supvr)
Menzies, Maria (offender supvr)
Ferguson, Barbara (offender supvr)
Spaven, Tracey (offender supvr)
Storr, Frank (offender supvr)

Public Protection Unit
Megan, Sarah (spo)
Gill, Barbara (spo)
Hill, Susan (office mgr)
Bennett, Maree
Carlton, Melanie
Cotterill, Sarah
Dargue, Darren
Devon, Alan
Ford, Allison
Pawson, Julie
Pritchard, Nick
Douglas, Lynn
Whitehead, Tony
Gardner, Gill
Hopton, Julie
Aldus, Beverly (vlo)
Edgar, Penny (vlo)

MAPPA
Brittain, Tracey (spo/mappa co-ord)
Elliott, Norma (office mgr)

Prolific & other Priority Offender Scheme (PPO) Middlesbrough
Nicolson, Kay (spo)
Barber, Jeremy
Rennie, Debbie
Hodgson, Jeanette
Beckett, Melissa (offender supvr)
Downing, Faye (offender supvr)

3. 154/156 Borough Road
    Middlesbrough TS1 2EP
    tel (01642) 210717 *fax (01642) 230621*

    Offender Management Unit
    Barnett, Sharon (spo)
    Morton, Helen (spo)
    Westmoreland, Lynda (perf mgr)
    Turbitt, James (dep ops mgr)
    Almond, Gail
    Ashton, Stephen
    Atkinson, Fiona
    Bentley, Michael
    Bullen, Carolyn

Dunn, Sheerie
Hird, Rebecca
Hunter, Claire
Iverson, Julie
Johnson, Gill
McGee, Kerri-Ann
Mahoney, Beth
Marshall, Joanne
Martell, Carolyn
Matthews, Barbara
Neasham, Laura
Raynell, Cora
Ubaka, Anselm
Whiteley, Sara
Williams (née Downing), Jennifer

Collingwood, Deborah (offender supvr)
Stewart, Pam (offender supvr)
Golden, Claire (offender supvr)
Armstrong, Janet (offndr supvr, ete)
Bedford, Jane (offender supvr)
Coates, Eddie (offender supvr)
Lawson, Alison (offender supvr)
Ayton, Lisa (offender supvr)
Naden, Jodie (offender supvr)

4. **Prolific & other Priority Offender Scheme (PPO) Middlesbrough**
    Middlesbrough Police Headquarters
    Bridge Street West
    Middlesbrough TS1 2AB
    tel (01642) 303305/6/7/8 *fax (01642) 303159*

    Taylor, David
    Motson, Sue (offender supvr)
    Finlay, David (police officer)

5. **Teesside Crown Court**
    Russell Street, Middlesbrough TS1 2AE
    tel (01642) 250469 *fax (01642) 230541*

    West, Doug (spo)
    Nolan, Mike
    Borg, Paul (offender supvr)
    Stott (née Clarke), Caroline (offndr supvr)
    Smith, Joan (offender supvr)

6. Mowlam House, 1 Oxford Street
    South Bank Middlesbrough TS6 6DF
    tel (01642) 452346 *fax (01642) 466021*

    note South Bank & Redcar work as one team across two sites

    Offender Management Unit
    Jan Bateman (spo)
    Armstrong, Ian (dep ops mgr)
    Blackett (née Edwards), Juliet
    Lane, Mike

McFee, Michelle
Suggett, Leigh
Waters, Nicola
Felstead, Carol (offender supvr)
Garbutt, Claire (offender supvr)
Smith, Debbie (offender supvr)
Williams, Linda (offender supvr, ete)

7. 38 Station Road
    Redcar TS10 1AG
    tel (01642) 494395 *fax (01642) 489424*

    *note South Bank & Redcar work as
    one team across two sites*

    Offender Management Unit
    Roy, Rosana (spo)
    Brown, John
    Close, Suzanne
    Edgar, Lisa
    Taylor, Peter
    Hernandez, Frieda
    O'Brien, Sue
    Urban, Lynne
    Ward, Ellen
    Ward, Kate
    Halasz, Emma (offender supvr)
    Moseley, Elizabeth (offender supvr)

8. **Prolific & other Priority Offender
    Scheme (PPO) Redcar**
    Langbaurgh District Police Headquarters
    Troisdors Way
    Kirkleatham Business Park
    Redcar TS10 5AP
    tel (01642) 302085/302086

    Parker, Richard (spo)
    Bell, Emma
    Devitt, Vicky
    Douglas, Chris (offender supvr)
    Rawson, Les (police officer)

9. Advance House, St Mark's Court
    Teasdale, Thornaby
    Stockton on Tees TS17 6QX
    tel (01642) 606111 *fax (01642) 607764*

    Offender Management Unit
    King, Peter (spo)
    John Graham (spo)
    Garbutt, Jenny (perf mgr)
    Boyd, Debbie
    Brown, Matt
    Clement, Sandra
    Coe, Emma
    Day, Joanne
    Day, Kim
    Ford, Dot

Fryett, Russell
Gallagher, Natalie
Grainger, Elizabeth
Greener, Lynne
MacDonald, Andrea
Nazir, Shahida
O'Neill, Jane
Rabjohns, Tracey
Ransome, Philip
Robson, Justine
Smart, Claire
Sowerby, Andrea
Vaux, Lizzie
Willett, Barbara (mentor)
Coyne, Laura (offender supvr)
Foster, Alison (offender supvr)
Hussain, Liaquet (offender supvr)
McConnell, Christine (offndr supvr, ete)
Maude, Catherine (offender supvr)
Raw, Stacey (offender supvr)
Richmond, Kay (offender supvr)
Ryan, Joanne (offender supvr)
Turner, Jean (offender supvr)
Walton, Victoria (offender supvr)

**Prolific & other Priority Offender
Scheme (PPO), Stockton**
Evans, Jeff (mgr)
Brown, Katie
Leishman, Martin
Moore, Louise
Eddon, Mark (offender supvr)
Evans, Keith (outreach wrkr)
Fleet, Jacqui (police officer)

10. Avenue Road
    Hartlepool TS24 8BL
    tel (01429) 265101 *fax (01429) 231854*

    Offender Management Unit
    Keay, Julie (spo)
    Spreadbury, Wendy (perf mgr)
    Adair, Steven
    Beard, Sylvia
    Gaffney, Sarah
    Hutchinson, Karen
    Robinson, Sheila
    Stoddart, Steve
    Harburn, Andrea
    O'Connor, Stella
    Robertson, Ann
    Jewett, Natalie
    Linighan, Louise
    Wood, Laura
    Caizley, Alison (offender supvr)
    Haston, Gilly (offender supvr)
    Horner, Pat (offender supvr)

Parkin, Pauline (offender supvr)
Ryan, Joanne (offender supvr)

Court Team
I'Anson, Dougie (offender supvr)

**Prolific & other Priority Offender
Scheme (PPO), Hartlepool**
Mulpetre, Gemma (spo)
Bailey, Louise
Turner, Sarah
Wilkinson, Julie
Faye, Jeremy (offender supvr)
Forsyth, Hayley (outreach wrkr)
Dunn, Brian (police officer)
Low, Sandra (ppo coord)

11. **'What Works' Programmes
& Case Management**
Advance House, St Mark's Court
Teasdale, Thornaby
Stockton on Tees TS17 6QX
tel (01642) 606111 *fax (01642) 607764*

Flanagan, Kath (dep mgr)
Horner, Gill
Westbrook, Andy
Johnson, Alan (action team advisor)
Davies, Bill (prog supt wrkr)
Henderson, Gary (offender supvr)
McKay, Debbie (offender supvr)
Maude, Catherine (offender supvr)
Whitaker, Elaine (offender supvr)

12. **Unpaid Work**
Milbank House, 1 Milbank Street
South Bank, **Middlesbrough** TS6 6DD
tel (01642) 515315/6 *fax (01642) 290677*

Bonas, Robin (spo)
Wooding, Gordon (dep ops mgr)
Cameron, Mark (offender supvr)
Charlton, Jack (offender supvr)
Cooper, Barry (offender supvr)
Currie, Bob (offender supvr)
Gilbey, Alan (offender supvr)
Hey, Anthony (offender supvr)
Johnson, Dave (offender supvr)
Lunn, Michael (offender supvr)
McKenna, Mike (offender supvr)
Marson, Louise (offender supvr)
Millar, David (offender supvr)
Paterson, Donald (offender supvr)
Pearce, Peter (offender supvr)
Simmonds, Tony (offender supvr)
Smallwood, Dave (offender supvr)
Smart, Olly (offender supvr)
Smithyman, Sue (offender supvr)
Vaughan, Brian (offender supvr)

What Works Programme
Gavaghan, Dave (dep mgr)
Bell, Simon (os 'what works')
Cotter, Melissa (os 'what works')
Hall, Andy (os 'what works')
Mackin, Christine (os 'what works')
Taylor, Rachel (os 'what works')
Catton, Bob (prog supt wrkr)
Hunter, Derek (prog supt wrkr)

**Housing, Employment, &
Learning Partnership**
Allan, Jim (offender supvr)
Winn, Nick (offender supvr)

13. **Practitioner Training Unit**
6th Floor, Centre North East
73-75 Albert Road
Middlesbrough TS1 2RU
tel (01642) 225021 *fax (01642) 252215*

Davy, Virginia (pda)
Dixon, Gill (pda)
Toyne, Margaret (pda)

Trainees
Askins, Liz
Baines, Wendy
Chapman, Erica
Doswell, Paul
Frostwick, Gemma
Hodge, Rachel
Stubbs, Adelle
Wright, Claire

Youth Offending Service

14. **Hartlepool**
The Archive Building
Upper Church Street
Hartlepool TS24 7EQ
tel (01429) 523986 *fax (01429) 523971*

Robinson, Sheila

15. **South Tees**
(Middlesbrough and Redcar)
51a Kings Road
North Ormesby
Middlesbrough TS3 6NH
tel (01642) 501500 *fax (01642) 501800*

James, Laurence

16. **Stockton**
Floor 3, Bayheath House,
Prince Regent Street
Stockton on Tees TS18 1DF
tel (01642) 527597 *fax (01642) 527598*

Hall, Maureen

Approved Premises (Hostels)

17. **Probation Hostel**
13 The Crescent
Linthorpe, Middlesbrough TS5 6SG
tel (01642) 826606 *fax (01642) 829782*

Smith, Paul (dep ops mgr)
White, Susan (office manager)
Palmer-Laidler, Charlotte (finance/admin asst)
Jackson, Rebecca (snr rsw)
Nichol, Paul (snr rsw)
Liebig-Denham (née Pearson), Annette (snr rsw)
Bielby, Aisha (rsw)
Bowers, Emma (rsw)
Dos Santos, Sarah (rsw)
Findlay, Pamela (rsw)
Manning, Karen (rsw)
Menzies, Russell (rsw)
Matthews, Carol (ncw)

18. **Nelson House Probation Hostel**
Middlesbrough Road
South Bank, Middlesbrough TS6 6LZ
tel (01642) 456811 *fax (01642) 468671*

Sam-Drysdale, Sandra (spo, hostels)
Glen Davis (dep ops mgr)
Watling, Steven (snr rsw)
Heaviside, Jennifer (snr rsw)
Lawton, Terry (ncw)
Ayton, Christopher (rsw)
Daniel, Malcolm (ncw)
Eastwell, Sue (ncw)
Jackson-Clapham, Deborah (rsw)
Welsh, Angela (rsw)
McCormick, Clark (rsw)
Moulsher, Philip (rsw)
Sparrow, David (ncw)
Stallard, Kay (rsw)
Thompson, Sid (rsw)
Warrior, David (rsw)

Institutions

19. H M Prison **Kirklevington Grange**
Yarm TS15 9PA
tel (01642) 781391 *fax (01642) 790530*

Discipline ext 201
Special visits (via communications office) ext 230

Kitching, Caroline (spo)
Hewerdine, Lynne
Michna, Jan
Thomas, Jeff (offender supvr)

20. H M Prison **Holme House**
Holme House Road
Stockton on Tees TS18 2QU
tel (01642) 744000 *fax (01642) 744001*
direct dial (01642) 74 + extn
probn clerk ext 4327
special visits ext 4280
probn fax (01642) 744264

Cooke, Sally ext 4143
Phillips, Joe ext 4106
Shaw, Jan ext 4106
Warrior, Joan ext 4137
Winn, Lesley ext 4143
Hatchwell , Victoria (accom officer)
Cassey, Nicola (accom officer)
Turver, Andy (offender supvr) ext 4157

Local Justice Areas

10 Hartlepool
6-7 Langbaurgh East
2-3, 9 Teesside

Crown Court

5 Teesside

THAMES VALLEY PROBATION AREA

e-mail: Firstname.Surname@thames-valley.probation.gsi.gov.uk

abbreviations:
(dam) Divisional Admin Manager
(pf) Programme Facilitator

1. **Head Office**
Kingsclere Road, Bicester
Oxon OX26 2QD
tel (01869) 255300 *fax (01869) 255344*

Marshall, Gerry (co)
Fearn, Malcolm (p, board chair)
Lawrence-Wilson, Richard (p, secy to board)
Marsh, Nicki (pa to co/chair)

Mackenzie, Gaynor (p, dir of hr)
Hudson, Lesley (p, dir of hr)
Gillbard, Paul (dir of operations)
Quiggin, Sean (dir of interventions)
Vine, Malcolm (dir of finance)
White, Debbie (quality imprvmnt mgr)
Medhurst, Elizabeth (bus proc imp mgr)
Smith, Greg (business proc imp mgr)
van Rensburg, Werner (business proc

imp mgr based at 3)
Tarrant, Fiona (comms mgr)
Hooper, Clare (comms off)
Jones, Karen (train & org devpt mgr)

Khanum, Naheed (hr advr)
Heron, Diane (hr advr)
Francis, Adele (hr advr, mgmt info & rec)
Bates, Heather (hr admin)
Peck, Jayne (p, hr admin)
Game, Elly (p, hr admin)
Sweetland, Judith (training admin)
Birtles, Lynda (p, training admin)
Fell, Sue (p, training admin)
Beckley, David (hr admin assist)
Mafham, Val (trainer)
Eaves, Eddie (health & safety advr)

Vacancy (finance mgr)
Harvey, Susie (p, snr finance off)
Fearn, Vicky (p, payroll mgr)
Dean, Vanessa (p, payroll off)
Smith, Sue (p, payroll off)
Chapple, Wendy (finance off)
Roberts, Sonia (finance off)
Durrant, Julia (p, senior facilities & est off)
Smith, Esther (p, asst facilities & est off)
Kempster, Helene (pa to dir int & oper)
Mitchell, Sarah (pa to dir hr & dir finance)
Hobbs, Lesley (p, admin services co-ord)
Ashton, Danielle (p, recap/admin)
Dally, Joe (p, recep/admin)

2. 1-3 Ock Street
   Abingdon Oxon OX14 5AL
   tel (01235) 535619 *fax (01235) 554511*

   Offender Management Unit
   Kueberuwa, Norma (spo)
   Evans, Sarah
   Lampton, Victoria
   Seddon, Andrew
   West, Sarah (p)
   Barry, Abigail (p, pso tracker link wrkr)
   Fisher, Laura (pso)
   Hudson, Natalie (pso)
   Wendon, Lois (pso)
   Moores, Derek (pso, courts)
   Perry, Alex (pso os)

   Training
   Galliers, Anna (trainee)

   Administration
   Irving, Deedee (dam, based 13)
   Robson, Angela (assist dam)

3. 2a Wynne-Jones Centre, Walton Road
   Aylesbury Bucks HP21 7RL
   tel (01296) 483174 *fax (01296) 415212*

Czajewski, Stephen (p, asst dir, based at 5)

Offender Management Unit
Gallagher, Gillian (spo)
Davis, Jan (spo)
Sparshott, Felicity (spo)
Sceeny, Wendy (p, spo)
Dow, Katherine
Elmore, Nicola
Evans, Catherine
Halliwell, Jenni
Jenner, Jeannie (p)
Matthews, Charlotte
Pickering, Linda
Shimeld, Irene
Waters, Martyn

Aburrow, Annette (p, pso)
Davis, Douglas (pso)
Karachiwala, Sahera (pso)
McElhinney, Lisa (pso)
Ody, Bill (pso)

Cowley, Pauline (pso, courts)
Malone, Cindy (pso, courts)
Rogers, Adrienne (p, pso, courts)

Wan, Gennae (pso os)

Subst Misuse Offender Mgmnt Unit
Keep, Margaret
Boots, Kate
Tomlin, Eve (p, subst misuse wrkr)
Butler, Terry (pso tracker link wrkr)
Mullaney, Louise (pso)
Roberts, Donna (pso)

Training
Adams-Rimmer, Jane (p, pda)
Carmichael, Jane (pda)
North, Kate (trainee)
Corquin, Jennifer (trainee)
Henderson, David (trainee)
Lowe, Liz (trainee)
Malone, Siobhan (trainee)
Peddie, Rachael (trainee)

B2E (Bridge to Employment) Unit
Simmons, Allister (b2e keyworker)

Administration
Deeks, Avril (dam)
Dale, Susan (assist dam, based at 8)

IT Unit
tel (01296) 393925 *fax (01296) 398490*

Baker, Ralph (snr IT supt off)
Briscoe, Neil (IT supt off)
Evershed, Tilly (p, IT supt off)
Shergill, Jas (IT supt off)
Shaw, Clare (IT admin bucks)
Mobeen, Shamah (IT admin ox)

Performance Information Unit
tel (01296) 484052

Gower, Alan (info mgr)
Harrison, Yvette (snr info analyst)
Searle, Mark (info analyst)
Grimes, Julie (perf info off)
Spayne, Chris (p, compli off)
Aulton, Michelle (p, res mgr)

3a. **Aylesbury Crown Court**
38 Market Square
Aylesbury, Bucks HP20 1XD
tel (01296) 339770 *fax (01296) 435665*

4. 15 Canada Close, Marley Way
Banbury Oxon OX16 2RT
tel (01295) 268436/7 *fax (01295) 268120*

Offender Management Unit
Toner, Michael (spo)
Burrell, Anne (p)
Hoggins, Michelle
McFarlane, Jane
Netten, Kate
Wilson, Pat
Yard, Gregory
Bryan, Rachel (pso)
Doolan, Mike (pso)
Gwynne, Lucinda (p, pso)
Ivory, Catrina (pso)
Jarvis-Aitoro, Megan (pso)
Walter, Dudley (pso)
Kirtley, Jane (pso tracker link wrkr)
Porter, Ian (p, legal proceedings mgr)

Training
Burrell, Anne (p, pda mentor)
Kenna, Karen (p, pda mentor)
Grant, Joy (trainee)
Robinson, Zoe (trainee)
Roe-French, Chris (trainee)
Ruff, Simon (trainee)
Sugarman, Donna (trainee)
Watt, Rachel (trainee)

Administration
Irving, Deedee (dam, based at 13)
Robson, Angela (asst dam)

5. Units 9 & 10 Talisman Business Centre
Talisman Road **Bicester**
Oxon OX26 6HR
tel (01869) 328500 *fax (01869) 328528*

Czajewski, Stephen (asst dir of intrvntns)
Pearce, Sue (asst dir of intrvntns)
Cowen, Caryl (pa)
fax (01869) 328543 (confidential fax line)

B2E Team
Mayson, Sarah (b2e mgr)
Yirrell, Shelley (b2e co-ord)
Cross, Carol (p, b2e admin)
Taylor, Karen (b2e admin)

Oxfordshire Unpaid Work Team
Swift, Erica (uw scheme mgr)
Clarke, Deborah (qa mgr)
Hall, Gemma (pcm)
Major, Diane (pcm)
Pittuck, Sue (pcm)
Price, Robyn (pcm)
Slocombe, Adam (pcm)
Spargo, Julia (pcm)
McCarthy, Dee (pso os)
Clayton, Julie (county uw admin)

Accredited Programmes Team
Reducing Reoffending Unit (RRU)
Myatt, Emma (prog mgr, rru)
Harvey, Julian (po treat mgr)
Phillips, Simon (p, treat mgr)
Stewart, Lucy (p, treat mgr)
Cockbill, Leona (pso, treat mgr)
Regan, Kate (pso, treat mgr)

Barr, Estelle (pf lev 3)
Carty, Angela (pf lev 3)
Crane, Rosalie (pf lev 3)
Dainty, Caroline (pf lev 3)
Earley, Michael (pf lev 3)
Edwards, Penny (pf lev 3)
Goswell, Samantha (pf lev 3)
Hughes, Oliver (pf lev 3)

Reducing Violence Unit (RVU)
(Domestic Abuse Offender Progr)
Johnson, Debbie (prog mgr, rvu)
Parker, Lynn (pf lev 3)
Ciotti, Megan (p, pf lev 4)
Faulkner, Sam (pf lev 4)
Gange, Callie (pf lev 4)
Phillips, Simon (p, pf lev 4)
Stewart, Lucy (p, pf lev 4)
Thornley, Ben (pf lev 4)
Weston, Kathryn (pf lev 4)
Court, Mary (admin mgr)
Wook, Sue (p, women's safety wrkr)

Thames Valley Unit (TVU)
(Sex Offender Programme)
tel (01869) 328600 *fax (01869) 328618*

Adamczyk, Liz (prog mgr, tvu)
Davis, Clive (treat mgr)
Liegis, Eduard (treat mgr)
Ricks, Linda (treat mgr)

Shah, Neeta (pf specific lev 3)
Vacancy (pf specific lev 3)

Loveday, Marian (p, pf lev 4)
Chapman, Rosemary (pf specific lev 4)
Lovelock, Jo (pf specific lev 4)
Morris, Bernard (pf specific lev 4)
Palmer, Corina (pf specific lev 4)
Sexton, Lesley (pf specific lev 4)
Stephenson, Maggie (pf specific lev 4)
Subenko, Pauline (p, pf specific lev 4)
Vince, Russell (pf specific lev 4)

Bates, Andrew (principal forensic psy)
(mobile no 07796 948297)
Clarke, Jackie (admin service mgr)

5a. **MAPPA Unit**
Thames Valley Police
Fountain Court, Kidlington, OX5 1NZ
tel (01865) 293101 *fax (01865) 293292*

Stirling, Bob (mappa mgr)

6. **Thames Valley Restorative
Justice Service**
Units 9 & 10 Talisman Business Centre
Talisman Road **Bicester**
Oxon OX26 6HR
tel (01869) 328562

Emerson, Geoff (rj mgr)

7. James Glaisher House
Grenville Place **Bracknell** RG12 1BP
tel (01344) 420446 *fax (01344) 301274*

Offender Management Unit
Rowlands, Jonathon (spo)
Powell, Vivian (p, spo)
Foxell, Oliver
May, Celia (p)
McGuigan, Steve
Rooke, Simon
Oztemel, Deniz (p)
Powers, Julia
Sutherland, Sarah (p)

Andrews, Catherine (p, pso)
Evans, Alessandra (pso)
Jones, Francesca (pso)
Russell, Christopher (pso)
Ungi, Marco (pso os)

Training
Bull, Richard (p, pda mentor)
Avarne, Grace (trainee)
Cudby, Teri (trainee)
Gash, Nicola (trainee)
Herd, Lucy (trainee)

Subst Misuse Offender Mgmnt Unit
Bull, Richard (p)

Administration
Coston, Jacqueline (dam based at 17)
Lagarde, Michelle (assist dam) (17)

B2E Team
Crawford, Mary (b2e keyworker)

8. Easton Court, 23a Easton Street
High Wycombe Bucks HP11 1NT
tel (01494) 436421 *fax (01494) 450132*

Offender Management Unit
Richards, Lyn (spo)
Walls, Charlie (spo)
Morris, Sally (spo)
Ayoub, Abid
Blowfield, Anna
Brown, Alma
Clark, Susan
Lang, Karen
McConnell, Elena
Morris, Helen
Richardson, Jo

Barker, Emily (pso)
Brown, Karen (pso)
North, Laura (p, pso)
Weston, Tim (pso)

Chapple, Paul (pso housing)

Bowell, Lynda (pso, court)
Glynn, Elisabeth (pso, court)

Pascal, Richard (pso os)

Derbyshire, Carol (pso tracker link wrkr)
Hafeez, Mohammed (legal proceedings
mgr)

Training
Ross, Marilyn (p, pda)
Fisher, Stella (trainee)
Pask, Jessica (trainee)
Urbanska, Jana (trainee)
Wood, Marie (trainee)

Administration
Deeks, Avril (dam based at 3)
Dale, Susan (assist dam)

B2E Team
McCarney, Laura (b2e keyworker)

9. Bridge Road
Maidenhead SL6 8PB
tel (01628) 770858 *fax (01628) 788675*

Subst Misuse Offender Mgmnt Unit
Walls, David (spo)

Powell, Vivian (p, spo)
Blakesley, Clive
Rees, Maryanne
Smith, Mark
Clarke, Frank (subst mis wrkr)
Bennett, Stepahnie (pso)
Gray, Lesley (pso, RoB co-ord)
Humphrey, Jean (p, pso)
Pawlow, Keely (pso os)
Perry, Richard (pso os)
Soor, Rajinder (pso os)
Stokes, Lauren (pso)
Wright, Cara (p, pso)

Administration
Coston, Jacqueline (dam based at 17)
Lagarde, Michelle (assist dam) (17)

10. 301 Silbury Boulevard, Witan Gate East
Milton Keynes MK9 2YH
tel (01908) 679734 *fax (01908) 230050*

Vigurs, Kilvinder (assistant director)
Hazell, Paulette (p, pa)

Offender Management Unit
St Amour, Paul (spo)
Butt, Denise (spo)
Carter-Philpott, Amanda (spo)
Newall, Jo (spo)
Bairstow, David
Fox, Mandy
Harris, Ann (p)
Kidd-White, Melanie
Litchfield, Theresa
Longley, Luke
Mathew, Bijoy (p)
Paintin, Gary
Passant, Rebecca
Potter, Mandy
Priseman, Nigel
Ridgway, Arlene
Rogers, Carol
Spencer, Johnson
Stebbens, Jo
Sylvester, Alison (p)

Beale, Katie (pso)
Bircham, Anne (pso)
Martin, Viv (pso)
Oldfield, Amanda (pso)
Stafford, Ruth (pso)
Stratfold, Deborah (p, pso)

Patterson, Sandra (pso, court)
Vickery, Sally (pso court)

May, Hayley (pso os)
Mcllwain, Carly (pso os)
Vippond, Keith (pso os)

Subst Misuse Offender Mgmnt Unit
Butt, Denise (drug services devpt mgr)
Cohen, Stan
Jones, Allan
Anstey, Susan (pso)
Duke, Vincent (pso)

B2E Team
Lant, Tracy (b2e key worker)

Training
Sylvester, Alison (p, pda)
Ali, Jay (trainee)

Accredited Programmes Team
Christie, Dod (pf)
Lindsay, Mary (p, pf)
Morse, Sharon (p, pf)
Smith, Eileen (p, pf)
Stubbs, Christine (p, pf)

Administration
Deeks, Avril (dam based at 3)
Atkinson, Angela (assist dam)

11. 20 Market Square
Stony Stratford
Milton Keynes MK11 1BE
tel (01908) 564812 *fax (01908) 262846*

Bucks & MK Unpaid Work Unit Unit
Coffey, Mike (uw scheme mgr)
Ayers, Paula (qa mgr)
Barber, Philippa (pcm)
Evans, Julie (pcm)
Hall, Jan (pcm)
Hopping, Eleanor (pcm)
Melisi, Hannah (pcm)
Spurrier, Sean (pcm)
Taylor, Ria (pcm)
Winch, Elliott (pcm)
Wright, Paul (pcm)
Jilo, Esther (pso os)

Administration
Ellens, Norma (admin service mgr)

12. Mill Lane
Newbury RG14 5QS
tel (01635) 43535 *fax (01635) 42103*

Offender Management Unit
Fisher, Claire (spo)
Aldridge, Richard
Quigley, Sandy
Randle, Gillian (p)
Tyson, Peter (p)
Foot, David (p, pso courts)
Moore, Niki (p, pso)
Willmott, Vickie (pso os)
Worthington, Frank (p, pso)

Subst Misuse Offender Mgmnt Unit
Loomes, Hazel (p, pso)

Training
Boden, Jim (trainee)
Constant, Aimee (trainee)

Administration
Bull, Helen (dam based at 16)
Smith, Paula (assist dam) (16)

13. Albion House
Littlegate Street **Oxford** OX1 1JN
tel (01865) 240750 *fax (01865) 240780*

McCartney, Graham (asst director)
Netting, Kathy (p, pa)

Offender Management Unit
Harvey, Vicki (spo)
Rogers, Katharine (spo)
Budgen, Penny (p)
Duffy, Andrea
Morrison, Donald
Payne, Giles
Richardson, Kay
Wickham, Tania (p)

Aitkins, Russell (pso courts)
Juggins, Tracy (pso courts)
Ashton, Ian (p, pso, court)
Baldauf-Clark, Beatrix (p, pso crt)
Colton, Lee (pso os courts)
Gannon, Sophia (pso, court)

Jackson, Piri (pso os)

Newman, Sarah (pso)
Williams, Caroline (p, pso)
Williams, Claire (pso)

Kelly-Ward, Pauline (pso accom)

Training
Smith, Sheila (p, pda)
Dutson, Kate (trainee)
Jennings, Lucy (trainee)
Mumford, James (trainee)

Programmes Team
Jolly, Ruth (p, pf)

B2E Team
Gardner, Valeria (b2e keyworker)
Halime, Aziz (p, b2e keyworker)

Subst Misuse Offender Mgmnt Unit
King, Linda (drug services devpt mgr)
Everatt, Lou (spo)
Waterston, Rob
Webb, Nicola
Bennett, Lynne (subst misuse wrkr)
Godin, Janet (subst misuse wrkr)

Merivale, Nicola (subst misuse wrkr)
Barletta, Kimberley (pso)
Lesnik, Andrew (pso)
Parveselli, Caroline (p, pso)
Winstone-Partridge, Elizabeth (pso)
Brammer, Pasquale (DAAT Sup off)

Administration
Irving, Deedee (dam)
Britten, Sandra (assist dam based at 14)

Oxford Magistrates' Court Office
tel (01865) 202039 *fax (01865) 200078*

14. Temple Cottage
164 Oxford Road **Cowley** Oxford OX4 2LA
tel (01865) 775482 *fax (01865) 770311*

Offender Management Unit
Hume, Duncan (p, spo)
Guthrie, Lydia (p, spo)
Banks, David
Bruce, Gary
Chapman, Margaret
Gowney-Hedges, Hannah
Haigh, Alex (p)
Hogg, Jo (p)
Medley, Stephanie
Garmen, Stuart (pso)
McCalmon, Colin (p, pso)
McKinley-Rodgers, Penny (p, pso os)

Training
Jefford, Michelle (trainee)

Administration
Irving, Deedee (dam based 13)
Britten, Sandra (assist dam)

15. The Old Shire Hall
The Forbury **Reading** RG1 3EH
tel 0118-967 4430 *fax 0118-967 4431*

Reading Crown Court Team
Evans, Grant (spo)
Cole, Jeanette (p, pso court)
Chrisp, Linda (pso, court)
Huggins, Terry (p, pso court)
Mead, Linda (p, pso, court)
Whyte, Peter (pso, court)

16. Greyfriars House
30 Greyfriars Road, **Reading** RG1 1PE
tel 0118-956 0466 *fax 0118-955 1300*

Vacancy (assistant director)
Browne, Carol (p, pa)

Offender Management Unit
Holland, Sarah (p, spo)
Clairmonte, Claire (spo)

Williams, Kevin (spo)
Davis, Geoff (spo)
Boyd, Gillian
Cannell, Sabina (p)
Ennis, John
Farrall Hyder, Ruth
Francis, Annabel
Graham, Debbie
Harding, Hannah
Hutchins, Lucy (p)
Newton, Nicole
Reeves, Catriona

Phillips, Caroline (p, pso, pqm)
McDonald, Linda (pso)
Jenkinson, Jan (pso)
Jackson, Tom (pso)
Honorata, Choloniewska (pso)
Pudge, Kayleigh (pso)

Collins, Sarah (pso trackr link wrkr)
Kent, Marion (pso trackr link wrkr)

Gibson, David (pso os)
Bonnello, Christine (p, pso os)
Niknejad, Leila (pso os)
Owen, James (pso os)

Stoddart, Gary (pso accom)

Reading Magistrates' Court Team
tel 0118-956 0466 *fax 0118-955 1305*

Evans, Grant (spo based at 15)
Oliver, David
Khan, Asma (legal proceedings mgr)
O'Boyle, Julie (pso os)
Heath, Jim (pso court)
Jenkinson, Jan (pso court)
Tompkins, Benjamin (pso court)
Taylor, Eileen (p, pso court)

Victim Liaison Unit
tel 0118-955 1255 *fax 0118-955 1304*
Honeysett, Clare (p, spo)
De Jongh, Caroline
Llewellyn, Heather
Oakes, Helen
Bailey, Nichola (pso)
Barraclough Kathryn (p, pso)
Bolton, Karen (p, pso)
Brent, Linda (p, co-ord)
Morgan, Helen (p, co-ord)

Berks Unpaid Work Unit
Mondaye, Andrew (uw scheme mgr)
Vacancy (qa mgr)
Leader, Frances (qa mgr)
Brazier, Carly (pcm)
Eggleton, Rebecca (pcm)
Fidler, Anna (pcm)

Godfrey, Joanna (pcm)
Hall, Rosy (pcm)
Harris, Laura (pcm)
Hawker, Emily (pcm)
Katuscakova, Julia (pcm)
Ladlow, Christina (pcm)
Senyah, Chris (pcm)
Vernon, Caroline (pcm)
Wells, Liz (pcm)
Jandu, Manjot (pso os)
Miljkovic Aleksander (pso os)
Pullen, Kim (admin serv mgr)

Subst Misuse Offender Mgmnt Unit
Amahwe, Gabriel (drug services
devpt mgr W Berks)
Powell, Hannah
Tagoe, Gina
Troup, Ian
Hartley, Ben (pso)
Hendrick, Maria (pso)
Lutaaya, Anthony (pso)

Training
Griffiths, Sue (practice devpt mgr)
Marshall, David (pda/mentor)
Greenwood, Judy (p, pda)
Warwick, Leah (p, pda)
Fairs-Billam, Toby (trainee)
Jara, Laura (trainee)
Knight, James (trainee)
Latawiec, Tomasz (trainee)
Oshan-Ellis, Berenice (trainee)
Raven, Rebecca (trainee)

B2E Team
Mills, Selina (b2e key worker)

Accredited Programmes Team
tel 0118-955 1222
Acteson, Doreen (treatment mgr)
Booth, Cathy (treatment mgr)
O'Kelly, Catherine (p, treatment mgr)
Arnold, Susan (pf)
Henstridge, Jenni (pf)
Hunt, Martin (pf)
Mayston, Greg (pf)
Nagib-Ali, Abdalla (pf)
Phasey, Rosalind (pf)
Odain, Lloyd (pf)
Reeves, Ella (pf)
Stokes, Denise (pf)
Wilson, Joanna (pf)
Wilson, Maxine (pf)

Administration
Bull, Helen (dam)
Smith, Paula (assist dam)

17. Revelstoke House, Chalvey Park
Slough SL1 2HF
tel (01753) 537516 *fax (01753) 552169*

Cooke, Sue (assistant director)
Williams, Tracy (p, pa)

Offender Management Unit
Brigue, Rekha (spo)
Cornwall, Simon (spo)
Geller, Eleri (spo)
Rich, Valerie (spo)
Le-Gendre, Kelita
Hewstone, Peter
Jordan, Hazel
Smith, Clare
Azad, Usha
Benson, Claire
Bourget, Robbie
Brown, Alma (temp po)
Caldecourt, Odele
Cunnington, Sarah
Hussey, Jonathan
Sims, Rebecca
Thornton, Hayley
Teodorescu, Christine
Ward, Maggi
Williams, Kevin I

Adebayo, Oluremi (pso)
Barraclough, Kathryn (p, pso)
Bullion, Leslie (pso os)
Ladha, Farzana (pso)
Nair, Renuka PSO
Panesar, Manjeet (pso)
Parwinder, Rakkar (pso)
Sahota, Jatinder (pso)
Smith, Matthew (pso)
Thomas, Sandra (pso)
Whelan, Siobhan (pso)

Ahsan, Saima (pso os)
Nyamakunda, Chorus (pso os)

Cann, Frances (pso accom)

Courts Team
Bartholomew, Amy (pso)
Bhatti, Jas (pso, court)
De Silva, Maureen (p, pso, court)
Gumbs, Veronica (pso)
Morris, Delia (pso)

Training
Cawdell, Mark (pda)
Clarke, Victoria (trainee)
Connell, Catherine (trainee)
Glenn, Ashleigh (trainee)
Kearns, Anthony

B2E Team
Kenny, Michael (b2e keyworker)
Stevens, Melanie (b2e keyworker)

Administration
Coston, Jacqueline (dam)
Lagarde, Michelle (assist admin mgr)

Approved Premises (Hostels)

18. **AP Central Referral Unit**
8 Straight Rd
Old Windsor SL4 2RL
tel (01753) 850586 *fax (01753) 852862*
Bradley, Felicity (project mgr)
O'Hara, Sue (cru co-ord)

19. 112 Abingdon Road **Oxford** OX1 4PY
tel (01865) 248842 *fax (01865) 794680*
Mobile 07836 235707

Perry, Sheila (ap area mgr)
Hearn, Lorraine (oper mgr)

20. **Clark's House** Clark's Row
Oxford OX1 1RE
tel (01865) 248841 *fax (01865) 790756*
Mobile 07836 637934

Simpson, Simon (ap area mgr)
Pritchard, Vicky (p, oper mgr)

B2E
Khalid, Asif (b2e keyworker)

21. **Manor Lodge**
8 Straight Road, Old Windsor SL4 2RL
tel (01753) 868807 *fax (01753) 620466*

Bradley, Felicity (ap area mgr)
Sandum, Shelley (oper mgr)

22. 1 Haddon, Great Holm
Milton Keynes MK8 9AL
tel (01908) 569511 *fax (01908) 265949*

Simpson, Simon (ap area mgr based at 20)
Walker, Vivien (oper mgr)

23. **St Leonard's**
2 Southcote Road, Reading RG30 2AA
tel 0118-957 3171 *fax 0118-956 0677*

Perry, Sheila (ap area mgr based at 19)
Billington, Kerry-Anne (oper mgr)

Voluntary Hostel

24. **Elizabeth Fry**
6 Coley Avenue, Reading RG1 6LQ
tel 0118-957 2385 *fax 0118-951 0340*

Titcomb, Fiona (mgr)
Oke, Caroline (p, deputy mgr)
Yapp, Anita (deputy mgr)

Institutions

25. HM YOI, Bierton Road
    Aylesbury Bucks HP20 1EN
    tel (01296) 444000 *fax (01296) 444001*

    Vacancy (spo)
    Lewis, Nick (p)
    Oke, Manny
    Phillips, Dave (p)
    Thorpe, Rodney
    Nelson, Sarah
    Cooper, Ian (pso)
    Robins, Hannah (p, pso)
    Taylor, Zoe (pso)

26. HMP **Bullingdon**
    P O Box 50, Bicester, Oxon OX25 1WD
    tel (01869) 353100 *fax (01869) 353101*

    Drake, Paul (spo)
    Eastwood, John
    Lebeanya, Uche
    Powell, Richard
    Wheatley, Dorothy (p)
    Winter, Kay (p)
    Chapman, Amanda (pso public prtctn)
    Howard, Dawn (pso hdc)
    Lewis, Christine (pso bail)
    Whareham, Lisa (pso)

    Bail Information Unit
    fax (01869) 353171

27. HMP **Grendon**
    Grendon Underwood
    Aylesbury, Bucks HP18 0TL
    tel (01296) 443000 *fax (01296) 443001*

    Charles, David
    Powell, Lesley
    Whymark, Gay

28. HM Remand Centre
    Forbury Road, **Reading** RG1 3HY
    tel 0118-908 5000 *fax 0118-908 5004*

    Yapp, Liam (po custody to work)
    Goodliffe, Joy (pso)
    Ibironke, Yenzile (pso)
    Naidoo, Sharon (pso)

29. HMP **Spring Hill**
    Grendon Underwood
    Aylesbury, Bucks HP18 0TH
    tel (01296) 443000 *fax (01296) 443002*

Foster, Karen (spo)
Carr, Diane
Cooper, Bridget
Gateley, Margaret (p)
Stokes, Paul
Adams, Hugh (pso)
Hall, Jonathan (p, pso)
Morris, Adam (pso)

30. HMP **Woodhill**
    Tattenhoe Street
    Milton Keynes, Bucks MK4 4DA
    tel (01908) 722000 *fax (01908) 867063*

    Hayat, Zareen (spo)
    Mansell, Lorraine
    Marais, Herman
    Nickles, Kate
    Burns, Heather (pso)
    Easthope Claire (pso)
    Kew, Debbie (pso)
    Parker, Natalie (pso)
    Shippen, Jane (pso)
    Snell, Martin (pso)
    Staff-Lonie, Sue (pso)
    Patidar, Prity (p, pso resettlement)
    Tate-Williams, Gill (pso resettlement)

31. HM YOI **Huntercombe**
    Huntercombe Place
    Nuffield, Henley on Thames RG9 5SB
    tel (01491) 643100 *fax (01491) 643101*

    Ellis, Lyn

Local Justice Areas

3 Central Buckinghamshire
2, 5 Southern Oxfordshire
10, 11 Milton Keynes
13, 14, 5 Oxford
17, 7, 16 East Berkshire
12, 16 West Berkshire
16 Reading
4, 5 Northern Oxfordshire
8 Wycombe & Beaconsfield

Crown Courts

3a Aylesbury
13 Oxford
15 Reading

WARWICKSHIRE PROBATION AREA

Out of hours emergency contact point
Augustus House Approved Premises (01926) 339331

Victim enquiries contact number tel 0845 1202325 *fax 0845 1202326*

Warwick Crown Court enquiries contact number tel (01926) 405840 *fax 01926 405801*

Human Resources enquiries contact number tel (01926) 405839

e-mail firstname.surname@warwickshire.probation.gsi.gov.uk

1. **Head Office**
2 Swan Street
Warwick CV34 4BJ
tel (01926) 405800 *fax (01926) 403183*

No reception/switchboard facility please use direct dial numbers below

Stafford, Liz (co) 405850
I'Anson, Cathy (pa) 405843

Wade, Andy (aco offender mngmnt) 405812
McGovern, Donald (aco intrvntns) 405815
Morrison, Christie (pa) 405807

Powell, Andrew (aco, business supt) 405813
Newbold, Sue (pa, training admin) 405811

Mason, Stephanie (staff devpt mgr) 405832

Crown Court Unit
fax (01926) 405801

Burt, Christine (pso) 405845
Furnivall, Pam (pso) 405824
Vacancy (admin) 405840

Finance Unit
Chappell, Sue (finance admin) 405831
Tew, Annette (finance admin) 405831

Human Resources Unit
Caswell, Heather (hr mgr) 405808
Jewsbury, Trish (deputy hr mgr) 405821
Elmhirst, Nicola (hr advisor) 405839
Jolly, Anne (temp hr advr) 405839

Information Unit
Goodyear, Kevin (IT mgr) 405823
Holmes, Clare (IT officer) 405835
Winstanley, Lorna (IT systems admin) 405806
Hobbins, Angela (IT admin) 405825

Programmes Team
O'Donoghue, Dee (mgr progs) 405818
Sharp, Jim (treatment mgr) 405837
Coles, Helen (treatment mgr) 405834
Hamid, Hana (prog admin) 405819

Partnerships Unit
Sutton, Sandra (ptnrshp projs mgr) 405878
Hardy, Len (ptnrshp unit co-or) 405817
Goodall, Nigel (emplt liaison off) 405844
Sambhi, Pam (temp accom off) 405805

1a. **Victim Contact Unit**
(part of Victim & Witness Information Partnership)
93-95 Bedford Street
Leamington Spa CV32 5BB
tel 0845 1202325 *fax 0845 1202326*

Kalm, Indi (pso) (01926) 680254
O'Brien Michelle (pso) (01926) 680254
Smith, Shirley (admin) (01926) 680253

2. Warwickshire Justice Centre
2nd Floor, Rosefield Place Entrance
Leamington Spa CV32 4LX
tel (01926) 682217/8 *fax (01926) 682241*

Ricketts, Louison (area probn mgr)

Team 1 South
Sahota, Kiran (spo)
Abram, Paula
Cory, Nick
Ghaiwal, Kanwal
Hewitt, Lucy
Kent, Stephen
Morgan, Cathy
Ramswell, Amy
Gallagher, Victoria (pso)
Jackson, Heather (pso)
Norman, Abigail (pso)

Team 2 South
Lawson, Neil (spo)
Caudell, Edna (aoa)
Basi, Kiran
Donnelly, Jim
Fox, Natalie
Hewitt Lucy
McConville, Patrick
Masonde, Kabel
Motler, Sarah
Savage, Corrina
Turner, Polly
Marsella, Lyn (pso)
O'Sullivan, William (pso)

Unpaid Work
Adams, Dave (qa mgr, cp)
Sandhu, Manny (pso, personal adv)

3. Grove Road
   Stratford-upon-Avon CV37 6QR
   tel (01789) 299520/267032 *fax (01789) 298264*

   Ghafoor, Mehmeena (sec to HMP Blakenhurst)
   Mannion, Danny (Team 1)
   Sullivan, Karen (Team 1)
   Wood, Paul (Team 1)

4. The Courthouse, Newbold Road
   Rugby CV21 2LH
   tel (01788) 534900 *fax (01788) 547576*

   Chapman, Thomasina (spo)
   Brown, Katie
   Cook, Val
   Cooper, Jolie
   Farthing, Mark
   Furnival, Monika
   Jones, Andrew
   Kelly, Hazel
   Mitchell, Kathleen
   Reeves, Gemma
   Treveil, Richard
   Moorie, Linda (pso, personal adv)
   Kenny, Julia (pso progs)
   Bullock, Sarah (pso)
   Hewitt, Joanne (pso)
   Hiron, Yvonne (pso)
   Clarke, Sally (aoa)

   PDA
   Chambers, Rosey

   Unpaid Work
   Eaves, Craig (cpo)
   Gallagher, Ann (cpo)
   Smith, Les (cpo)

5. Warwickshire Justice Centre
   Vicarage Street **Nuneaton** CV11 4JU
   tel (02476) 483140 *fax (02476) 482864*

   Bains, Peter (area probn mgr)

   Team 1 North
   Evans, Bev (spo)
   Burnett, Chris
   Chapman, Sarah
   Crunkhorn, Sue
   Farndon, Suzanne
   Goodman, Carol
   Kiggell, Jackie
   Kockelbergh, Marion
   Parmar, Deena
   Wood, Kelly
   Dewis, Hayley (pso)
   Howe, Faith (pso)
   Patten, Sharon (pso)

Team 2 North
Guru, Sam (acting spo)
Ademefun, Ade
Birchall, Daphne
Davies, Janice
Doughty-Lee, Niki
Dowse, Liz
Gilbert, Beverley
Hill, Natalie
Hill, Sarah
van der Molen, Jenny
McKenzie, Dan (pso progs)
Oldham, Nicola (pso progs)
Price, Simon (pso progs)
Devine, Catherine (pso)
Lewis, Linda (aoa)

PDA
Burns, Roy

Unpaid Work
Gravenor, Frank (unpaid wk mgr)
Mawby, Chris (qa mgr)
Baxter, Sue (cpo)
Fowler, Des (cpo)

Warwickshire Youth Offending Team

6. Montague House
   12 Hamilton Terrace, Holly Walk
   Leamington Spa CV32 4LY
   tel (01926) 736200 *fax (01926) 736201*

   Johnson, Diane (hd of yo services)
   Moore, Tara (yot pract)
   Weatherall, Brian (yot pract)

7. Newton Hall
   Lower Hillmorton Road
   Rugby CV21 3TU
   tel (01788) 331256 *fax (01926) 476900*

Drug Action Resettlement Team

   Godfrey, Leroy (pso, Leamington Team 2)
   Stewart, Margaret (pso, Nuneaton Team 2)

Community Punishment Unit

8. **Warwick Workshop**
   Montague Road, Warwick CV34 5LL
   tel (01926) 413448 *fax (01926) 411265*

   Dalman, Martyn (cpo)
   Griffin, Velma (cpo)

Approved Premises (Hostels)

9. **Augustus House**
   33 Kenilworth Road
   Leamington Spa CV32 6JG

tel (01926) 339331 *fax (01926) 312518*

Baxendale, Nadine (area probn mgr)
Hanks, Rosemarie (deputy mgr)
Chamberlain, Chris (asst warden)
Frost, Melanie (asst warden)
Kavanagh, Maxine (asst warden)
Kettyle, Heather (asst warden)
Wallis, Steve (asst warden)
Vacant (administrator)

10. **McIntyre House**
    125 Edward Street, Nuneaton CV11 5RD
    tel 024 7638 2889 *fax 024 7635 3982*

    Measom, Jack (deputy mgr)
    Allen, Angela (asst warden)
    Barlow, James (asst warden)
    Pickard, Rosanna (asst warden)
    Power, Joy (asst warden)
    Wallis, Julia (asst warden)
    Simons, Sharon (administrator)

Local Justice Area

2-6 Warwickshire

Crown Court

1 Warwick

WEST MERCIA PROBATION TRUST
Herefordshire, Shropshire, Worcestershire, Telford & Wrekin

Out of hours emergency contact point:
Braley House (01905) 723975

e-mail Firstname.Surname@west-mercia.
probation.gsi.gov.uk

1. **Head Office**
   Stourbank House
   90 Mill Street **Kidderminster**
   Worcs DY11 6XA
   tel (01562) 748375 *fax (01562) 748407*

   Chantler, David (co)
   Kelly, James (trust chair)
   Allen, Helen (hd of interventions,
   community devpt & performance)
   Masters, Julie (hd of offender mngmnt)
   Rudd, Alec (hd of resources)

Mallinson, Graham (hd of bus
services & org devpt)
Frampton, Lesley (p, area mgr intrvntns)
(7)
Ritson, Catherine (area mgr perf)
Fletcher, Deb (culture mgr)
Warrington, Brian (employment mgr)
Chiverton, Steve (spo holding)
Williams, Jane (spo holding)
Simmonds, Karen (hd off bus mgr)
Fisher, Vicki/Jennings, Sarah (business
ops mgr)
Lewis, Jane (location mgr)
Bell, Jackie (p.r. off)
Bury, Shirley (board accountant)
Champken, Tina (finance services mgr)
Fraser, Shelley (contracts off)
Smith, Linda (i.c.t. mgr)
Lewis, Darren (systems mgr)
Jones, Jeff (info mgr)
Ashmore, Tina (income generation mgr)

1a. **Training & Development Suite**
    36 Leswell Street, **Kidderminster** DY10
    1RP
    tel (01562) 66150 fax (01562) 825899

    Bramford, Kate (training mgr)
    Vose, Derrick (training off)
    Derrick, Sarah (training admin)
    Reeves, Catherine (upw h&s co-ord)
    Thomas, Jason (partnerships mgr)

Area Wide

2. **Accredited Programmes (South)**
   3-4 Shaw Street **Worcester** WR1 3QQ
   tel (01905) 723591 *fax (01905) 724833*

   Farebrother, Jim (spo mgr)
   Stephenson, Jenny (spo mgr)
   Stewart, Jayne (treatment mgr, did)
   Taylor, Audrey (treatment mgr, osap)
   Wilks, Helen (treatment mgr, ets, calm)
   Davenne, John
   Foster, Andy
   Morris, Lin
   Stevens, Dave
   Wright, Karen
   Ball, Kathryn (pso)
   Dufty, Katy (pso)
   Evans, Eddie (pso)
   Hewitt, Stephen (pso)
   Laurenson, Neil (pso)
   McLeod, Steve (pso)
   Newton, Tony (pso)
   Slater, Leanne (pso)
   Bettison, Jan (location mgr)

RCSOG
Daly, Maggie
Parsons, Kate

3. **Accredited Programmes (North)**
Courtside House, Telford Square
Malinsgate **Telford** TF3 4EQ
tel (01952) 299366 *fax (01952) 200896*

Law, Tom (spo mgr)
Barrington, Karyn (csog po)
Briscoe, Mark (treatment mgr)
Hankinson, Ian (treatment mgr)
Willetts, Diane (treatment mgr)
Wright, Karen (pso)
De Vos, Les (pso)
Challenger, Paul (pso)
Loviett, Carrie-Ann (pso)
McCarthy, Sarah (pso)
Mansel, Carey (pso)
Newcombe, Gillian (pso)
Pugh, Karli (pso)
Price, Iain (pso)
Birch, Roberta (upw procurement mgr)

Shrewsbury
Pearce, Wendy
Smith, Alan
Clarke, Janet (pso)
Norfolk, Gael (pso)
Pearce, Anna (pso/drr)
Pugh, Karli (pso)

Telford Division

4. Telford Square
Malinsgate **Telford** TF3 4HX
tel (01952) 214100 *fax (01952) 214111*

Branch, George (area mgr)
Davies, Glyn (dist team mgr)
Southwell, Debra (dist team mgr)
Cotton, Louise (risk mgr)
Kelly, Doug (upw mgr)
Beeston, Nicola
Cox, Dorethy
Danesi, Rosa
Emanual, Jennifer
Grant, Desmond
Kwarteng, Michelle
Larkin, Dave
Pawsey, Ruth
Wheeler, Clare
Wilson, Jessica
Kaleta, Phil
Aldridge, Tina
Hinde, Christopher
Armstrong, Guy
Stephens, William

Watts, Jim
Bond, Kelly (pso)
Morrow, Ann (pso)
Russell, Michelle (pso)
Muffit, Lynne (vlo)
Hughes, Chris (pso enforcement)
Brown, Godfrey (upwo)
Gorse, Derek (upwo)
Richardson, Wendy (upwo)
Murray, Phil (upwo)

DRR
Pawsey, Ruth (drr)
Herd, Clare (drug wrkr)
Hood, Della (drug wrkr)

Gittins, Amanda (location mgr)

Telford Magistrates' Court
tel/fax (01952) 210074

New Shropshire Division
Shrewsbury, Ludlow, Market Drayton
Oswestry, Whitchurch

5. 135 Abbey Foregate
Shrewsbury SY2 6AS
tel (01743) 231525 *fax (01743) 244914*

Hatfield, Michele (area mgr)
Holland, Glyn (dist team mgr)
Smith, Ruth (dist team mgr)
Gandon, Michelle (risk mgr)
Kelly, Doug (upw mgr)
Adams, Sheila
Buckley, Carol
Cannon, Helen
Chilton, Lis
Goodban, Diana
Harvey, Carrie (p)
Jeffries, Sandra (p)
Law, Margaret (p)
Morgan, David (p)
Obertelli, Joanne
Pennal, Jesse
Ruffell, Clare (p)
Castle, Lindsay (pso)
Dean, Ruth (pso)
Joyce, Rose (pso)
Price, Bev (pso)
Johnson, Colin (enforcement off)
Cox, Lesley (vlo)
Edwards, Sally (offender learning mgr)

Coleman, Annita (upwo)
Heskey, Richard (upwo)
McIntyre, Don (upwo)
Telford, Dawne (upwo)

DRR
Owen, Lynne

Proctor, Anne
Pearce, Anna (pso)
Aston, Phil (drug wrkr)
Groves, David (drug wrkr)

Goodban, Diana (pda/csog tutor)
Heywood, Sue (pda)
Prince , Katherine (trainee)
Russell, Michelle (trainee)
Slawson, Robert (trainee)
Susan M Smith (trainee)
Varnham, Maxine (trainee)

Konkel, Carolyn (location mgr)

5a. **Crown Court Probation Office**
The Law Courts, Shirehall
Abbey Foregate **Shrewsbury** SY2 6LU
tel (01743) 252934 fax (01743) 252936

Marshall-Clarke, Vincent

Herefordshire Division

6. Gaol Street
Hereford HR1 2HU
tel (01432) 272521 *fax (01432) 350408*

Baker, Paul (area mgr)
Ashworth, Julie (dist team mgr)
Smith, Ursula (dist team mgr)
Powell, John (risk mgr)
Anderson, Kathleen (cp unit mgr)
Beard, Richard
Bennett, David
Chambers, Lucy
Clarke, Lloyd
Denning, Andrew
Greig, Dennis
Matthews-Jones, Nigel
Mills, Sue
Rees, Sharon
Rosoman, Richard
Armstrong, Nicola (pso, programmes)
Chilton, Barbara (pso, programmes)
Dovey, Amanda (pso, programmes)
Jones, Pam (cpo)
Leeuwangh, John (pso)
Morris, Sarah (pso)
Parsons, Nicola (cpo)
Swan, Jane (pso)
Wainwright, Urszula (pso, programmes)
Wilkinson, Mike (pso)
Guy, Ginny (enforcement officer)
Petts, Susannah (vlo)

Fuller, Catherine (pda)
Cannon, Leila (trainee)
McFarlane, Moira (trainee)

Bettison, Jan (location mgr)

North Worcestershire Division

7. 1-4 Windsor Court
Clive Road **Redditch**
Worcestershire B97 4BT
tel (01527) 585152 *fax (01527) 596459*

Haywood, Jonathon (area mgr)
Frampton, Lesley (p, area mgr intrvntns)
(1)
Davis, Hyacinth (dist team mgr)
Lee, W Martin (dist team mgr)
Jenkins, Neil (snr pract, risk mgr)
Breen, Jan (unit mgr upw) (8)
Chaudhry, Aftab
Da Silva, Claira
Fowler, Claire (p)
Gurney, Daniel
Hammes, Anthony
Harding, Emma (p)
Middleton, Penny
Ramsay, Sheena
Rees, Sara (p) (mat leave)
Southwell, Keith (cso)
Elmes, Robert (cso)
Thompson, Mark (cso)
Clarke, Alex (pso)
Heighway, Lee (pso)
Potter, Julia (pso) (mat leave)
Prince, Lis (pso)
Underwood, M (pso, temp)
Bawler, Tim (p, location mgr)

8. Stourbank House, 90 Mill Street
Kidderminster
Worcestershire DY11 6XE
tel (01562) 820071 *fax (01562) 862425*

Haywood, Jonathon (area mgr)
Moran, Paula (dist team mgr)
Sinclair, Margaret (snr pract, risk mgr)
Breen, Jan (unit mgr, cp) (7)
Akhtar, Azeem
Haycock, Natasha
Hulston, Debbie
Johnson, Adam
Nicholls, Jacqui
Thorp Elizabeth
Turner, Rob
Wall, Tania Maria (pso cp)
Webster, Trevor (pso cp)
Betts, Lynn pso
Green, Kate pso
Smith Jason pso
Thompson, Kirsty pso
Darlow, Teresa pso
Prince, Lis (enforcement off)
Mowbray, Nicola (vlo)

Andrews, Louise (pmo)
Lewis, Jane (location mgr)

South Worcestershire Division

9. 3-4 Shaw Street
    Worcester WR1 3QQ
    tel (01905) 723591 fax (01905)
    20516/29057

Smith, Liz (area mgr)
Morgan, Jane (dist team mgr)
Skelton, Dave (dist team mgr)
Stennett, Susannah (dist team mgr)
Grove, John (risk mgr)
Akhtar, Zafran
Batsford, Louis
Britton, Christine
Concannon, Iggy
Cox, Jane
Drever, Marita
Fields, Alistair
Greenman, Hilary
Gualano, Marco
Guest, Kerry
Hackett, Nina
Harris, Emma
Hutchinson, Chris
Marshall, Rachel
McLean, Paula
Murphy, Carol
Perkins, Joanne
Purewal, Davs
Rimoncelli, Polly
Sheath, Jan
Young, Tania
Barton, Liz (pso)
Charles, Kim (pso)
McDonald, Dee (pso)
Schwab, Richard (pso)
Smith, Kirsty (enforcement officer)
Teale, Gemma (pso)
Sirman, Catherine (pso)
Wall, Martin (pso)
Martin, Carol (vlo)

Atkins, Sara (js, upw unit mgr)
Anderson, Kathleen (js, upw unit mgr)
Bovington, Sarah (upwo)
Gibbons, Jennifer (upwo)
Hampton, Ian (upwo)
Jones, Pete (upwo)
Morgan, Louise (upwo)
Penney, Craig (upwo)
Rushton, Doug (upwo)
Taylor, Lou (upwo)
Thompson, Pete (upwo)
Weston, Mike (upwo)

Willis, Pete (upwo)
Secrett, Rebecca (pda)
Allen, Karen (trainee)
Cadmore, Dave (trainee)
Jones Dan (trainee)
Wroblewska-Fairless, Dorota (trainee)
Bearcroft, Gill (location mgr)

Worcester Crown Court
tel (01905) 723591

10. **Acclaim Project**
    Youth Support Services
    Unit 3, Ryelands Business Centre,
    Ryelands Lane, Elmley Lovett, Droitwich
    Worcestershire WR9 0PT
    tel (01299) 252300 *fax (01299) 252310*

    Baynton, Glen (proj mgr)
    Glen.baynton@yss.org.uk

    Hereford/Worcester
    Bennett, Ben (acclaim off)
    Bennett, Jeannie (acclaim off)
    Swann, Karen (acclaim off)

    Telford/Shropshire
    7 Badham Court, Castle Street
    Telford, Shropshire TF1 5QX
    tel (01952) 257467 *fax (01952) 246113*

    Baynton, Glen (area case mgr)
    Jarrett, Jill (acclaim off)
    McGlue, Suzie (acclaim off)

Youth Offending Services

11. PO Box 13827
    Bromsgrove B60 9DR
    tel (01527) 556200

    Oliver, Sarah

12. 24 Victoria Road
    Wellington, **Telford** TF1 1LG
    tel (01952) 257477

13. Tolladine Road
    Worcester WR4 9NB
    tel (01905) 732200

    Walters, Steve

Approved Premises (Hostels)

14. **Braley House Approved Premises**
    89 Ombersley Road
    Worcester WR3 7BT
    tel (01905) 723975 *fax (01905) 617687*

    Bentley, Mike (hostel mgr)

Baynton, Jenny (po dep mgr)
Baker, Fred (asst warden)
Crouch, Carole (asst warden)
Coleman, Neil (asst warden)
Harding, Wendy (asst warden)
Khan, Nadim (asst warden)

15. **Iris House Voluntary Hostel**
68 Bath Road
Worcester WR5 3EW
tel (01905) 353884

Institutions

16. HM YOI **Stoke Heath**
Market Drayton TF9 2JL
tel (01630) 636000 *fax (01630) 636001*
probn fax (01630) 636164

Gaffney, Jane (spo)
Busk, Bob
Sheppard, Felicity
Barrow, Marie
Collin, Chris
Johnstone, Kerrie (pso)
White, Ashleigh (pso)

17. H M Prison **The Dana**
Shrewsbury SY1 2HR
tel (01743) 273000 *fax (01743) 273001*
probn fax (01743) 273003
probn tel (01743)273054

Smith, Ruth (p, spo)
Cummings, John
Wilson, Fiona

18. H M Prison **Hewell**
Redditch B97 6RD
tel (01527) 785000 *fax (01527) 785001*
legal visits (01527) 785087
legal visits fax (01527) 785010

Williams, Pete (spo)
Fraser, Margaret
Koser, Razwana
Chung, Dawnn ext 851
Taylor, Lee ext 854
Meese, Sharon (pso)

19. H M Prison **Long Lartin**
South Littleton, Evesham WR11 3TZ
tel (01386) 835100 *fax (01386) 835101*

Wain, John (spo)
Concannon, Ignatius
Cox, Jane
Wildig, Sarah
McLean, Paula
Weston, Mike (pso)

Local Justice Areas

5 Drayton
7 Bromsgrove & Redditch
6 Herefordshire
5 South Shropshire
5 Oswestry
8 Kidderminster
5 Shrewsbury
9 South Worcestershire
4 Telford & Bridgnorth

Crown Courts

6 Hereford
5a Shrewsbury
9 Worcester

WEST MIDLANDS PROBATION AREA

Victim enquiries contact number
tel 0121-248 6100

e-mail Firstname.Surname@west-midlands.
probation.gsi.gov.uk

1. **Head Office**
1 Victoria Square, Birmingham B1 1BD
tel 0121-248 6666 *fax 0121-248 6667*

Maiden, Mike (cpo)
Bates, Ged (dir of operations)
Holland, Catherine (dir of people &
business devpt)
Steer, Richard (secretary/solicitor)
Nelson, Andy (dir of finance & facilities)
Gill, Stephen (aco, interventions &
business devpt & quality)
Madders, Michael (aco, i.t. services)
Daly, William (aco, business supt)
Whitehouse, David (aco, finance)
Knott, David (hr business partner)
Allcott, Ros (area planning mgr)
Cutayar, Mark (estates & facilities mgr)
Flaxman, James (perf & systems info mgr)
Kerslake, Mike (qual imp mgr)
Mitchell, Rita (risk mgr)
Noble, Jackie (hr manager)
Sawbridge, Judith (info & comms mgr)

2. **King Edward House**
5th Floor, King Edward House
135A New Street, Birmingham B2 4QJ
tel 0121-248 2700 *fax 0121-248 2701*

Equality & Diversity Unit
Green, Richard (aco equality & diversity)

Kelly, Tony (e&d off)
Sharma, Ushma (e&d off)
Whelan, Paula (e&d off)

Assistant Chief Officers Unit
Green, Richard (aco, Courts, EOASys,
expedited breach & deaths under
supervision, diversity & victims)
Byford, Nigel (aco offender mgmnt,
west of area)
Wall, Chris (aco offender mgmnt,
Birmingham & Solihull)
Taylor, Richard (aco)
Appleby, Neil (aco intrvntns, Coventry)
Tennant, Mike (aco interventions)

Effective Practice
Aziz, Naheed (spo)

**Bail & Support Services
Project (BASS)**
West Midlands Area
Jones, Stuart (spo)
Kneller, Jo (pso)
Nott, Elaine (pso)
Vacancy (pso)
Warwickshire Area
Vacancy (pso)
Staffordshire Area
Evans, Susan (pso)
Palin, Rachel (pso)
West Mercia Area
Wheeldon, John (pso)
Vacancy (pso)

Partnerships & Interventions Unit
(including Skills For Life)
Vacancy (admin mgr)
Singh, Harjinder (ext prtnrshp comm mgr)
Cole, Diane (ptnrshps monitoring off)
Phul, Sharon (dtto/drr commissioning off)
Carr, Caroline (prtnrshp & commissioning
mgr for skills for life & ete)
Pymm, Lesley (dist mgr ptnrshps &
intrvntns)
Badasha, Dalbir (progs implmntatn mgr)
Tudor, Barbara (victim offender devpt off)

Treatment Managers
*(located in various offices across West
Midlands)*
Burton, Carol (based at 9)
Gray, Deborah (based at 9)
Campion, Sally (based at 36)
Edgar, Karen (based at 36)
Ballard, Claire (based at 33)
Afzal, Kaiser (based at 33)
Appleton, Jane (based at 11)
Ford, David (based at 11)

White, Elaine (based at 22)

**Employment Training & Education
Unit**
Carr, Caroline (prtnrshp & commissioning
mgr for skills for life & ete)
Emplt & Skills for Life Co-ordinators

French, Emily (Birmingham)
Evans -Cole, Annice (Coventry & Solihull)
Talbot, Emma (West of County)

at Centenary House 0121- 248 3660
Gaughan, John (ete pso)
at Coventry 024-7663 0555
Lowndes, Jackie (ete pso)
at Dudley (01384) 440682
Pearce, Gavin (ete pso)
at Erdington 0121-248 5600
Henry, Jackie (ete pso)
at Greencoat House 0121-248 5705
McGowan, Yvonne (pso)
at Hamstead Rd 0121-248 6500
Mohammed, Sohail (ete pso)
at Harborne 0121-248 6230
Cook, Steve (ete pso)
at Lower Essex St 0121-248 6400
Henry, Jackie (ete pso)
at Perry Barr 0121-248 6348
Mohammed, Sohail (ete pso)
at Unity House, 0121-533 4500
Smith, Richard (ete pso)
at Saltley 0121-248 6150
Cook, Steve (ete pso)
at Selly Oak 0121 2486720
Henry, Jackie (pso)
at Stonnall Road Hostel (01922) 459574
 Vacancy (pso all hostels)
at Walsall (01922) 721341
Iftikhar, Ali (ete pso)
at Wolverhampton (01902) 576000
Stevens, Chris (ete pso)
Rees, Jennie (ete pso)

3. **Area Victim Liaison Unit**
    at 52 Newton Street
    Birmingham B4 6NF
    tel 0121-248 6100 *fax 0121-248 6101*

    Beckford, Audrey (spo)
    Gallagher, Nicola (po)
    Collier, Catherine (po)
    Madeley, Helen (po)
    Fitzmaurice, Tracey (pso)
    Garrow, June (pso)
    Nembhardt, Osbourne (pso)
    Ferber, Rozanne (women's safety wrkr)

    at 5th Floor, King Edward House
    135A New Street, Birmingham. B2 4QJ

tel 0121-248 2700 *fax 0121-248 2701*

Tudor, Barbara (vodo)

at 70 Little Park Street
Coventry, CV1 2UR
tel 024-7655 3268 *fax 024-7623 0925*

Meir, Janice (po)
Patton, Brian (pso)

at Minerva Wharf, Horseley Fields
Wolverhampton WV1 3LX
tel (01902) 576001 *fax (01902) 454212*

Gallagher, Nicola
Durbin, Jacque (pso)
Vacancy (women's safety wrkr)

3a. **The Violent & Sex Offender Joint
Management Team**
W Midlands Area MAPPA
c/o West Midlands Police
FCSB, PO Box 52
Lloyd House, Colmore Circus Queensway
Birmingham B4 6NQ
tel 0121-609 6954 *fax 0121-609 6950*

Briscoe, John (spo, co-ord)
Fox, Valerie
Paten, Sarah (snr admin)

Dudley District

4. **District Management Unit**
Suite 5, Trafalgar House
47-49 King Street, Dudley DY2 8PS
tel (01384) 326020 *fax (01384) 326021*

Townsend, Viv (dist mgr)
Brown, Steve (admin mgr)

5. 44 New Road **Stourbridge** DY8 1PA
tel (01384) 440682 *fax (01384) 441354*

Batham, Angie (spo)
Garratt, Liz
Chohan, Sharnjit
Kaur-Thandi, Palbinder
Storer, Jim
Jerrison, Jayne
Fountain, Joanne
Taylor, Barbara
Baker, Sonia (pso)
Cox, Ira (pso)
Farrar, Susan (pso)
Fearon, David (pso)
Simmons, Rachel (pso)
Walker-Smith, Jenny (pso)

6. The Court House, The Inhedge
Dudley DY1 1RR

tel (01384) 862424 *fax (01384) 862425*

Aston, Heather (spo)
Clark, Mandy (spo)
Brierley, Sally
Dimmock, Katy
Hampton, Jane
Hogan, Marie
Langstone, Diane
Reid, Karen
Richards, Monesha
Vaughan-Phillips, Louise
Whittam, Jayne
Brown, Shirley (pso)
Dixon, Christian (pso)
Grizzle, Subs (pso)
Jones, Chris (pso)
Leather, Debbie (pso)
Partridge, Susan (pso)
Round, Deborah (pso)
Tyler, Ami (pso)

7. Laurel Lane **Halesowen** B63 3DA
tel 0121-550 1496 *fax 0121-585 5582*

Fergus, Michael (spo)
Bishop, Claire
Mann, Caroline
Mills, Phil
Page, Saundra
Dee, Elaine (pso)
Hawley, Anne (pso)
Nash, Paul (pso)

Courts and Allocation
Vacancy (spo)

Halesowen Magistrates' Court Office
tel 0121-550 1496 *fax 0121-585 5582*
Brecknell, Davina
Vickers, June
Barrett, Ann Marie (pso)
Darlington, Daphne (pso)

Dudley Magistrates' Court Office
tel (01384) 862424 *fax (01384) 862437*

Fitzgerald, Kevin
Jordan, Oliver (pso)
Spiteri, Paula (pso)

8. **Dudley Youth Offending Team**
Brindley House, Hall Street
Dudley DY2 7DT
tel (01384) 813060 *fax (01384) 813270*

Platt, Andy
Higgit, Gary

Sandwell District

9. 14-16 New Street
    West Bromwich B70 7PN
    0121-533 4500 *fax 0121-533 4501*

    Royal, Pat (dist mgr)
    Brown, Steve (admin mgr)
    Talbot, Emma (ete co-ord West of Area)

    OM Team 1
    Hudson, Sue (spo)
    Cookson, David
    Glean, Janice
    Kooner, Juskaran
    Overthrow, Karen
    Balasubramaniam, Malini (pso)
    Copson, Kerry (pso)
    Dee, Brian (pso)
    Hubbold, Melissa (pso)
    Riley, Paul (pso)

    OM Team 2
    Thompson, Jacky (spo)
    Kaur-Pahal, Rashpal (spo)
    Bibi, Shaida (spo)
    Brown, Adele
    Chand, Geeta
    Crawford-Brown, Junior
    Forrest, Sean
    Francis, Vanessa
    Kernarne, Emma
    Kuffa, Tony
    Littlehales, Sue
    Morgan, Claradell
    Queely, Claudine
    Samria, Daljit
    Spence, Audrey
    Summers, Susan
    Adams, Natalie (pso)
    Browne, Philippa (pso)
    Booth, Samantha (pso)
    Edwards, John (pso)
    Oakley, Stacey (pso)
    Sendur, Leila (pso)
    Stewart, Cynthia (pso)

    OM Team 3
    Coxall, Mary (spo)
    Baden, Asha
    Greensill, Carole
    Price, John
    Rai, Harmail
    Robinson-Wright, Lorraine
    Taylor, Owen
    Vasia, Archana
    Ward, Jenny
    Bevin, Fay (pso)
    Buchanan, Sonia (pso)
    Reeve, Adam (pso)

Whale, Paul (pso)

Interventions
Gould, Ian (spo)
Cowles, Jasmine (pso)
Hothi, Sak (pso)
James, Jane (pso)
Saddler, Stephen (pso)
Sarai, Kulvinder (pso)

ETE
Smith, Richard (pso)

Substance Misuse & PPO Team
Ellis, Philip J (spo)
Pritchard, Andy
Williams, Morene
Anderson-Stevens, Heather (pso)
Lewis, Linda (pso)
Radford, Edwina (pso)
Wheeler, Monica (pso)

Courts & Allocation
Ellis, Philip J (spo)
Abrams, Pat
Edwards, Alyson
Kaye, Peter
McGhee, James

Warley Magistrates' Court Office
tel 0121-533 3427 *fax 0121-525 6751*
Bloice, Lawrence (pso)
Mervyn Jackie (pso)
Shaw, Bhartiben (pso)

W. Bromwich Magistrates' Crt Office
tel 0121-525 5381 *fax 0121-525 6751*
Alexander, Marion (pso)
Balu, Amarjit (pso)
Facer, Rebecca (pso)
Oldham-Smith, Trevor (pso)
Smith, Karen (pso)

10. **Sandwell Youth Offending Team**
     SGS House, Johns Lane, Off Tipton Road,
     Tividale, Oldbury B69 3HX
     tel 0121-557 8804 *fax 0121-521 0991*

     Botham, Michael
     Trainor, Timothy

Coventry District

11. Bishop Street
     Coventry CV1 1HU
     tel 024-7655 5638

     District Management Unit
     fax 024-7663 0183
     Chand, Sarah (district mgr)
     Kaur, Christine (admin mgr)

Coventry Programmes
O'Donoghue, Deirdre (spo)
Appleton, Jane (treatment mgr)
Ford, David (treatment mgr)
Darragh, David (pso)
Griffin, Leigh (pso)

12   70 Little Park Street
Coventry CV1 2UR
tel 024-7663 0555 *fax 024-7663 1531*

Coventry Crts & Allocation Team
fax 024-7655 3393

Winston, Muhammad (spo)
Cosser, Mike
Norton, Debra
O'Neil, Jim
Purdy, Lynn
Whittem, Gavin
Allder, Heather (pso)
Bolland, Patrick (pso)
Cowley, Steve (pso)
Gill, Ciara (pso)
Hall, Michael (pso)
Lee, Mark (pso)
Miller, Cath (pso)
Oakley, Jon (pso)

OM Team 1
Killeen, Chris (spo)
Atwal, Ranjit
Davies, Sandra
Jones, Ray
McGeoghan, Fiona
Newell, Diane
Wibberley, Steve
Fisher, Mathew (nqpo)
Lennon, Anna (nqpo)
Briffa, Colin (pso)
Ferron, Lynne (pso)
Heath, Peter (pso)
Paul, Anthony (pso)
Porter, Kevin (pso)

OM Team 2
Dunkley, Rose (spo)
Hayward, Mark
James, Emma
Jaspal, Sunny
Lynch, Leanna
Newbold, Denise
Sugden, Joseph
Thorpe, Elaine
Browett, Guy (nqpo)
Butler, Anita (nqpo)
Gordon, Lindsay (nqpo)
David, Sabrina (pso)
Goolding, Melanie (pso)

Melville, Donna (pso)
Nutting, Marie (pso)
Rich, Brian (pso)
Rudd, Charlotte (pso)

OM Team 3
Yeap, Chris (spo)
Coope, Kirstin
Day, Stuart
Flemming, Sandra
Gibbs, Amy
Golby, Chris
Harris, Faith
Mole, James
Rose, Samantha
Bilverstone, Stuart (pso)
Johnson, Barbara (pso)
McEwan, Aaron (pso)
Rana, Rae (pso)
Rollason, Karen (pso)

OM Team 4
fax 02476 655012

Toor, Haramandeep (spo)
Gheent, Harvi
Holten, Noelle
Humphrey, Joanne
Laidler, Karen
Robertson, Helen
Taylor, Caroline
Willett, Andrea
Sanderson, Emily (nqpo)
Gardner, Chris (pso)
Kane, Lorraine (pso)
Killeen, Mick (pso)
Lusby, Nichole (pso)
Mellor, Jackie (pso)
Patrick, Ray (pso)

Substance Misuse, PPOs & Custody
Laura Treacy (spo)
Green, Bev
Windridge, Kelly
Groves, Rose (pso)
Khan, Imtiaz (pso)
Springer, Enmore (pso)

ETE
Evans-Healey, Annice (ete co-ord)
Lowndes, Jackie

13. **Coventry Youth Offending Team**
Ground Floor, Christchurch House
Greyfriars, Lane, Coventry CV1 2GY
tel 024-7683 1414 *fax 024-7683 1400*

Almquist, Debbie
Gill, Duljit
Miekle, Caron

East Birmingham & Solihull District

14. **Centenary House**
Mackadown Lane, Kitts Green
Birmingham B33 0LQ
tel 0121-248 3660 *fax 0121-248 3661*

District Management Unit
Connelly, Jane (dist mgr)
Kaur, Christine (admin mgr)

OM Team 1
Ditchburn, Margaret (spo)
Dickenson, Nicole
Dodd, Claire
Jellett, Victoria
Mitchell, Kathleen
Walsh, Leisha
Foster, Maria (pso)
Holmes, Carly (pso)
Nevin, Louise (pso)

OM Team 2 *inc Substance Misuse*
Rogers, Marj (spo)
Buckley, Susan
Kaur, Gurpreet
Murphy, Majella
Smith, Claire
Whitehurst, John
Brenan, Helen (nqpo)
Mills, Stephen (nqpo)
Bebbington, Chris (pso)
Chapman, Sarah (pso)
Lalwal, Oluwole (pso)
Thomas, Ian (pso)

OM Team 4
Kennedy, Jennifer (spo)
Davenport, Jen
Farmer, Louise
Taylor, Sarah
Kelley, Steve (pso)
McLaughlin, Eddie (pso)

OM Team 5
Kennedy, Jennifer (spo)
Chatwin, Pat
Dickenson, Nicole
Spillane, Kerry (nqpo)
Chaplin, Eileen (pso)
Kelly, Linda (pso)
Longthorne, Debra (pso)

Solihull Magistrates' Court Team
Allder, Marian (spo)
McCauley, Chris

Solihull Magistrates' Court
Homer Road, Solihull B91 3RD
tel 0121-711 7331 *fax 0121-711 7050*

Atkins, Jenny (pso)

Fitzsimmons, Elaine (pso)
Hipkiss, Andy (pso)
Lambden, Anne (pso)
Murland, Richard (pso)
Reeve, Max (pso)

ETE
Gaughan, John (pso)
Connelly, Bill (pso)

15. **7 Herbert Road**
Solihull B91 3QE
tel 0121 248 6849 *fax 0121 248 6848*

OM Team 3
Hockin, Trevor (spo)
Buckley, Jane
Gissey, Sharon
Littleford, Ceri-Lisa
McLarnon, Nonnie
O'Donoghue, Claire
Walker, Yvonne
Worley, Nick

16. **Solihull Youth Offending Team**
Keeper's Lodge, Chelmsley Road
Chelmsley Wood
Birmingham B37 7RS
tel 0121-779 1750 *fax 0121-779 1755*

Peynado, Fenton

Wolverhampton District

17. **Prue Earle House**
Union Street, Horseley Fields
Wolverhampton WV1 3JS
tel (01902) 576000 *fax (01902) 455180*

District Management Unit
Pejatta, Jas (dist mgr)
Vann, Barbara (admin mgr)

Audit, Quality & Improvement
Ashby, Ted (spo)

Team 1
Dee, John (spo)
Anand, Vijay
Easthope, Norma
Lloyd, Fran
Parmar-Poynter, Bhavna
Smith, Richard
Thackwray, Michelle
Uppal, Pinder
Colburne, Gemma (pso)
Goodman, Danielle (pso)
Lockley, Sheila (pso)
Ramzan, Mohammed (pso)
Williams, Odette (pso)

Team 2
Patel, Lalita (spo)
Aston, Jenny
Chamberlain, Sarah
Chumber, Amrit
Cooper, Heather
Grant, Sheena
Meredith, Nina
Wallace, Clare
Wilson, Jean
Davies, Katie (pso)
Heer, Kuljit (pso)
Phipps, Sally (pso)
Teale, Tracey (pso)
Thompson, Gemma (pso)
Wilson, Lisa (pso)

Team 3
Gleadall, Vikki (spo)
Evans, Jo
Malik, Assifa
Mangot, Harbinder
Marsh, David
Mitchell, Carol
Moore-Graham, Merna
Wilkins, Ian
Daley, Carol (pso)
Garrett, Joan (pso)
Grant, Carol (pso)

Team 4
McConnell, Kate (spo)
Brittle, Emma
Caine, Louise
Charmling, Swaroop
Cooper, Judith
Fincher, Jenny
Mail, Stephanie
Pschenyckyj, Denise
Sharman, Dave
Teale, Ian
Williams, Gerry
Chahal, Rajinder (pso)
Russon, Janet (pso)

Skills for Life
Murdoch, Mike (spo)
Rees, Jennie (pso)
Stevens, Chris (pso)

18. **Wolverhampton Programmes Unit**
Minerva Wharf, Horseley Fields
Wolverhampton WV1 3LX
tel (01902) 871659 *fax (01902) 452496*

Murdoch, Mike (spo)
Joslyn, Jean
Whitehouse, Sally
Hale, Rebecca (pso)

Court & Allocation Unit
tel (01902) 576000 *fax (01902) 576010*
Walker, Stephen (spo)

19. **Wolverhampton Magistrates' Crt**
Law Courts, North Street
Wolverhampton WV1 1RA
tel (01902) 711449 *fax (01902) 772361*

Walker, Stephen (spo)
Male, Anita
Pearson, John
Robinson, Angela
Tatton, Tracey
Dyke, Marjorie (pso)
Garcha, Daive (pso)
McManus, Sally (pso)
Randle, Katy (pso)
Ross, Peter (pso)
Timmins, Chuchie (pso)
Worsey, Ruth (pso)

20. **Wolverhampton Crown Court**
Pipers Row, Wolverahmpton WV1 3LQ
tel (01902) 481108/9 *fax (01902) 713355*

Walker, Stephen (spo)
Davis, Hortense
Grewal, Ami
Jones, Jackie (pso)
Nash, Kate (pso)
Phipps, Sally (pso)

21. **Wolverhampton Youth
Offending Team**
c/o Social Services Department
Beckminster Houses, Birches Barn Road
Wolverhampton WV3 7BJ
tel (01902) 553722 *fax (01902) 553733*

Denny, Nicola
Kaur, Rajinder
Osbourne, Annette
Dee, Jill (pso)
Winstone, Diane (pso)

Walsall District

22. Walsall Probation Complex
Midland Road **Walsall** WS1 3QE
tel (01922) 721341 *fax (01922) 725616*

District Management Unit
McNulty, Adrian (dist mgr)
Vann, Barbara (admin mgr)

Team1/2
Russell, Pete (spo)
Billingham, Ruth
Brown, Vassel

Jones, Lisa
McGovern, Kathleen
Robertson, Les
Roberts, Beccy
Austins, Alan (pso)
Bull, Martin (pso)
Cross, Dave (pso)
Goode, Debbie (pso)
Panesar, Paramjit (pso)
Wood, Stephen (pso)

Team 3
Blake, Sonia (spo)
Ainslie, Sam
Cornwell, Rachel
Fiero, Roma
Head, Nigel
Hewitt, Christine
Jordan, Carla
Kelsey, Hayley
Kendrick, Carol
Ball, David (pso)
Kaur, Bilwinder (pso)
Richards, Marjorie (pso)

Team 4
Brownsword, Andrew (spo)
Thawait, Pratima (snr pract)
Ball, Pamela
Corbett, Victoria
Linton, Hazelle
Sagar, Vid
Ball, Sarah (pso)
Evans, Yvonne (pso)
Gainer, Martin (pso)
Preedy, Karen (pso)
Tarajia, Zaynab (pso)
Wallbank, Jenny (pso)

Substance Misuse & PPO Team
Cunningham, Julian
Mills, Pamela
Ball, Sarah (pso)
Evans, Yvonne (pso)
Tarajia, Zaynab (pso)
Wallbank, Jenny (pso)

Interventions
Coyle, John (spo)
Nash, Karen (pso)
Ali, Iftikhar (pso skills for life)
Carolan, Bernie (pso)
Hunter, Kerrie (pso)
Jackson, Charles (pso)
Wells, Angela (pso)

Walsall/Aldridge Magistrates' Crt
Burnham, Dolores (spo)
Hamkalo, Michelle
McLeish, Gillian

Osmond, Andy
Dhani, Hasmukh (pso)
Ford, Lesley (pso)
Titley, Janine (pso)

23. **Youth Offending Team**
Blakenhall Village Centre, Thames Rd
Blakenhall, Walsall WS3 1LZ
tel (01922) 714966 *fax (01922) 492462*

Russell, Pete (spo)
Arrowsmith, Ben
Dhillon, Surrinder

Birmingham District

24. **Birmingham ACO & Admin Unit**
5th Floor, King Edward House
135A New Street, Birmingham B2 4QJ
tel 0121-248 2700 *fax 0121-248 2701*

Wall, Chris (aco Birmingham & Coventry)
Elphick, Bronwen (dist mgr) (32)
Lomas, Simon (dist mgr) (31)
Brown, Len (dist mgr) (30)
Brown-Richards, Pat (dist mgr) (36)
Kidson, Gay (dist mgr)
Walton, Neil (admin mgr)
Carr, Caroline (basic skills co-ord)

24a. **Violent & Sex Offender Joint Management Team**
W Midlands Area MAPPA
c/o West Midlands Police
FCSB, PO Box 52
Lloyd House, Colmore Circus Queensway
Birmingham B4 6NQ
tel 0121-609 6954 *fax 0121-609 6950*
Briscoe, John (spo)
Fox, Val

25. **Victoria Law Courts**
PO Box 4081, Corporation Street
Birmingham B4 6QU
tel 0121-248 6080
crt info fax 0121-248 6081
crt liaison fax 0121-248 6096

Henderson, Jane (spo)
Burt, Tania
Dooley, Phil
Edwards, Althea
Edwards, Cheryl-Ann
Flynn, Val
James, Donna
Murphy, Brian
Samrai, Dalwinder
Thompson, Sally
Wilkinson, Sara

Allen, Julie (pso)
Andrews, Fay (pso)
Bennington, Claire (pso)
Gregson, Susie (pso)
Grimes, Sarah (pso)
Kaur, Ranjit (pso)
Palmer, Maureen (pso)
Ram-Jakhu, Sodhi (pso)
Samuels, Lorraine (pso)
Young, Mary (pso)
Williams, Martin (pso)

Drug Intervention Programme
tel 0121-248 1283 *fax 0121-248 1276*
Dippolito, Angela (spo)
Smith, Liz (pm)
Clarke, Cynthia (pso)
Spencer, Christopher (pso)
Clarke, Anne (pso)
Hadley, Paula (pso)
Smith, Anne (pso)
Tandy, Rachel (pso)

26. **Queen Elizabeth II Law Courts**
1 Newton Street, Birmingham B4 7NA
tel 0121-248 0099 *fax 0121-248 0045*

Sutton Coldfield Magistrates' Crt
The Court House, Lichfield Road
Sutton Coldfield, Birmingham B74 2NS
tel 0121-354 3715 *fax 0121-355 8984*

Crown Court Team
& Sutton Court Team
Hughes, Phillip (spo)
Jones, Martin (based at Sutton Mags Crt)
Astley, Denise
Durbin, Ray
Kyne, Chris (temp)
Gessey, Vanessa (pso Sutton)
Rollason, Juliette (pso)
Grundy, Victoria (pso)

Larman, Karen (pso)

Peripatetic Team
Matile, Miles
Belboda Queeley, Claudine
Collins, Yvonne
Phillipides, Toni

27. **11-15 Lower Essex Street**
Birmingham B5 6SN
tel 0121-248 6460 *fax 0121-248 6461*

Homeless Offenders
Resettlement Unit
Mullis, Dave (spo)
Bailey, Rema
Cooner, Sanjit

Carman, Stephen
Minto, Sharon
O'Shea, Rebecca
Phillips, Rebecca
Reynolds, Gillian
Sandhu, Jagjit
Whitehouse, Lynne
Braithwaite, Kevin (pso)
Millwood, Pauline (pso)

28. **Saltley Programmes Unit**
12 High Street, Saltley
Birmingham B8 1JR
tel 0121-248 6184 *fax 0121-248 6151*
Ballard, Claire
Barnacle, Sharon
Chester, Sarah
Dewitt, Sandeep
Simms, Arlene
Anderson, Patricia (pso)
Aston, Brent (pso)
Richards, Laurie (pso)

29. **Programmes Unit**
326-328 Hamstead Road
Birmingham B20 2RA
tel 0121-248 6500 *fax 0121-248 6501*

Edgar, Karen
Campion, Sally (pso)

30. 12 High Street
Saltley Birmingham B8 1JR
tel 0121-248 6150 *fax 0121-248 6151*

Team 1
Pasha, Naveed (spo)
Britton, Matthew
Cain, Claudia
King, Maxine
Lau, Natalie
Lowe, Eve
Morris, David
Overthrow, Karen
Smythe, Karen
Tudor, Pam
Batchelor, Dawn (pso)
Eason, George (pso)
Groves, Linda (pso)
Kalia, Reena (pso)
Thomas, Mark (pso)

Team 2
Octigan, Mike (spo)
Astley, Deborah
Blackman, Gywllym
Branson, Jennifer
Heslop, Mike

Johnson, Debbie
Jordan, Pat
Muir, Elizabeth
Slater, Malcolm
Woods, Pat
Anderson-Stevens, Heather (pso)
Ciccone, Leeza (pso)
Johns, Sue (pso)
McPherson, Stuart (pso)
Panton, Shirley (pso)
Raphael, Melissa (pso)
Watts, Leonard (pso)

31.   Greencoat House, 259 Stratford Road
      Sparkbrook Birmingham B11 1QS
      tel 0121-248 5611 *fax 0121-248 5613*

      Team 1
      McCarthy, Terry (spo)
      Alden, Andy
      Baker, Joanne
      Brown, Carolyn
      Campbell, Jennifer
      Fergus, Paul
      Lam, Angela
      Phillips, David
      Thomas, Kat
      Barker, Louise (pso)
      Brissett, Maxine (pso)
      Stephens, Faye (pso)
      Williams, Claudette (pso)

      Team 2
      Francis, Ireca (spo)
      Bond, Jon
      King, Maria
      Lidell, Catherine
      Milinkovic, Victor
      Mohammed, Weddad
      Rahim, Mohammed
      Rehman, Rafia
      Rhoden, Sonia
      Brown, Vanessa (pso)
      Gooch, Amy (pso)
      Jordan, Althea (pso)
      Millard, Adrianna (pso)
      Perkins, Eve (pso)

      Team 3
      Smith, Paul (spo)
      Ahmed, Shaheen
      Benjamin, Audrey
      Caesar, Yvette
      Carrol, Andrew
      Felton, Stuart
      Bath, Jaspal (pso)
      Beardmore, Rennie (pso, dip)
      Colburn, Gemma (pso)

Hedderick, Bev (pso)
Poller, Gemma (pso)
Pratty, Claire (pso)
Wint, Patsy (pso)

Team 4
Baker, Kirsty (spo)
Bailey, Nadia
Hyman, Joy
Islam, Mohammed
Philippides, Toni
Thurman, Berney
Barnett, Pat (tpo)
Dennis, Bev (pso)
Gibbs, Charlie (pso)
Moulton, Patricia (pso)
Williams, Claudette (pso)

32.   826 Bristol Road **Selly Oak**
      Birmingham B29 6NA
      tel 0121-248 6680 *fax 0121-248 6681*

      Jones, Rodderick (spo)
      Levy, Paul (spo)
      O'Connell, Michael (snr pract)
      Anderson, Dawn
      Beard, Helen
      Cansfield, Karen
      Francis, Aaron
      Hanley, Richard
      Harper, Keely
      Hughes, Anna
      Knowles, Ann
      Maye, Owen
      Mordecai, Josephine
      Morton, Jon
      Mullings, Janet
      Stevenson, Fiona
      Tyler, Annie
      Watkins, Laurence
      Abanikanda, Tunde (pso)
      Bryan, Alan (pso)
      Cooper, Roger (pso)
      Gordon, Michael (pso)
      Gordon, Pat (pso)
      Johnson, Julia (pso)
      Nott, Elaine (pso)
      Robinson, Keith (pso)
      Rowley, Glenda (pso, dip)
      Swingler, Claire (pso)
      Walker, Jackie (pso)
      Woolley, Malcolm (pso)

33.   **18-28 Lower Essex Street**
      Birmingham B5 6SN
      tel 0121-248 6400 *fax 0121-248 6401*

      Hird, Maria (spo)

Johnson, Eric (spo)
O'Connell, Michael (snr pract)
Altaf, Samina
Chopra, Kulvinder
Fountain, Joanne
Lindo, Elizabeth
Penney, Kevin
Stewart, Mervin
Zanab, Be
Bailey, Eileen (pso)
Crawford, Jean (pso)
Gray, Diane (pso)
Hamilton, Nyasha (pso)
Shinji, Rajinder (pso)

34. 76 Walsall Road
Perry Barr Birmingham B42 1SF
tel 0121-248 6340 *fax 0121-248 6341*

Team 1
Richards, Sandra (spo)
Brookes, Angie (snr pract)
Akram, Safraz
Bevan, Catherine
Dillon, Jennifer
Green, Janet
Harvey, Victoria
Oakley, Patricia
Powell, Wayne
Scott, Andrew
Ward, Rosaleen
Wilkinson, Paula
Young, Jodie
Bassan, Ravinder (pso)
Boylan, Lindsay (pso)
Caines, Rianne (pso)
Creighton, Denise (pso)
Finch, Andre (pso)
Hamilton, Adele (pso)
Scott, Dominique (pso)
Sohail, Mohammed (elo)

Team 2
Poland, Michael (spo)
Ayee, Jacqui
Birdi, Sharon
Burns, Louise
Gaddu, Diamond
Heatherley, Janine
Mair, Patsy
Vernon, Maureen
Williams, Paul
Byrne, Sarah (pso)
Mills, Olive (pso)
Smith, Les (pso)
Uppal, Dalvinder (pso)

Team 3
Rai, Ravinder (spo)

Collins, Yvonne
Hazeley-Jones, Christopher
McGrainor, Katie
Scott, Andrew
Lerenzo, Sebastian (pso)
Madders, Lynn (pso)
Riley, Laura (pso)
Sheard, Mary (pso)

35. Stuart Court, 73/75 Station Road
Erdington Birmingham B23 6UG
tel 0121-248 5600 *fax 0121-248 5605*

Morris, Paulette (spo)
Moss, Alison (snr pract) Mon-Wed
Barnett, Mabel
Bassi, Baljinder
Brown, Keren
Canicle, Jakki
Coombs, Caroline
Crisp, Ruth
Davey, Melanie
Hunk, Emma
Key, Martin
Smith, Keith
Thompson, Angela
Edwards, Dot (pso)
Franklin, Charlene (pso)
Minnott, Marsha (pso)
Pankhania, Manjula (pso)
Robins, Toby (pso)
Rollins, Gina (pso)
Stannard, Andrew (pso)
Wiggan, Tammy (pso)

36. 326/328 Hamstead Road
Handsworth Birmingham B20 2RA
tel 0121-248 6500 *fax 0121-248 6501*

Edwards, Jamie-Ann (spo)
Mayers, Julie (spo, guns & gangs)
Williams, Ruth (snr pract)
Bonas, Leon
Caines, Michelle
Clarke, Tracy
Dale, Rebecca
Driscoll, Steve
Eggleton, Joanne
Field, Richard
Griffiths, Sîan
Hoo, Marcus
Marchant, Mel
Mukwamba, Michael
Parkes, Barbara
Perkins, Colin
Young, Therese
Green, Ben (pso, dip)
Badesha, Jas (pso)

Bhopal, Varinder (pso)
Forde, Noel (pso)

37. **4 Albany Road**
    Harborne Birmingham B17 9JX
    tel 0121-248 6230 *fax 0121-248 6231*

    Tier 3
    Tracey, Daniel (spo)
    Moss, Alison (snr pract)
    Antrobus, Lisa
    Aziz, Zanfar
    Baker, Barbara
    Blake, Sarah
    Dickman, Susan
    Frati, Catherine
    Lambert, Genene
    Seadon, Sally
    Sewell, Jean
    Wookey, Stephen
    Adams, Karl (pso)
    Blewitt, Juliet (pso)
    Chapasuka, Judith (pso)
    Grant, Stacey (pso)
    Scott, Valerie (pso)
    Sterling, Conrad (pso)

38. **11-15 Lower Essex Street**
    Birmingham B5 6SN
    tel 0121-248 6460 *fax 0121-248 6461*

    Jackson, Judith (spo)
    Vassalo, Carmela (spo)
    Afzal, Kaiser (treatment mgr)
    Boulton, John (pso)
    Moulton, Patricia (pso)
    Smart, Charles (pso)
    White, Elaine (pso)

39. **Birmingham Youth Offending Service**

39a. **Youth Offending Service Head Office**
    18 Gravelly Hill North
    Erdington, Birmingham B23 6BQ
    tel 0121-464 0600 *fax 0121-464 0609*

    Vacancy

39b. **Youth Offending Service (North)**
    Pype Hayes Hall, Pype Haye Park
    Pype Hayes, Birmingham B24 0HG
    tel 0121-303 0252 *fax 0121-464 0921*

    Cain, Claudia
    Jones, Sezal

39c. **Youth Offending Service (South)**
    Halescroft Square, off Shenley Hill
    Birmingham B31 1HD
    tel 0121-476 5111 *fax 0121-411 2198*

Heath, Jeanette (admin asst)
Southall, Joanne

39d. **Youth Offending Service (East)**
    15 Commons Lane, Washwood Heath
    Birmingham B3 2US
    tel 0121-464 7719 *fax 0121-464 6261*

    Brydson, Davlin
    Coleman, Angela

39e. **Youth Offending Service (West)**
    115 All Saints Street
    Hockley, Birmingham B18 7RJ
    tel 0121-464 8484 *fax 0121-464 7575*

    Hazell, Liz
    Myerscough, Karen

39f. **Youth Offending Service
    (Highgate Centre)**
    157-159 St Lukes Road, Highgate
    Birmingham B5 7DA
    tel 0121-464 1570 *fax 0121-464 1596*

    Morgan Daniel
    Parchment, Lorna

39g. **Youth Offending Service
    (Birmingham Youth Court)**
    c/o 52 Newton Street
    Birmingham B4 6NF
    tel 0121-233 3600 *fax 0121-236 0828*

    Browne, Bev (pso)
    McIntear, John
    Moss, Gwyneth (admin asst)

Unpaid Work Division

40. 5th Floor, King Edward House
    135a New Street **Birmingham** B2 4QJ
    tel 0121-248 2700 *fax 0121-248 2702*

    Hall, Kobina (dist mgr)
    Tolley, Pat (admin mgr)
    Huckerby, Keith (health & safety off)

41. Unity House, 14-16 New Street
    West Bromwich B70 7PN
    tel 0121-533 4500 *fax 0121-533 4501*

    Unpaid Work Unit
    Walton, Martin (unit mgr)
    Loft, Lesley (qa mgr)
    Hewitt, Alan (pso)
    Showell, Leonard (pso)
    Williams Charles (pso)

42. 162 Halesowen Road
    Netherton **Dudley** DY2 9TS

tel (01384) 456482 *fax (01384) 457441*

Unpaid Work Unit
Mills, John (unit mgr)
Coley, Trevor (qam)
Busby, Marinda (pso)
Warmer, Barry (pso)
Woolridge, John (pso)

43. Bishop Street
Coventry CV1 1HU
tel 024-7625 1166 *fax 02476630183*

Unpaid Work Unit
Smith, Penny (unit mgr)
Farmer, Terry (qa mgr)
Emslie, Gabrielle (pso)
Hughes Charlotte (pso)
Massey Stephen (pso)

44. Minerva Wharf, Horseley Fields
Wolverhampton WV1 3LX
tel (01902) 351518 *fax (01902) 452496*

Unpaid Work Unit
Brown, Barry (imp mgr)
Kennedy, Yvonne (unit mgr)
Hardy, Neil (pso)
Hill, Karen (pso)
Portsmouth, Brian (pso)

UPW Offender Management
Cookson, Geof (pso)
Vacancy (pso)

45. Walsall Probation Complex
Midlands Road **Walsall** WS1 3QE
tel (01922) 721341 *fax (01922) 723080*

Unpaid Work Unit

Brown, Roger (unit mgr)
Gibney, Audrey (pso)
Irving, Marshall (pso)
Leslie, Tracey (pso)

46. United Friendly House
76 Walsall Road
Perry Barr Birmingham B42 1SF
tel 0121-248 6348 *fax 0121-248 6324*

Unpaid Work Unit
Choudhury, Sheku (unit mgr)
Barlow, Lynne (qa mgr)
Badesha, Jas (pso)
Heath, Lisa (pso)
Stokes, Tony (pso)

47. **11-15 Lower Essex Street**
Birmingham B5 6SN
tel 0121-248 6334 *fax 0121-248 6109*

*(covering Saltley, Chelmsley Wood
Selly Oak & Sparkbrook)*
Unpaid Work Unit
Walker, Steve (unit mgr)
Hawkins, Craig (qa mgr)
James, Will (qa mgr)
Al-Moghraby, Mazen (pso)
Balfour, Richard (pso)
Gee, Alan (pso)
James, Donna (pso)
Meacham, Robert (pso)
Mohammed, Khalik (pso)
Oram, Andrew (pso)
Reid, Kenneth (pso)
Walker, Lionel (pso)

Human Resources Division

48. **People & Business Development**
826 Bristol Road
Selly Oak Birmingham B29 6NA
tel 0121-248 6720 *fax 0121-248 6721*

Armstrong, Kim (admin mgr, hr)
Bailey, Claudette (head of training
& staff devpt)
Gill, Andy (pre-qualifying mgr)
Geach, Mary (spo, post-qualifying mgr)
Aston, Jeff (dep, pre-qualifying mgr)
Harman, Lucy (bus supt training mgr)
Bannister, David (bus supt trainer)
Rattigan, Sylvia (pract developer)
Makin, Nick (pract developer)
Hunter, Eileen ('what works' trainer)
Richardson, Sue ('what works' trainer)
Beard, Julie (pre-qualifying admin)

Practice Development Assessors
Allison, Una (based at 22)
Altaf, Azhar (based at 41)
Chaudhry, Geet (based at 37)
Glennie, Karin (based at 17)
Jester, Katie (based at 41)
Palmer, Caroline (based at 14)
Richmond, Rita (based at 30)

49. **Health & Safety Unit**
5th Floor, 1 Printing House Street,
Birmingham, B4 6DE
tel 0121-248 6328 *fax 0121-248 6327*

Lowe, Paul (health & safety mgr)
Singh, Amrik (health & safety off)

Regional Sex Offender Unit

50. **Regional Sex Offender Unit**
5th Floor, King Edward House,
135A New Street

Birmingham B2 4QJ
tel 0121-248 2700 *fax 0121-248 2701*

Sutton, Heather (regnl mgr)
Vacancy (admin mgr)

In West Midlands Area

51. **Sex Offender Unit**
826 Bristol Road
Selly Oak Birmingham B29 6NA
tel 0121-248 6760 *fax 0121-248 6761*

Clarke, Dave (spo/prog mgr, W Midlands
& Warwickshire Area)
Barrington, Karyn (po/facilitator)
Barzdo, Veronica (treatment mgr)
Fitzer, Zelda (po/facilitator)
Gibbs, Caroline (po/facilitator)
Halawin, Kath (po/facilitator)
Heath, Alison (po/facilitator)
Henderson, Vicky (po/facilitr based at 52)
Houston, Sally (po/facilitator)
James, Rachel (po/facilitator)
Joslyn, Jean (po/ facilitr based at 52)
Millington, Sonia (po/facilitator)
Rees, David (po/facilitator)
Twist, John (po/facilitator)
Twist, Lorraine(po/facilitator)
Ring, Lindsey (psychologist, W Mids
& Staffs)

In Staffordshire Area

52. **Regional Sex Offender Unit**
Stafford Programmes Unit
Dorrington Drive
Dorrington Industrial Park
Common Road, Stafford ST16 3DG
tel (01785) 279951 *fax (01785) 279959*

Cooper, Sally, (spo)
Vacancy (treatment mgr)
Dwight, Ellie (treatment mgr)
Raven, Mark (treatment manager)
Baverstock, Laura (po/facilitator)
Daubner, Jackie (po/facilitator)
Gilbride, Sue (po/facilitator)
Henderson, Victoria (po/facilitator)
Joslyn, Jean (po/facilitator)

In West Mercia Area

53. **Regional Sex Offender Unit**
Courtside House
Telford Square, Malinsgate
Telford TF3 4EQ
tel (01952) 299366 *fax (01952) 200896*

Willetts, Diane (treatment mgr)
Barrington, Karyn (po/facilitator)

54. **Regional Sex Offender Unit**
135 Abbey Foregate
Shrewsbury SY2 6AS
tel (01743) 231525 *fax (01743) 244914*

Goodban, Diana (po/facilitator)

55. **Regional Sex Offender Unit**
3-4 Shaw Street
Worcester WR1 3QQ
tel (01905) 723591 *fax (01905) 724833*

Farebrother, Jim (spo)
Daly, Maggie (po/facilitator)
Parsons, Kate (po/facilitator)

Approved Premises & Prisons Division

56. **Approved Premises & Prisons
Division Admin Unit**
King Edward House
135a New Street
Birmingham B2 4QJ
tel 0121-248 2828 *fax 0121-248 6490*

Garton, Kashmir (dist mgr)
Morgan, Ms Chloris (admin mgr)

Approved Premises (Hostels)

57. **Bilston Approved Premises**
23 Wellington Road
Bilston, Wolverhampton WV14 6AH
tel (01902) 497688 *fax (01902) 498150*

Clark, Joseph (spo mgr)
Walker, Glenford (po dep)

58. **Carpenter House Approved Premises**
33 Portland Road, Edgbaston
Birmingham B16 9HS
tel 0121-248 3680 *fax 0121-248 3690*

Wride, David (spo mgr)
Joseph, Drayton (po deputy)

59. **Crowley House Approved Premises**
(for women)
31 Weoley Park Road, Selly Oak
Birmingham B29 6QY
tel 0121-472 7111 *fax 0121-415 4072*

Moran, Lynne (spo mgr)
Williams, Sarah (po deputy)

60. **Elliott House Approved Premises**
(for mentally disordered offenders only)
96 Edgbaston Road, Moseley
Birmingham B12 9QA
tel 0121-440 2657 *fax 0121-446 6818*

Dunbar, Janet (spo mgr)

Kaur, Inderbir (po deputy)

61. **Welford House Approved Premises**
31 Trinity Road, Aston
Birmingham B6 6AJ
tel 0121-523 4401 *fax 0121-515 1355*

Wride, David (spo mgr)
Richards, Sandra (po deputy)

62. **Stonnall Road Approved Premises**
85 Stonnall Road
Aldridge, Walsall WS9 8JZ
tel (01922) 459574 *fax (01922) 455373*

Clark, Joseph (spo mgr)
Canning, Michael (po deputy)

63. **Sycamore Lodge Approved Premises**
Clay Lane, Langley
Oldbury B69 4TH
tel 0121-552 9930 *fax 0121-544 6994*

Norford, Herman (spo mgr)
Vacancy (po deputy)

Institutions

64. H M Prison, Winson Green Road
Birmingham B18 4AS
tel 0121-345 2500 *fax 0121-345 2501*
hdc fax 0121-554 7793

Special visits ext 2565

Finucane, Gabe (spo) ext 2748
Ashley, Wendy ext 2412
Bassi, Hardeep ext 2578
Fellowes, Richard ext 2680
Holt, Helen ext 2601
Leach, Magaret ext 2473
Ormsby, Janet ext 2413
Byron-Scott, Sharlene (pso) ext 2609
Oram, Rachel (pso) ext 2527

65. H M YOI & Remand Centre **Brinsford**
New Road, Featherstone
Wolverhampton WV10 7PY
tel (01902) 532450 *fax (01902) 532451*
Special visits tel (01902) 532605

Burns, Louise ext 3678
Clarke, Yvonne ext 3564
Hunter, Colin ext 3526
John, Alan ext 3528
Shotton, Julie ext 3526
Pratley, Jacqueline (pso) ext 3453
Tabberer, Phil (pso, bail info) ext 3571
Vogan, Jayne (pso, bail info) ext 3571

West Mercia
Seconded to HMP **Blakenhurst**
tel (01527) 400500 *fax (01527) 400501*
Williams, Pete (spo) (01527) 794080
Kyle, Susanna (01527) 785230

Local Justice Areas
25-38 Birmingham
11, 12 Coventry
6, 7 Dudley
14, 15 East Birmingham and Solihull
5, 7 Stourbridge and Halesowen
26 Sutton Coldfield
22 Walsall and Aldridge
9 Warley
9 West Bromwich
17-19 Wolverhampton

Crown Courts
26 Birmingham
12 Coventry
20 Wolverhampton

WILTSHIRE PROBATION AREA

Victim enquiries contact number:
Swindon (01793) 509709

e-mail Firstname.Surname@wiltshire.
probation.gsi.gov.uk

1. **Head Office**
Rothermere, Bythesea Road
Trowbridge BA14 8JQ
tel (01225) 781950 *fax (01225) 781969*
Direct dial (01225) + number

Fulbrook, Diana (co) 781960
Wilkinson, Tom (p, treasurer) 710905
Hazeltine, Mike (aco off mgmt) 781954
Munday, Mal (aco bd&p) 781956
Strike, Martyn (aco int) 781957
Powell, Diane (aco hr) 781966
Henderson, Gavin (proj/imp mgr) 710904
Vacancy (hr mgr) 710908
Standfield, Heather (hr off) 781965
Quinney, Gemma (hr asst) 710906
Mills, David (finance mgr) 781967
Sullivan, Sandra (finance off) 781968
Mullerworth, Debbie (p, staff devpt mgr) 781966
Topping, Nicola (staff devpt asst) 781955
Fairgrieve, Simon (area mgr info/tech) 781951
Hungerford, Lesley (data qual officer) 781952
Elkins, Adrian (IT off) 781953

Parker, Eileen (admin co-ord) 781963
Green, Hilary (pa to aco) 781959
Parfitt, Tracy (pa to aco) 781958
Tawn, Jan (pa to co) 781962

2. 2 Prospect Place
    Trowbridge BA14 8QA
    tel (01225) 763041 *fax (01225) 775667*

    Beddis, Anna (ppm)
    Hickey, Liz (ppm)
    Dyer, Felicity
    Larcombe, Laura
    Loft, Sarah
    Owen, Gwyneth
    Race, Heather
    Rhodes, Emma
    Sexton, Laura
    Coombs, Laura (p, pso)
    Fuller, Lester (pso)
    Lauder, Caroline (pso)
    Wilshire, Tanya (pso)

    Murray, Andrew (pda)
    Brown, Jo (trainee)
    Drew, Sharon (trainee)
    Parker, Charlotte (trainee)

    Heydon, Carolyn (p, case admin)
    Cole, Alison (gen admin)
    Peerman, Kelly (case admin)
    Lancashire, Cheryl (admin off)
    Reeve, Sara (p, case admin)
    Thornton, Karen (case admin)
    Wilkinson, Rhona (team co-ord)
    Knight, Philip (ext svcs off)
    Jackson, Sue (ete co-ord)
    Vacant (ete off)
    Gerrish, Ray (accom pso)

    Programmes Team
    Bennett, Mark (prog supvr)
    Kelley, Tom
    Parmenter, James
    Arnold, Christopher (qa sup)
    Frost, Simon (prog tutor)
    Gage, Emma (p, prog tutor)
    Rai, Prith
    Williams, Victoria (prog tutor)

    Unpaid Work Office
    Trowbridge (01225) 753508

    Davies, Cheryle (upw team mgr)
    Thornton, Teresa (dev off upw)
    Ashman, Anne (admin off)
    Bird, Dale (upwo)
    Pimpernell, Linda (upwo)
    Fryer, John (p, upws)
    Line, Mette (p, upws)

Rainbow, Malcolm (upws)
Morrison, Stuart (p, upws)
Gibbins, Alan (peripatetic upws)

3. 51-52 Parkfields
    Chippenham SN15 1NX
    tel (01249) 656836 *fax (01249) 445497*

    Minch, Alison (off mgmt mgr)
    Phillips, Jan (ppm)
    Cope, Simon
    Holmes, Ann
    Knight, Georgina
    Bull, Vicky (pso)
    Jackson, Terry (pso)
    Love, Sandi (p, pso)
    Taylor, Maxine (forensic psychologist)
    Lowe, David, (info mgmt officer)
    Lomanovskis, Claire (case admin)
    Easden, Vivien (team co-ord)
    Newman, Tracy (case admin)
    Scoble, Karen (case admin)

4. The Boulter Centre
    Avon Approach **Salisbury** SP1 3SL
    tel (01722) 327716 *fax (01722) 339557*

    Dillon, Monica (ppm)
    Flynn, Lisa (p, ppm)
    Tobin, Kerry (ppm/po)
    Ryan, Tony (h&s mgr)
    Beale, Jessica
    Jay, Tina
    O'Shaughnessy, Debbie (p)
    Manning, Charlotte
    Taylor, Ann
    Taylor, Michael
    Williams, Ruth
    Baldwin, Joanna (pso)
    James, Avril (pso)
    Patrick, Gina (pso)
    Robinson, Rosemary (pso)
    Roscow, Susan (pso)
    Wells, Laura (pso)

    Franklin, Veronica (ext svcs)
    O'Pray, Andy (pda)
    Capon, Lisa (trainee)
    Hurst, Emma (trainee)
    Miles, Deborah (trainee)
    Piper, Stephen (trainee)
    Rees-Jones, Stephen (trainee)
    Udale, Bridget (trainee)
    Whittle, David (trainee)

    McKenzie, Ray (off mgr)
    Adlam, Joanna (case admin)
    Regan, Sarah (team co-ord)
    Scott, Michelle (gen admin)

Sally Kerley (case admin)

Unpaid Work Office
tel (01722) 320897

Uphill, Amanda (upwo)
Dinley, Steve (upws)

5. Centenary House, 150 Victoria Road
    Old Town **Swindon** SN1 3UZ
    tel (01793) 534259/536612
    General fax (01793) 509707
    Off Mgmt fax (01793) 509701
    Interventions fax (01793) 509702

Offender Management
Murray, Amanda (area mgr, eff pract)
Wootton, Lynne (acting am, eff)
Weedon, Tom (ppm)
Glasscoo, Stephanie (ppm)
Kennedy, Angela (ppm)
Attree, Nicholas
Bamford, James
Bath, Chris
Davies, Albertine (p)
Derbyshire, Wayne
Hall, Louise
Hellier, Emma
Kipling, Laura
Maull, Gerald
Rhoades, Doreen
Ross, Emma

Ashraf, Omara (pso)
Evans, Gareth (pso)
James, Michelle (pso)
Lansdowne, Lesley (pso)
Nash, Jody (pso)
Martin, Nicola (pso)
Matsushima, Carol (p, vlo)
O'Hara, John (pso)
Sheeran, Joanna (pso)
Sheldon, Laura (pso)
Winning, Dawn (vlo)

Fardon, Howard (info/data off)
Bird, Kelly (ppm)
Truman, Claire (ppm)
Austen, Mary (p, case admin)
Brooks, Lisa (case admin)
Dipierro, Alicia (p, gen admin)
Edmonds, Pat (p, case admin)
Greenslade, Julie (case admin)
Probets, Joe (case admin)

Programmes Team
Coleshill, Joe (am interventions)
Jones, Rhiannon (p, snr pract, drr)
Brazier, Andrea (p, snr pract, drr)

Fry, Chris (prog supvr)
Henry, Marilyn (p, prog supvr)
Gooden, Eleanor
Mack, Leanne (prog tutor pt)
Mason, Sara (prog tutor)
Blacklock, Sue (womens safety worker)

Headon, Sheila (off mgr)
Affleck, Annette (int admin)
Graham, Karen (int co-ord)
McMullan, Carol (team co-ord)
Dempster, Chloe (admin off)
Woodward, Hilary (admin off)

Unpaid Work Office
Swindon (01793) 534259/496622

Simpson, Tracey (qual ass mgr)
Frankham, Rachel (upwo)
Sargeant, Maryann (upwo)
Soane, Melanie (upwo)
Geiran, Tracy (unpaid work co-ord)
Benfield, Roy (upws)
Beresford, Kim (upws)
Garratt, Marilyn (p, upws)
Holland, John (upws)
O'Connor, Christine (upws)
Affleck, Annette (int admin)
Fortune, Evelyn (admin off)

Training
Dudman, Jennifer (trainee)
Fuller, James (trainee)
Freeman, Kerry (trainee)
Melvin, Joanna (trainee)
Norton, Melissa (trainee)

6. **Youth Offending Team**
    The Limes, 21 Green Road
    Upper Stratton **Swindon** SN2 6JA
    tel (01793) 823153 *fax (01793) 820578*

    Owen, Karen
    Scarle, Jane

6a. The Martins, 56a Spa Road
    Melksham SN12 7NY
    tel (01225) 793616 *fax (01225) 793556*

    Clarke, Simon

6b. 1st Floor, Salisbury Activity
    Centre, Wilton Road
    Salisbury SP2 7GX
    tel (01722) 341644 *fax (01722) 341655*

    Glassock, Karen

7. **MAPPA Co-ordination**
    Room 54, Devizes Police Station
    New Park Street, **Devizes** SN10 1DZ

tel 0845 408 7000 *fax (01380) 733260*

Hemming, Alan (MAPPA co-ord) ext
7372398
e-mail alan.hemming@wiltshire.pnn.
police.uk
Caple, Amy (ViSOR admin) ext 737580
e-mail amy.caple@wiltshire.pnn.police.uk

Institution

8. HM Prison **Erlestoke**
    Devizes SN10 5TU
    tel (01380) 814250 *fax (01380) 818663*

    Davis, Caroline (spo) 814436
    Clifford, Maggie 814437
    Greaves, Andrew (pso)
    Otto, Melanie (pso)
    Walsh, Mike (pso)

Local Justice Areas

2 NW Wiltshire
3, 4 SE Wiltshire
5 Swindon

Crown Courts

4 Salisbury
5 Swindon

NORTH YORKSHIRE PROBATION AREA

Out of hours emergency contact point
Southview App Premises (01904) 780358

e-mail firstname.surname@north-yorkshire.
probation.gsi.gov.uk

1. **Head Office**
    Thurstan House, 6 Standard Way
    Northallerton DL6 2XQ
    tel (01609) 778644 *fax (01609) 778321*

    Brown, Pete (co)
    Burns, Walter (aco corporate governance)
    Marginson, Lynda (aco offender mgmnt)
    Sheard, Jon (treasurer)
    Ryan, Mike (aco interventions)
    Seed, Kevin (organisational devpt mgr)
    Widmer, Jacqui (pa to co)
    Jameson, Felicity (snr secy, board chair)
    Johnson, Sheila (snr secy, offender mgmnt)
    Williams, Lorraine (snr secy, corp gov)
    Minns, Tracy (snr secretary, hr/training)
    McClelland, Shirley (snr secretary, hr/
    training)
    Bennet, Helen (snr secy, interventions)

Taylor, Justine (h.r. mgr)
Moule, Kay (training co-ordinator)
Bateson, Julie (personnel off))
Foster, Clare (personnel asst)
Wetherell, Sue (personnel asst)

Boston, Jamil (diversity officer, North/
West Yorks 01924 885300)
Elsworth, Clare (NVQ assessor)

IT
Bunton, Ken (info systems asst)

2. Essex Lodge, 16 South Parade
    Northallerton DL7 8SG
    tel (01609) 772271 *fax (01609) 772931*

    Offender Management
    Capes, Wendy (spo)
    Fitzwalter, Sarah
    Minchin, Alison
    McCormack, Helen
    Wilkes, Sue
    Wright, Laura Jane
    Yeo, Laura
    Digby, Sharon (pso)

    Corporate Governance
    Topping, Diane (snr secretary)
    Burke, Alison (ca)
    Croser, Becky (ca)
    Dinsdale, Deborah (ca)

3. 5/7 Haywra Crescent
    Harrogate HG1 5BG
    tel (01423) 566764 *fax (01423) 565790*

    Offender Management
    Stephen Gallagher (spo)
    Wilkinson, Pauline (spo)
    Corney, Beverley (perf & quality mgr)
    Alm, Rebecca
    Bear, Daniel
    Grainger, Christine
    Langston, Helen
    Jones, Wilma
    Sanders, Karen
    Wright, Laura-Jane
    Sorah, Philip
    Stewart, Mark
    Eastwood, Tony (pso)
    Elias, Annie (pso)
    Halliday, Clare (pso)
    Kettlewell, Daniel (pso, spotlight)
    Watson, Andrew (pso)
    Harrison, Nicola (pp admin)

    Corporate Governance
    Vennart, Liz (office mgr)
    Graves, Mandy (snr secretary)

Brittan, Holly (ca)
Cunningham, Moira (ca)
Ellis, Emma (ca)
Garforth-Collinson, Sally (ca)
Smith, Kirsty (ca)
Hirst, Jayne (ca)

Interventions
Gibson, Mark (spo unpaid work)
Hughes, Heather (pract mgr)
Hird, Charlotte
Pearson, Clare
Walker-Johnson, Katrina
Dcaccia, Teresa (pso)
Musson, Ruth (pso vlo/wsw)
Rushton, Liz (pso)
Waters, Joyce (pso)
Terry, Peter (upw manager)
Brown, John (upw pso)
Coles, Mick (upw supvr)
Downs, Fred (upw supvr)
Procter, Mandy (upw supvr)
Sadler, Richard (upw supvr)
Smith, Ian (upw supvr)
Southwell, Danielle (pso)
Turner, Alvin (upw supvr)

Human Resources
Kirk, Paul (pda)
Hall, Claire (trainee)
Statner, Karen (trainee)

3a. The Court House
Bunkers Hill, **Skipton** BD23 1HU
tel (01756) 794797 *fax (01756) 798614*

Offender Management
van der Gucht, Sheila
Gallagher, Margaret
Hall, Lynda (pso)
Smith, Ann (snr secretary)
Howe, Victoria (ca)

4. 3rd Floor, Pavilion House
Pavilion Square
Scarborough YO11 2JN
tel (01723) 366341 *fax (01723) 501932*

Offender Management
Ansell, Gill (spo)
Hilton, Wendy (spo)
O'Brien, Vikki (perf & quality mgr)
Biggs, Christopher
Barton, David
Collins, Caroline (pt)
Davidson, Malcolm (pt)
Gaddass, Sarah
Hutchinson, Ian
Grassie, Briony

Hardy, Melissa
Maughan, Stephen
Race, Liz (ppo coordinator)
Rose, Linda
Ruth, Paul
Owen, Diane
Smith, Ian
Wray, Lesley (pso)
Broadbent, Dave (pso, spotlight)
Connor, Faye (pso)
Garbutt, Matthew (pso)
Harper, Mal (pso)
McFarlane, Peter (pso)
Naylor, Debbie (pso)
Walker, Dawn (pso)
Willan, Paul (pso, bail info)

Corporate Governance
Lukehurst, Beryl (office manager)
Lumsden, Sarah (snr secretary)
Austwick, Wendy (recep p/t)
Burnhill, Anita (ca)
Campion, Jan (ca)
Carter, Melanie (ca)
Ellis, Linda (ca)
Foster, Margaret (ca)
Groves, Margaret (ca)
Henley- Welch, Lynda (pp admin)
Woodhead, Tina (ca)
Wright, Karen (rcarecep p/t)

Interventions
Wilkinson, Vikki
Holmes, Geoff (pract mgr)
Burke, Alan (locum po)
Barber, Ian
Pattison, Yvonne
Ruth, Rachel (pso vlo/wsw)
Broadbent, Sarah (pso)
Rank, Zoe (pso)
McFarlane, Peter (pso)
Moseley, Susan (pso)
Wilson, Maureen (pso)
Young, Irene (pso)
Parkin, Karl (upw manager)
Farrell, Gordon (upw pso)
Barclay, Iain (upw supvr)
Daniels, Glen (upw supvr)
Hopper, Mick (upw supvr)
Hutchinson, Geoff (upw supvr)
Monsey, Simon (upw supvr)
Pratt, Paul (upw supvr)
Timmins, Stephen (upw supvr)
Watson, Dennis (upw supvr)

IT
Richards, Mark (info services mgr)
Day, Malcolm (info systems officer)
Rounce, Christopher (info systems officer)

Human Resources
Toole, Paul (trainee)
Wilson, Natalie (trainee)

5. 108 Lowther Street
    York YO31 7WD
    tel (01904) 526000 *fax (01904) 526001*

Offender Management
Burns, Fran (spo)
Pavlovic, Michael (spo)
Chapman-Gibbs, Petra (perf & quality mgr)
Brogan-Hewitt, Gemma
Daley, Michelle
Dawson, David
Entwistle, Gemma
Hamilton, Elaine
Hardy, Felicity
Jackson, Sarah
Lewis, Chris
Littler, Jon
McBurney, Don
Maule-Cole, Louise
Nasson, Sara
Ives, Lucy Rawcliffe, Maria
Smith, Leo
Spadone, Dominic
Stewart, Nicola
Waters-kelly, sally
Yarrow, Julie
Barmby, Sandra (pso)
Duncan, Lynne (pso)
Kamara, Ros (pso)
McKnight, Marilyn (pso)
Moss, Andrew (pso)
Nunns, Jane (pso)
Reeve, Phil (pso)
Thornber, Patrick (pso, spotlight)
Vennart, Ian (pso)
Wilkinson, Maria (pso)

Kelly, Elaine (mental health nurse)

Corporate Governance
Harding, Sara (office mgr)
Thorley, Gela (snr sec)
Clark, Caroline (recep)
Cox, Jayne (ca)
Hall, Helen (pp admin)
Jacques, Barbara (ca)
Jaques, Eileen (ca)
Read, Valerie (ca)
Renshaw, Ruth (ca)
Riddiford, Liz (ca)
Tipper, Shelley (ca)
York, Michaela (ca)
Ward, Fiona (ca york mags ct)

Interventions
Cooper, Kathryn (pract mgr)
Ferris, Shane
Gough, Lesley
Mayes, Emma
Wright, Howard
Davison, Laura (pso)
Heron,Dave (pso)
Gosling, Sarah (pso)
Langford, Lyn (pso vlo/wsw)
Rowbottom, Joanna (pso)
Sullivan, John (pso)
Wilton, Christine (pso)
Gray, Edward (upw manager)
Cowood, Sheredan (upw pso)
Bell, Rachel (upw supvr)
Bickerdike, Noel (upw supvr)
Bremner, Michelle (upw supvr)
Craft, Stephen (upw supvr)
Doney, Julian (upw supvr)
Heron, David (upw supvr)
Millhouse, Rebecca (upw supvr)
Trotter, Stephen (upw supvr)

Human Resources
Cawthorne, James (trainee)
Whitham, Lyndsey (trainee)

IT
Czarnecki, Sarah (proms co-ord)
North, Angelique (info systems asst)

6. Pavilion 2000 (P2K), Amy Johnson Way
    Clifton Moor **York** YO3 4XT
    tel (01904) 698920 *fax (01904) 698929*

Offender Management
Bourton, John (area mgr, public protctn)
Chatters, Sandra (area mgr, offender mgmnt)
Stokell, Pauline (mappa stategic mgr)
Fiona Shingles (snr secretary)

Interventions
Atkin, Joanne (spo prog mgr)
Hart, Peter (spo housing services mgr)
Weatherstone, Paul (pract mgr)

Human Resources
Wilkes, Patrick (North/West Yorks learning/develop mgr)

Coporate Governance
Brown, Garvey (h&s officer)
Clement, Emma (comms/p.r. officer)
Richardson, Dianne (office mgr)
Ford, Diane (snr secretary)
Freeman, Paula (snr secretary)
Gill, Jenny (snr secretary)

7. **York Crown Court**
   The Castle, York YO1 9WZ
   tel (01904) 651021 *fax (01904) 652397*

   Franks, Joyce (snr sec)
   Hilton, Wendy (cclo mon, tue, alt wed)
   Lewis, Chris (cclo thur, fri, alt wed)

8. Union Lane
   Selby YO8 4AU
   tel (01757) 707241 *fax (01757) 213911*

   Offender Management
   Powell, Ann (spo/circles of supt &
   accountability mgr)
   Bushby, Emma
   Struthers, Jenny
   Morley, June (pso)
   Westwood, Marie (pso)
   Wace, Carol (pso vlo/wsw)
   Anderson, Josephine (snr secretary)

9. **CRI** (Crime Reduction Iniatives)
   6 Peckitt Street, York YO1 9SF
   tel (01904) 675040 *fax (01904) 521108*

10. **Public Protection**
    North Yorkshire Police Headquarters
    Newby Wiske DL7 9HA
    tel (01609) 789299 *fax (01609 789214)*

    Watkins, Elaine (public protection mgr)
    Horridge, Sheena (mappa admin)

Youth Offending Teams

11. **N Yorkshire Youth Offending Team**
    Delta House, 12B North Park Road
    Harrogate HG1 5PG
    tel 0845 0349478 *fax (01423) 522949*

    Almond, Tracy

12. **N Yorkshire Youth Offending Team**
    2nd Floor, Pavilion House
    Pavilion Square
    Scarborough YO11 2JN
    tel 0845 0349497 *fax (01723) 361368*

    Pentland, Heather

13. City of York Council
    1st Floor, George Hudson Street
    York YO1 6ZE
    tel (01904) 554565 *fax (01904) 554566*

    Yarrow, Julie

Approved Premise (Hostel)

14. **Southview Approved Premises**
    Southview, 18 Boroughbridge Road

York YO26 5RU
tel (01904) 780358 *fax (01904) 780475*

Lomas, Neil (spo)
Ripley, Ann-Marie (pract mgr)
Baguley, Sylvia (pso)
Davies, Lynn (pso)
Hildred, Rod (pso)
Holmes, Gary (pso)
Lawson, John (pso)
Nicholson, Judith (pso)
Galloway, Wendy (night support wrkr)
Gray, George (night support wrkr)
Houghton, Robert (night support wrkr)
Stephenson, Michael (night support wrkr)
Bosworth, Sue (snr sec)

Institutions

15. HM YOI East Road
    Northallerton DL6 1NW
    tel (01609) 785100 *probn fax (01609)
    785102*

    HDC Clerk (01609) 785183
    Sentence Planning Clerk (01609) 785177
    Public Protection Clerk (01609) 785179
    Offender Mgmnt Clerk (01609) 785182

    Tweddell, Elise (pso)

    O'Neill, Pamela

16. HM Prison **Askham Grange**
    Askham Richard, York YO32 3FT
    tel (01904) 772000 *fax (01904) 772001
    probation fax (01904) 772003*

    Griffiths, Gina (spo)
    Richardson, Vanessa
    Scarrott, Rosie
    Shey, Anne (pso)
    Berry, Shirley (ca)

Local Justice Areas

3 Harrogate
2 Northallerton & Richmond
4 Scarborough
8 Selby
3a Skipton
5, 6 York

Crown Court

7 York

Secondments

Martin, Jonathan (aco)
Knowles, Liz (spo)
Weblin, Martin (spo)
Cockerham, Janet (pract mgr)
Race, Liz

SOUTH YORKSHIRE PROBATION AREA

Central bail referral no: 0114-278 0075
fax 0114-278 8520

Out of hours emergency contact point
Norfolk Park Hostel 0114-275 3054

Victim enquiries contact number
0114-276 7276

e-mail Firstname.Surname@south-yorkshire.
probation.gsi.gov.uk

1. Head Office
    45 Division Street
    Sheffield S1 4GE
    tel 0114-276 6911 *fax 0114-275 2868*
    fax (reception) 0114-276 1967

    Brown, Roz (chief off)
    Fox, Julian (secy to the board)
    Jones, Graham (aco)
    Scott, Rachel (aco)
    Wright, Marion (aco)
    Hannant, Janice (divnl mgr)
    Kerr, Janet (divnl mgr) (1)
    Colleyshaw, Julie (spo)
    Smith, Jaqueline (spo)
    Swinden, David (spo)
    Brown, Janice
    Gilmour, Claire
    Brown, Kaniz (strategic supt off)
    Dale, Sarah (strategic supt off)
    McNaney, Teresa (strategic supt off)
    Hunt, Laura (strategic supt off)
    Brookman, Janet (pa)
    Chapman, Vicky (strategic supt off)

    Kerslake, Brian (dir of finance)
    Linley, Robert (finance mgr)
    Andrews, David (snr finance off, accounts)
    Heap, Catherine (payments off)
    Susan Woodhouse (snr finance off, accounts)

    Cullen, Amanda (director HR & org devpt)
    Greene, Imelda (head of HR)
    Anderson, Kathy (head of diversity and inclusion)
    Thompson, David (Health & Safety welfare advr)

    Grant, Shaun (info service off)
    Myers, Gail (snr computer off)
    Pashley, Pat (snr computer off)

    Tarr, John (PR & comms mgr)
    Green, Katherine (PR & comms off)
    Chufungleung, Samantha (psychologist)

Henry, Caroline (research off)
Lawrenson, Hilary (data protctn off)
Maughan, Ann (devpt & implemention mgr)
Doyle, Tina (info services mgr)
Naylor, Jennifer (info services team ldr)
Tinker, Angela (HQ admin & resources mgr)
Wadsworth, Michael (business risk mgr)

2. 3 West Bar
    Sheffield S3 8PJ
    tel 0114-272 6477 *fax 0114-276 5267*

    Divisional Management Unit
    Dyson, Michael (divnl mgr)
    Adey-Johnson, Ann (divnl supt mgr)
    Parkin, Gillian (divnl admin mgr)

    Offender Mgmnt Unit 1
    Kime, Sheena (spo)
    Mansaram, Rayan (spo)
    Murray, Elizabeth (spo)
    Crawford, Angela
    Cruickshank, Tim
    Gayle, Hyacinth
    Harley, Bryan
    Johnson, Susan
    Keeton, Jane
    Mchale, Anne
    Moreland, Gregory
    Scott, Samantha
    Ward, Adele
    Carroll, Steven (pso)
    Kerslake, Stephen (pso)
    O'Neil, Isobel (pso)
    Barber, Linda (snr admin)

    Offender Mgmnt Unit 2
    Clarke, Dean (spo)
    Bufton, Sally
    Drabble, Philip
    Hermiston, Paul
    Hurst, Jane
    Machin, Helen
    Mclaughlin, Marie
    Robson, Sheila
    Stephenson, Christine
    Sykes, Karen
    Woodhouse, Joan
    Macpherson, Niki (pso)
    Wall, Michelle (pso)
    Considine, Vanessa (snr admin)

    Offender Mgmnt Unit 3
    Buckley, Ellen (spo)
    Came, Suzanne
    Jones, Karen
    Langsley, Joy

Lawrence, Aimee
Mellor, Sonya
Shaw, Ruth
Stocks, Christine
Stoddart, Barbara
Sullivan, Jeremy
Taylor, Samantha
Foster, Julie (pso)
Macdonald, Gwendoline (pso)
Holdsworth, Gillian (snr admin)

Offender Mgmnt Unit 4
Reading, Neil (spo)
Betts, Melissa
Broadhead, Julian
Highfield, Melissa
Johnson, David
Moss, Susan
Newton, Andrea
Penney, Sallyann
Smith, Andrew
Storey, Ruth
Wake, Sarah
Williams, Elizabeth
Clayton, Francine (pso)
Winter, Jane (snr admin)

Offender Mgmnt Unit 5
Connelly, John (spo)
Rejaie, Kaveh (spo)
Kenny, Helen
Kerr, Laura
Lockington, James
Perch, Michael
Smith, Hannah
Taylor, Nicholas
Walker, Rebecca
Herron, Janine (pso)
Perrelli, Ruth (pso)
Roe, Margaret (pso)

Offender Mgmnt Unit 8 (West Bar)
Colleyshaw, Julie (spo)

Offender Mgmnt Unit 9
Allen, Elaine (pso)
Crookes, Joan (pso)
Horbury, John (pso)
Hughes, Denise (pso)

Sheffield TPO Training
Doherty, Anthony (pda)
Beet, Hannah (trainee)
Fenwick, Jessica (trainee)
Fowler, Andrew (trainee)
Tether, Laura (trainee)
Maud, Rebecca (trainee)

2a. **Magistrates Court** c/o
3 West Bar

Sheffield S3 8PJ
all post to office 2

tel 0114 2760760 *fax 0114-2756373*

Offender Mgmnt Unit 8
Parkin, Maxine
Akpaka, Berthrand (pso)
Barber, Sheila (pso)
Beresford, John (pso)
Morgan, Ann (pso)
Oates, Daniel (pso)
Revill, Deborah (pso)
Rhodes, Stephen (pso)
Howard, Sadie (pso)
Antcliffe, Cynthia (bail supt off)

2b. **Crown Court**
50 West Bar, Sheffield
tel 0114-270 1060 *fax 0114-275 9816*

all post to office 2

Offender Mgmnt Unit 8
Bunting, Kathryn (pso)
Gill, Linda (pso)
Askew, Sarah (pso)
Wood, Jospehine (snr admin off)

3. 269 Pitsmoor Road
Sheffield S3 9AS
tel 0114-272 5058 *fax 0114-275 4997*

Offender Mgmnt Unit 6
Cotterell, Robert (spo)
Afzal, Taira
Daughtry, Emma
Gordon, Colin
Hermiston, Susanne
Reeves, Sheila
Titus, Karen
Everett, Susan (pso)
Hatton, Rachael (pso)
McDonnell, Coleen (pso)
Meades, Louise (pso)
Walton, Christine (pso)

4. 8 Eastern Avenue
Sheffield S2 2FY
tel 0114-241 6097 *fax 0114-239 4675*

Offender Mgmnt Unit 7
Small, John (spo)
Edwards, Angela
Gregory, Sharon
Hogan, Katy
Jackson, Melvin
Tully, Marianne
Bostock, Graham (pso)
Edmunds, Katy (pso)

Hodgkinson, Michael (pso)
Hurst, David (pso)
Keyworth, Tony (pso)
Mcevoy, Declan (pso)
Neville, Helen (pso)
Smith, Jennifer (snr admin)

5.   7 St Peter's Close
Sheffield S1 2EJ
tel 0114-228 8555 *fax 0114-228 8500*

Youth Offending Team
Manifold, Garry
Price, Sharon
Shann, Christine
Galton, Jill (pso)

6.   Barnsley Division
6 Victoria Road
Barnsley S70 2BB
tel (01226) 283411 *fax (01226) 287441*

Landon, Tracey (snr admin off)
Waller, Lynda (snr admin off)

Offender Mgmnt Unit 1
Westley-Morris, Raymond (spo)
Allsopp, Sarah
Barton, Esther
Green, Andrew
Jones, Samantha
Kennedy, Sarah
Lindley, Kathryn
Swift, Andrea
Rock, Julie (pso)

Offender Mgmnt Unit 2
Firth, Emma
Hesselden, Kathryn
Horridge, Peter
Kenny, Elanor
Middleton, Emma
Rose, Samantha
Ormrod, Heather (pso)
Richardson, Neil (pso)
Steele, Betty (pso)
Whyke, Larry (pso)

Offender Mgmnt Unit 3
Pidwell, David (spo)
Dyson, Rita
Heeley, Rachael
Ibbotson-Devine, Kerry
Jones, Andrew
Nicol, Kelly
Shaw, Josephine
Skidmore, Louise (pso)
Morrisroe, Simon (pso)
Padgett, Rosemary (pso)

Barnsley TPO Training
Holdsworth, Suzanne (pda)
Baker, Jennifer (trainee)
Jones, Rachael (trainee)
Pearson, Joy (trainee)
Phillips, Darren (trainee)
Sherriff-Jones, Jo (trainee)
Shepherd, Luke (trainee)
Spivey, Katherine (trainee)

7.   Court House
Churchfields **Barnsley** S70 2HW
tel (01226) 243331 *fax (01226) 294908*
divnl mgr fax (01226) 295080

Divisional Management Unit
Forbes-Williams, Paulette (divnl mgr)
Britton, Jennifer (divnl supt mgr)
Gilly, Ann (divnl admin mgr)
Speight, Alison (snr admin off)

Offender Mgmnt Unit 4
Delamore, Susan (spo)
Harper, Clare (spo)
Beckford-Peart, Marjorie
Bougnot, Anna
Brown, Thomas
Couldwell, Amber
Handy, Jill
McCuish, Linda
Marziano, Cristina
Pollard, Roderick
Sykes, Amy
Taylor, Helen
Coniston, Diane (pso)
Dixon, Harry (pso)
Garrett, Sharon (pso)
Hewitt, Keith (pso)

Offender Mgmnt Unit 5
Avison, Jacqueline (spo)
Andrews, Stella (pso)
Chambers, Tracy (pso)
Crossland, Amy (pso)
Denton, Rachel (pso)
Mcdermid, Charles (pso)
Stanley, Eileen (pso)

8.   **Youth Offending Team**
Phase 1-2, County Way
Barnsley S70 2DT
tel (01226) 774986 *fax (01226) 774968*

Birkbeck, Barbara
Scott, Alison
Slimon, David

9.   The Law Courts
College Road **Doncaster** DN1 3HU
tel (01302) 366585 *fax (01302) 320853*

Court Team
Turgoose, Josephine (spo)
Townsend, Mark
Allison, Tracy (pso)
Barends, David (pso)
Siddons, Christine (pso)
Steen, John (pso)
Varney, Christine (pso)
Weerdmeester, Maia (pso)
Wilkinson, Melanie (pso)
Corby, Tracy (snr admin off)
Bartholomew, Erica (snr admin off)

10. Bennetthorpe, 34 Bennetthorpe
Doncaster DN2 6AD
tel (01302) 730099 *fax (01302) 730220*
divnl mgr/dsu fax (01302) 730720

Divisional Management Unit
Montgomery, Avril (divnl mgr)
Bowie, Christopher (divnl supt mgr)
Jones, Carol (divnl admin mgr)

Human Resources
Room, Vicki (divnl HR mgr)

Offender Mgmnt Unit 1
Vernon, Glyn (spo)
Barrow, Louise
Chesters, Joanne
Dallas, William
Hetherington, Jayne
Mombeshora, Davie
Wheatcroft, Deborah
Wormley, Zoe
Dix, Cathryn (pso)
Hopson, Hannah (pso)
Rachwalski, Gemma (pso)
Torn, Shelley (pso)

Offender Mgmnt Unit 2
Porter, Jennifer (spo)
Beadle, Sally
Howkins, Sallyanne
Huber, Tacita
Potter, Helen
Satchwell, Dorothy
Spence, Judith
Walker, Lorraine
McMaster, Valerie (pso)
Mitton, David (pso)
Bishop, Rowena (snr admin off)

Offender Mgmnt Unit 3
Kendell, Pauline (spo)
Bertie, Susan
Hosfield, Christopher
Latibeaudiere, June
Honey, Graeme (pso)
Thomas, Patricia (pso)

Offender Mgmnt Unit 4
Page, Paulette (spo)
Critchlow, Deborah
Harris, Clare
Pass, Clare
Peat, Sarah
Popple, Teresa
Richards, Donna
Shaw, Lorna
Lambert, Aaron (pso)
Mills, Nichola (pso)
Thomas, Janice (pso)
Wilson, Sharon (pso)
Jane, Cheryl (snr admin off)

Offender Mgmnt Unit 5
Jackson, Ian (spo)
Badcoe, Elizabeth
Broadbent, Anthony
Ellis, Paul
Jones, Helen
Wilson, Kerry
Hill, Jayne (pso)
Jackson, Sharron (pso)
Houghton, Michelle (pso)
Porritt, Patricia (pso)
Davidson, Jackie (pso)
Hamill, Kerry (snr admin off)

Doncaster Enforcement Unit
Hamill, Kerry (snr admin off)

Doncaster MARAC/Interventions
Johnson, Imelda (pso)

Doncaster Drug Interventions Programme
Brown, Duncan (pso)
Gordon, Sophia (pso)

Doncaster TPO Training
Edwards, Lynda (pda)
Brown, Peter (trainee)
Emmerson, Laura (trainee)
Havenhand, Kate (trainee)
Lloyd-Jones, Gwen (trainee)

11. **Youth Offending Team**
Rosemead Centre, May Avenue
Balby Doncaster DN4 9AE
tel (01302) 736100 *fax (01302) 736103*

Heathcote, Michael
Moss, Samantha
Cocker, Glynn (pso)

12. 12 Main Street
Rotherham S60 1AJ
tel (01709) 376761 *fax (01709) 838715*

Divisional Management Unit
Holmes, Ruth (divnl mgr)

Hadfield, Susan (snr admin off)
Saxton, Kathleen (snr admin off)

Human Resources
Slater, Carrie (divnl hr mgr)

Offender Mgmnt Unit 1
Lubienski, May (spo)
Wells, Emma (spo)
Ayub, Shaqoor
Carrington, Diane
Deen, Shaheen
Ducker, Andrew
Holland, Lindsey
Jones, Carol
Newsum-Brown, Anthony
Norton, Julia
Ogden, David
Peacock, Jane
Pullan, Stuart
Taylor, Jill
Turner, Emma
Walker, Katy
Cottam, Helen (pso)
Goodrich, Jennifer (pso)
Hirst, Richard (pso)
Lane, Sarah (pso)
Maw, Claire (pso)
Patterson, Claire (pso)
Pickup, Eileen (pso)
Turner, Sheila (pso)
Walker, Victoria (pso)
Wragg, Karen (pso)

Offender Mgmnt Unit 2
Gregory, Ian (spo)
Cureton, Debbie
Hoole, Paul
Morris, Lisa
Phillips, Staffel
Saville, Jane
Tweddle, Claire
Ullah, Ali
Heeds, Charlotte (pso)
Murphy, Lynda (pso)
Pullar, Derv (pso)
Tindall, Elizabeth (pso)

Offender Mgmnt Unit 3
Maillie, Douglas (spo)
Brennan, Lenday
Burnett, Ian
Crookes, Fraser
Davitt, Rachel
Dutton, Toni (pso)
Lester, Kevan (pso)
Rimmer, Julia (pso)
Watson, Margaret (pso)

Rotherham TPO Training
Ford, Elizabeth (pda)

Booth, Rebecca (trainee)
Glover, Andrew (trainee)
Tapudzai, Menford (trainee)
Weston, Lisa (trainee)

13. **Youth Offending Team**
4/6 Moorgate Road
Rotherham S60 2EN
tel (01709) 516999 *fax (01709) 836584*

Broadhead, Melanie
Sharman, Anne
Hoole, Michelle (pso)

14. **Rotherham Magistrates' Court**
The Statutes, PO Box 15
Rotherham S60 1YW
tel (01709) 361321 *fax (01709) 370172*

Offender Mgmnt Unit 4
Welch, Simon (spo) (based at 12)
Hayes, Kay (pso)
Land, Judith (pso)
Rhodes, Janet (pso)
Wainwright, Jeanett (pso)

Groupwork Programmes

15. **Groupwork Programmes Unit**
Masborough Street
Rotherham S60 1HW
tel (01709) 561533 *fax (01709) 550952*

Turvey, Maryke (divnl mgr)
Lee, Malcolm (spo)
Platt-Hopkin, Gill (spo)
Cosgrove, Caroline
Edge, Philip
Ellis, Rhys
Glover, Lynda
Ibbotson, Bryan
Jenkinson, Paul
Jones, Paula
Nowell, Peter
Pratley, Mary
Simpson, Rachel
Suddaby, Jane
Turner, Kate
Walton, Frank

Castleton, Tracie (pso)
Grocott, Wayne (pso)
Hadfield, Joanne (pso)
Hutchinson, Geraldine (pso)
Manduzeh, Liisa (pso)
Miller, Fiona (pso)
Millington, Gillian (pso)
Narracott, Katherine (pso)
Parker, Tracey (pso)
Parry, Stephen (pso)

Cowan, Libby (pso)
Ulman, Stephen (pso)
Wales, Steven (pso)
Welch-Jasnoch, Nicky (pso)
Wilkinson, Emma (pso)

Akers, Berrnard (gp prog supt wrkr)
McFarlane, Natalie (gp prog supt wrkr)
Smith, Deborah (gp prog supt wrkr)

Beard, Sarah (divnl admin & supt off)
Crossland, Gillian (snr admin)

Unpaid Work

16. Masborough Street
    Rotherham S60 1HW
    tel (01709) 561533 *fax (01709) 550952*

    Turvey, Maryke (divnl mgr)

17. 269 Pitsmoor Road
    Sheffield S3 9AS
    tel 0114-272 5058 *fax 0114-275 4997*

    Walker Steve (team mgr)
    Henry, Roy (proj off)
    Hunter, Kevin (proj off)
    Slack, Phil (proj off)
    Badger, Brian (supvr)
    Fleet, Judith (proj off)
    Grubb, David (supvr)
    Hayes, James (supvr)
    Headen, Mark (supvr)
    Illingworth, Peter (supvr)
    Layhe, Mary (supvr)
    Longmuir, John (supvr)
    Tomlinson, Ian (supvr)
    Turton, David (supvr)
    White, Ron (supvr)
    Whitworth, Stephen (supvr)
    Cadet, David (supvr)
    Smith, Debbie (snr admin)

18. 12 Main Street
    Rotherham S60 1AJ
    tel (01709) 376761 *fax (01709) 838715*

    Renshaw, Ann, (team mgr)
    Shaw, Steven (dep/qa mgr)
    Bargh, Alan (proj off)
    Fallowfield, Ron (supvr)
    Gordon, Martin (proj off)
    Hancock, Stuart (supvr)
    Lumwai, John (supvr)
    Moule, Graham (supvr)

19. Victoria Road
    6 Victoria Road
    Barnsley S70 2BB

tel (01226) 283411 *fax (01226) 287441*

Dixon, Phil (dep/qa mgr)
Cullumbine, Lynn (proj off/supvr)
Staves, Glyn (proj off/supvr)
Barrowclough, Susan (supvr)
Hodgson, Stanley (supvr)
Lean, Philip (supvr)
Lockie, Trish (supvr)
Sigfusson, Tony (supvr)
Smith, Russell (supvr)
Swallow, Ian (supvr)

20. Yarborough Terrace
    Bentley **Doncaster** DN5 9TH
    tel (01302) 787758 *fax (01302) 390865*

    Renshaw, Ann, (team mgr)
    Doyle, Brenda (proj off)
    Murdoch, Scott (proj off)
    Barks, Terry (supvr)
    Dutchak, Peter (supvr)
    Gant, Chris (supvr)
    Stanton, John (supvr)
    Tottie, John (proj off)
    Wilson, Paul (supvr)

    Lynas, Julia (divnl admin & supt mgr)

Approved Premises (Hostels)

Central bail referral number
tel 0114-278 0075 *fax 0114-278 8520*

Hostel Administrative Support
tel (01709) 361001 *fax (01709) 835496*

Abbott, Penny (dvnl mgr) (at office 22)

21. **Norfolk Park Hostel**
    100-108 Norfolk Park Road
    Sheffield S2 2RU
    tel 0114-272 1950 *fax 0114-275 3054*

    Williams, Barbara (spo)
    Greaves, Rita (probn hostel wrkr)
    Hodgkinson, Faye (probn hostel wrkr)
    Prince, Gemma (probn hostel wrkr)
    Ellams, Stephen (night care wrkr)
    Flintham, Jacqueline (hostel supt wrkr)
    Peters, Sandra (night care wrkr)
    Sampson, Ann (night care wrkr)
    Senior, Lowgan (night care wrkr)
    Skubala, June (night care wrkr)
    Wood, Charlotte (hostel supt wrkr)

22. **Rookwood Hostel**
    Doncaster Road
    Rotherham S65 1NN
    tel (01709) 361001 *fax (01709) 835496*

Abbott, Penelope (divnl admin mgr)
Andersson, Pamela (spo)
Lupton, Clare
Andrews, Diane (probn hostel wrkr)
Bennett, Delroy (probn hostel wrkr)
Berry, Tracy (probn hostel wrkr)
Evans, Jodi (hostel supt wrkr)
Wadsworth, Ian (hostel supt wrkr)
Benfold, Coleen (night care wrkr)
Bintcliffe, Kenneth (night care wrkr)
Fretwell, Darren (night care wrkr)
Isle, Valerie (night care wrkr)
Marsh, Donna (night care wrkr)
Legat, Lisa (snr admin off)
Laksevics, Abigail (snr admin officer)

23. **Town Moor Bail Hostel**
    38/40 Christchurch Road
    Doncaster DN1 2QL
    tel (01302) 739127 *fax (01302) 761920*

    Niven, Christopher (spo)
    Cox, Joan
    Bourne, Rodney (probn hostel wrkr)
    Faulkner, Brian (probn hostel wrkr)
    Machin, Pamela (probn hostel wrkr)
    Chehata, Paula (hostel supt wrkr)
    Christiansen, Stephen (night care wrkr)
    Faulkner, Kim (night care wrkr)
    Fox, Michelle (night care wrkr)
    Hall, John (night care wrkr)
    Slater, Stephen (night care wrkr)
    Gauden, Susan (snr admin off)

Institutions

24. H M Prison & YOI **Doncaster**
    Marsh Gate, Doncaster DN5 8UX
    tel (01302) 760870 *fax (01302) 760851*

    Discipline (edr enquiries) ext 308
    Discipline (discharge) ext 265
    Special visits (01302) 342413

    Probn direct dial (01302) 763 + ext
    Probn clerk ext 203
    Houseblock 1 probn ext 287
    Houseblock 2 probn ext 290
    Houseblock 3 probn ext 291
    Bail info ext 293
    Bail info fax (01302) 368034

    Eastwood, Michael (spo)
    Fells, Helen
    Gasper, John
    Marsh, Martin
    Mockford, Mark
    Petersen, Lynn
    Cokeham, Michelle (pso)
    Milne, Pamela (pso)
    Wright, Patricia (pso)

25. H M Prison **Lindholme**
    Bawtry Road, Hatfield Woodhouse
    Doncaster DN7 6EE
    tel (01302) 524700 *fax (01302) 524750*

    Aspden, Paul (spo)
    Forrest, Janet
    Mackenzie, Philip
    Musgrave, Rita
    Thompson, Carole
    Hookway, Beverly (pso)
    Marriott, Granville (pso)
    Willerton, Clair (pso)
    Winstanley, Jacqueline (pso)

26. H M Prison & YOI **Moorland (Closed)**
    Bawtry Road, Hatfield Woodhouse
    Doncaster DN7 6BW
    tel (01302) 523000 *fax (01302) 523001*

    Probn clerk ext 3108

    Odusanya, Julie (spo)
    Harrison, Janet
    Hornsby, Helen
    Morgan, Gaynor
    Toole, Alison
    Tyson, Carla
    Pearson, Samantha (pso)

27. HM Prison & YOI **Moorland (Open)**
    Thorne Road **Hatfield**
    Doncaster DN7 6EL
    tel (01405) 746500 *fax (01405) 746501*

    Skelding, Stephen
    Carlisle, Jennifer (pso)
    Phipps, Serena (pso)

Interventions Staff (Various Locations)

Number shows office location
Bostock, Graham (pso) (4)
Clarke, Lesley (pso) (6)
Henry, Christina (pso) (12)
Keye, Christy (pso) (12)
Knowles, Alexandra (pso) (2)
Newett, Sarah (pso) (12)
Unsworth, David (accom services wrkr) (6)

Local Justice Areas

2-5 Sheffield
6-8 Barnsley
9-12 Doncaster
13-17 Rotherham

Crown Courts

2a Sheffield
7 Rotherham
9 Doncaster

WEST YORKSHIRE PROBATION AREA

Out of Hours Emergency Contact Point
Elm Bank Hostel (01274) 851551

e-mail firstname.surname@west-yorkshire.
probation.gsi.gov.uk

1. **Head Office**
Cliff Hill House
Sandy Walk, Wakefield WF1 2DJ
tel (01924) 885300 *fax (01924) 885395*

Hall, Sue (chief officer)

Joint Secretarial Unit
Beale, Cristina (supt to co)
Gage, Susan (secy to co)
Todd, Vicky (pa to chair/secy to brd)
Beresford, Jayne (pa to chair/secy to brd)
Illingworth, Charlotte (secy/pa to directors)
Palmer, Amanda (secy/pa to directors)
Johnston, Peter (rgnl bus devpt mgr)

Offender Management
Siddall, Mark (dir offender mngmnt)
Ball, Kevin (area mgr)
Beatson, Max (devpt & progr mgr)
Hines, Janine (proj & implmtn mgr)
Mills, Elizabeth (devpt & progr mgr)

Interventions
Myatt, Maxine (dir interventions)
Johnson, Diana (aco)
Voakes, Robert (aco)
Morris, Ann (pa to aco)
Burns, Janine (temp are mgr app prem)
Dugdale, Ian (mgr)
Fraser, Simon (area mgr, progrs)
Harrison, Susan (progrs admin mgr)
Kyle, Jerry (devpt & progr mgr)
Parkin, John (interventions admin mgr)
Sinclair, Andrew (area mgr, upw)
Garg, Sarah (sao)
Emmett, Deborah (sao)
Williams, Barbara (secy)
Walker, Craig (emplt services devpt mgr)
Hooson, Christopher (empl engagement mgr)
Killey, Emma (skills for wk co-ord)
Eaglen, Joanne (skills for wk off, Leeds W)
Gerrard-Ehrlich, Melanie (skills for wk off, Leeds E)
Milczanowski, Richard (skills for wk off, Calderdale)
Mooney Revell, Gail (skills for wk off, Bradford)

Human Resources
Brandwood, Ian (dir of HR)
Blackburn, Kay (pa to director)
Bradley, Stephen (HR systs off)
Brereton, David (diversity & devpt mgr)
Denham, Vicki (org devpt mgr)
Wilkes, Patrick (training & devpt mgr)
Wallace, Robert (training off)
Hemingway, Helena (assessor Level 3 CJA)
Watts, Ian (assessor Level 3 CJA)
Mason, Barbara (personnel mgr)
France, Chelsey (personnel off)
Holland, Kate (personnel off)
Tyreman, Charlene (personnel off)
Wood, Matthew (personnel off)
Everitt, Sarah (personnel asst)
van der Wal, Janice (personnel asst)
Walton, Linda (personnel asst)
Wilby, Anna (personnel asst)
Oldroyd, Rachel (admin asst, personnel)
Holding, Stephanie (admin mgr, personnel)
Taylor, Colleen (sao)
Tomlinson, Lisa (admin officer)
Walton, Sara (admin officer)

Head Office Peripatetic PO Team
Lynch, Timothy
White, Martin
Woodrow, Michelle
Young, Michelle

Head Office Peripatetic AO Team
Backhouse, Nick (admin officer)
Bennett, Kathleen (admin officer)
Denny, Charlotte (admin officer)
Franklin, Stuart (admin officer)
Wilkinson, Lindsey (admin officer)

Finance Section
King, Jayne (dir finance)
Hunter, Janet (pa to director)
Sweeney, Mary (pa to dep director)
Sheard, Jon (aco)
Bland, Karen (finance syst proj mgr)
Bruce, Mandy (snr financial off)
Brace, Denise (payroll & expenses mgr)
Goznik, Denise (policy mgr, finance & estates)
Porteus, Richard (financial accountant)
Mason, Louise (mgmnt accountant)
Chen, Helen (accounting off, mgmnt accounts)
Lee, Hue (accounting off, financial accounts)
Moody, Julie (snr payroll & expenses off)
Prendergast, Susan (payroll & expenses admin off)

Preston, Sandra (snr accounting off, fin accounts)
Sutton, Ian (snr accounting off, fin accounts)
Reed, (snr accounting off, man accounts)
Wilkinson, Malcolm (facilities mgr)
Taylor, Nicola (sao)
Easton, Pamela (admin officer)
Ainsworth, Gemma (admin officer finance & estates)
Sims, Michael (admin officer, systems)
Allatt, Jennifer (pay & expenses admin asst)
Sharpe, Adele (finance asst, payments)
Wilson, Kelly (finance asst, payments)

Legal/Health & Safety Section
Thorpe, Nigel (secy to the brd)
Ainsworth, Linda (secy to legal services section)
Aveyard, Lisa (contracts & ptnrshps mgr)
Slawinski, Diane (dep area contracts mgr)
Bond, Bob (H&S off)
Charlton, Glennis (legal asst)
Edmunds, Susan (legal asst)
Farrar, Jane (snr legal asst)
Harman, Tracie (admin officer)
Peacock, Donna (admin officer)

Information Services
Brown, Imogen (aco)
Burgess, Steve (knowledge mgr)
Sheppard, Ben (performance info mgr)
Manktelow, John (it mgr)
Manktelow, John (it mgr)
Temple, John (quality mgr)
Harris, Rochelle (research mgr)
Robinson, Emma (snr research off)
Chana, Rajinder (research off)
Rennison, Claire (research & info supt off)
Clapson, Gillian (sao)
Holdinga, Marcel (info off)
Reynolds, Ian (info off)
Brailsford, Natalie (info systs supt)
Charlton, Donna (info systs supt)
Denny, Margaret (info systs supt)
Foxcroft, Brenda (info systs supt)
Haigh, Tracey (info systs supt)
Lee, Matthew (info systs supt)
Nesbitt, Patricia (info systs supt)
Spink, Lorraine (info systs supt)
McQueen, Paul (technical proj specialist)
Robinson, David (technical proj specialist)
Cheng, David (technical supt)
Beardsall, Jason (technical supt)
Pullein, Heather (helpdesk supvr)
Marshall, Alison (helpdesk supt)
Sufi, Mehmoona (helpdesk admin supt)

Kimber, Sarah (it training supvr)
Allred, Ian (it trainer)
Ramsden, Julia (it trainer)
Thomis, Ann (library admin asst)

Public Relations
Grazin, Elaine (coms & pr mgr)
Watson, Simon (pro)
Gray, Bronwen (case wrkr)

Trainee Development Team
Fisher, Alison (trainee devpt team mgr)
Lee, Gavin (trainee devpt team mgr)
Doherty, Eugene (pda)
Godley, Simon (pda)
McLeish, David (pda)
Peace, Melanie (pda)
Dewey, Cristina (pda)
Bray, Sheila (pda)
Schlaberg, Yvonne (pda)
Pitchford, William (int verifier)
Nellist, Alexene (admin officer)

Trainees C10
Ackroyd, Danielle (trainee C10)
Arif, Altaf (trainee C9, City Courts)
Arthington, Lauren (trainee C10)
Atkinson, Tracy (trainee C10)
Bailey, Jacqeline (trainee C10)
Barber, Jayne (trainee C10)
Bowden, Melissa (trainee C10)
Bowen, Victoria (trainee C10)
Bray, Michael (trainee C10)
Burnham, Gemma (trainee C10)
Callaghan, Sarah (trainee C10)
Crawford, Rachel (trainee C10)
Crockett, Helen (trainee C10)
Dickinson, Mandy (trainee C10)
Farrar, Justin (trainee C10)
Foote, Ellen (trainee C10)
Gilmore, Ruth (trainee C10)
Godfrey, Lisa (trainee C10)
Hanson, Graham (trainee C10)
Hartley, Teresa (trainee C10)
Holt, Jessica (trainee C10)
Hunter, Charlotte (trainee C10)
Johnson, Claire (trainee C10)
Johnson, Judith (trainee C10)
Khan, Ziaullah (trainee C10)
Lloyd, Rachel (trainee C10)
Petgrave, Clive (trainee C10)
Richardson, Angela (trainee C10)
Sohanpal, Gurdev (trainee C10)
Woods, Anja (trainee C10)
Wright, Bonnie (trainee C10)

Bradford District

2. **Fraternal House**
45 Cheapside **Bradford** BD1 4HP
tel (01274) 703700 *fax (01274) 703701*

District Administration Team
Moloney, Neil (aco)
Wall, Beverley (pa to aco)
MacPherson, Stuart (area mgr)
Tibbetts, Phillippa (ptnrshp mgr)
Moody, Linda (pract mgr)
Nolan, Karen (pract mgr)
Bailey, Christine (supt services mgr)
Ali, Abid (supt services mgr)
Maud, Karen (supt services mgr)
Hall, Louise (team supt off)
Mistry, Reshma (team supt off)
Bastow, Anne (team supt off)
Corkindale, Louise (admin officer)
Akhlaq, Monis (admin officer)

Bradford Offender Mgmnt Unit 1
Bryan, Jim (team mgr)
French, Penny
Gilbert, Stephen
Hanley, Michelle
Hughes, Sarah
Ibrahim, Shahid
Kubala, Henryk
Richardson, Naomi
Smith, Helen
Wallis, Rob
Bashir, Mohammed (pso)
Morley, David (pso)
Nash, Michael (pso)
Phillips, Ann (case admin)
Robinson, Linda (case admin)
Sebah, Shahista (case admin)

Victim Services/Public Protection Unit
Prescott, John (pract mgr)
Armitage, Mark (pso)
Caine, Heidi (pso)
Gromitt, Jo (pso)
Tilbury, Carol (pso)
Cartwright, Janette (admin officer)
Crabtree, Sarah (admin officer)

MAPPA
Sheikh, Bushra (team mgr)
Grey, Nadia (supt off)
Riaz, Noreen (supt off)
Hird, Louise (admin officer)

3. **The City Courts**
P O Box 6 **Bradford** BD1 1LB
tel (01274) 704500 *fax (01274)*
721010/704501

Bailey, Christine (supt services mgr)

Bradford Offender Mgmnt Unit 2
Teasey, Marc (team mgr)
Hussain, Amjad
Laird, Matthew
Lamb, Jacqueline
Ross, Helen
Sharif, Azra
Armitage, Kenny (pso)
Ashton, Sarah (pso)
Karim, Shahina (pso)
Myers, David (pso)
Cook, Rebecca (case admin)
Minchella, Christine (case admin)
Moore, Ian (case admin)
Murphy, Anya (case admin)

Bradford Offender Mgmnt Unit 3
Wilson, Margaret (team mgr)
Ball, Clare
Bilney, Jo-Anne
Bunyan, Debbie
Mallows, Glynis
Small, Seb
Thompson, Michelle
McNulty, Michelle (pso)
Mistry, Narendra (pso)
Rowe, Donna (pso)
Siraj, Mohammed (pso)
Baig, Shazeeda Uddin (supt admin)
Large, Katherine (case admin)
Ramzan, Ishtiaq (case admin)
Wilkinson, Sandra (case admin)

Bradford Offender Mgmnt Unit 4
Moore, Colin (team mgr)
Ali, Shaista
Beech, James
Lang, Eleanor
Nash, Gareth
Cowgill, Judy (pso)
Doggett, Adam (pso)
Iluk, Rachel (pso)
Karim, Zenab (pso)
Parker, Christopher (pso)
Stansfield, Rebecca (pso)
Calpin, David (admin officer)
Kirkham, Elizabeth (case admin)
Nessa, Lorelai (case admin)
Ramsden, Emily (case admin)
Williams, Dianne (case admin)

Bradford Offender Mgmnt Unit 5
James, Peter (team mgr)
Burke, Maureen
Khan, Hikmat
Medd, Catherine
Miller, Lorraine

Ward, Michael
Burran, Eileen (pso)
Khan, Alia (pso)
Magill, Martin (pso)
Woolley, Alison (pso)
Greenough, Nicky (case admin)
Hodgson, Susan (case admin)
Walsh, Jenny (case admin)

Bradford Offender Mgmnt Unit 6
Doyle, Mary (team mgr)
Brennan, Deborah
Khan, Sadaqat
Lewis, Denis
Long, Jim
Mahmood, Shahid
Suggett, Angela
Wilson, Laura
Khan, Abdul (pso)
Khan, Ferzana (pso)
Roberts, Vicky (pso)
Jan, Elizabeth (case admin)
Kausar, Razwana (case admin)
Whitaker, Stacy (case admin)

Bradford Offender Mgmnt Unit 7
Ridley, Alison (team mgr)
Alam, Sajid
Ali, Momosar
Anjum, Zahida
Crossley, Shane
Day, Helen
Iqbal, Tahir
Jandzio, Edward
Stringfellow Shaw, Rachael
Martinus, Justine (pso)
Pollard, Daniel (pso)
Mirza, Tayaba (case admin)

4.   Merchant's House
     1-7 Leeds Road **Shipley**
     Bradford BD18 1BP
     tel (01274) 809801 *fax (01274) 809884*

Substance Misuse OMU
Burden, Simone (team mgr)
Atkin, Sarah
Crossley, Louisa
Green, Gareth
Nelson, Marva
Akrigg, Donna
Sharma, Kiran
Chalk, Emily (pso)
Manir, Parveen (admin officer)
Almond, Lesa (case admin)

5.   **The Law Courts**
     Exchange Square

Drake Street **Bradford** BD1 1JZ
tel (01274) 742140 *fax (01274) 726394*

Court Team
Hadcroft, Marie (team mgr)
Bonfield, Jacqui (team mgr)
Miller, Michael
Bell, Nowell
Clarke, Christine (pso)
Dalgleish, Marie (pso)
Fox, Helen (pso)
Hardy, Maggie (pso)
Harris, Claire (pso)
Hirst, Dorota (pso)
Horsman, Karl (pso)
Page, Richard (pso)
Raper, Gerald (pso)
Wensley, Susan (pso)
Woods, Martin (pso)
Christie, June (sao)
Bowles, Nicola (admin officer)
Bulsara, Pragna (admin officer)
Butt, Sohaib (admin officer)
Coates, Ann (admin officer)
Diabira, Brenda (admin officer)
Greenwood, Leanne (admin officer)
Kumar, Nikki (admin officer)
Mairs, Eileen (admin officer)
Mitchell, Jane (admin officer)
Priestley, Elaine (admin officer)
Spark, Anne-Marie (admin officer)
Waldron, Russell (admin officer)

6.   11/19 Cavendish Street
     Keighley BD21 3RB
     tel 01535 662771/2 *fax 01535 611346*

Bradford Offender Mgmnt Unit 8
Austwick, Martin (team mgr)
Mullinder, Lynne
Parkin, Sally
Terrington, Tina
Timlin, Carol
Walker, Marcia
Croker, Simon (pso)
Eloi, Jules (pso)
Thorp, Julie (pso)
Watt, Nicola (pso)
Hussain, Rozbana (case admin)
Kelly, Sandra (case admin)
Szuszko, Barbara (case admin)
Ward, Rachel (case admin)

Leeds West District

7.   **Waterloo House**
     58 Wellington Street **Leeds** LS1 2EE
     tel 0113-243 0601 *fax 0113-399 5374*

fax 0113-234 4057

District Administration Team
Smallridge, Margaret (aco)
Gosling, Wendy (pa to aco)
Evans, Dave (pract mgr)
Miller, Lynn (pract mgr)
Glazier, Tamsin (pract mgr)
Schofield, Susan (supt services mgr)

Substance Misuse OMU
Hawley, Nick (team mgr)
Chambers, Emma
Eggleton, Matt
Greensmith, Jenny
Musgrove, Eme
Charnley-Richards, Elizabeth (pso)
Love, Mark (pso)
Ehrlich, Sergio (pso)
Mountain, Gail (pso)
Silver, Andrea (pso)
Shiel, Jodie (pso)
Sorhaindo, Evans (pso)
Ratcliffe, Janette (pso)
Bradley, Cheryl (case admin)
Briggs, Alison (case admin)
Illingworth, James (case admin)
Tennant, Steph (case admin)

Leeds West Offender Mgmnt Unit 1
Tate, Karen (team mgr)
Cheyne, Rebecca
Crombie, Julie
Flanagan, Kate
Forster, Aiden
Hudson, Karen
Jones, Kate
McBride, Eimear
Newbould, Samuel
Sadler, Fiona
Cazan, Sorin (pso)
Kilbane, Angela (pso)
Summan, Mukhtiar (pso)
Harper, June (case admin)
Keane, Sandra (case admin)
Machell, Jenna (case admin)

Leeds West Offender Mgmnt Unit 2
Melaugh, John (team mgr)
Afzal, Nazia
Hymas, Stephen
Lomas, Katie
Moss, Sarah
Tedstill, Lisa
Wilson, Kerryanne
Fowler, Marie (pso)
Khan, Ghohar (pso)
Reynolds, Graham (pso)
Wilkins, Stephanie (pso)

Hegarty, Adele (case admin)
Jefferson, Kolleen (case admin)
Thomson, Nichola (case admin)

Leeds West Offender Mgmnt Unit 3
Dersley, Ian (team mgr)
Horsfall, Ruth
Johnson, Anne
Nicol, Catherine
Olbison, Sheree
Prior, Clare
Truelove, Robert
Burns, Carol (pso)
Clark, Thomas (pso)
Mann, Ranjit (pso)
Paul, Gavin (pso)
Acaster, Lisa (case admin)
Johnson, Amanda (case admin)
Mendy, Mary (case admin)
Rai, Jasmandeep (case admin)

Leeds West Offender Mgmnt Unit 4
Roberts, Jude (team mgr)
Cherry, Helen
Hartley, David
Hussain, Wajid
Lewis, Ruth
McDonnell, Simon
Conway, Martin (pso)
Costello, Michelle (pso)
Jowett, Angela (pso)
McPhail, Ian (pso)
Parker, Catherine
Bateson, Laura (case admin)
Bird, Helen (case admin)
Denman, Kerry Anne (case admin)

8. **Magistrates' Court**
28 Westgate, Leeds LS1 3AP
tel 0113-399 5440 *fax 0113-245 0967*

Court Team
Maud, Graham (team mgr)
Jarosz, Josie
Everett, Margaret
Forster, Karen (pso)
Hunt, Trevor (pso)
Scott, Margaret (pso)
Lloyd, Rozanne (pso)
Sowerby, Catherine (pso)
Eggleston, Mark (pso)
Beck, Lynn (pso)
Walker, Norah (pso)
Dinsdale, Rod (pso)
Broadhurst, Vicki (sao)
McIlvenny, Irene (sao)
Baldwin, Ann (admin officer)
Bradley, Mark (admin officer)

Gaffney, Marie (admin officer)
Gerald, Sue (admin officer)
Hunt, Diane (admin officer)
MacFadyen-Speight, Janet (admin officer)
Mesie, Andrew (admin officer)
Reynolds, Karen (admin officer)
Shaw, Katherine (admin officer)

9. **Drug Intervention Programme (DIP)**
   Millgarth Police Station
   Millgarth Street, Leeds LS2 7HX
   tel 0113-241 3133 *fax 0113-241 3140*

10. **Crown Court**
    1 Oxford Row, Leeds LS1 3GE
    tel 0113-243 1107 *fax 0113-234 1952*

    Steed, Mary (team mgr)
    Rodney, Brian
    Berry, Michael (pso)
    Gordon, Carole (pso)
    Jeffers, Joan (pso)
    Lenski, Rosemary (pso)
    Cox, Felicity (sao)
    Butler, Sandra (admin officer)
    Butterfield, Kathleen (admin officer)
    Butterworth, Lindsay (admin officer)
    Dawber, Jennifer (admin officer)
    Shillito, Julie (admin officer)

Leeds East District

11. **379 York Road**
    Leeds LS9 6TA
    tel 0113-285 0300 *fax 0113-285 0301*

    District Administration Team
    Chandler, Andrew (aco)
    Miller, Adele (pa to aco)
    Johnson, Louise (area mgr)
    Jarvis, Sarah (ptnrshp mgr)
    Harrison, Lisa (supt services mgr)
    Evans, Steve (supt services mgr)
    Jones, Susan (team supt off)
    Blanc, Johny (pract mgr)
    Brotton, Richard (pract mgr)
    Cockerill, Tanya (pract mgr)

    Leeds East Offender Mgmnt Unit 1
    Hudson, Jennifer (team mgr)
    Bowkett, Emma
    Brennan, Helen
    Hussain, Zaffar
    Mair, Sarah
    McGlinchey, Richard
    Sherwood, John
    Smith, Sarah
    Brown, John (pso)
    Bygrave, Joanne (pso)

Packer, Anne (pso)
Phillip, Ruby (case admin)
Sheridan, Caroline (case admin)

Leeds East Offender Mgmnt Unit 2
Ward, Marianne (team mgr)
Ashworth, Matthew
Davies, Lisa
Heatley, Kirsty
Heptinstall, Donna
Hooson, Michael
van Rossum, Henk
Watkins, Rachael
Bircumshaw, Edwin (pso)
Gray, Charlotte (pso)
Kilbride, Gary (pso)
Munden, Angharad (pso)
Seavers, Heidi (pso)
Walker, Jonathan (pso)
Binks, Jane (case admin)
Graham, Andrea (case admin)
McEvoy, Charlotte (case admin)

Leeds East Offender Mgmnt Unit 3
Button, Sue (team mgr)
Burrows, Ray
Field, Clare
Glenn, Joanne
Jeffers, Lennie
Roberts, Trish
Robinson, Kirstie
Akhtar, Shameem (pso)
Gunn, Sorrell (pso)
Murgatroyd, Peter (pso)
Saunderson, Helen (pso)
Wales, Sharon (pso)
Jackson, Beckie (case admin)
Kane, Allan (case admin)
Liburd, Pat (case admin)

Leeds East Offender Mgmnt Unit 4
Garry, Rachel (team mgr)
Clark, Sarah
Hines, David
Powell, Catherine
Quinn, Elizabeth
Spink, Ben
Storey, Gemma
Mills, Rachel (pso)
Morton, Jodie (pso)
Phillips, Amanda (pso)
Walker, Lorraine (pso)
Audsley, Denise (case admin)
Holmes, Lisa (case admin)
Schofield, Janette (case admin)

Leeds East Offender Mgmnt Unit 5
Pickering, John (team mgr)
Atkinson, Natalia

Baxter Crisp, Karen
Green, Andrew
Halstead, Diane
Vickers, Anne
Watt, Ollwyn
Bell, Gillian (pso)
Nunns, Helen (pso)
Scott, Alison (pso)
Laister, John (case admin)
Mayhew, Lyndsey (case admin)
Walker, Dawn (case admin)

Leeds East Offender Mgmnt Unit 6
Maxwell, Chris (team mgr)
Crute, Emma
Curtis, Laura
Dickinson-Ramsden, Issy
Gulzar, Mohammed
McNamara, Siobhan
Tuckley, Beth
Westbrooke, Louise
Ali-Khan, Ansar (pso)
Bellwood, Irene (pso)
Sinclair, James (pso)
Pritchard, Elizabeth (case admin)
Raby, Mavis (case admin)

Victim Services
Wood, Avril (pract mgr)
Baker, Debbie (pso)
Coates, Glynnis (pso)
Henshaw, Karen (pso)
Pitchford, Angela (pso)
Ryder, Sue (pso)
Boomer, Margaret (admin officer)
Coulson, Donna (admin officer)

MAPPA Leeds East
Charlesworth, Sue (team mgr)
Turner, Peter (team mgr)
Chadwick, Helen (supt off)
Kennedy, Christine (supt off)
Kilcommins, Denise (supt off)
Whelan, Polly (supt off)
Aspin, Nicola (admin officer)
Jefimovs, Indra (admin officer)

Calderdale District

12. Probation Centre,
    173a Spring Hall Lane
    Halifax HX1 4JG
    tel (01422) 340211 *fax (01422) 320998*

District Admin Team
Scott, Joan (aco)
Flint, Margaret (pa to aco)
Devenport, William (pract mgr)
Hall, Vicky (supt services mgr)
Barker, Amanda (supt services mgr)

King, Julie (team supt off)

Calderdale Offender Mgmnt Unit 1
Wright, Catherine (team mgr)
Baxendale, Carole
Cartwright, Judith
Gardner, Pauline
Pierre-Madigan, John
Sherriff, Leanne
Biesty, Sarah (pso)
Richardson, Hilary (pso)
Thomson, Jessica (pso)
Ashcroft, Suzanne (case admin)
Gray, Tracy (case admin)
Jones, Joanne (case admin)

Calderdale Offender Mgmnt Unit 2
Gallagher, Tony (team mgr)
Bonham, Nicola
Chambers, Lynn
Griffith, Gail
Kerr, Richard
Radicke, Maria
Walsh, Charlotte
Friessner-Day, Shayne (pso)
Kite, Alison (pso)
Pedley, Michael (pso)
Bennett, Dawn (case admin)
Johnson, Susan (case admin)
Nolan, Sarah (case admin)

Court Team
Pilling, Kay (team mgr)
Rudderforth, Jeff
Chapman, Gary (pso)
Lister, Georgia (pso)
Sladdin, Anna (pso)
Jordan, Tracey (sao)
Beevers, Barbara (admin officer)
Devenport, Michelle (admin officer)
Walton, Jade (admin officer)

Substance Misuse OMU
Hillas, Deryck (team mgr)
Gregory, Jill
Holdsworth, Charlotte
Khan, Mohammed
Lester, Liz
Nowell, Frances
Jennison, Margaret (pso)
Nicholl, Helen (pso)
Powell, Mark (pso)
Berry, Suzanne (case admin)
Robinson, Pamela (case admin)

Kirklees District

13. Broadway House, Crackenedge Lane
    Dewsbury WF13 1PU
    tel (01924) 464171/3 *fax (01924) 453279*

Substance Misuse OMU
Fagg, Caterina (team mgr)
Tolson, Matthew
Walker, Claire
Wallace, Mona
Moore, Julie (pso)
Mulla, Nasim (pso)
Oldroyd, Philip (pso)
Byrne, Claire (case admin)
Faulkner, Rosemarie (case admin)
Gaskin, Katie (case admin)
Stephenson, Diane (case admin)

Kirklees Offender Mgmnt Unit 4
fax (01924) 460382

Higgins, Paula (team mgr)
Anforth, Patricia
Endeacott, Anthony
Foster, Sara
Hattersley, Patricia
Nash, Jessica
Wilson, Gail
McNamara, Eva (pso)
Perrot, Matthew (pso)
Sumner, Nicola (pso)
Sykes, Tracey (pso)
Mould, Susan (admin off)
Mallender, Lynn (case admin)
Ward, Deborah (case admin)

Kirklees Offender Mgmnt Unit 5
Branton, Christine (team mgr)
Aveyard, Heidi
Buch, Nina
Payne, Sarah
Richmond, Mike
Roberts, Jean
Canning, Steven (pso)
Gardner, Sandra (pso)
Sykes, Karen (pso)
Crossley, Ruth (case admin)
Lane, Rachel (case admin)

14. 21 St John's Road
Huddersfield HD1 5BW
tel (01484) 826100 *fax (01484) 422218*

District Admin Team
Loney, Kathryne (aco)
Hodgson, Adele (pa to aco)
Bramley, Liz (ptnrshp mgr)
Taylor, Lucy (pract mgr)
Swanson, Gaynor (pract mgr)
Dawson, Steph (supt services mgr)
Ambler, Anita (supt services mgr)
Finneran, Catherine (team supt off)
Kaye, Kimberley (team supt off)
Andrews, Annmarie (recep)

Ellam, Gwendolen (recep)
Howard, Yvonne (recep)

Court Team
Daniels, Gerard (team mgr)
Newsome, Melanie (pso)
Bohanna, Glenn (pso)
Daniel, Karen (pso)
Ledger, Karen (pso)
Lees, Sharon (pso)
Lee, Adele (pso)
Stones, David (pso)
Munir, Samaina (pso)
Ray, Leanne (pso)
McLeod, Richard (sao)
Hamilton, Marcela (admin off) (p)
Lumb, Debbie (admin off)
McEwen, Emma (admin off)
Shaw, Patricia (admin off) (p)
Wilkinson, Meryl (admin off)
Deane, Laura (case admin)

Kirklees Offender Mgmnt Unit 1
Firth, Cassy (team mgr)
Cooper, Ian
Cummings, Rachael
Kellett, Helen
Lawrence, Penelope
Martin, Emma
Roberts, Helen
Simpson, Jacqui
Hinds, Dominy (pso)
Kennedy, Nicky (pso)
Martin, Graham (pso)
Clay, Jane (case admin)
Goodchild, Sharon (case admin)
Kaur, Baljinder (case admin)

Kirklees Offender Mgmnt Unit 2
Ralcewicz, Elizabeth (team mgr)
Bentley, Alison
Edmondson, Alison
Montgomery, Alison
Osborne, Monday
Varlow, Jolene
Carrig, Katie (pso)
Hinchcliffe, Veronica (pso)
Todd, Nathan (pso)
Green, Alison (case admin)
Johnson, Victoria (case admin)
Noble, Sharlene (case admin)

Kirklees Offender Mgmnt Unit 3
Barnes, Irena (team mgr)
Daley, Lorna
Fenby, Neil
Haider, Halima
Ridgeway, Lorraine
Scott, Debbie

Sheeky, Emma
Thorpe, Emily
Atkinson, Hannah (pso)
Charlesworth, Benjamin (pso)
Ellis, Belinda (pso)
Williams, Becki (pso)
Ali, Tahira (case admin)
Drinkwater, Kathleen (case admin)
Lambert, Karin (case admin)

Wakefield District

15. 20/30 Lawefield Lane
Wakefield WF2 8SP
tel (01924) 361156 *fax (01924) 291178*
aco (01924) 885425 *fax (01924) 885440*

District Admin Team
Lanfranchi, Maximilian (aco)
Bentley, Julie (pa to aco)
Brearton, Julie (ptnrshp mgr)
Reid, Dave (pract mgr)
Clark, Carol (pract mgr)
Gilling, Shevon (supt services mgr)
Halloran, Anne (supt services mgr)

Court Team
Todd, Viv (team mgr)
Brettell, James
Borrill, Steve (pso)
Rainforth, Paul (pso)
Turner, Maria (pso)
Evans, Stephen (pso)
France, Martin (pso)
Hayward, Pamela (pso)
Jeans, Julie (sao)
Brown, Joan (admin officer)
Newton, Sarah (admin officer)
Haggerty, Diane (admin officer)
McKenna, Brenda (admin officer)
Woodfine, Kate (admin officer)

Victim Services
Brook, Margaret (pract mgr)
Appleyard, Tracey (pso)
Jenkinson, Suzy (pso)
Kerry, Ruth (pso)
Sheard, Ruth (pso)
Hobbs, Julie (admin officer)
Senior, Victoria (admin officer)

MAPPA Wakefield
Parsisson, George (team mgr)
Crossley, Julie (supt off)
Hirst, Marie (supt off)
Neill, Hazel (supt off)

Wakefield Offender Mgmnt Unit 1
Oliver, Maureen (team mgr)
Brown, Phillip

Mitchell, Rhonda
Munro, Donald
Wood, Susan
Fiksen, Victoria (pso)
Gavins, Christine (pso)
Wardle, Susan (pso)
Barlow, Marjorie (case admin)
Schofield, Cathryn (case admin)
Stickland, Simone (case admin)

Wakefield Offender Mgmnt Unit 2
Sweeting, Christopher (team mgr)
Bergin, Susan
Cadamarteri, Sharon
Fields, Louise
Hanby, Pamela
Noor-Foster, Dawn
Razaq, Mohammed
Scarlett, Jane
Johnson, Lynn (pso)
Stansfield, Bernadette (pso)
Wharton, Nicola (pso)
Barraclough, Nicola (case admin)
Bennett, Karen (case admin)
McCarthy, Gareth (case admin)

16. 2 Harropwell Lane
Pontefract WF8 1QY
tel (01977) 791357 *fax (01977) 602041*

Wakefield Offender Mgmnt Unit 3
Goodchild, Jennifer (team mgr)
Clay, Rowan
Jones, Lynne
Payne, Philip
Spence, Robert
Johnson, Don (pso)
Palmer, Gail (pso)
Redman, Gillian (pso)
Steel, Deborah (pso)
Walker, Lindsay (pso)
Briggs, Julie (case admin)
Coleman, Amy (case admin)
Curtis, Simon (case admin)
Dee, Diane (case admin)
Wolfe, Carole (case admin)

Wakefield Offender Mgmnt Unit 4
Johnson, Imogen (team mgr)
Heslop, Lynne
Jordan, Cathy
Shields, Katie
Zaszlos, Sarah
Jones, Stephen (pso)
Jowsey, Robert (pso)
Campsall, Cathy (case admin)
Stringer, Tracy (case admin)

17. Grosvenor House
8-20 Union Street
Wakefield WF1 3AE
tel (01924) 784999 *fax (01924) 781405*

Substance Misuse OMU
Todd, Viv (team mgr)
Maguire, Clare
Nolan, Stephen
Smith, Miles
Henry, Sarah (pso)
Holmes, Fiona (pso)
Mack, Karen (case admin)

Programmes

18. **Bradford/Calder Programmes**
Fraternal House
45 Cheapside **Bradford** BD1 4HP
Edwards, Richard (pract mgr)
tel (01274) 703700 *fax (01274) 703701*

Bennett, Barbara (pso team mgr)
Morris, Michael (pract mgr)
Vikse, Hilary (pract mgr)
Wright, Christine (pract mgr)
Elsom, Jo
Lynch, Jacqueline
Ryan-Appleby, Mary
Baldwin, Catherine (pso)
Bates, John (pso)
Clarkson, David (pso)
Dobson, Sarah (pso)
Dunne, Susan (pso)
Forber, Gillian (pso)
Hay, Angela (pso)
Kavanagh, Karen (pso)
Markey, Gillian (pso)
Naheed, Farzana (pso)
Pickles, Catherine (pso)
Richardson, Carolyn (pso)
Silson, Eve (pso)
Thackray, Andrew (pso)
Welsh, Sophie (pso)
Wickham, Ralph (pso)
Ashworth, Sarah (admin officer)
Chatfield, Donna (admin officer)
Morley, Deena (admin officer)
Smith, Venetta (admin officer)
Tahir, Asim (admin officer)

19. **Kirklees/Wakefield Programmes**
5 Albion Street
Dewsbury WF13 2AJ
tel (01924) 457744 *fax (01924) 458564*

McAvoy, Jackie (team mgr)
Barber, Jean (pract mgr)
Kruthoffer, Jane (pract mgr)

Wrighton, Libby (pract mgr)
Yates, Angela (pract mgr)
Crabtree, Dawn
Duggan, Sharna
Johnson, Jolene
Neto-Claringbold, Ana
Akbar, Zahir (pso)
Armitage, Sally (pso)
Bell, Andrew (pso)
Cruse, Ann (pso)
Evdokiou, Katy (pso)
Flynn, Paula (pso)
Foster, Kelly (pso)
Hartley, Sarah (pso)
Just, Simon (pso)
Mundin, Leanne (pso)
Ridge, Gemma (pso)
Todd, Andrew (pso)
Wilkinson, Graham (pso)
Bailey, Amanda (admin officer)
Holdsworth, Julie (admin officer)
Illingworth, Lynn (admin officer)
Lambert, Andrea (admin officer)
Roberts, Tracey (admin officer)

20. **Leeds Programmes**
Waterloo House
58 Wellington Street **Leeds** LS1 2EE
tel 0113-243 0601 *fax 0113-399 5374*

Maxwell, Mary (team mgr)
Ashford, Rita (pract mgr)
Braithwaite-Vare, Tracey (pract mgr)
Lowton, Mark (pract mgr)
Ashton, Julie
Boynton, Timothy
John, Gareth
Osman, Paul
Tebbutt, Russell
Westerman, Yvette
Acornley, Nicola (prog tutor)
Bhogal, Iqbal (prog tutor)
Carter, Natalie (prog tutor)
Coulthard, Penelope (prog tutor)
Dix, Thomas (prog tutor)
Evans, Peter (prog tutor)
Knights, Adrian (prog tutor)
Newton, Danielle (prog tutor)
Rai, Sukbinder Kaur (prog tutor)
Morrill, Ruth (pso)
Swan Francis, Jane (pso)
Szostak, Catherine (pso)
Beba, Slawka (admin officer)
De Asha, Andrew (admin officer)
Hayes, Deborah (admin officer)
Standing, Gaynor (admin officer)

Unpaid Work

21. **Bradford/Calder Unpaid Work**
Fraternal House
45 Cheapside **Bradford** BD1 4HP
tel (01274) 703700 *fax (01274) 703701*

Milner, Christine (team mgr)
Booker, Tracey (dep mgr)
Hall, Brian (dep mgr)
Bartholomew, Bill (proj off)
Brooks, Gillian (proj off)
Jones, Nicola (proj off)
Kirrane, Mark (proj off)
Blakeley, Carol (upw supvr)
Finney, David (upw supvr)
Gilmartin, Susan (upw supvr)
Hinkins, Beres (upw supvr)
Hussain, Abid (upw supvr)
Hussain, Zeena (upw supvr)
Jno - Baptiste, Michael (upw supvr)
Moore, Heather (upw supvr)
Morley, Sue (upw supvr)
Netherwood, Stuart (upw supvr)
Ozupak, Volkan (proj off)
Parvez, Faeisal (upw supvr)
Richards, Paul (upw supvr)
Robson, Neil (upw supvr)
Schofield, Stacey (admin officer)
Simmonds, Sean (upw supvr)
Sladdin, Edward (upw supvr)
Sultan, Mohammed (upw supvr)
Taylor, Kenny (upw supvr)
Uddin, Nadeem (upw supvr)
Larkin, Julie Carole (sao)
Hellowell, Irene (admin officer)
Towers, Patricia (admin officer)
Williams, Marilyn (admin officer)

22. **Kirklees/Wakefield Unpaid Work**
21 St John's Road
Huddersfield HD1 5BW
tel (01484) 826100 *fax (01484) 422218*

Walker, Mandy (team mgr)
Roach, Walter (dep mgr)
Thompson, John (dep mgr)
Ingram, Kim (proj off)
Oliver, Michelle (proj off)
Pedley, Janine (proj off)
Simpson, Diane (proj off)
Thorpe, Wendy (proj off)
Barry, William (upw supvr)
Bohanna, Paul (upw supvr)
Caton, Andrew (upw supvr)
Cramm, Eric (upw supvr)
Davies, John (upw supvr)
Frankland, Gordon (upw supvr)

Frisby, Andrew (upw supvr)
Hewitt, Jean (upw supvr)
Sheridan, Paul (upw supvr)
Smith, Jeannie (upw supvr)
Turner, Philip (upw supvr)
Wales, Granville (upw supvr)
Ward, Andrew (upw supvr)
Watson, Lynne (upw supvr)
Francis, Norma (sao)
Brummitt, Anne (admin officer)
Collins, Brenda (admin officer)
Hughes, Susan (admin officer)
Moxon, Wanda (admin officer)
Ward, Maura (admin officer)

23. **Leeds Unpaid Work**
379 York Road
Leeds LS9 6TA
tel 0113-285 0300 *fax 0113-285 0301*

Ambler, Margaret (team mgr)
Hainsworth, Jonathan (dep mgr)
Parrish, Diane (dep mgr)
Lewis, Angela (proj off)
Guthrie, John (proj off)
Oldroyd, James (proj off)
Armitstead, David (upw supvr)
Ashton, Rose (upw supvr)
Bodrozic, Mark (upw supvr)
Davis, Hugh (upw supvr)
Gata-Aura, Satpal (upw supvr)
Godsell, Gail (upw supvr)
Laurenson, Allan (upw supvr)
Matharu, Jagdish (upw supvr)
McNichol, Laraine (upw supvr)
Osahn, Balwinder (upw supvr)
Roe, Peter (upw supvr)
Selby, Richard (proj off)
Thomas, Abbie (proj off)
Watson, Roy (upw supvr)
Wilson, Richard (upw supvr)
Shelley, Sabrina (sao)
Bulsara, Daxa (admin officer)
Emmott, Anne (admin officer)
Johnson-Newton, Jackie (admin officer)
Paton, Gill (admin officer)

Secondments

Addlestone, Deborah (team mgr DIP Leeds)
Charles, Shirley (DIP)
Oddy, Richard (pso DIP Leeds)
Akhter, Nasim (contracts mgr)
Boyle, Ann-Louise (prof supt off)
Clark, Debbie (employer engagmnt mgr)
Cooper, Mike (spo, int offender mgmnt)
Gartland, Louise (NOMS ptnrshp mgr)

Golden, Becky (probn intelligence off)
Hirons, David (community chaplaincy)
Khan, Quaiser (choices)
McNerney, Val (com & ptnrshp mgr)
Mills, Howard (aco,ROMS)
Moran, Natalie (pso)
Nelson, Richard (unison)
Quarmby, David (bus stdrds specifier)
Shackleton, Alyson (bail info off, nacor)
Evans, Maureen (bail inf off, nacro)
Thornton, Janet (perf info mgr)
Townend, Karen (Home Office)
Wallace, Julie (employer engagmnt mgr)
Whitehead, Gini (com mgr, probn)

Youth Offending Teams

24. Bank House, 41 Bank Street
     Bradford BD1 1RD
     tel (01274) 436060 *fax (01274) 436061*

     McNulty, Bernard

25. **Leeds North**
     The District Centre
     Town Street **Chapel Allerton**
     Leeds LS7 4NB
     tel 0113-214 5662 *fax 0113-214 5684*

26. **Leeds West**
     Hough Lane Centre, Hough Lane
     Bramley, Leeds LS13 3RD
     tel 0113-395 0101 *fax 0113-395 0102*

27. **Leeds East**
     Halton Moor Centre
     Neville Road, Leeds LS15 0NW
     tel 0113-214 1369 *fax 0113-214 1377*

     Begley, Laura
     Cooke, Nadine
     Hooson, Cindy
     McCluskey, Ian
     Meek, Sarah
     Neech, Jennifer
     Sattar, Musrat

28. **Leeds South**
     38 Sweet Street, Holbeck
     Leeds LS11 9DB
     tel 0113-214 5300 *fax 0113-214 5299*

29. **Intensive Supervision &
     Surveillance Programme**
     47 Marshall Street, Holbeck
     Leeds LS11 9RZ
     tel 0113-214 1514 *fax 0113-214 1517*

30. 3 Trinity Place
     Halifax HX1 2BD
     tel (01422) 368279 *fax (01422) 368483*

     Ogden, Tracey

31. 1st Floor, Somerset Buildings
     Church Street **Huddersfield** HD1 1DD
     tel (01484) 226263 *fax (01484) 226919*

     Tock, Heather
     Rashid, Ayesha (admin off)

32. 5 West Parade
     Wakefield WF1 1LT
     tel (01924) 304155 *fax (01924) 304156*

     Plant, Carol
     Walker, Lyndsey

33. **Yorkshire & Humberside Consortium**
     2nd Floor, Devonshire House
     38 York Place, Leeds LS1 2ED
     tel 0113-244 6044 *fax 0113-245 1394*
     e-mail *yhpcgen@yhpc.co.uk*

     Geeson, Roger (learning & devpt mgr)
     Woodward, Nicola (sao)
     Atkinson, David ('what wks' mgr)
     Beier, Claire (admin officer)
     Marchant, Janet (admin off)
     Ridsdale, Janette (admin off)

**Approved Premises (Hostels)
West Yorkshire Probation Managed**

34. **Holbeck House Approved Premises**
     Springwell View, Springwell Road
     Leeds LS12 1BS
     tel 0113-245 4220 *fax 0113-245 4910*

     Neal, Elise (mgr)
     Jones, Keith (ro)
     Rawsthorne, Anna (ro)
     Sheehan, Caroline (ro)
     Young, Grace (ro)
     Hall, Monika (asst ro)
     Cooper, Frances (admin off)
     Kinder, Nicola (admin off)

35. **Elm Bank Approved Premises**
     59 Bradford Road
     Cleckheaton BD19 3LW
     tel (01274) 851551 *fax (01274) 851079*

     Stadward, Chris (mgr)
     Cox, Maureen (ro)
     Dalawar, Ifzal (ro)
     Elliott, Marsha (ro)
     Iredale, Katie (ro)
     Brown, Donnavon (asst ro)
     Higson, Trudie (admin off)

36. **Albion Street Approved Premises**
30 Albion Street
Dewsbury WF13 2AJ
tel (01924) 452020 *fax (01924) 455670*

Trevitt, Joanne (mgr)
Elliott, David (ro)
Evans, Andrew (ro)
Lee, Julia (ro)
Smith, Stuart (ro)
Lynch, Alistair (asst ro)
Hirst, Alison (admin off)

37. **Westgate Project**
188-198 Westgate
Wakefield WF2 9RF
tel (01924) 203730 *fax (01924) 203731*

Haddrick, David (mgr)
Hanson, Phil
Gillespie, Janice (pso)
Hickman, James (pso)
Sharrock, Julie (pso)
Ablett, Nicola (asst ro)
Bennett, Dawn (asst ro)
Hamilton, Scott (asst ro)
Parvez, Gaz (asst ro)
Ramsden, Devon (asst ro)
Windsor, Louise (asst ro)
Hill, Michelle (admin off)

Voluntary Managed Approved Premises (Hostels)

38. **Cardigan House Approved Premises**
84 Cardigan Road
Leeds LS6 3BJ
tel 0113-275 2860 *fax 0113-274 5175*

Cantley, Louise (mgr)
Schofield, Bill (team mgr)

39. **St John's Approved Premises**
259/263 Hyde Park Road
Leeds LS6 1AG
tel 0113-275 5702 *fax 0113-230 5230*

Berry, Tony (mgr)
Bradley, Laura (dep mgr)

40. **Ripon House Approved Premises**
(women only hostel)
63 Clarendon Road
Leeds LS2 9NZ
tel 0113-245 5488 *fax 0113-242 3675*

Pickin, Rod (mgr)
Willcock, Karen (dep mgr)

Institutions

41   HM Prison **Wealstun**
Thorp Arch, Boston Spa
Wetherby LS23 7AZ
tel (01937) 444400 *fax (01937) 444401*

Hutchings, Tanya (team mgr)
Dixon, Fiona (case mgr)
Neave, Zoe (case mgr)
Rowe, Jayne (case wrkr)
Whittemore, Rebecca (case wrkr)
Wolstenholme, Christine (case wrkr)

Intensive Community Order Team
Ali, Sajid (mgr)
Armitage, Nigel
Brooksbank, Kate
Richards, Gemma

42. HM Prison **Armley**
Leeds LS12 2TJ
tel 0113-203 2600 *fax 0113-203 2601*

Wallis, Clare (team mgr)
Klaus, Jude (offender mgr)
Langton, Cris (case mgr)
Lawless, Tim (case mgr)
Cole, Helen (case wrkr)
Khan, Zaq (case wrkr)
Rozee, Andrew (case wrkr)
Sellars, Ashley (case wrkr)

Bail Information
ext 2648/2640
bail info fax 0113-2032869

43. HM Prison, Love Lane
Wakefield WF2 9AG
tel (01924) 246000 *fax (01924) 2462799*

Odunze, Rachael (team mgr)
Barker, Katherine (case mgr)
Burkinshaw, Clare (case mgr)
Fell, Michelle (case mgr)
Gill, Sarah (case mgr)
Wilmot, Denise (case mgr)

44. HM Women's Prison
New Hall Dial Wood
Flockton, Wakefield WF4 4AX
tel (01924) 803000 *fax (01924) 803001*
probn fax (01924) 844248

Parker, Lisa (team mgr)
Redhouse, Liz (case mgr)
Coupland, Claire (case mgr)
Denniss, Maria (case wrkr)
Dunstan, Lauren (case mgr)
Nightingale-Clark, Lorraine (case wrkr)
Wilson, Alison (case mgr)

Local Justice Areas

2-4 Bradford
6 Keighley
7, 9 Leeds
12 Calder
13, 15 Batley & Dewsbury
14 Huddersfield
16 Wakefield
17 Pontefract

Crown Courts

5 Bradford
11 Leeds

DYFED POWYS PROBATION TRUST YMDDIRIEDOLAETH PRAWF DYFED POWYS

e-mail Firstname.Surname@dyfed-powys.
probation.gsi.gov.uk

1. **Headquarters**
   Llangunnor Road, Carmarthen SA31 2PD
   tel (01267) 221567 *fax (01267) 221566*

   Morgan, Caroline R (ce)
   Rutter, Frances (dir of offender mgmnt)
   Remigio, Rebecca (dir of interventions)
   Pearce, Jan E S (dir of fin and ict)
   Davies, Geoffrey L (dir of h.r.)
   Wheatley, Lynn (area mgr offender
   mgmnt, Carmarthenshire, Pembrokeshire)
   John, Jackie (snr ce pa)
   James, Catrin (pa to dir of fin and ict)
   Dilworth, Susan (pa to dir of offender
   mgmnt)
   Dadson, Anita / Taylor, Louise (pa
   to dir of interventions)
   Leeman, Patsy (p,pa to area mgr offender
   mgmnt, Carmarthenshire, Pembrokeshire)
   Raby, Pauline/Cadd, Theresa (p,pa to dir
   of hr)
   Johns, Helen (learning and development
   mgr)
   Bundock, Sarah (h.r. off)
   James, Tracey (h.r. off)
   Pritchard, Wayne (ict systems mgr)
   Glasson, Steve (ict off)
   Williams, Neil (ict off)
   Ladbrook, Martin (ict admin)
   Lee, Craig (ict admin)
   Cooke, Cerys (ict admin)
   Scott-Davies, Andrew (fin mgr)
   Bale, Shirley (finance off)
   Davies, Arfon (finance off)
   Griffiths, Alison (p, finance admin,
   transport)
   Nash, Terri (p, finance admin)

2. 7a & 7b Water Street
   Carmarthen SA31 1PY
   tel (01267) 222299 *fax (01267) 222164*

   **Carmarthenshire Offender
   Management Division: Carmarthen**
   Greenhill, Peter (divnl mgr)
   Brosnan, Mark (pract mgr offender
   mgmnt)
   Elliott, Helen (p, pract mgr, intrvntns divn)
   Coleridge, Tom

Davies, Catherine
Jones, Jayne
Lloyd, Ben
Morgan, Debbie

Kettle, Emily (trainee)
Owen, Robert (trainee)
Payne, Clare (trainee)
Williams, Lynne (trainee)

Burd, Judith (pso, om)
Cuthell, Keith (pso, om)
John, Gaye (pso, om)
Inglesant, Bob (p,pso, int)
King, Rosemary (pso, int)
Rees-Thomas, Michelle (pso, int)
Foster, Michael (vlo)

Saunders, Sian (divnl admin)
Davis, April (p, case admin)
Evans, Jane (p, case admin)
Wright, Peter (case admin)
King, Kathleen (case admin)
Hodge, Iris (p, victim liaison admin)
Vacancy (recep)

3. Lloyd Street
    Llanelli SA15 2UP
    tel (01554) 773736 *fax (01554) 758491*

    **Carmarthenshire Offender
    Management Division: Llanelli**
    Greenhill, Peter (divnl mgr)
    Churchill, Janet (p, pract mgr, offender
    mgmnt)
    Hoyles, Lee (pract mgr, offender mgmnt)
    Grant, Desmond (pract mgr, intrvntns
    divn)
    Brennan Jackie (p, yot)
    Brenton, Liz (p)
    Creed, Martyn
    Edwards, Christine (p)
    Hiscocks, Karen
    Jackson, Rachael
    Jones, David
    King, Peter
    Ripley, Carol (p, yot)
    Rosser, Mandy (p)
    Thomas, Lowri

    Morgan, Paul (trainee)
    Perdu, James (trainee)
    Jenkins, Tim (pso, om)
    Harries, Christine (pso, om)
    Thomas, Sian (pso, om)
    McDowell, Kirsty (pso, om)
    Waters, Sîan (pso, int)

    Belton, Mike (pso, int)
    Bouleghlimat, Janet (pso, int)

Freshwater, Ian (pso, int)
John, Clive (cwo)

Harries, Janet (divnl admin)
Thomas, Janet (p, divnl secy)
Standfield, Will (case admin)
Davies, Gloria (case admin)
Jones, Susan (p, case admin)
Samuel, Barbara (case admin)
Millar, Rhyla (p, ops admin & p, case
admin)
Ransome, Harriet (p, cwcs admin)
Warwick, Susanne (interventions admin)
Vacancy (recep)

4. 14 High Street
    Haverfordwest SA61 2DA
    tel (01437) 762013 *fax (01437) 765423*

    **Pembrokeshire Offender
    Management Division**
    Houton, Janet (divnl mgr)
    Caveille, Loraine (pract mgr, offender
    mgmnt)
    Linck, Jacquie (p, pract mgr, intrvntns
    divn)
    Birks, Sandra
    Chappill, Frank
    Davies, Nicola (p)
    Davis, Steven (yot)
    Horner, Jim
    Jarvis, Tara
    Jenkins, Georgina
    Parker, Claire
    Sheehan, Matthew
    Thomas, Sarah

    James, Keri (trainee)
    King, Laura (trainee)
    Welsby, Clare (trainee)

    Norman, Julie (pso, om)
    Owen, Bob (pso, om)
    Phillips, Clare (p,pso, om)
    Quinnell, Diane (pso, om)
    Wilford, Huw (pso, om)
    Giacci, Blanche (pso, int)
    Rees, Nicola (pso, int)
    Inglesant, Bob (p, pso, int)
    Jenkins, Myfanwy (cwo)

    Sladden, Mair (divnl admin)
    Phillips, Julia (case admin)
    Kidd, Margaret (case admin)
    Smith, Helen, (case admin)
    Johnson, Luke (case admin)
    Williams, Kate (p, admin)
    Worsell, Joanne (p, ops admin)
    Rackham, Amy (recep)

5. 23 Grays Inn Road
   Aberystwyth SY23 1DE
   tel (01970) 636460 *fax (01970) 624713*

   Ceredigion Offender Mngmnt Divn
   Wakelam, Ruth (divnl mgr)
   Ayriss, Debbie (p, pda)
   Llewellyn, Sera (p, pda)
   Gawthorpe, Aine (pract mgr, offndr mgmnt)
   Frisby, Daniel
   Jones, Gary
   Moore, Alistair (p, yot)
   Rennie, Gemma
   Simpson, Laura (p)

   Hurren, Jackie (trainee)
   Rees, Sian (trainee)

   Bowen, Elizabeth (pso, om)
   Davies, Julian (pso, om)
   Griffiths Sharon (pso, om)
   Davies, Ruth (pso, int)
   Maguire, Allan (pso, int)
   Vacancy (p, pso, int)
   Price, Jane (divnl admin)
   Cafferelli, Mauro (case admin)
   Juffernholz, Lyn (p, case admin)
   Lindsay, Helen (case admin)
   Jones, Tania (case admin & recp)

6. Ground Floor, Plas y Fynnon
   Cambrian Way
   Brecon LD3 7HP
   tel (01874) 614150 *fax (01874) 610602*

   **Powys Offender Management
   Division: Brecon**
   Powis, Kathy (powys divnl mgr)
   Daniel, Darren (interventions mgr)
   Livesley, Julia (po & pract mgr)
   Burdett, Andrea (p)
   Gregory, Janet (p)
   Harris, Nicola (p, yot)
   Williams, Helen
   Wooldridge, Jonathan (interventions)
   Worth, Tracey

   Craig, Graham (trainee)
   Kerr, Bridget (trainee)
   Dodds, Maureen (cwo)
   Hickey, Nigel (cwo)

   Price, Philip (p, pso, om)
   Scott, Jenny (pso, om)
   Ward, Anna (pso int)
   McAllister, Jessica (pso int)

   Carter, Charlie (pract mgr, ETE intrvntns)

   Williams, Margaret (divnl admin)

   Leakey, Gillian (p, case admin)
   Thomas, Rose (case admin)
   Higgins, Tracy (divnl secy)
   Vacancy (ete admin)
   Vacancy (p, recep)

7. Straight Lines House
   New Road **Newtown** SY16 1BD
   tel (01686) 611900 *fax (01686) 611901*

   **Powys Offender Management
   Division: Newtown**
   Alman, Mark (area mgr offender mgmnt Ceredigion/Powys)
   Powis Kathy (powys divnl mgr)
   Arrowsmith, Stevie (pract mgr interventions divn)
   Cookson, Trish
   Jarman, Nicola
   Taylor, Helena
   Vacancy (p)
   Williams, Hannah (trainee)
   Hickman, Tracey (cwo)

   Brown, Anna Marie (pso, om)
   Phillips, Leah (p, pso, om)
   Williams, Jane (p, pso, om/yot)
   Arrowsmith, Stuart (pso, int)
   Sandford, Tracey (pso, int)
   Farrington, Rebecca (pso, int)
   Harvey, Laura (p,divnl admin)
   Purnell, Lesley (p, pa to Mark Alman)
   Robinson, Jennifer (case admin)
   Roberts, Nicola (case admin/recep)
   Evans, Rebecca (case admin/recep)
   Vacancy (p, recep)

8. **MAPPA Unit**
   Dyfed-Powys Police Headquarters
   Llangunnor Road, Carmarthen SA31 2PD
   tel (01267) 226154 *fax (01267) 226054*
   mappa@dyfed-powys.pnn.police.uk

   Williams, Yvonne (MAPPA co-ord)
   Vacancy (p, MAPPA admin)
   Thomas, Emma (p, MAPPA admin)

9. **Drug Interventions Programme**
   Block 1, St David's Park
   Jobswell Road, Carmarthen, SA31 3HB
   tel (01267) 236862 *fax (01267) 237317*

   Fisher, Kevin (DIP mgr)
   Vacancy (p,DIP data mgr)

   Richards, Mair (DIP admin)

10. **Intensive Alternatives to Custody
    (IAC) Demonstrator Project**

Lloyd Street, **Llanelli** SA15 2UP
tel (01554) 773736 *fax (01554) 758491*

Spencer, Lesley (IAC project mgr)
Hunter Katie
Weinzweig, Nicole
Lester, Michelle (pso)
Vacancy (p, pso)
Vacancy (case admin)
Vacancy (p, admin)
Leeman, Patsy (p, research asst)

Youth Offending Services

11. **Pembrokeshire YOS**
Customer Services Centre
Argyle Street
Pembroke Dock SA72 6HL
tel (01437) 776036/8 *fax (01646) 684563*

Davis, Steven

12. **Carmarthenshire YOS**
1 West End, Llanelli
Carmarthenshire SA15 3DN
tel (01554) 740120 *fax (01554) 740122*

Brennan, Jacqueline (p)
Ripley, Carol (p)

13. **Ceredigion YOS**
Marine Terrace,
Aberystwyth, SY23 2DE
Tel (01970) 633730 *fax (01970) 633745*
Moore, Alistair (p)
Williams, Jane (p)

14. **Powys YOS**
Ground Floor, Watton Mount,
The Watton, Brecon, LD3 7AW
tel 01874 615986 *fax (01874) 615990*

Harris, Nicola (p)

Local Justice Areas

2 Carmarthen
5 Ceredigion
7 De Brycheiniog
8 De Maldwyn
4 Dinefwr
3 Llanelli
4 North Pembrokeshire
6 Radnorshire & N Brecknock
4 South Pembrokeshire
7 Welshpool

Crown Court

3 Carmarthen
3 Haverfordwest

GWENT PROBATION AREA
GWASANAETH PRAWF GWENT

e-mail Firstname.Surname@gwent.probation.
gsi.gov.uk

1. **Head Office**
Cwmbran House, 3rd Floor
Mamhilad Park Estate
Pontypool NP4 0XD
tel (01495) 762462 *fax (01495) 762461*
direct dial (01495) 74 + ext

Coates, Jane (co) 5702
Ryan, Mary (pa to co) 5707)
Blease, Adrian (aco) 5703
Gotley, Adam (aco) 5705
Seymour, Carolyn (aco) 5706
Langdon, Christopher (aco) 5704
Holland, Susan (pa to aco's) 5709

Caple, Michelle (board admin off) 5708

Coombes, Mark (hr mgr) 5713
Fisher, Bärbel (hr off) 5717
Zafar, Andrea (hr off) 5974
Fearn, Samantha (hr off) 5745

Jones, Neil (fin mgr) 5714
Hamilton, Joanne (fin off, payroll) 5720
Howells, Helen (fin off, accounts) 5715
Phillips, Cherryl (fin off, facilities) 5701

Butler, Tomos (it & perf supt mgr) 5721
Ballard, Stephen (info off) 5972
Edwards, Gail (info off) 5710
Gajic, Gemma (info off) 5724
Hencher, Della (info off) 5723

Bell, Doreen (team mgr, staff devpt) 5712
Humphreys, Gaynor (training off) 5718

Oram, Dawn (snr clerical officer) 5719
Davies, Hannah (telephonist) 5730
Perkin, Lesley (telephonist) 5731
Walters, Frances (telephonist) 5730

Hale, Gareth (mappa co-ordinator) 5725
Trotman, Rhonwen (mappa registrar) 5711

2. 50 Bethcar Street
Ebbw Vale NP23 6HG
tel (01495) 309799 *fax (01495) 306997*
direct dial (01495) 35 + ext

Ebbw Vale Team
Fields, Dave (team mgr) 6462
Harris, Theresa (office mgr) 6454
Goulding, David 6477
Hopkins, Michelle 6481
Johnson, Emma 6487
Lloyd, Rhiannon 6480

Pizey, Sarah 6473
Williams, David (6472
Bynon, Julie (pso) 6468
Hughes, Suzanne (pso) 6476
Price, Natasha (pso) 6471
Thomas, Iwan (pso) 6495
Timothy, Sarah (pso) 6482
Williams, Timothy (pso) 6488
Heard, Keri (case admin) 6469
Whitcombe, Judith (case admin) 6470
Richards, Wendy (case admin) 6494

Staff Development Team
Vowden, Nicole (pract teacher) 6486
Humphreys, Laura (trainee) 6467
Price, Katie (trainee) 6467
Salathiel, Louise (trainee) 6467

ETE Team
Davies, Andrews (pso) 6456

3. Centenary House, De Clare Court
    Pontygwindy Industrial Estate
    Caerphilly CF83 2WA
    tel (02920) 885861 *fax (02920) 760123*

Rhymney Valley Team 1
Walters, Sharon (team mgr) 0092
Bidgway, Bev (office mgr) 0001
Bailey, Helen 0022
Blake, Alexandra 0044
Howse, Sarah 0033
Phillips, Kelly 0060
Partridge, Christopher 0019
Robinson, Sinead 0020
Robinson, Lisa 0036
Shaw, Linda 0046
Tetley, Nick 0037
Adams, Sharon (pso) 0054
Alexander, Sharon (pso) 0050
Cribb, Christine (pso) 0042
Davies, Siân (pso) 0021
Jones, Beth (pso) 0038
Taylor, Rachel (pso) 0053
Lambeth, Kathryn (case admin) 0045
Nightingale, Rebecca (case admin) 0049
Simmons, Deborah (case admin) 0052

Rhymney Valley Team 3
Richley, Linda (team mgr) 0090
Allen, Barbara 0065
Connolly, Lisa 0075
Hamed, Janine 0011
Hood, Maree 0013
Jones, Kristina 0027
Nash, Katie 0015
O'Connell, Siobhan 0029
Thomas, Liz 0012
Coles, Linda (pso) 0018
Dixon, Grace (pso) 0028

Powell, Nadine (pso) 0025
Ravenhill, Sandra (pso) 0014
Turner, Vicki (pso) 0023
Carey, Catherine (case admin, crts) 0010
Davey, Susan (case admin) 0024
Mann, Sara (case admin) 0016

Staff Development Team
Sullivan, Jane (pract teacher) 0008/0082
Jones, Ceri (trainee) 0025
Jones, Gwenno (trainee) 0007
Richmond, Ruth (trainee) 0006

ETE Team
Palmer, Rosa (pso) 0115

4. **Accredited Programmes Team**
    The Highway, Croesyceiliog
    Cwmbran NP44 2HF
    tel (01633) 877716 *fax (01633) 867251*
    Direct dial (01633) 83 + ext

Bowkett, Stephen (team mgr) 5935
Holder, Rachael (office mgr) 5930
Curtis, Sherrie (treatment mgr) 5931
Thomas, Fiona (treatment mgr) 5934
Vallely, Gillian 5934
Callow, Leah (pso) 5933
Davies, Frank (pso) 5937
Halligan, Jean (pso) 5936
Hier, Emma (pso) 5934
Preece, Kim (pso) 5936
Tew, Stephanie (pso) 5937
van Biljon, Yvonne (intrvntns admin) 5939

5. Torfaen House, Station Road
    Sebastopol **Pontypool** NP4 5ES
    tel (01495) 755221 *fax (01495)763233*
    direct dial (01495) 74 + ext

East Gwent Team 1
Turner, Karen (team mgr) 5030
Henniker-Gotley, Julie (office mgr) 5050
Flage, Leeanne 5026
Harrison, Susan 5027
Jones, Leigh 5018
Owen, Peter 5023
Taylor, Janice 5013
Thorne, Stephen 5012
Thorpe, Keiron 5024
Wright, Hannah 5015
Goodall, Lianne (pso) 5044
Morris, Janice (pso) 5042
Sellick-Brown, Ann (pso) 5022
Walters-Moore, Andrew (pso) 5001
Williams, Sarah (pso) 5021
Young, Mark (pso) 5017
Andrews, Hannah (case admin) 5025
Evans, Caroline (case admin) 5020
Hamiton, Cath (case admin) 5020
Pembridge, Helen (case admin, crts) 5042

East Gwent Team 2
Davies, Alan (team mgr) 5005
Collier, Rowena 5032
Lavelle, Kate 5041
Pearson, Ann 5013
Jenkins, Jason (pso) 5011
Price, Marilyn (pso) 5003
Sims, Jim (pso) 5004
Howells, Zoe (case admin) 5002
Price, Susan (case admin) 509

Public Protection Team
Reed, Gail (team mgr) 5031
Holloway, David 5036
Mason, Heather 5039
Morris, Lucy 5034
Thomas, Siân 5037
Webb, Ellen 5033
Goode, Liz (case admin) 5038

MAPPA
Richardson, Ann-Marie (visor admin) 5047

6. 19/20 Gold Tops
   Newport NP20 4UG
   tel (01633) 213221 *fax (01633) 221568*
   direct dial (01633) 84 + ext

   Newport Team 1
   Vernon, Claire (team mgr) 4658
   Richards, Liza (office mgr) 4627
   Butcher, Michelle (office mgr) 4627
   Boulter, Paul 4650
   Dacey, Ian 4648
   Gilder, Gayle 4653
   Llewellyn-Rowe, Janet 4655
   Richards, Kelly 4654
   Sarwar, Zaheen 4643
   Gabica, Zoe (pso) 4656
   Gibbon, Louise (pso) 4649
   Harrison, Laura (pso) 4657
   Ivens, Luke (pso) 4651
   Lloyd, Susan (pso) 4652
   Davey, Fran (case admin) 4747
   Quick, Anne (case admin) 4647

   Newport Team 2
   Gillo, Debbie (team mgr) 4639
   Edwards, Sarah 4630
   Sabor, Monika 4646
   Powell, Kate 4630
   Brass, Erin (pso) 4630
   Edwards, Sharon (pso) 4630
   Owen, Peter (pso) 4630
   Parisi, Gino (pso) 4645
   Smith, Rebecca (pso) 4630
   Whittington, Fiona (pso) 4644
   Williams, Brian (pso) 4630
   Blight, Susan (case admin) 4640

Appleton, Elizabeth (case admin, crts) 4630

Newport Team 3
Watkins, Cath (team mgr) 4667
Hatfield, Catherine 4666
Johns, Kirsty 4660
Peckham, Tracey 4659
Porter, Rick 4662
Asher, Kate 4641
Jenkins, Rebecca 4624
Clemson, Patricia 4663
McCormack, Caroline 4664
Beck, Ruth (pso) 4661
Brown, Joanne (pso) 4642
Lewis, Frances (pso) 4625
McGuire, Eleanor (pso) 4626
Moore, Kate (pso) 4643
Sagoo, Sharan (pso) 4663
Lippiatt, Carole (case admin) 4623
Kendall, Sally (case admin) 4665

7. 27 Argyle Street
   Newport NP20 5NE
   tel (01633) 822007 *fax (01633) 820839*

   Unpaid Work Team
   King, Mike (team mgr)
   Hughes, Meryl (office mgr)
   Bidgood, David (snr unpaid work off)
   Axenderrie, Paul (unpaid work off)
   Mogford, Mike (unpaid work off)
   Morgan, Robin (unpaid work off)
   Morgan, Glyn (unpaid work off)
   Bartlet, Claire (interventions admin)

   Education, Training & Employment Team
   King, Mike (team mgr)
   Abdalla, Janey (pso)
   Cresswell, Sarah (pso)
   Mitchell, Valerie (basic skills co-ord)
   Hawkins, Samara (interventions admin)

8. The Annexe
   Rear of Pentonville Magistrates' Court
   Newport NP20 5XQ
   tel (01633) 840298 *fax (01633) 840334*
   direct dial (01633) 84 + ext

   Drug Rehabilitation Team 1
   Packham, Jill (team mgr) 8125
   Powell, Norma (office mgr) 1254
   Collins, Katharine 0295
   Gittoes, Cath 0297
   Haskins, Lee 0292
   Nicholls, Heather
   Bullock, Donna (pso) 0284
   Vaughan, Karen (pso) 0301
   Plant, Deborah (case admin) 0294

Drug Rehabilitation Team 2
Spacey, Nigel (team mgr) 1255
Anderson, Laura 0284
Forman, Louise 0301
Howe, Emma 0291
Pudge, Lindsey 0310
Wilding, Laura 0295
Jenkins, Helen (pso) 0310
Walsh, Johanna (pso) 0284
McCormack, Siân (case admin) 0296

Based at Blackwood
tel (01495) 228829
Birchmore, Alan
Powell, Claire
Wan, Lisa
Warry, John (pso)
Jones, Gail (case admin)

9. Rear of Pentonville Magistrates' Court
Newport NP20 5XB
tel (01633) 841249 (staff devpt team)
(01633) 841256 (Newport team 2)
fax (01633) 841278
direct dial (01633) 84 + ext

Staff Development Team
Warke, Clifford (pract teacher)
Crescenzi, Jane (case admin)
Horton, Christian (trainee)
Lang, Gemma (trainee)
Williams, Sarah (trainee)

Newport Team 2
Mukhtar, Kauser 1272
Nicholas, Zara 1271
Phillips, Emma 1271
Thomas, Siân 1275
Wesley, Michelle 1273
Clarke, Tony (pso) 1275
Cross, Susan (case admin) 1256
Johns, Melissa (case admin) 1256

Prolific Offender Team
Davies, Alan (team mgr) (based at 5)
Dunne, Michael 1260
Nicholls, Robert 1258
Strange, Jeffrey 1258
Thomas-Owen, Mandy 1258
Cook, Amanda (case admin) 1262

Institutions

10. H M Prison, 47 Maryport Street
Usk NP15 1XP
tel (01291) 671600 *fax (01291) 671752*
direct dial (01291) 67 + ext

Hopkins, Michelle 3694
Sheppard, David 3693

11. H M Prison
Prescoed, Coed-y-Paen
Nr Pontypool NP4 0TB
tel (01291) 675000 *fax (01291) 675158*
direct dial (01291) 67 + ext

Daniel, Peter (pso) 5118

Local Justice Areas

2, 3 NW Gwent
5, 6, 9 SE Gwent

Crown Court

6 Newport

NORTH WALES PROBATION AREA (Counties of Anglesey, Denbighshire, Flintshire, Wrexham, Gwynedd, Conwy) GWASANAETH PRAWF GOGLEDD CYMRU (Siroedd Ynys Mon, Ddinbych, Fflint, Wrecsam, Gwynedd, Conwy)

Out of hours emergency contact point
Ty Newydd Hostel (01248) 370529
Plas y Wern Hostel (01978) 814949

Victim enquiries contact number
(01492) 524000

e-mail Firstname.Surname@north-wales.
probation.gsi.gov.uk

Offices

1. **Head Office**
Alexandra House, Abergele Road
Colwyn Bay LL29 9YF
tel (01492) 513413 *fax (01492)513373*

Moore, Carol R (co)
Neal, David (dir of resources & treasurer)
Ray, Stephen G (aco interventions)
Driver, Matthew (aco offender mngmnt)
Adlam, Doris (area mgr, perf, planning, diversity, qual assurance, staff devpt & research)
Long, Suzie (area personnel mgr)
Roberts, Simon (perf/info off)
Jones, Pam (info off)
Webb, Rob (info off)
Rush, Ruth (hr officer)
Catton, Tessa (projects mgr,p)
Gilio, Janet (snr finance officer)
MacDonald, Fergie (business devpt mgr)

Staff Training & Development
Owen, Lucie (spo devpt, diversity, research)
Dance, Sheila (staff devpt/NVQ co-ord)

Duckett, Sarah (trainee)
Evans, Claire (trainee)
Evans, Ruth (trainee)
Griffiths, Angharad (trainee)
James, Angharad (trainee)
Jones, Hannah (trainee)
Jones, Mari (trainee)
Lamb, Stephen (trainee)
Moon, Kelly (trainee)
Murt, Carly (trainee)
Owen, Marina (trainee)
Roberts, Sian (trainee)
Smart, Jodie (trainee)
Thompson, Rachael (trainee)
Waldron, Sarah (trainee)
Williams, Caryl (trainee)
Williams, Margaret (trainee)
Woolford, Elen (trainee)

All trainees may be contacted through the Staff Training & Devpt Unit

2. Llys Garth, Garth Road
    Bangor Gwynedd LL57 2RT
    tel (01248) 370217 *fax (01248) 372422*

Offender Management
Evans, Jane (area mgr)
Griffiths, Hannah (spo)
Riou, Jill (practice devpt mgr)
Roberts, Alona (business admin)

Jones, Delyth
Jones, Rhys
Kidd, Gareth
Owen, Lowri
Owen, Samantha
Davies, Emma
Williams, Ffion
Williams, Lynne
Whatling, Mike (pso)
Healy, Diane (pso)
Phillips, Liz (pso)

Programmes
Vacancy (team leader)
Hughes, June (interventions off)
Hughes, Karen (interventions off)
Owen, Cathy (interventions off)
Tyrer-Thomas, Cathy (intervntns off)
Williams, Sîan (interventions off)

Unpaid Work/Community Payback
Thomas, Graham (unit mgr)
Hughes, Ken (cs off)

Wilding, Bob (placement supt off)

3. 14 Market Street
    Caernarfon Gwynedd LL55 1RT
    tel (01286) 674346 *fax (01286) 672668*

Offender Management
Evans, Jane (area mgr)
Williams, Sharon (spo)
Griffiths, Mimma (bus/building admin)
Dawson, Linda
Farrer, Susie
Martin, Sue
Thomas, Catrin
Rees, Awen
Williams, Eira
Peters, Llyr
Pugh, Richard (pso)
Roberts-Price, Lynne (pso)

4. Lombard Street, Dolgellau
    Dolgellau Gwynedd LL40 1HA
    tel (01341) 422476 *fax (01341) 422703*

Programmes
Cumming-Watt, Karen (p, ca)
Harrison, Mrs. Marian (interventions off)

5. 25 Conway Road,
    Colwyn Bay, Conwy LL29 7AA
    tel (01492) 530600 *fax (01492) 532283*

Offender Management
Jones, Andy (area mgr)
Partington, Catherine (business admin)
Morris, Marie (building admin)
Owen, Tracey (spo)
Amirech, Mohammed (spo)
Lowe, Sheila (pract devpt mgr)
Lewis, Elenid (pract devpt mgr)
Byfield-Jones Anna
Cran, Melanie
Dhaliwal, Jaspal
Jones, Tim
Markwick, Nerys
Puw, Rhodri
Griffith, Gerallt
Honan, Carole
Swinden, Elizabeth
Marston, Joanna
Roberts, Sue
Schofield, Eleri
Sowinska-Pritchard, Bernadetta
Williams, Paul
Donnelly, Paul
Jones, Gillian
Kelly, Louise (pso)
Nicholls, Sîan (pso)

Roberts, Eirian (pso)
Thomas, Rachel (pso)

Unpaid Work/Community Payback
Hughes, Elizabeth (area mgr)
Marsh, Sue (business admin)
Thomas, Graham (unit mgr)
Wright, John (cs project devpt off)
Parry, Paul (placement support off)

Jervis, Allison (cso)

Programmes
Livingston, Wulf (area mgr)
Vacancy, (team leader)
Richardson, Judy (business admin)
Roberts, Jan (intervntions off)
Pritchard, Vivian (intervntions off)
Burton, Maxine (p, intervntns off)
New, Tony (intervntions off)
McIntyre, Karen

VLU
McKeaveney, Siobhan (svlo)
Owen-Rees, Nia (vlo)
Kerr, Cassie (vlo)

McCabe, Julieanne (case admin)

Wales Training Constortium
Gwilym, Ceinwen (regnl training off)

6. Unit 6, Acorn Business Centre
    Flint Flintshire CH6 5YN
    tel 01352 792140 *fax (01352 792141)*

    Offender Management
    Williams, Judith (area mgr)
    Ryan, Jane (spo)
    Garvey, Margaret (bus/building admin)
    Aitken, Jackie
    Conway, Angela
    Hooley, Emily
    Jones, James
    Lord, Christine
    Maggs, Ceri
    Maggs, Chris
    Preece, Llinos
    Richards, Cerren
    Waldron, Sarah
    Richards, Stif
    Jones, Ceri (pso)
    Shepherd, Natasha (pso)
    Quinn, Mike (pso)
    Wynn, Mair (pso)

7. Ellice Way, Wrexham Technology Park
    Wrexham LL13 7YX
    tel (01978) 346200 *fax (01978) 346206*

    Offender Management
    Williams, Judith (area mgr)
    Oats, Lis (spo)

Brett, Emma (spo)
Vacancy (pract devpt mgr)
Hands, Angela (pract devpt mgr)
Laing, Angharad (p, pract devpt mgr)
Ellis, Phil (H&S mgr)
Vacancy (building admin)
Stewart, Chris (bus admin)
Allmark, Nigel
Thornburn, Anna
Evans, Edwyn
Carrison, Janet
Clarke, Jonathon
Hughes, Paula
Humphries, Kathleen
McAlley, Ian
McKenzie, Kirstin
Mooney, Claire
O'Keeffe, Alex
Partington, Michelle
Pawulska, Jacqui
Quinn, Katherine
Roberts, Lynsey
Smith, Katherine
Taylor, Joanne
Taylor, Julie
Waldron, Sarah
Webster, Frances

Davies, Patrick (pso)
Roberts, Pamela (pso)
Connah, Andrew (pso)
Mitchell, Emma (pso,p)
Seward, Derek (pso)
Woolford-Tab, Ffion (pso)

Programmes
Goodwin, Phil (team mgr)
Haggett, Carol (psychologist)
Davies, Teresa (interventions off)
Griffiths, Myfanwy (intervntns off)
Owen, Elain (interventions off)
Wrzeszcz, Halina (intervntns off)

Unpaid Work/Community Payback
Evans, Charlie (unit mgr)
Davies, Chris (cso)
Purton, Richard (cso)
Harry, Brian (placement supt off)
Lloyd, Dave (placement supt off)

8. **Drug Interventions Programme (DIP)**
    13 Princes Drive
    Colwyn Bay LL29 8HT
    tel (01492) 536672 *fax (01492) 531652*

    Playle, Katy (proj mgr)
    Williams, Lisa (data perf mgr)
    Robinson, Sue (bus admin)

"Hafod"
21 Grosvenor Road
Wrexham LL11 1BT
tel (01978) 366941 *fax (01978) 366945*

10-12 Salisbury Street
Shotton
Flintshire CH5 1DR
tel (01244) 845920 *fax (01244) 836483*

63 High Street
Bangor
Gwynedd LL57 1NR
tel (01248) 354602 *fax (01248) 353400*

1 Glanhwfa Road
Llangefni
Anglesey
Gwynedd LL77 7EN
tel (01248) 750732 *fax (01248) 750732*

9. **Youth Offending Teams**
    6th Floor, County Hall
    Mold Flintshire CW7 5BD
    tel (01352) 702603 *fax (01352) 750601*

    Evans, Tracey

    Swyddfa Menai
    Glan y Mor, Felinheli
    Bangor LL56 4RQ
    tel (01248) 679183 *fax (01248) 679180*

    Hughes, Fred

    Unit 21, Whitegate Industrial Estate
    Caia Park **Wrexham** LL13 8UG
    tel (01978) 268140 *fax (01978) 268169*

    Dyment, Joy (operations mgr)
    Jones, Caren

    68 Conway Road
    Colwyn Bay LL29 7LD
    tel (01492) 523500 *fax (01492) 523555*

    Parry, Glynne

10. **MAPPA Unit**
    Crimes Services Division
    North Wales Police
    Ffordd William Morgan
    St Asaph LL17 0HQ
    tel (01745)588078/588005 *fax
    (01745)588498*

    Clark, Carolyn (MAPPA co-ord)
    Ellis, Paula (MAPPA admin)

11. **Crown Courts**
    Mold Crown Court

Law Courts, Civic Centre
Mold CH7 1AE
tel & fax (01352) 751649

Carrison, Janet (crown crt liaison)

Caernarfon Crown Court
Shire Hall Street
Castle Ditch
Caernarfon LL55 2AY
tel (01286) 675717/674346 *fax (01286) 675717*

Martin Sue (crown crt liaison)

Approved Premises (Hostels)

12. **Plas y Wern** Approved Premises
    Ruabon, Llangollen Road. Nr Wrexham
    LL14 6RN
    tel (01978) 814949 *fax (01978) 810435*

    Higgins, Chris (area mgr)
    Hughes, Sharon (ap unit supt)
    Shone, Norman (pso)
    Hughes, Donna (pso)
    Forster, Ceri (rso)
    Harrocks, Bridget (rso)
    Higgins, Gareth (rso)
    Scott-Melville, Ricky (rso)
    Vacancy (rso)
    Jones, Helen (ap business admin)

13. **Ty Newydd Approved Premises**
    Llandygai Road
    Bangor, Gwynedd LL57 4HP
    tel (01248) 370529 *fax (01248) 371204*

    Higgins, Chris (area mgr)
    Parry, Trish (ap unit supt)
    Jones, Tina (pso)
    Phillips, Len (po)
    Jones, Hefina (rso)
    Sawicz, Philip (rso)
    Mead Damon (rso)
    Williams Emyr (rso)
    Williams, Gwenno (rso)
    Cox, Karen (ap business admin)

Local Justice Areas

2 Anglesey/Ynys Mon
5 Conwy
5 Denbighshire
6 Flintshire
2, 3, 4 Gwynedd
7 Wrexham Maelor

Crown Courts

11 Caernarfon
11 Mold

SOUTH WALES PROBATION TRUST
GWASANAETH PRAWF DE CYMRU

Out of hours emergency contact numbers
Mandeville House Approved Premises
029-2039 4592
e-mail Firstname.Surname@south-wales.
probation.gsi.gov.uk

1. **Head Office & Central Support Services**
   Tremains House, Tremains Road
   Bridgend CF31 1TZ
   tel (01656) 674747 *fax (01656) 674799*
   direct dial (01656) 67 + ext

   Lankshear, Ian (ce) ext 4798
   Cossins, Angela (director of ops) ext 4801
   Potter, Mark (director of resources) ext 4803
   Ace, Christine (aco, intrvntns) ext 4790
   Richards, Tony (aco, crts & public prtctn) ext 4771
   Eirian Evans (dist mgr, courts) ext 4832
   Peter Morgan (comms mgr) ext 4818
   James, Russell (trust admin mgr) ext 4794
   Viant, Gwenllian (sec/pa to ce) ext 4798
   Jones, Ceri J (exec asst) ext 4796
   John, Clare (exec asst) ext 4834
   Kenny, Joscelin (exec asst) ext 4812
   Smith Jayne (exec asst) ext 4789
   Browning, Bernice (trust admin) ext 4793
   Jenkins, Helen (diversity admin) ext 4836

Commissioning, Partnerships & Service Development
Liz Rijnenberg, (aco, commissioning, prtnrshps & prison estab) ext 4753
Blower, Dawn (dist mgr, commissioning & prtnrshps) ext 4831
Hyett, Wendy (project mgr) ext 4833
O'Leary Susan, (qual & imp mgr) ext 4830
Davies, Melanie, (proj supt) ext 4796
Richards, Sarah (research asst) ext 4764
Evans, Shelley (exec asst) ext 4834
Meredith, Siân (exec asst)

Human Resources Unit
Ferris, Cathryn (head of hr) ext 4715
Pring, Maxine (hr mgr) ext 4777
Cotgias, Jessica (snr hr off) ext 4817
Light, Sheena (hr officer) ext 4779
Riddiford, Colette (hr officer) ext 4780
Llewellyn, Ruth (hr officer) ext 4781

Staff Development & Training Unit
Moss, Pamela (mgr) ext 4759

Bickerton, Ian (comm just training devpt off) ext 4758
Olson, Carl (crams training off) ext 4755

Information Unit
Curtis, Simon (mgr) ext 4748
Jones, Phillip W (snr info off) 4746
James, Carley (info officer) ext 4750
Mohammed, Shamim (info officer) ext 4752
Pritchard, Leon (info off) ext 4743
Arnold, Michael (info off) ext 4750

Finance Unit
Dixon, Janis (head of finance) 4774
Arnott, Aneurin (principal accntnt) ext 4776
MacDonald, John (principal accntnt) ext 4775
Rowles, Philomena (principal accntnt) ext 4805
Fowler, Ian (fin off) ext 4782
Mordecai, Kim (fin off) ext 4785
Rees, Lindsey (fin off) 4783
Cooke, Lee (fin off) ext 4784

Property/Facilities Unit
Burridge, Gareth (head of prop & fac) ext 4786
Kembery, Tracey (asst) ext 4787
Cowmeadow, Elaine (asst) ext 4769

IT Services Unit
Rees, Lisa (helpdesk mgr) ext 4761
Dalling, Stephen (snr it serv supt) ext 4763
Head, Andrew (it serv supt) ext 4760
Hewitt, Christopher (it serv supt) ext 4762
Morgan, Jonathan (it serv supt) ext 4762

Health and Safety Unit
Johns, Chris (h&s mgr) ext 4823
Berriman, Jeff (h&s off) ext 4807

Trainee PO Scheme
Emery, Eirlys (mgr) (01685) 728902
Allen, Mike (pda) (01792) 478102
Bouleghlimat, Abdel-Aziz (pda) (01792) 478182
Cowan, Pat (pda) (01685) 728910
Evans, Robert (pda) 029-2078 5137
Hughes, Lowri (pda)
Jones, Jessica (pda) 029-2078 5086
Loring, Alison (pda) (01792) 478182

Cardiff & Vale of Glamorgan Districts

2. 33 Westgate Street
   Cardiff CF10 1JE
   tel 029 2023 2999 *fax 029-2023 0384*
   direct dial 02920 78 + ext

Brunt, Granville (aco) ext 5007
Stone, Neil (dist mgr) ext 5003
Bradbury, Suzanne (p, sec/pa to aco) ext 5003
Meakin, Tracy (p, sec/pa to aco) ext 5003
Summers-Atkins, Keri (business svcs mgr) ext 5005
Singh, Suckvindar (diversity mgr) ext 5021
Bertram Sheila (diversity off) ext 5021
Morris, Claire (basic skills co-ord) ext 5126

Offender Management
Pallister, Sheila (team mgr) ext 5006
Foulner, Jane (team mgr) ext 5009
Edwards, Meinir (team mgr) ext 5009
Costigan, Rachel (team mgr) ext
Dyer, Charlotte (team mgr) ext 5088
Bedwell, Marcus (team mgr) ext 5104
Hughes, Michael (team mgr) ext 5122
Shellens, Peter (team mgr) ext 4996

Atherton, Moira ext 5106
Bailey, Ken ext 5107
Brown, Lynsey ext 5135
Chandler, Rachael ext 5108
Davies, Gavin ext 5114
Enos, Estella
Gibbons, Kathleen ext 5142
Halsey, James ext 5147
Hygate, Zoe ext 5102
James, Debbie
Lesauter, Alice
Lucking, Bethan
Lofdhal, Miriam
Morris, Graham ext 5084
Morris, Leanne ext 5106
Morley, Rebecca
Nicholas, Charisse
Price, Sally ext 5091
Reddington, Terry
Stephens, Joanne ext
Sheppard, Anita ext
Skyrme, Natalie ext
Waters, Lindsey
Williams, Lisa ext 5148

Bamford, Aimee (pso) ext 5091
Bellamy, Nicola (pso) ext 5132
Clinton, Lisa (pso) ext 5098
Galvin, Suzanne (pso)
Hailes, Zoe (pso) ext 5019
Hatherly, Colin (pso)
Jenkins, Catherine (pso) ext 4502
Jones, Bethan (pso) ext 5073
Jones, Kate (pso, vale team) ext
Olding, Karen (pso) ext 5077
Wareham, Karen (pso)

Walsh, Timothy (pso) ext 5118
Williams, Lucy (pso) ext 5169

Vale Team
Horsell, Katie ext 6270
Jones, Kate ext 5068
Stockley, Pru
Williams, Tara ext
Witts, Adrian ext

Arthur, Stephen (pso) ext 5062
Fisher-Sharp, Tracey (pso) ext 5100
Floyd, Nicola (pso) ext 4209
Sullivan, Steve (pso) ext 5618
Thomas, Michael (pso) ext 5117
Wools, Emma (pso) ext 5082

Victim Liaison
Hailes Zoe (pso) ext 5017
Watts, Amanda (women's safety wrkr) 5017
Williams, Amanda (pso) 5018

Interventions/Programmes
Hooper, Nicola (team mgr) ext
Martin, Anne (po/treatment monitor) ext 5085
Mulligan, Dairmuid ext 5140
Williams, Jo ext 5085
Morgan, Leah (treatment monitor)
Vowles, Gus (treatment monitor)
Williams, Sarah (treatment monitor)
Baker, Byron (pso) ext 5097
Evans, Sara (pso) ext 5097
Ewing, Sashika (pso) ext 5124
Goldsworthy, Jason (pso) ext 5140
McTair, Grace (pso) ext 5125
Moore, Kirsty (pso)

Offender Accomm/Emplt Resources Unit
Guise, Anne ext 5027
Smithson, Mandy ext 5028
Wilkinson, Chris ext 5026
Mayne, Ruth (pso) ext 5025
Neale, Andrea (pso) ext 5072

3. 2a Lewis Street, Canton
Cardiff CF10 8JX
tel 029 20660 611 *fax 029-2066 7870*
direct dial 029-20660 + ext

Offender Management
Warner, Helen (team mgr) ext 614
Aston, Ted (pso) ext 619
Newton Robert (pso)
Taylor, Yvonne (pso) ext 622

Interventions/Unpaid Work
Martin, Philip (team mgr) ext 615
Jones, Dennis (plcmnt off) ext 612

Maidment, Liam (workshop mgr)
Davies, Paul (interv supvr)
Jefferies, Nigel (interv supvr)
Jones, Kim (interv supvr)
McTair, Kelly (interv supvr)
Powell, Richard (interv supvr)
Powell, Stephen (interv supvr)
Steer, Gerard (interv supvr)
Thomas, Alan (interv supvr)
Zeigler, Simon (interv supvr)
(all interv supvrs ext 5040)

4. **Cardiff Crown Court**
    Cathays Park, Cardiff CF10 3NL
    tel 029-2034 8890 *fax 029-2034 5705*
    direct dial 029-2034 + ext

    Irwin, Claire (team mgr)
    Humphries, Siân ext
    Nicholas, Colin ext 8896
    Smythe, Anne ext 8891
    Williams, Jane ext 5062
    Williams, Joan ext 8898
    Adams, Darren
    Franklin, Anna (pso) ext 8895
    Hathaway, Rebecca (pso) ext 8894

5. **Cardiff Magistrates' Court**
    Fitzalan Place, Cardiff CF24 1RZ
    tel 029-2035 8460 *fax 029-2049 8587*
    direct dial 029-2035 + ext

    Irwin, Claire ext
    Feniuck, Jan ext
    Pearson, Maria ext
    Sharp, Steven ext
    Alecock, Tricia (pso) ext 8462

    Vale of Glamorgan Mags Court
    Thompson Street, Barry CF63 4SX
    tel 01446 729964 *fax 01446 734180*

    Holmes, Louise (pso)
    Moyle, Gaynor (pso)

Bridgend District

6. Tremains House
    Tremains Road **Bridgend** CF31 1TZ
    tel (01656) 674747 *fax (01656) 674702*
    direct dial(01656) 67 + ext

    Brunt, Granville (aco, based at 2)
    McAllister, Wil (dist mgr)

    Offender Management
    Osuji, Iain (team mgr) ext 4726
    Girton, Tracey (team mgr) ext 4725
    Bray, Tony
    Burridge, Lynne
    Jury, Caren ext 4721

Jackson, Jackie ext 4741
Jenkins, Kate
Salerno, Lawrence
Thomas, Siânelen ext 4727
Williams, Emma ext 4739
Brown, Reg (pso) ext 4705
Francis, Yvonne (pso) ext 4709
John, Pen (pso) ext 4730
Nye, Kelly (pso) ext 4736
Roche, Anne (pso) ext 4740
Williams, Peter (pso) ext 4708
Yip, Deborah (p, pso) ext 4837

Court Team
Clatworthy, Nicola (team mgr)
Allen, Graham ext 4706
Walton, Helen
Wybron, Stephanie
Jones, Anna (pso) ext 4706

Interventions/Programmes
Harley, Christine (team mgr) ext 4153
Rees, Abbie, (area trtmnt mgr) 4795
Perriam, Helen (trtmnt mntr, pso) ext 4745
James, Paul ext 4718
Wanklyn, Delyth ext 4724
Thomas Donna ext 4724
Bowman, Lisa (pso) ext 4816
Clarke Robert (pso) ext 4703
James, Karen (prog admin) ext 4721
McNally, Aileen (pso) ext 4703
Perriam, Helen (pso) ext 4745
Wybron, Nicola (pso)

Interventions/ Unpaid Work
Fraser, Tony (team mgr)
Woolcock, Mark (placement ofr)
Payek, Christopher (interv supvr)
Bowen, William (interv supvr)
Halliday, Bryan (interv supvr) ext 4737
Hogg, Phillip (interv supvr) ext 4737
Stephens, Melissa (interv supvr) ext 4737

Merthyr Tydfil & Rhondda Cynon Taff District

7. 4-7 The Broadway
    Pontypridd CF37 1BA
    tel (01443) 494200 *fax (01443) 494284*
    direct dial (01443) 49 + ext

    Barrow, Ian (aco) ext
    Davies, Nicola (dist mgr)
    Sartin, Joanna (sec/pa) ext 4245

    Offender Management
    Goodman, Gail (team mgr) ext
    Hall, Victoria (team mgr)
    Richards, Emma (team mgr) ext 8912
    Suggett Hannah (team mgr)

Boswell, Sarah ext 4270
Bozzola, Gail ext
Cain, Dominic ext 4209
Carvalho, David
Cottrell, Nicola ext 4241
Davies, Melissa ext 4242
Eynon, John ext 4265
Griffiths, Helen
James, Heulwen ext 4217
Jones, Karen (p) ext 4260
Li, Xue Bin
Lovell, Rhian
Millard, Debbie ext 4239
Morgan, Catherine
Powell, Sally
Roberts, Stephen ext 4268
Williams, Simone
Andrews, Angela (pso) ext 4205
Cornwall, Sarah (pso) ext 4207
Cox, Joanne (pso)
Williams, Judith (pso) ext 4206
Davies, Siân (pso) ext 4211
Elston, Diane (pso) ext 4204
Howells, Cliff (pso)
Hughes, John (pso) ext 4231
Jones, Ceri (pso) ext 4203
Price, Alison (pso)
Robertson, Allan (pso) ext 4229
Williams, Andrea (pso)
Williams, Siwan (pso) ext 4212

Victim Liaison
Thomas, Denise (women's safety wrkr)
ext 4269

Interventions/Programmes
Hegarty, Patricia ext 4258
Barratt, David (pso)
Evans, Simon (trtmnt mntr) ext 4257
Gerrard, David (pso) ext 4256
Wilce, Andrew (pso)
Davies, Maxine (perf admin)

Court Services
Smith, Earl (team mgr)
Nowaparast, Shida
Jones, Karen
Owen, Emma
Cox, Joanne (pso) ext 4255
Llewellyn, Ann (pso)

Interventions/Unpaid Work
Evans, Lyn (team mgr, based at 7)
Tredinnick, John
Holder, Mike (plcmnt off) ext 4230
Bailyes, Gary (interv supvr)
Davies, Barrie (interv supvr)
Jones, Simon (interv supvr)
Williams, Gareth (interv supvr)

8. Oldway House, Castle Street
   Merthyr Tydfil CF47 8UJ
   tel (01685) 728900 *fax (01685) 728921*
   direct dial (01685) 72 + ext

   Barrow, Ian (aco, based at 7)
   Davies, Nicola, (dist mgr, based at 7)

Offender Management
Bebb, David (team mgr) ext 8912
Osowicz, Debbie (team mgr) ext 8943
Billingsley, Lee ext 8923
Carvalho, David
Lewis, Nicola ext 8923
Scott-Cowan, Pippa ext 8907
Davies, Melissa ext 8925
Haselhurst, Laura ext 8916
Jones, Emma ext ext 8918
Reynolds, Andrew
Lewis, Catrin ext 8914
Reynolds, Andrew ext 8920
Davies, Natalie, (pso) ext 8917
James, Claire (pso) ext 8903
Price, Alison (pso) ext 8913
Thomas, Nicola (pso) ext 8924
Townsend, Lawrence (pso)

Court Services
Smith, Earl (team mgr)
Beaumont, Patricia ext 8908
Billingsley, Lee ext 8933
Evans, Paula (pso) ext 8934
Jones Fred (pso) ext 8917
Owen, Bernadette (pso) 8931
Watkins, Hywel (p, pso) ext 8918

Interventions/Programmes
Gibbins, Chantal (team mgr) ext 8929
Norgorve, Ross (pso, treatment
monitor) ext 8931/8933
Boden, Emma (pso)
Haines, Beth (pso)
Boden, Emma (pso)
Coleman, Phil (pso) ext 8935
Nauth, Joanne (pso) ext 8918

Interventions/Unpaid Work
Evans, Lyn (team mgr) ext 8929
Davies, Barrie (inter supvr)
Dermody, David (interv supvr)
Powell, Gareth (interv supvr)
Williams, Mark (interv supvr)
Wright, Dennis (interv supvr)

Victim Liaison
Kirby, Alison (pso) ext 8927

Swansea District

9. West Glamorgan House
   12 Orchard Street **Swansea** SA1 5AD

tel (01792) 645505 *fax (01792) 478132*
direct dial (01792) 47 + ext

Barrow, Ian (aco, based at 7)
Kirk, Tony (district mgr) ext 8322
Clancy, Sarah (bus svcs mgr) ext 8121
Ford, Mike (it services mgr) ext 8188
Allender, Steve (pso) ext 8160
Atkinson, Marie Louise (ca) ext 9316

Offender Management
Colbeck, David (team mgr) ext 9323
Duckfield, Nicola (ca) ext 9320
Durgan, Roger (team mgr) ext 8193
Maynard, David (team mgr) ext 9324
Hughes, Gwyneth (team mgr) ext 9398
Meredith, Roger (team mgr) ext 8155
Roberts, Collette (team mgr) ext 9302
Mason, Deanne ext 9319
Jones, Rebecca ext 8104
Beckers, Helen ext 8124
Banner, Helen
Guite, Cerys ext 9353
Hunt, Bill ext 8198
Lewis, Audra ext 8115
Macdonald-Mohan, Melissa ext 9304
Matthews, Johnathan
Miles, Nicholas ext 9394
Morgan, Ian
Morgans, Leon ext 8129
Nantel, Caroline ext 8134
Owen, Emma 8111
Rees, Julie ext 9303
Roberts, Ken ext 8173
Rowlands, Eleri ext 8102
Stringer, Sue ext 8110
Tyler, Sue ext 9327
Walsh, Jed ext 8101
Young, Joanne ext 8167
Young, Marie ext 8196

Davies, Ian (pso) ext 9309
Edwards, Suzanne (pso) ext 9333
Fox, Melanie (pso) ext 8175
Ganz, Lisa (pso) ext 8120
Grimes, Sarah (pso) ext 8103
Howells, Simon (pso) ext 8133
Jones, Jayne (pso)
Lewis, Helen (pso) ext 9330
Matthews Fred (pso) ext 8127
Meadowcroft, Sarah (pso) 8127
Mobbs, Susan (pso) ext 9326
Poiner, Bev (pso) ext 9339
Reece, Karan (pso) ext 8169
Richardson, Darren (pso) ext 8168
Williams, Kerry (pso) ext 9310

Interventions/Programmes
Turner, Monica (team mgr) ext 9348

Lewis, Hannah (trtmnt mntr) ext 9357
Walsh, Jed ext 8101
Jones Ian (pso, trtmnt mntr) ext 9358
Adams, Lynne (pso/trtmnt mntr) ext 9356
Bartlett, Judy (pso) ext 9359
Budge, Steve (pso) ext 9312
Davies, Dorian (pso) ext 9349
Davies, Ian (pso) ext 9399
Frame, Susan (pso) ext 9354
Ganz, Lisa (pso) ext 8160
Hazzard, Karl (pso) ext 9360
Lee, Peter (pso) ext 8120
Owen, Neil (pso) ext 9351
Thomas, Sharon (pso) ext 9350
Bulpitt, Emma (prog admin) ext 9352
Cornelius, Katherine (admin) ext 9336

Victim Liaison
Edwards, Andrew (pso) ext 9334
Scullion, Rachel (pso) ext 9333
McSweeny, Joanna (wsw) ext 9332

Court Services
Maynard, David (team mgr)
Beckers, Helen
Rees, Bernie
Macdonald-Mohan, Melissa
Evans, Heather
Hughes, David
Flowers, Greg (pso)
Thomas, Jayne (pso)
Kovacs, Tina (pso) ext 9314
Steadman, Joanne (pso) ext 9313
Williams, Kerry (pso) ext 9310

Interventions/Unpaid Work
Rees, Paul (team mgr) ext 9305
Morse-Jones, Simon (plcmnt off) ext 8122
Griffiths, Nigel (interv supvr)
Hall, Ian (interv supvr)
Lloyd, Gareth (inter supvr)
Morgan, Andrew (interv supvr)
Stock, Nathan (interv supvr)
Seabright, Chris (interv supvr)
Uzzell, Laurence (interv supvr)
Williams, Noel (interv supvr)

Neath/Port Talbot District
Rabaiotti, Ella (team mgr) 8177
Purchase Sue (team mgr) 8153
Barker, Cliff ext 8116
Hinder, Vic
Jones, Rebecca ext 8131
Lewis, Audra ext 8115
Porter, Michelle ext 8115
Protheroe, Tammy ext 8114
Page, Eleanor ext 9395
Rowlands Emma-Jane ext 8108
Thomas, Donna

Trinder, Joel ext 8164
Grimes, Sarah (pso) ext 8103
Reece, Karan(pso) ext 8169
Richardson, Darren (pso) ext 8172
Sparks, Ian (pso) ext 8171

Neath/Port Talbot Court
(01639) 765951 (Neath) (m,w,f)
(01639) 894064 (Port Talbot) (t-th)
Evans, Sheila (pso) ext 9328
Lewis, Libby (pso)

10. **Swansea Crown Court**
St Helens Road, Swansea SA1 4PF
tel (01792) 461381 *fax (01792) 457783*

Maynard, David (team mgr) (9) ext 9324
Llewelyn Einir (pso)
Richards, Claire (pso)
Richards, Susan (pso)

11. **Youth Offending Teams**
Bridgend Youth Offending Team
Tremains House, Tremains Road
Bridgend CF31 1TZ
tel (01656) 657243 *fax (01656) 648218*

Strong, Rebecca (seconded po)

Cardiff Youth Offending Team
The Rise, Penhill, Cardiff CF11 9PR
tel 029 2056 0839 *fax 029-2057 8746*

Hearnden, Alex (seconded po)
Waite, Leny (seconded po)
Watkins, Leon (seconded po)
Manley, Sarah (pso)

Merthyr Tydfil Youth Offending Team
Merthyr CBC Youth Justice
47-48 Pontmorlais Centre
Merthyr Tydfil CF47 8UN
tel (01685) 389304 *fax (01685) 359726*

Lewis, Stephanie (seconded po)

Neath Port Talbot Youth Offending Team
Cramic Way, Port Talbot SA13 1RU
tel (01639) 885050 *fax (01639) 882809*

Thomas, Emyr (seconded po)

Rhondda Youth Offending Team
Unit 2, Fairway Court, Tonteg Road
Treforst Industrial Estate, Pontypridd
CF37 5UA
tel (01443) 827300 *fax (01443) 827301*

Harris, Robert (seconded po)
Davies, Charlotte (seconded po)
O'Brien, Michael (pso)

Swansea Youth Offending Team
Llwyncelyn Campus
Cockett Road, Cockett
Swansea SA2 0SJ

tel (01792) 522800 *fax (01792) 522805*
Hoare, Philip (snr pract)
James, Jackie (seconded po)

Vale Youth Offending Team
91 Salisbury Road, Barry
Vale of Glamorgan CF62 6PD
tel (01446) 745820 *fax (01446) 739549*

Heaton-Jones, Saul (seconded po)

12. **S Wales Area MAPPA Unit**
Public Protection Bureau
Police HQ, Cowbridge Road
Bridgend CF31 3SU
tel (01656) 306043/48 *fax (01656) 303464*

Rees, Nigel (MAPPA mgr co-ord)
Higgins, Bernard (dep MAPPA mgr co-ord)
Francis, Kate (admin)
O'Brien, Carole (admin)
Richards, Lynda (admin)

Approved Premises (Hostels)
Richards, Tony (aco based at 1)

13. **Mandeville House Hostel**
9 Lewis Street, Canton
Cardiff CF11 6JY
tel 029 2039 4592 & 029-2023 2999 ext 4530
fax 029-2023 3857

Protheroe, Ann (team mgr)
Taylor, Phil (dep mgr)
Barrett, Nicola (appr prem serv off)
Driscoll, Janice (appr prem serv off)
Davies, Siobhan (appr prem serv off)
Griffiths, Stuart (appr prem serv off)
Lundbech, Dave (appr prem serv off)
Batten, Edgar (waking night supvr)
Butt, Kate (waking night supvr)
Burland, Michell (waking night supvr)
Woodward, Anthony (waking night supvr)
Miles, Kay (admin)

14. **Quay House Probation Hostel**
The Strand, Swanea SA1 2AW
tel (01792) 641259 *fax (01792) 641268*

Protheroe, Ann (team mgr)
Long, Peter (dep mgr)
Frudd, Andrew (appr prem serv off)
Jones, Alan (appr prem serv off)
Oakley, Angela (appr prem serv off)
Powell, Andy (appr prem serv off)
Williams, Nigel (appr prem serv off)
Edwards, Alan (waking night supvr)
Morgan, Richard (waking night supvr)
Litchfield, Terrence (waking night supvr)
Newcombe, Jeff (waking night supvr)
Bevan, Helen (admin)

Institutions

Rijnenberg, Liz (aco, based at 1)

15. **HM Prison**
Knox Road, **Cardiff** CF24 1UG
tel 029-2092 3100 *fax 029-2092 3318*

Griffiths Carolyn (team mgr)
Bicknell, Helen
Driscoll, Wayne Jarvis, Barbara
Wareham, Robert
Bailey, Jonathan (pso)
Evans, Margaret (pso)
Wanty, Simon (pso)

16. **HM Prison Parc**
Heol Hopcyn John, Bridgend CF35 6AR
tel (01656) 300200 *fax (01656) 300201*

Griffiths, Carolyn (team mgr, based at 15)
Davies, Wynne Holland, Emma
Lewis,Amanda
Francis, Sean (pso)
Slee, Laura (pso)
Thomas, Nicola (pso)
Thomas, Lindsey (pso)

17. **HM Prison**
Oystermouth Road **Swansea** SA1 3SR
tel (01792) 485300 *fax (01792) 632979*

Osowicz, Debbie (team mgr, based at 7)
Carley, Michael
Codling, Jenny (pso)
Evans, Vivian (pso)

Secondments

Attwell, Julia (aco) Wales Training
Consortium
Jones, Bobbie (area mgr) MoJ
Pickles, Janet (po) Women's Safety Unit
Cardiff
Zammit, Ingrid (team mgr) MoJ
Mulligan, Zelda (po) MoJ

Local Justice Areas

2 Cardiff
6 Cynon Valley
7 Merthyr Tydfil
6 Miskin
8 Newcastle & Ogmore
9 Neath Port Talbot
9 Swansea County
2 Vale of Glamorgan

Crown Courts

4 Cardiff
7 Merthyr Tydfil
10 Swansea

NORTHERN IRELAND

Northern Ireland Office

Criminal Justice Services Division, Massey
House, Stoney Road, Belfast BT4 3SX
tel 028-9052 7348

The NIO is the sponsoring Department for the
Probation Board for Northern Ireland. Enquiries
about operational matters should be directed
to the PBNI (see separate entry). Criminal
Justices Services Division develops and
supports the legislative and policy environment
in which PBNI operates. In conjunction with
the Department's Financial Services Division,
CSJD ensures that the Board carries out its
activities within the overall policy and resources
framework set by the Secretary of State; and
adheres to the requirements and procedures
attaching to its expenditure of public money.

Statistics and Research Branch
Massey House, Stoney Road, Belfast BT4 3SX
tel 028-9052 7534

The Branch supplies professional statistical and
research advice and services to the Northern
Ireland Office. It also disseminates statistical
and research information via requests from
parliament, academia, official publications and
the public in general.

Northern Ireland Prison Service

Dundonald House, Upper Newtownards Road,
Belfast BT4 3SU
tel 028-9052 5065 email info@niprisonservice.
gov.uk

Parole Commissioners

5th Floor, Windsor House, Bedford Street,
Belfast BT2 7SR
028-9054 9424 *fax 028-9054 9427*
www.lsrcni.org.uk

Functions The Parole Commissioners are
an independent body that make decisions on
the release of all life sentence prisoners in
Northern Ireland. The Parole Commissioners
replace the Life Sentence Review
Commissioners, the hitherto existing body for
that purpose.

Chief Commissioner Peter Smith QC

Criminal Justice Inspection, Northern Ireland

6th/7th Floor, 14 Great Victoria Street,
Belfast BT2 7BA
tel 028-9025 8000 *fax 028-9025 8033*

e-mail firstname.surname@cjini.org

Under the Justice (Northern Ireland) Act 2002, the new Criminal Justice Inspectorate took over from the Social Services Inspectorate responsibility for inspection of the Probation Board for Northern Ireland. CJI is responsible for inspecting all the criminal justice agencies in Northern Ireland, except for Courts.

Chief Inspector
Dr Michael Maguire   028-9025 8001
Personal Secretary Linda Boal

Deputy Chief Inspector
Brendan McGuigan   028-9025 8002

Inspectors
Tom McGonigle	028-9025 8003
John Shanks	028 9025 8004
James Corrigan	028 9025 8005
Bill Priestly	028 9025 8006
Rachel Tupling	028 9025 8010

PROBATION BOARD FOR NORTHERN IRELAND

Emergency out of hours contact point
028-9079 6220

e-mail firstname.surname@pbni.org.uk

1. **Head Office**
   80/90 North Street, Belfast BT1 1LD
   tel 028-9026 2400 *fax 028-9026 2470*

   McCaughey, Brian (cpo)
   van der Merwe, David (cmo)
   Canavan, Maura (aco finance)
   Doran, Paul (aco)
   Hamill, Hugh (aco)
   Kelly, Graham (aco)
   Lamont, Ms Cheryl (aco)
   Muldoon, Ms Roisin (aco)
   Doherty, Terry (aco)
   Moss, Peter (secy to the board)
   McGurnaghan, Mrs Gayle (training mgr, L&D)
   McCutcheon, Brian (it mgr)
   Bailie, Ms Rosemary (mgr)
   Maginnis, Mrs Lisa (pr/communications)
   Carson, Nick (temp pr/communications)

Policy/Planning Devpt
Bailie, Ms Rosemary (area mgr)
Hamilton, Stephen (p)

Assessment Unit
tel 028-9026 2400 *fax 028-9026 2472*

O'Hare Miss Rita (area mgr)
Davies, Chris (area mgr)
Ball, Mrs Rosemary (p)
Carville, Ms Carol (p)
Cubillo, Bill
Cumming, Miss Mary (p)
Darnbrook, Alan (p)
Gillespie, Mrs Barbara
McKee, Ms Briege
McKee, Ms Mary
Mills, Rory (p)
Nicholson, Mrs Jacqueline
O'Neill, Mrs Oonagh (p)
Reid, Maurice (p)
Richardson, Mrs Eileen
Robinson-McDonald, Mrs Rosaleen
Sands, Miss Caroline (p)
Taylor, Mrs Siobhan (p)
Milburn, Mrs Rhonda (pso)
McIlveen, Paul (pso)
Nash, Paul (pso)
Nawaz, Mrs Eileen (pso)

Psychology Department
tel 028-9026 2408 *fax 028-9026 2472*
O'Hare, Ms Geraldine (principal psych)

2. **330 Ormeau Road**
   Belfast BT7 2GE
   tel 028-9064 7156 *fax 028-9064 1409*

   Bourke, John (area mgr)
   McCusker, Paul (area mgr) (8, 9, 10)
   Brecknell, Ms Patricia (p)
   Cahir, Seamus (p)
   Farrelly, Ciaran
   Greer, Bill
   Lenzi, Ms Shauneen
   McMahon, Fergal (p)
   McNicholl, Ms Sally (p)
   Murphy, Ms Christine
   Quinn, Ms Niamh (p)
   Woods, Mrs Geraldine (p)
   Forsythe, Mrs Claire (pso)
   Scroggie, Mrs Shauna (pso)

3. Unit 4, Wallace Studios
   27 Wallace Avenue
   Lisburn BT27 4AE
   tel 028 9267 4211 *fax 028-9260 4018*

   Arthur, Mrs Liz (area mgr)
   Grant, Mrs Jill (p)

Johnston, Ms Emma
Quail, Ms Moira
Stirling, Miss Mairi (p)

4. **306 Antrim Road**
    Belfast BT15 5AB
    tel 028-9075 7631 *fax 028-9074 3983*

    McKenna, Mrs Jane (area mgr)
    Bell, Ms Sarah-Jane (p)
    Crawley, Declan (p)
    Graham, Brian
    Hopkins, Mrs Shirley
    McAuley, Ms Nicola
    MacNeill, Eoin
    Mooney, Ms Angela
    O'Shea, Ms Johanna (p)
    Ramsey, Ms Angela
    Russell, Miss Gael (p)
    Sheppard, Paul (isu)
    Flanagan, Edward (pso)
    Nicholl, Ms Irene (pso)

5. **Antrim Technology Park**
    Belfast Road, Antrim BT41 1QS
    tel 028-9448 0140 *fax 028-9448 0199*

    Learning & Devpt Centre
    Cavan, Mrs Mary (p)
    Christie, Ms Patricia
    Maguire, Ms Catherine (p)
    O'Neill, Mrs Noreen (p)

    Information Services Team
    tel 028-9448 0150 *fax 028-9448 0199*

    Willighan, Stephen

6. Glenshane House
    202a Andersonstown Road
    Belfast BT11 9EB
    tel 028-9060 2988 *fax 028-9061 9313*

    Coogan, Ms Nicola (p)
    Cummings, Kyle (p)
    Gadd, Ms Anna (p)
    Grant, Ms Deirdre
    Harper, John
    McCarthy, Vincent (p)
    McConnell, Ms Rachel (p)
    McKenna, Miss Gloria
    Paterson, Ms Carolyn (youth justice)
    White, Miss Philippa (p)
    Maitland, Michael (pso)

7. **297 Newtownards Road**
    Belfast BT4 1AG
    tel 028-9073 9445 *fax 028-9046 0119*

    McRoberts, Mrs Claire (p, area mgr, multi

agency procedures for assessment &
management
of sex offenders [masram])
Beggs, Miss Kathryn
Davies, Ms Jenni (p)
Doran, Ms Andrea
Douglas, Alain (p)
McKee, Chris
Shaw, Stephen
Jordan, Robin (trainee forensic psy)
Nethercott, Ray (pso)
Watters, Ms Eilis (pso)

8. 15 Castle Street
    Newtownards BT23 3PA
    tel 028-9181 7778 *fax 028-9181 8905*

    Leckey, Mrs Roisin (area mgr) (p)
    Breen, Mrs Siobhan
    Doran, Ms Andrea
    McKee, Chris
    Ritchie, Jim (isu)
    Spence, Ms Melissa (p)

9. 2 Church Street
    Downpatrick BT30 6EJ
    tel 028-4461 4061 *fax 028-4461 2506*

    reporting centre only

10. 12 Lodge Road
    Coleraine BT52 1NB
    tel 028-7035 3141 *fax 028-7035 2442*

    Archibald, Ms Julie
    Dorsett, Ms Caroline (p)
    Dyer, Patrick (p)
    Holmes, Mrs Paula
    Turner, Ms Seanagh
    Nelis, Liam (pso) (p) (also at 11)
    Quigley, Mrs Marlyn (pso)

11. The Bridge House, 106 Bridge Street
    Ballymena BT43 5EP
    tel 028-2565 2549 *fax 028-2565 5523*

    Smyth, Miss Julie (mgr) (10)
    Rodgers, Ms Brigie (proj mgr)
    Lees, Ray (p)
    Wiseman, Paul
    Wilson, Mrs Dorothy

12. 8 Crawford Square
    Londonderry BT48 7HR
    tel 028-7126 4774 *fax 028-7126 7374*

    O'Kane, John (area mgr) (13)
    Clifford, Miss Briege
    Curran, Ms Lisa (p)
    Devlin, Ms Anne

Higgins, Michael
Maguire, Ms Eileen (p)
Nash, Miss Martina

13. 7 Limavady Road
Londonderry BT47 1JU
tel 028-7134 6701 *fax 028-7134 1034*

Archibald, Ms Selina
Barr, Mrs Nicola
Dunlop, Raymond
Frazer, Jason (p)
Monaghan, Ms Siobhan
Stewart, Ms Densie (p)
Wetherall, Miss Kathleen
Ferguson, Liam (pso)
Kelly, Mrs Donna (pso)

14. 38 Fountain Street
Antrim BT41 4BB
tel 028-9442 8475 *fax 028-9446 9123*

Graham, Ms Joan (area mgr) (15, 16)
Dempsey, Mrs Kirsteen
McClintock, Ms Liz
McMillan, Mrs Pauline
Ralph, Chris
Potts, Gordan (pso)

15. Tower House, 33-35 High Street
Carrickfergus BT38 7AN
tel 028-9336 2088 *fax 028-9336 3049*

Campbell, Miss Pamela
Cunningham, Ms Julie (p)
Smith, Mark (p)
Winnington, Michael

16. 41 Point Street
Larne BT40 1HU
tel 028-2827 9231 *fax 028-2827 5990*

Rainey, Stuart (pso)

17. 1d Monaghan Street
Newry BT35 6BB
tel 028-3026 3955 *fax 028-3026 9548*

Doran, Mrs Mary (p)
Lamb, Mrs Linda (p)
McCann, Dermot (p)

18. McGredy Buildings, 31-33 High Street
Portadown BT62 1HY
tel 028-3833 3301 *fax 028-3839 4334*

Connolly, Mike (area mgr) (17)
Cousins, Ms Joanne
McElnea, Miss Siobhan
Miller, Michael

Quigley, John
Smyth, Ms Stephanie
McCreery, David (pso)

19. 11A High Street
Omagh BT78 1BA
tel 028-8224 6051 *fax 028-8224 8437*

McKeever, Mrs Patricia (area mgr) (20)
Brady, Mrs Julie
Montgomery, Harry (p) (also at 20)
McKelvey, Ms Ruth (p)
O'Hagan, John (p)
Young, David (p)
McCrory, Thomas (pso)

20. 14 Dublin Road, Cathcart Square
Enniskillen BT74 6HH
tel 028-6632 4383 *fax 028-6632 5988*

Carty, Ms Selina
Flynn, Mrs Susan
Lattimore, Collette (p)

21. 9 Kirk Avenue
Magherafelt BT45 6BT
tel 028-7963 3341 *fax 028-7963 1197*

Feeney, Ms Geraldine
Grant, Mrs Michelle (p)
McLaughlin, Terry
McConomy, Martin (p)
Teague, Grainne (p)
Grace, Vincent (pso)
McMullan, Mrs Joanne (pso)
Wilkinson, Stephen (pso)

22. 30 Northland Row
Dungannon BT71 6AP
tel 028-8772 2866 *fax 028-8775 2318*

Johnston, Ms Jo-anne
Nealon, Ms Bernadette (p)
Devlin, Ms Fiona (pso)
Powell, Gary (pso)

23. 25 College Street
Armagh BT61 9BT
tel 028-3752 5243 *fax 028-3752 8530*

Duffy, Damien
Montgomery, Miss Gillian
McAnallen, Mrs Annie (p)
Abernethy, Ms Jayne (pso)
Bedard, Ms Beverley (temp pso)
Donaldson, Victor (pso)
Hazlett, Miss Louise (pso)

24. **40-44 Great Patrick Street**
Belfast BT1 2LT

tel 028-9033 3332 *fax 028-9043 8990*

Programme Delivery Unit
Best, Mrs Pat (area mgr) (p)
McClinton, Ms Janet (co-ord)
McCourt, Ms Eileen (projs)
McWilliams, Ms Jacqueline (also at 31)
Andrews, Tommy (temp pso)
McClenaghan, Joe (probn comm off)
Mottram, Ronald (pso)

25. **Alderwood House (Integrated Supervision Unit)**
Hydebank Wood, Purdysburn Road
Belfast BT8 7SL
tel 028-9064 4953 *fax 028-9064 1435*

O'Neill, Mrs Jean (area mgr)
Thompson, Paul (area mgr)
Owens, Ms Valerie (specialist facilitator)
Barry, Mrs Patricia (p)
Boyle, Thomas
Carswell, Ms Lyn (p)
Gately, Ms Madonna (p)
McCarthy, Vincent
McGlade, Ian (p)
McSherry, Mrs Tina
Mullan, Ms Brigeen
McVeigh, Ms Josephine (pco)
O'Loughlin, Mrs Kathryn (p)
Roberson, Mrs Brigid (p)
Simpson, Mrs Simone (p)
McVeigh, Ms Josie (probn comm off)

26. **Impact (Inclusive Model of Partnership Against Car Theft)**
Sally Gardens Community Centre
Sally Gardens Lane, Belle Steele Road
Poleglass, Belfast BT17 0PB
tel 028-9062 7321 *fax 028-9062 9428*

McGowan, William (operations mgr seconded)
Brennan, Miss Tracy (proj wrkr)
Gadd, Tim (proj wkr)
Cahill, Ms Maria (pso)
Watson, Gary (pso)

27. **Victim Information Scheme**
Office 40, Imperial Buildings
High Street, Belfast
tel 028 9032 1972 *fax 028 9032 1973*

Hunter, Mrs Christine (p, area mgr)
Dougan, Mrs Carol
McCaughey, Miss Mary

Institutions
28. Welfare Unit
H M Prison **Magilligan**

Co Londonderry BT49 0LR
tel 028-7775 0434/5 *fax 028-7775 0312*

Shiels, Mrs Marlene (area mgr)
Cunningham, Mrs Bernie
Canning, Ms Donna (p)
Dempsey, Colin
O'Donnell, Noel
Pegg, Ms Jackie
Quigg, Ms Martina
Quigley, Michael

29. Welfare Unit
Hydebank Wood
Hospital Road, Belfast BT8 8NA
tel 028-9049 1015 *fax 028-9064 2868*

O'Neill, Mrs Jean (p, area mgr)
Bell, Mrs Lesley (p)
Calvin, Mrs Marilyn (p)
Sinnamon, Ms Karen (p)
Tracey, Damien
Weir, Mrs Stephanie (p)
Wylie, Mrs Margaret (p)

30. Welfare Unit
HM Prison **Maghaberry**
17 Old Road, Upper Ballinderry
Lisburn BT28 2PT
tel 028-9261 2665 *fax 028-9261 9976*

Devlin, Paul (area mgr)
Lappin, Mrs Jane (area mgr) (split locatn)
Brannigan, Miss Oonagh
Conlon, John (p)
Connolly, Gary (p)
Ferguson, Philip
Haslett, Ms Andrea
McEvoy, Niall
Nicholson, Mark
Robinson-McDonald, Mrs Rosaleen (p)
Rooke, Mrs Genivene
Sloan, Ms Allison
Willighan, Stephen (p)

On Secondment
Lennox, Ms Julie
Noade, Mrs Deirdre
Richardson, Mrs Eileen
Rooke, Andrew

On career break
Bartlett, Ms Patricia
McKelvey, Ms Claire
Reynolds, Ms Aisling (p)
Smith, Ms Helen

REPUBLIC OF IRELAND
THE PROBATION SERVICE
An tSeirbhís Phromhaidh

Abbreviations

appo Assistant Principal Probation Officer
spo Senior Probation Officer
apo Assistant Principal Officer
heo Higher Executive Officer
eo Executive Officer
ypp Young Persons' Probation

where no letters appear after a name, that person is a Probation Officer

Dialing from UK 00 (international code) 353 (country code) and omit the first 0 of the local code (so, for example, for the Headquarters dial 00 353 46 9090992 or Haymarket, Smithfield Officer 00 353 1 8173600.

1. **Headquarters**
   Athumley House
   IDA Business Park
   Johnstown
   Navan, Co. Meath.
   tel 046 909 0992 *fax 046 909 0992*

   Donnellan, Michael (director)
   Geiran, Vivian (director of operations)
   O'Donovan, David (director of research/ training & devpt)
   Vella, Suzanne (director of corp affairs/HR)
   Dack, Brian (asst director of young persons probation and family law)
   Cooney, Paula (appo operations, programme and projects devpt)
   Wilson, Mark (appo of prisoners & risk resettlement)
   Marlborough, Marina (heo)
   King, Eileen (eo)
   Lynagh, Suzanne (admin, pa)
   Martin, Monica (admin)
   Gavagan, Mags (admin)

1a. **Haymarket**
   Smithfield, Dublin 7
   tel 01 817 3600 *fax 01 872 2737*

   Operations Directorate
   McNally, Gerry (asst director community service & funded projects)
   Connolly, Anna (appo Value for Money Reviews CS & funded projects)
   Comerford, Frances (ap CS & funded projects)
   Glennon, Ailish (spo community service & funded projects)

Moore, Mary (appo, ypp)
Foley, Tony (spo family law)
Kelly, James (spo operations)

Corporate Affairs/H.R.
Burke, Ita (appo H.R.)
Hanney, Christine (apo corp services)
Callanan, Valerie (accountant)

Research/Training and Devpt
Fernee, Ursula (appo)
Kennedy, Ciaran (appo)

Staff Training & Devpt Unit
McNamara, Joan (spo)
Boylan, John
Christie, Irene
Geiran, Elaine
Lawton, Jerry (Cork)
Boland, Maria (admin)

Admin staff
Boland, Liam (admin operations)
Cawley, Leona (admin H.R.)
Coleman, Stephanie (admin corp affairs)
Commins, Pat (admin corp affairs)
Cornish, Simon (eo, community funded projects)
Daly, Chris (eo, admin estate mngmnt & i.t.)
Fay, Margaret (admin corp affairs)
Finglas, Keith (admin operations)
Grimes, Carmel (admin finance)
Higgins, Lilibeth (heo, admin H.R.)
Irwin, Paula (admin young persons probn and family Law)
Jordan, Karen (eo, admin operations)
Jordan, Lisa (eo, admin PA/Freedom of Information)
Kennedy, Geraldine (admin registry)
Lally, Paul (heo, corp services & estate management)
Lynch, Darren (eo, registry)
McPartland, Lisa (admin registry)
Mooney, Graham (eo, finance)
Mooney, Noel (admin operations)
O'Connor, Deirdre (admin finance)
O'Doherty, Fiona (admin finance)
Rodgers, Noreen (eo, corp affairs)
Sullivan, Grainne (admin community service and funded projects)
Sweeney, Bill (eo, info mgr)
Treacy, Patricia (eo, corp affairs)
Wade, Linda (heo, corp affairs)

O'Keeffe, Karen (heo,mgr i.t. & foi)
Brennan, Natasha (eo, info i.t.)
Gormley. Aidan (statistician)
Cummins, Yvonne (admin i.t.)
Smith, Brenda (admin i.t.)

Dublin South & Wicklow Region

2. **Haymarket**
Smithfield, Dublin 7
tel 01 817 3600 *fax 01 872 2737*

Dublin Court Liason Team
Hanna, Emer (spo)
Balfe, John
Donnelly, Declan
Treacy, Marie

Dublin South Assessment Team
Benson, Gerry (spo)
Crowe, Andrew
Curtis, Victoria
Lowe, Helen
McGuire, Leah
Molloy, James
Nagle, Susan
Richardson, Michelle
Rock, Mark

*Homeless Offenders Team and
Cloverhill Remand Centre*
Timoney, Lena (spo)
Darragh, Sandra
Geary, Marie Anne
Keane, Marie Anne
Kelly, Maire
Lavin, Dermot
Murphy, Elaine

Cloverhill Courthouse
Cloverhill Road
Clondalkin, Dublin 22
tel 01 630 4942 *fax 01 630 4939*

Joyce, Phyllis (admin)

3a. The Cualann Centre Main Street
Bray Co Wicklow
tel 01 204 2662 *fax 01 204 2663*

Wicklow Team
Linnane Paul (spo)
Corcoran, Cathy
Doyle, Catherine
Morahan, Marion
Murphy, Andrew
Twomey, Anne
Johnston, Elizabeth (admin)

3b. Over Extra Vision Wexford Road
Arklow Co.Wexford
tel 0402 91 066 *fax 0402 91 114*

Cullen, Anne Marie (admin)

4. Le Fanu Road
Ballyfermot Dublin 10
tel 01 623 3666 *fax 01 623 3737*

Dublin South Central Team
Macken, Nuala (spo)
Buggy, Aoife
Meenaghan, Fiona
O'Higgins, Muireann
Connaughton, Linda (admin)

5. Mark's Lane Neilstown Road
Clondalkin Dublin 22
tel 01 623 6235 *fax 01 623 6236*

Dublin South Central Team
Macken, Nuala (spo)
Brosnan, Caitriona
Groome, Tommy
Phibbs, Tracey
Aughney, Brenda (admin)
Gibson, Marguerite (admin)

6. 390-396 Clonard Road
Crumlin Dublin 12
tel 01 492 5625 *fax 01 492 5631*

Regional Manager's office
Cotter, Anthony (appo)
Callery, Dot (admin)
O'Neill, Yvonne (admin)

7. **Carmens Hall**
Garden Lane (off Catherine Street)
Dublin 8
tel 01 709 3530 *fax 01 709 3539*

Dublin South Inner City Team
Jennings, Pat (spo)
Barry, Eleanor
Broomsfield, Darren
Claffey, Helen
Cole, Jennifer
Gates, Paul
Trainor, Mary
Krivtsova, Oksana
Kenny, Maurice (admin)

8. Westpark **Tallaght**
Dublin 24
tel 01 462 3033 *fax 01 462 3767*

Dublin South West Team
O'Connor, Ciara (spo)
Algottson, Gallagher, Anna
Cahill, Sharon
Charles, Anita
McMahon, Kathryn
O'Reilly, Dorothy
Ward, Liz (admin)

9. Foundation House
Northumberland Avenue

Dun Laoghaire Co. Dublin
tel 01 230 1860 *fax 01 230 1870*

Dublin South East Team
King, Jim (spo)
Kelly, Anthony
McCabe, Janice
McQuaid, Emily
O'Doherty, Ann
O'Neill, Martina
Needham, Mavis
Ryan, Mary
Reid, Vincent (admin)

Dublin North & North East Region

10. **Haymarket**
   Smithfield, Dublin 7
   tel 01 817 3600 *fax 01 872 2737*

   Dublin North Assessment Team
   Kenny, Dave (spo)
   Duffy, Paul
   Fogarty, Fliona
   Hynes, John Roderick
   McArdle, Rita
   Murphy, Claire
   Power, Linda
   Stapleton, Una
   Taylor, Scarlett

   Dublin West Team
   O'Sullivan, Cathal (spo)
   Hickey, Bernadette
   Murphy, Dave
   O'Connell, Valerie
   Odimuke, Victor
   Sharma, Champa

   *Intensive Probation Supervision
   (Bridge Project) Team*
   Horgan, Brian (spo)
   Anderson, Lisa
   Connell, Brian
   Croghan, Paul
   McGarrigle, Sarah
   Trant, Aidan

11. Second Floor Office Block
   Donaghmede Shopping Centre
   Grange Road **Donaghmede**
   Dublin 13
   tel 01 816 6800 *fax 01 816 6801*

   Regional Manager's Office
   Brian Santry (appo)
   Moore, Karen (admin)

   Dublin North East Team
   Leetch, Judith (spo)
   Campbell, Fiona

Corrigan, John
Cotter, Laura
Dooley, Niamh
Ferguson, Darren
O'Connor, Joan

12. Unit 3, Parnell Business Centre
   24 Parnell Street Dublin 1
   tel 01 814 6760 *fax 01 814 6762*

   Dublin North Inner City Team
   O'Sullivan, Mary (spo)
   Boyle, Olivia
   Loughrey, Sile
   McGuigan, Sarah
   Zagibova, Danica
   Jones, Steve
   Kelly, Sarah (admin)

13. Poppintree Mall
   Finglas Dublin 11
   tel 01 864 4011 *fax 01 864 3416*

   Dublin North Central Team
   Ansbro, Ann (spo)
   Adesida, Ademilole
   Claffey, Thomas
   Codd, Avril
   Doyle, Barbara
   O'Brien, Tim
   Stone, Clive
   Lawlor, Breda (eo)
   O'Grady, James (admin)

14a. St. Laurence's Street
   Drogheda Co. Louth
   tel 041 980 1580 *fax 041 980 1583*

14b. Government Offices
   Millenium Centre
   Alphonsus Road **Dundalk**
   Co. Louth
   tel 042 933 2163 *fax 042 933 2501*

   Louth Team
   McDonald, Mary (spo)
   Farry, Neasan
   Faulkner, Monica
   Murphy, Margaret
   Norton, Sheena
   Roche, Melanie
   Jordan, Ita (admin)
   McKeever, Sinead (admin)

15. Government Offices, Kilcairn
   Navan Co. Meath
   tel 046 909 0941 *fax 046 909 0142*

Meath Team
Quinn, Kerry (spo)
Brennan, Mary
Kearney, Ian
Ruane, Mary
Wason, Laura
McHugh, Martina (admin)

Prisons Region

16. **Haymarket**
Smithfield, Dublin 7
tel 01 817 3600 *fax 01 872 2737*

Sex Offender & High Risk Management Team
Reade, Ann (spo, risk mngmnt)
Bailey, Darragh
Broderick, Geraldine
Coffey, Aisling
Glynn, David
O'Dwyer, Geraldine

17. **Arbour Hill Prison**
Arbour Hill, Dublin 7
tel 01 671 9519 *fax 01 671 9565*

O'Sullivan, Donal (spo)
Clark, Nick
Dardis, Sandra
Finnegan, Sarah
McCarthy, Justin

18. **Wheatfield Place of Detention**
Cloverhill, Dublin 22
tel 01 620 9437 *fax 01 620 9457*

Downey, Pauline (spo)
Devine, Andrea
Kavanagh, Elaine
Kelly, Paula
Nichol, Derek
O'Neill, Jenny (admin)

19. **Shelton Abbey**
Arklow, Co. Wicklow
tel 0402 32912 *fax 0402 39924*

Alvey, Jan

20. **Mountjoy Prison (Male)**
North Circular Road, Dublin 7
tel 01 806 2834 *fax 01 830 2712*

Williamson, David (spo)
Clarke, Susan
Kane, Tara
O'Byrne, Ambrose
Lowde, Sean
Commins, Susan

O'Reilly Rachel (admin)

21. **Mountjoy Female Prison**
Dochas Centre, North Circular Road
Dublin 7
tel 01 806 2834 *fax 01 830 2712*

Skehan, Gerri (spo)
McCarthy, Liz
Morris, Aine
Mulpeter, Maria
Nemala, Raja

22. **Midlands Prison**
Dublin Road
Portlaoise, Co. Laois
tel 0502 72210 *fax 0502 72209*

Matthews, Deirdre (spo)
Farrell, Eileen
Hanlon, Joy
Heffernan-Price, Majella
Kavanagh, Jane Sarah
Carolan, Patricia
Delahunt, Claire (admin)

23. **Castlerea Prison**
Harristown, Castlerea
Co. Mayo
tel/fax 094 962 5277

Brett, Maeve (spo)
Caldwell, Katie
Connolly, Kieran
Quinlan, Judy

24. **Loughan House**
Blacklion, Co. Cavan
tel/fax 072 53026

Brett, Maeve (spo)
Fallon, Oliver

25. **Cork Prison**
Rathmore Road
Cork
tel 021 4503829 *fax 021 450 1702*

Coakley, Deirdre (spo)
O'Farrell, Tim
Carmody, Mairead
Murphy, Siobhan (admin)

26. **Limerick Prison**
Mulgrave Street
Limerick
tel 061 294718 *fax 061 419812*

Coakley, Deirdre (spo)
Condon, Joan

Young Persons' Probation Region

27. **Haymarket**
Smithfield, Dublin 7
tel 01 817 3600 *fax 01 872 2737*

    YPP Dublin Court Liason
    Brennan, Claire (spo)
    Bentley, Philip
    Kelly, Frankie
    Foley, Liz
    Hickey, Majella
    Kangley, Jacinta
    McCarroll, Jane

28. 390-396 Clonard Road,
Crumlin Dublin 12
tel 01 492 5625 *fax 01 492 5631*

    YPP Dublin South Team
    O'Donoghue, Liz (spo)
    Connor, Siobhan
    Egan, Amanda
    McLoughlin, Ruth
    O'Shea, Olivia
    Pickles, Rob

29. Main Street,
Ballymun Dublin 9
tel 01 842 1810

    YPP Dublin North Team
    McGagh, Mary (spo)
    Gunn, Emma
    Lillis, Rachel
    Martin, Catriona
    O'Toole, Ann-Marie
    Purcell, Denise
    Brady, Margaret (admin)

30a. St. Laurence's Street
Drogheda Co. Louth
tel 041 980 1580 *fax 041 980 1583*

30b. Government Offices
Millenium Centre
Alphonsus Road **Dundalk**
Co. Louth
tel 042 933 2163 *fax 042 933 2501*

    YPP North East Team
    Gibbons, Maria (spo)
    McCourt, Caroline
    McAloon, Eadaoin
    O'Malley, Rachel
    Jordan, Ita (admin)
    Walsh, Fionna (admin)

31. **St Patrick's Institution**
North Circular Road, Dublin 7

tel 01 806 2941 *fax 01 830 1261*
Cronin, Rosemary (spo)
Milne, Sarah
O'Brien, Maria
O'Halloran, Caoimhe
Kenny, Renee (admin)

32. Government Buildings
Cranmore Road **Sligo**
tel 071 914 5203 *fax 071 914 4840*

    YPP North West
    Mannion, John (spo)
    Keogh, Valerie
    Meehan, Eileen (admin)

33. Abbey Arch
8 Upper Abbeygate Street
Galway
tel 091 565375 *fax 091 567286*

    Halpin, Mary
    Myles, Bridget

34. 48-50 Lower Main Street
Letterkenny Co. Donegal
tel 074 912 5264 *fax 074 912 6008*

    Halligan, Colin

35. The Crescent, Ballymahon Road
Athlone Co. Westmeath
tel 090 648 3500 *fax 090 647 5843*

    Leonard, Sinead

36. 3 Catherine Street
Waterford
tel 051 872 548 *fax 051 878 238*

    YPP South East
    Goode, Mary (spo)
    Brooks, Veronica
    Fisher, Sean

37. Harbour House, The Quay
Clonmel Co. Tipperary
tel 052 23880 *fax 052 25874*
Costigan, Marita
O'Connor, Jacqueline

38. Government Buildings
Abbeyleix Road
Portlaoise Co. Laois
tel 057 862 2644 *fax 057 866 0218*
Kenny, David

39. Theatre Court
15 Lower Mallow Street
Limerick

tel 061 206 320 *fax 061 206 339*

YPP Limerick
Brosnahan, John (spo)
Kirwisa, Linda
McNulty, Brian
Murphy, Sean
O'Connor, Tracey
Moore, Michelle
Dwane, Mary (admin)
Minogue, Anne (admin)
Quigley, Gerard (admin)

40. St. Nicholas Church
     Cove Street **Cork**
     tel 021 483 6700 *fax 021 484 5146*

     YPP Cork
     Fox, Rosemary (spo)
     Buckley, Hilary
     Desmond, Tom
     Henley, Karen
     McCarthy, Ken
     O'Leary, Paula

     Cork Court Liaison
     Ahern, Maria
     Walsh, Mary

41. **Family Law**
     Haymarket Smithfield
     Dublin 7
     tel 01 817 3600 *fax 01 872 2737*

     Foley, Tony (spo)

West/North West & Westmeath Region

42. The Crescent, Ballymahon Road
     Athlone Co. Westmeath
     tel 090 648 3500 *fax 090 647 5843*

     Regional Manager's Office
     Doyle, Una (appo)
     Hannon, Clare (eo)

     Westmeath/Longford/
     Roscommon Team
     Gavin, Alma (spo)
     Byrne Fallon, Collette
     Gilmore, Irene
     Carney, Mary (admin)
     Ward, Enda (admin)

43. Mill House, Friar's Mill Road
     Mullingar Co. Westmeath
     tel 044 35666 *fax 044 35663*

     Westmeath/Longford/
     Roscommon Team
     Hartley, Moya
     Ryder, Tom

44. Abbey Arch
     8 Upper Abbeygate Street
     Galway
     tel 091 565 375 *fax 091 567 286*

     Prendergast, Margaret (spo)
     Brady, Brid
     Burke, Brigetta
     Devine, Corina
     Ganly, Sheila
     Halpin, Una
     Mitchell, Patrick
     Mulligan, Noirin
     Flanagan, Marian (admin)
     O'Grady, Marion (admin)

45. Government Buildings
     Cranmore Road **Sligo**
     tel 071 914 5203 *fax 071 914 4840*

     Sligo/Mayo Team
     Morrin, Helena (spo)
     Kelly, Tracey
     Leahy, Denise

46. 1st Floor, 3 Castle Street,
     Sligo
     tel 071 914 1616 *fax 071 914 9937*

     Operations Office
     Cooney, Paula (appo)
     Wasylocha, Klara (admin)

47. Unit 10 F, N 5 Business Retail Park
     Moneen **Castlebar** Co. Mayo
     tel 094 902 8404/5 *fax 094 9044218*

     Sligo/Mayo Team
     Morrin, Helena (spo)
     Sheppard, Sue
     Tallon, Miriam
     Duffy, Siobhan (admin)

48. 48-50 Lower Main Street
     Letterkenny Co. Donegal
     tel 074 912 5264 *fax 074 912 6008*

     Donegal Team
     Devine, Josephine (spo)
     Coughlan, Tim
     Duke, Anne
     Lennox, Yvonne
     McDermott, Michelle
     Connery, Ian (admin)

49. Unit 15, Churchview
     Cavan
     tel 049 432 7474 *fax 049 4327461*

Cavan/Monaghan/Leitrim Team
Donnelly, Carmel (spo)
Gervin, Alice
Murray, Aine
Reilly, Sinead
Noone, Catherine (admin)

Midlands & South East Region

50. Government Buildings
    Abbeyleix Road
    Portlaoise Co. Laois
    tel 057 862 2644 *fax 057 866 0218*

    Laois/Offally Team
    Brennan, Mary (spo)
    Cuddy, Pat
    Cummins, Mary
    Doyle, Alan
    Fahy, Caroline
    Scully, Agnes
    Walshe, Ann
    Mannion, Carmel (admin)

51. 3 Catherine Street
    Waterford
    tel 051 872 548 *fax 051 878 238*

    McCarthy, Vanessa (appo)
    Keen, Jane (spo)
    Bourke, Andrea
    Darnell, Rosemarie
    Kennedy, Sharon
    Leahy, Deirdre
    Fisher, Geraldine
    Murphy, Mary T.
    O'Brien, Thomas
    Mansfield, Patricia (admin)
    Tobin, Margaret (admin)

52. Government Buildings
    Anne Street **Wexford**
    tel 053 914 2076 *fax 053 912 3565*

    Weir, Michelle (spo)
    Corcoran, Anna Mai
    Duffy, Christine
    Gurrin, Catherine
    Halpenny, Seamus
    Lyons, Philip
    Long, Carol (admin)
    Waters-Kehoe, Margaret (admin)

53. Over Extra Vision
    Wexford Road,
    Arklow Co. Wicklow
    tel 0402 91 066 *fax 042 91 114*

    Cullen, Anne-Marie (admin)

54. Harbour House, The Quay
    Clonmel Co. Tipperary
    tel 052 23880 *fax 052 25874*

    Devereux, Della (spo)
    Aylward, Mary
    Cooney, John
    Gleeson, Carole
    Hughes, Ina
    Lynam, Elizabeth
    O'Dwyer, Niamh
    Lyons, Mandy (eo)
    Feighery, Shane (admin)

55. Quinn House
    Mill Lane **Carlow**
    tel 059 913 5186 *fax 059 913 5194*

    Kavanagh, Billy (spo)
    Brown, Carolyn
    Young, Dolores
    Macken, Lorna
    McGagh, Aisling (admin)

56. Government Offices
    Hebron Road, **Kilkenny**
    tel 056 776 5201 *fax 056 776 4156*
    Kavanagh, Billy (spo)
    Lacey, Joan
    Walsh, Geraldine
    O'Sullivan, Moyra (admin)

57. 82 Leinster St
    Athy Co. Kildare
    tel 059 863 3387

    Kildare Team
    Redmond, Helen spo
    Boyle, Jennifer
    Canty, Elaine
    Cowzer, Elaine
    Kelly, Lorraine

South West Region

58. St Nicholas Church
    Cove Street **Cork**
    tel 021 483 6700 *fax 021 484 5146*

    Regional Manager's Office
    Boyle, Terry (appo)
    O'Riordan, Jennifer (eo)
    Desmond, Maria (admin)
    O'Brien, Margaret (admin)
    Barry, Kenneth (admin)
    Keohane, Peter (admin)
    Berkery, Madeline (admin)

    Assessment Team
    O'Connell, Sinead (spo)

Coveney, Eugene
Gallahue, Liz
Lynch, Dympna
Moriarty, Theresa
Walsh, Bernie

South Cork Community Supervision
Coughlan, Tony (spo)
Busteed, Eleanor
Casey, Sue
Kelleher, Roseanne
McAuley, Robert
Moylan, Breda
Steffans, Ton

North Cork Communty Supervision
Corcoran, John (spo)
Campbell, Susan
Kemp, Wyndham
O'Brien, Joe
O'Connell, Sinead S.
O'Sullivan, Tracey

59. Ashe Street,
Tralee Co. Kerry
tel 066 712 2666 *fax 066 712 1764*

Kerry/South Limerick
Norma Keane (spo)
Brassil, Nora
Hickey, Patrick
Holly Eileen
Keane, Siobhan
O'Donnell Helena
O'Connor, Hannah (admin)

60. Theatre Court
15 Lower Mallow Street
Limerick
tel 061 206 320 *fax 061 206 339*

Limerick City Supervision
Coughlan, Hedvig (spo)
Cahill, Frank
Ryan, Cathy
Tierney, Catherine

Assessment
Kelly, Janice (spo)
Griffin, Gerry
King, Mary
McLoughney, Caroline
Mohan, Sadie
Purcell, Patricia

Intensive Probn & Offending Behaviour
Griffin, Margaret (spo)

CHANNEL ISLANDS, ISLE OF MAN, AND THE COURTS-MARTIAL REPORT SERVICE

The Channel Islands and the Isle of Man are separate jurisdictions. Community Orders are not formally transferable to or from them. Special procedures exist for the transfer of post custodial Licences. Contact should be made with the relevant Service before any offender moves to the Channel Islands or the Isle of Man.

GUERNSEY PROBATION SERVICE

The Market Building, Fountain Street
St Peter Port, Guernsey GY1 1BX
tel (01481) 724337 *fax (01481) 710545*
e-mail probation@gov.gg

Guilbert, Anna (cpo)
Harvey, Greg (snr pract)
Crisp, Stuart (snr pract)
Tardif, Kerry (prison)
Clark, Kate
Guilbert, Sarah
Greening, Gemma
Murphy, Cathy
Ozanne, Carol
Richmond, Issy
Speers, David
Sullivan, Mark (trainee)
Hill-Tout, Laurence (cso)
Ogier, Gill (cj drug wrkr)
Lowe, Vanessa (admin mgr)

Victim enquiries to Anna Guilbert (cpo)

ISLE OF MAN PROBATION SERVICE

2nd/3rd Floors, Prospect House
27-29 Prospect Hill
Douglas, Isle of Man IM1 1ET
Tel (01624) 687323/24 *fax (01624) 687333*

Sellick, David B L (cpo)
Devereau, Anne (pa to cpo)
Ingram, Pat (deputy) (dir of operations)
Callow, Andrea (pa to dir of ops)
Quayle, Eddie (admin)
Dooley, Anne (admin)
Christian, Louise (secy)
Britain-Jones, Elizabeth (secy)

Erani, Hilary
Ledger, Ian
Robertson, John
Stott, Elaine
Wheeler, Mark

Wildman, Frank (drug & alc team) 617889

Gilbert, Marilyn (family crt welfare)
Strickland, Briana (family crt welfare)

Morphet , Kirstie (youth justice) 687572

Cubbon, Dawn (pso)
Dunne, Tim (pso)
Watts, Lynda (cso)

Bass, John (prison) 01624 891008
Hunter, Gillian (prison) 01624 891006

JERSEY PROBATION SERVICE

PO Box 656, 1 Lempriere Street
St Helier JE4 8YT
tel (01534) 441900 *fax (01534) 441944*
e-mail initial.surname@gov.je
www.gov.je

Heath, Brian (cpo)
Cutland, Michael (acpo)
Cooley, Jenny (office mgr)
Miles, Dr Helen (p, research & info mgr)
Trott, David (team ldr)
Austin, Natalie (js)
Brown, Susan (js)
Carré, Marilyn (marilyn.carre@gov.je)
Ferguson, Jane (js)
Ibbotson, David
Langford, Chris
Lister, Lisa (js)
Luce, Emma
Ormesher, Adelaide
Pike, Chay
Saralis, Mark (crt liaison/subst misuse)
Taylor, Robert
Urquhart, Janette
Whittaker, Jane

Christmas, Jane (p,psa)
Vacancy (p, psa)
Machon, Barbara (psa) (trainee po)
Rose, Chantelle (p, psa restorative justice)

Castledine, Alisha (p, case
mgmnt asst) (trainee po)
Child-Villiers, Norah (case mgmnt asst)
Gosselin, Gillian (p, case mgmnt asst)
Soley, Tina (case mgmnt asst)
Wakeham, Maura (case mgmnt asst)

Banks, Shaun (p, cs mgr)
Allix, Nicky (p, asst cso)
Le Marrec, Andy (asst cso)
De Abreu, Rui (p, cs supvr)
Hague, Philip (p, cs supvr)
Irwin, Marcus (p, cs supvr)
Langlois, Kerrie (p, cs supvr)
Lennane, John (p, cs supvr)

Najib, Ghazi (p, cs supvr)
Syvret, Jason (p, cs supvr)

THE COURTS-MARTIAL REPORT SERVICE
formerly known as the Army Probation Service

Courts-Martial Report Service (CMRS)
Building 183, Room 3
Trenchard Lines, Upavon, Pewsey
Wilts SN9 6BE
tel (01980) 618050/618101/618065
fax (01980) 618048

Carruthers, George (mgr)
Vacancy (office mgr)
Hogan, Sarah (admin officer)
Dyke, Carole (admin officer)

CMRS Germany Office
Direct dial from UK (use mobile numbers below)
fax (contact staff below for details)

Hurley, Michael (po) 0049 1734 425049
(mobile)
Varty, Jan (po) 0049 1768 5060 132
(mobile)

In Germany CMRS have responsibility for the following:
* representing NPS in the British Forces Germany community
* supervision of Court Orders imposed on civilian employees working for the army and their dependants
* supervision of Community Orders imposed by UK civilian courts on soldiers based overseas

SCOTLAND

DIRECTORATE FOR CRIMINAL JUSTICE

Community Justice Services Division
Room GW-07, St Andrew's House, Regent
Road, Edinburgh EH1 3DG
tel 0131-244 5454 *fax 0131-244 3548*
e-mail Firstname.Surname@scotland.gsi.gov.uk

**Depute Director for Community Justice
Services**
Policy lead on community sentences and
supervision, framework for delivery of criminal
justice social work services and electronic
monitoring.

Depute Director Wilma Dickson
PS Fiona Cowan

COMMUNITY JUSTICE AUTHORITIES

The Management of Offenders etc
(Scotland) Act 2005 established eight local
Community Justice Authorities (CJAs)
in Scotland to provide a co-ordinated
approach to planning and monitoring the
delivery of offender services by planning,
managing performance and reporting on
the performance of offender management
services. The aim of these partnership
arrangements is to target services to
reduce re-offending and to ensure close
co-operation between community based
services and the Scottish Prison Service,
and the voluntary sector.

Each CJA consists of elected members of
local authorities. The CJA is supported by
the Chief Officer and support staff. CJAs
have been fully operational from April
2007.

Central Support Manager
CJANAT@glasgow.gov.uk
Based in Glasgow CJA Office

1.   **Fife & Forth Valley Community
Justice Authority**
Kilncraigs Business Centre
Greenside Street, Alloa FK10 1EB
tel 01259 727 434

*local authorities: Fife, Clackmannanshire,
Falkirk, Stirling*

2.   **Glasgow Community Justice Authority**
4th Floor, Westergate
Glasgow G2 6AB
tel 0141 287 0916

local authority: Glasgow

3.   **Lanarkshire Community Justice
Authority**
Council Offices
Floor 2
Beckford Street
Hamilton ML3 0AA
tel 01698 454234

*local authorities: North & South
Lanarkshire*

4.   **Lothian & Borders Community
Justice Authority**
Scottish Borders Council Area Office
Rosetta Road
Peebles EH45 8HL
tel 01721 726314

*local authorities: Edinburgh, East Lothian,
West Lothian, Midlothian, Scottish Borders*

5.   **North Strathclyde Community
Justice Authority**
Room 1.5, North Building
Cotton Street
Paisley PA1 1TZ
tel 0141 840 3237

*local authorities: Argyll and Bute,
East Dunbartonshire, West Dunbartonshire,
East Renfrewshire, Renfrewshire, Inverclyde*

6.   **Northern Community Justice
Authority**
Woodhill House Annexe
Westburn Road
Aberdeen AB16 5GJ
tel 01224 665780

*local authorities: Aberdeenshire, Aberdeen
City, Moray, Highland, Orkney, Shetland,
Eilean Siar*

7.   **South West Scotland Community
Justice Authority**
Suite 6, Sovereign House
Academy Road, Irvine KA12 8RL
tel 01294 277 968

local authorities: East, North & South Ayrshire, Dumfries & Galloway

8. **Tayside Community Justice Authority**
    7th Floor, City House, Overgate
    Dundee DD1 1UH
    tel 01382 435394

    local authorities: Angus, Dundee, Perth & Kinross

SOCIAL WORK INSPECTION AGENCY: CRIMINAL JUSTICE TEAM

Ladywell House, Ladywell Road, Corstorphine EH12 7TF

The Social Work Inspection Agency undertakes the following functions:
Inspection, review and reporting across social work and social care services.
Sectoral and aspect evaluations of social work and social care services.
Commissions from the Scottish Ministers, relevant Departments of the Scottish Executive and other bodies.
Provision of professional advice to Scottish Ministers and others.

Depute Chief Inspector
Gill Ottley   0131-244 3603
Gill.ottley@swia.gsi.gov.uk

Personal Secretary
Dylais Mattison   0131-244 5340

Inspectors

John Waterhouse   0131-244 5449
john.waterhouse@ swia.gsi.gov.uk

Irene Scullion   0141 249 6831
Irene.scullion@ swia.gsi.gov.uk

Clare Wilson   0141 249 6835
Clare.wilson@swia.gsi.gov.uk

Gerry Hart
0141 249 6863
Gerry.hart@swia.gsi.gov.uk

Audrey Mistry
0131 244 3529
Audrey.mistry@swia.gsi.gov.uk

David Rowbotham   0131 244 5091
David.rowbotham@swia.gsi.gov.uk

Katie Lamb   0141 249 6834
Katie.lamb@swia.gsi.gov.uk

Willie Paxton   0131 249 5494
Willie.paxton@swia.gsi.gov.uk

Paolo Mazzoncini   0141-249-6798
Paolo.mazzoncini@swia.gsi.gov.uk

PAROLE AND LIFE SENTENCE REVIEW DIVISION

2nd Floor Rear, St Andrew's House, Regent Road, Edinburgh EH1 3DG
0131-244 8524/8530 *fax 0131-244 8794*

Functions Administration of the release and sentence management of offenders under the Prisoners and Criminal Proceedings (Scotland) Act 1993. Sentence management policy. Managing children sentenced to custody under the Criminal Procedure (Scotland) Act 1995. Sponsorship of the Parole Board for Scotland and the Risk Management Authority. Prisons Commission Secretariat. There are three casework teams and a policy team.

Casework teams deal with the release, supervision and recall of life, determinate and extended sentence prisoners: set licence conditions for short-term (sentences of 6 months to under 4 years) sex offenders; present Scottish Ministers' views at Tribunals on suitability for release on licence of life sentence prisoners and recalled extended sentence prisoners. Work distributed on an alphabetical basis.

Prisoners' surnames A-Ge and Sentenced Children
0131 244 8547
Prisoners' surnames Gf-Mac/Mc
0131 244 8530
Prisoners' surnames M-Z
0131 244 5744

PAROLE BOARD FOR SCOTLAND

Saughton House, Broomhouse Drive, Edinburgh EH11 3XD
general enquiries 0131-244 8373 *fax 0131-244 6974*

Professor Sandy Cameron (chair of the board)

Carolyn Girvan (head of parole brd executive)
e-mail carolyn.girvan@scotland.gsi.gov.uk
tel 0131-244 3404

Janet Sneddon (head of casework)
e-mail janet.sneddon@scotland.gsi.gov.uk
tel 0131-244 8755

Lesley Macaulay (head of policy)
e-mail lesley.macaulay@scotland.gsi.gov.uk
tel 0131 244-1409

ABERDEEN CITY COUNCIL

Emergency out of hours contact point
(01224) 693936

e-mail oohs@socialwork.aberdeen.net.uk

Central Services

1. St Nicholas House
    Broad Street **Aberdeen** AB10 1BY
    tel (01224) 522110 *fax (01224) 523195*

    Power, Sandra (chief social work officer)
    e-mail spowerh@aberdeencity.gov.uk

1a. St Nicholas House
    Broad Street Aberdeen AB10 1BY
    tel (01224) 522457 *fax (01224) 522605*

    Taylor, Liz (hd of service (health & care)
    neighbourhood services (central)
    e-mail LiTaylor@aberdeencity.gov.uk

1b. Neighbourhood Services (Central)
    Criminal Justice Social Work
    Exchequer House, 3 Exchequer Row
    Aberdeen AB11 5BW
    tel (01224) 765000 *fax (01224) 576109*

    Simpson, Lesley (team mgr cj)
    e-mail lsimpson@aberdeencity.gov.uk

    Simpson, Mark (risk mgmnt co-ord)
    e-mail masimpson@aberdeencity.gov.uk

    Balme, Jane (research/info officer)
    e-mail jbalme@aberdeencity.gov.uk

Specialist Criminal Justice Teams

2. Exchequer House, 3 Exchequer Row
    Aberdeen AB11 2BW
    tel (01224) 765000 *fax (01224) 576109*

    ### Team 1
    (level 1 probn, crt services, sao, diversion)
    John Connon (ssw)
    Trew, Carrie (ssw)
    Brady, Ruth (sw)
    Delaney, Elaine (p, sw)
    Fogg, Noreen (sw)

Fullerton, Mick (sw)
Henderson, Norma (p, sw)
Lorimer, Leanne (sw)
McAllister, Anne (p, sw)
McCubbin, Lyn (sw)
MacKenzie, Angela (sw)
Plumbridge, Brenda (sw)
Rutherford, Jean (p, sw)
Sandison, Steve (sw)
Smith, Edwina (p, sw)
Whyte, Claire (sw)
Wilkie-Clark, Pam (sw)
Mearns, Kathleen (p, sao)
Rennie, Margaret (p, sao)

Team 2
(level 2 & 3 probn)
Rennie, Kate (ssw)
Buchanan, Neil (ssw)
Ashwood, Tina (sw)
Cameron, Claire (sw)
Edgar, Jackie (sw)
Fyffe, Karaina (p, sw)
Goodman, Kerry (sw)
Logan, Alistair (sw)
McCloy, Marion (sw)
Michel-Stephen, Tina (sw)
Roach, Philip (sw)
Robertson, Sam (sw)
Sellens, Diane (sw)
Wallace, Iona (sw)
Wilson, Claire (sw)

Team 3
(throughcare)
Youngson, Nicola (ssw)
Aitken, Adelle (sw)
Douglas, Julie (sw)
Forbes, Lora (sw)
Gillan, Gillian (sw)
McKerron, Gayle (sw)
McLean, Rachel (p, sw)
MacPherson, Zara (sw)
Robertson, Marianne (sw)

Campbell, Karen (comm supt wrkr)
Fraser, Caroline (comm supt wrkr)
Gaunt, Paul (comm supt wrkr)

3. **Drug Treatment & Testing Orders**
    137 Gallowgate, Aberdeen AB25 5BU
    tel (01224) 267100 *fax (01224) 645473*

    Murray, Lorna (team ldr)
    Halford, Vina (sw)
    McLachlan, Louise (sw)
    Ure, Amanda (sw)
    Donald, Abbey (subst misuse nurse)
    Vacancy (subst misuse nurse)

Russell, Ann (subst misuse nurse)
Edwards, Stacy (subst misuse wrkr)
Watt, Gillian (subst misuse wrkr)
Vacancy (subst misuse wrkr)
Mitchell, Janice (mandatory drug testing)
Tarkenter, Audrey (mandatory drug testing)
Shirran, Jackie (arrest referral wrkr)
Vacancy (arrest referral wrkr)

Community Service

4. 11 Willowdale Place
    Aberdeen AB24 3AQ
    tel (01224) 624317 *fax (01224) 626544*

    Community Service Resource Team
    Thain, Martin (acting team leader)
    Paterson, Neil (projects officer)
    Cormack, Emma (order supving off)
    Finnie, Pamela (order supving off)
    Freeman, Derek (order supving off)
    McWilliam, Shona (order supving off)
    Murdoch, Colin (order supving off)
    Riches, Carson (order supving off)
    Peacock, Carol (personal placement off)

Probation Hostel

5. **St Fitticks House**
    36 Crombie Road, Torry
    Aberdeen AB1 3QQ
    tel (01224) 877910 *fax (01224) 894303*

    (males & females aged 18+)
    Dawson, Gary (unit mgr)

Penal Establishment

6. Social Work Unit
    HM Prison, Craiginches
    Aberdeen AB9 2HN
    tel (01224) 238315 *fax (01224) 238343*

    Williamson, Sheena (ssw)
    Bruce, Lauren (sw)
    Hendry, Christine (sw)

Health Services

7. Social Work Department
    Royal Cornhill Hospital
    Cornhill Road, Aberdeen AB9 2ZH
    tel (01224) 557734/557781 *fax (01224) 557730*

Independent Sector

8. **APEX Scotland**
    1st floor, 48a Union Street
    Aberdeen AB10 1BB

    tel (01224) 611875 *fax (01224) 611890*

    supervised attendance orders, employment
    Crawford, Susan (unit mgr)

8a. **Victim Support (Scotland)**
    32 Upperkirkgate
    Aberdeen AB10 1BA
    tel (01224) 622478 *fax (01224) 625439*

    Bell, George (area co-ord)
    Scott, Mary (co-ord)

8b. **SACRO**
    110 Crown Street, Aberdeen AB11 6HJ
    tel (01224) 560550

    Proe, Mike (snr mgr ops North)
    Fakhet, Claire (cj mgr)

Courts

Aberdeen High Court
Aberdeen Sheriff and Justice of the Peace Court

ABERDEENSHIRE COUNCIL

1. Carlton House
    Arduthie Road
    Stonehaven AB39 2DL
    tel (01569) 768447 *fax (01569) 768450*

    Booth, Chris (director of child care & cj)

2. 53 Windmill Street
    Peterhead AB42 1UE
    tel (01779) 477333 *fax (01779) 474961*

    Watson, Sheena (acting sw mgr for cj)
    Witts, David (info & research officer)

3. **Joint Sex Offender Project**
    88 King Street
    Peterhead AB42 1HH
    tel (01779) 499950 *fax (01779) 474961*

    Innes, Corinne (acting team mgr)
    Delaney, Elaine (sw)
    Herd, Lindsey (sw)
    Selkirk, Deirdre (sw)
    Stoddart, Fiona (sw)
    McWilliam, Dianne (p, sw)
    Vacancy (sw)
    Vacancy (sw)
    Mackland, Fiona (project wrkr)
    Stuart, Gayna (project wrkr)
    Linton, Philippa (p, project wrkr)
    Rowland, Lynn (admin)

4. **Addictions Team**
88 King Street
Peterhead AB42 1UH
tel (01779) 499950 *fax (01779) 476435*

Dickson, Stewart (team mgr)
Ackroyd, Kim (ssw)
Gibson, Neil (sw)
Goodman, Theresa (sw)
Jamieson, Sean (sw)
MacDonald, Kathy (sw)
Ogilvie, Claire (sw)
Black, Carol-Ann (th'care support, North)
Staines, Anne (th'care support, South)
Vacancy (support wrkr)
Vacancy (support wrkr)
Rowland, Lynn (admin)

5. **Community Service**
P.O. Box 42
56 Cameron Street
Stonehaven AB39 2HE
tel (01569) 767553 *fax (01569) 767906*

Westland, Fiona (ssw)
Christie, Gillian (proj off, South)
Birse, Kim (admin)

14 Saltoun Square
Fraserburgh AB43 9DA
tel (01346) 513281 *fax (01346) 516885*

Clark, John (proj off, North)

6. **Supervised Attendance Orders**
53 Windmill Street
Peterhead AB42 1UE
tel (01779) 477333 *fax (01779) 474961*

Black, Celia (proj off)
Keith, May (admin)

7. **Voluntary Throughcare**
53 Windmill Street
Peterhead AB42 1UE
tel (01779) 477333 *fax (01779) 474961*

Vacancy (support wrkr)

Aberdeenshire North Team

8. 88 King Street
Peterhead AB42 1UH
tel (01779) 499950 *fax (01779) 476435*

Leslie, Dawn (team mgr)
Rowland, Lynn (admin)

9. 53 Windmill Street
Peterhead AB42 1UE
tel (01779) 477333 *fax (01779) 474961*

Black, Celia (sw)
Hamilton, John (sw)
Lauder, Wullie (p, sw)
Richardson, Deborah (p, sw)
Dowding, Margaret (admin)

10. Winston House
39 Castle Street
Banff AB45 1FQ
tel (01261) 812001 *fax (01261) 813474*

Mason, Barbara (sw)
Richardson, Deborah (p, sw)
Vacant (admin)

11. 14 Saltoun Square
Fraserburgh AB43 9DA
tel (01346) 513281 *fax (01346) 516885*

Henderson, Angie (sw)
Lauder, Wullie (p, sw)
Smith, Sarah (sw)
Walsh, Joe (sw)
Thores, Sheila (admin)

Aberdeenshire South Team

12. P.O. Box 42
56 Cameron Street
Stonehaven AB39 2HE
tel (01569) 767553 *fax (01569) 767906*

Westland, Fiona (team mgr)
Bartram, Christine (sw)
Rhodes, Jayne (sw)
Birse, Kim (admin)
Vacant (p, admin)

13. 25 Station Road
Ellon AB41 9AE
tel (01358) 720033 *fax (01358) 723639*

Wilson, Susan (p, sw)

14. 93 High Street
Inverurie AB51 3AB
tel (01467) 625555 *fax (01467) 625010*

Clark, Michele (sw)
Donnelly, Fidelma (p, sw)
Rhodes, Susan (p, sw)
Wilson, Susan (p, sw)
Hay, Lorna (admin)

15. 25 Gordon Street
Huntly AB54 8AL
tel (01466) 794488 *fax (01466) 794624*

Donnelly, Fidelma (p, sw)

Penal Establishment

16. Social Work Unit
HMP Prison, Invernettie
Peterhead AB42 2YY
tel (01779) 485086 *fax (01779) 471269*

Gibson, Eileen (team mgr)
Christie, Norma (sw)
Horan, Teresa (sw)
Millar, Nanette (sw)
Magill, Sach (sw)
Sutherland, Scott (sw)
Wallace, Chrissie (sw)
Vacancy (sw)
Guild, Joan (admin)

Courts

Banff Sheriff Court (01261) 812140
Peterhead Sheriff Court (01779) 476676
Stonehaven Sheriff Court (01569) 762758
Banff JP Court (01261) 812140
Peterhead JP Court (01779) 476676
Stonehaven JP Court (01569) 762758

ANGUS COUNCIL

Emergency out of hours contact point
(01382) 436430

e-mail surname and initial of forename@angus.
gov.uk

1. Social Work and Health
St Margaret's House, Orchard Loan
Orchardbank Business Park
Forfar Angus DD8 1WS
tel (01307) 461460 *fax (01307) 474899*

Peat, Robert (director of social work
& health)

1a. Social Work and Health
Ravenswood, New Road
Forfar Angus DD8 2AF
tel (01307) 462405 *fax (01307) 461261*

McIntosh, Gordon (snr mgr,
children's services & criminal justice
services)

2. Criminal Justice Services
9 Fergus Square **Arbroath** DD11 3DG
tel (01241) 871161 *fax (01241) 431898*

Townsend, Isobel (service mgr)
Fyfe, John (ssw)
Herbertson, Sylvia (ssw)
Lorimer, Vicki (ssw)
Cavill, Steve (research & info officer)

Beierlein, Jackie (sw)
Calvert, Elizabeth (sw)
Cashley, Kathryn (sw)
DeVries, Linzi (sw)
Hendry, Alison (sw)
Jenkins, Wendy (sw)
McIntyre, Becky (sw)
Pert, Angie (sw)
Richardson, Aileen (sw)
Smith, Colin (sw)
Wilson, Lesley (sw)
Catherall, Philip (cso)
Bancroft, Paul (cja)
Coutts, Bruce (cja)
Daly, Mark (cja)
Ness, Maureen (cja)
Reilly, Bernadette (cja)
Richards, Lynn (cja)
Smith, Lynn (cja)
Dickson, Fiona (admin asst)

Courts

Arbroath Sheriff Court
Forfar Sheriff Court
Angus District Court at Arbroath
Angus District Court at Forfar

ARGYLL & BUTE COUNCIL

*Part of Argyll, Bute & Dunbartonshire's Criminal
Justice Social Work Partnership*

e-mail firstname.surname@argyll-bute.gov.uk

Secure e-mail firstname.surname@argyll-
bute.gsx.gov.uk

1. **Criminal Justice Services
(Headquarters)**
Argyll & Bute Council
Dalriada House, Lochnell Street
Lochgilphead PA31 8ST
tel (01546) 604580 *fax (01546) 604588*
direct dial (01546) + number

Belton, Jon (cj services mgr) 604567
Green, Kirsteen (planning & eval off)
604583

**Criminal Justice Services (Mid-Argyll
Area)**
Nail, Steve (team ldr, Kintyre, Mid-Argyll,
Lorn) 604580
Unsworth, Jayne (sw) 604580
For CS, see Kintyre entry (5)
Vacancy (employment support worker)
604580

Throughcare/High Risk Offenders
(all of Argyll & Bute)
Smith, Nancy (sw) 604580
Unsworth, Jayne (sw) 604580

2. **Criminal Justice Services
(Cowal Area)**
16 Church Street
Dunoon PA23 8BG
tel (01369) 707829 *fax (01369) 703641*
direct dial (01329) + number

Kelsall, Pat (team ldr, Cowal & Bute)
700616
Brown, Rita (sw) 700613
Cameron, Liz (sw) 700615
MacNiven, Kathrine (cs Cowal & Bute)
700612

3. **Criminal Justice Services
(Isle of Bute)**
35 Union Streeet
Rothesay, Island of Bute PA20 0HD
tel (01700) 501300 *fax (01700) 505408*

all CJ Services for the Island of Bute
Sillars, Brigid (sw) 501300
For CS, see Cowal entry (2)

4. **Criminal Justice Services (Lorn Area
Isles of Mull, Colonsay, Coll & Tiree)**
Soroba Road **Oban** PA34 4JA
tel (01631) 572955/563068 *fax (01631)
566724*
direct dial (01631) + number

Gordon, Rosalind (sw) 572934
MacLeod, Susan (sw) 572954
Anderton, Ann (cj asst & cs) 572937

5. **Criminal Justice Services (Kintyre,
Isles of Gigha, Islay & Jura)**
Old Quay Head **Campbeltown** PA28 6ED
tel (01586) 559068 *fax (01586) 554912*
direct dial (01586) + number

Gray, Ruth (sw) 559081
Anderson, Jillian (cj asst & cs, Kintyre &
Mid Argyll) 559082

6. **Criminal Justice Services
(Helensburgh
& Lomond)**
West Dumbarton Council
Municipal Buildings, Station Road
Dumbarton G82 1QA
tel (01389) 738484 *fax (01389) 738480*
direct dial (01389) + number

Stevens, Craig (ssw assessment team)
738471
Daddy, Phil (ssw supvn team) 738497
Pryce, Ruth (cs mgr) 738385

Courts

*Court social work services run by local CJ
team*

Campbeltown Sheriff Court
Castlehill, Campbeltown PA28 6AN
tel (01586) *fax (01586) 554967*

Dunoon Sheriff Court
George Street, Dunoon PA23 8BQ
tel (01369) 704166 *fax (01369) 702191*

Oban Sheriff Court
Albany Street, Oban PA34 4AL
tel (01631) 562414 *fax (01631) 562037*

Rothesay Sheriff Court
Eaglesham House, Mountpleasant Road
Rothesay, Isle of Bute PA20 9HQ
tel (01700) 502982 *fax (01700) 504112*

Argyll & Bute District Court at Bowmore
Argyll & Bute District Court at
Campbeltown
Argyll & Bute District Court at Dunoon
Argyll & Bute District Court at
Lochgilphead
Argyll & Bute District Court at Oban
Argyll & Bute District Court at Rothesay

CLACKMANNANSHIRE COUNCIL

1. Services to People - Social Services
Lime Tree House, Castle Street
Alloa FK10 1EX
tel (01259) 452371 *fax (01259) 452400*

Cilliers, Deirdre (hd of social services &
cwso)
McHale, Eileen (secy)

2. A.L.L.O.A. Centre
8 Hillcrest Drive, **Alloa** FK10 1SB
tel (01259) 721069 *fax (01259) 723998*

Shovlin, Ian (service mgr, c.j. services)
ishovlin@clacks.gov.uk

Criminal Justice Team
Buchanan, June (team mgr)
jbuchanan2@clacks.gov.uk

Elflain, Lynne (ssw)
Miller, Anne (ssw)

Bagley, Elizabeth (sw)
Conoboy, Catherine (p, sw)
Craig Alison (sw)
Duncan, Shona (p/t sw)
Vacancy (sw)
McCourt, Michele (sw)
McGibbon, Mandy (sw)
McVeigh, Janet (p, sw)
Paterson, Caroline (sw)
Rennie, Tom (sw asst)
Vacancy (sw asst)

Community Service Team
Binnie, Chris (cs officer)
Drysdale, Ken (wk supvr)
Lennon, Cheryl (wk supvr)
Lumsden, Irene (p, wk supvr)

Admin
Coyle, Tricia
Lambert, Jeni
McDougall, Marilyn
Williamson, Julie

3. Social Work Unit
HM Prison & YOI **Glenochil**
King O'Muirs Road
Tullibody FK10 3AD
phone & fax (01259) 767315

Banyard, Libby (team mgr)
Libby.Banyard@sps.gov.uk
Bond, Michael (sw)
Brown, Caroline (sw)
Collin, Eleanor (sw)
Couldridge, Amanda (sw)
Vacancy (sw)
Gray, Dawn (sw)
Stewart, Karen (sw)

Admin
Fox, Susan
Thomson, Diana

Courts

Alloa Sheriff Court
Clackmannanshire District Court at Alloa

COMHAIRLE NAN EILEAN SIAR WESTERN ISLES COUNCIL

Out of hours contact: (01851) 701702

e-mail imacaulay@cne-siar.gov.uk
margaret.macleod@cne-siar.gov.uk

1. Criminal Justice Service
Social and Community Services Dept
Council Offices
Sandwick Road **Stornoway**
Isle of Lewis HS1 2BW
tel (01851) 703773 *fax (01851) 709532*

Macaulay, Iain (depute director of sw)
Macleod, Margaret (cj services mgr)
Fletcher, Reg (cj sw)
MacDonald, Maggie (cj sw)
Murray, Donald (cj sw)

Courts

Lochmaddy Sheriff Court
Stornoway Sheriff Court
Western Isles District Court at Stornoway

DUMFRIES & GALLOWAY COUNCIL

Out of hours contact no 030 33 33 3000

e mail AllanMo@dumgal.gov.uk

1. Education and Community Services
Woodbank, Edinburgh Road
Dumfries DG1 1NW
tel (01387) 260417 *fax (01387) 260453*

Smith, B (group mgr-children's services)

2 Criminal Justice Social Work
39 Lewis Street
Stranraer DG9 7AD
(01776) 706167 *fax (01776) 706884*

Monteforte, A (operations mgr, cj social work)

Criminal Justice Social Work East

3. 79 Buccleuch Street
Dumfries DG1 2AB
tel (01387) 262409 *fax (01387) 267964*

Glynn, J (team mgr)
McNish, G (acting business info officer)
Beattie, D (prison liaison officer)
Fortune, P (sw asst)
Dudgeon, W (sw asst throughcare)

Smeaton, E (cso)
Mulholland, R (cso)
Moffat, G (cso)
Herd, L (snr clerical asst)
Pagan, G (snr clerical asst)
McDowell, C (snr clerical asst)
Kirk, A (modern apprentice)

4. 52A/B Buccleuch Street
Dumfries DG1 2AP
Please send all mail to office 3
tel (01387) 262409 *fax (01387) 262431*

Monteforte, A (operations mgr, cj)
Kerr, A (admin mgr)
Sturgeon, J (team mgr-east)
Davies, R (team mgr-dtto)
Knipe, C (snr sw)
Fitzpatrick, E (sw dtto)
Henderson, A (sw dtto)
MacDonald, C (sw student dtto)
Hall, J (sw throughcare)
Thinsmith G (sw prog delivery)
Wells, D (swa prog delivery)
Baillie, A (sw)
Jamieson K (sw)
McCarron, A (sw)
McMeikan, E (sw)
McNaught, A (sw)
Muir, T (sw)
O'Sullivan, A (sw)
Turnbull, S (sw)
Wilson, I (sw)
Wuerffel, V (sw)
Peacock, J (swa)
Brown, J (snr clerical asst)
Shannan, C (snr clerical asst)
Sturgeon, L (snr clerical asst)

5. Community Service
8 King Street
Dumfries DG2 9AN
tel (01387) 248495 *fax (01387) 248495*

operational depot only

East - Annandale & Eskdale Area

6. 2 Bank Street
Annan DG12 6AA
tel (01461) 203411 *fax (01461) 205964*

Hall, J (sw throughcare) (based at 4)
Mackay, F (sw)
Race, H (sw)
Mulholland, R (cso) (based at 3)

Stewartry/Throughcare

7. Daar Rd, **Kirkcudbright** DG6 4JG
tel (01557) 330291 *fax (01557) 332537*

McKenzie, R (team mgr-throughcare)
Blackwell, L (sw)
Lindsay, A (sw)
Hamilton, B (cso)
Ferries, A (snr clerical asst)

West

8. 39 Lewis Street
Stranraer DG9 7AD
tel (01776) 706167 *fax (01776) 706884*

McCallum, A (team mgr)
Stead, J (acting ssw)
Walsh, P (sw-dtto)
Guest, G (sw)
Hollis, K (sw)
Beagrie, S (swa)
Carnochan, C (swa prog delivery)
McDevitt, P (swa)
Findlay-Dean, R (prison liaison officer)
Milligan, A (snr clerical asst)
Loudon Hughes, M (snr clerical asst)

9. Penninghame Centre
Auchendoon Road
Newton Stewart DG8 6HD
tel (01671) 403933 *fax (01671) 403017*

contact office 8

Penal Establishment

10. HM Prison **Dumfries**
Terregles Street, Dumfries DG2 9AX
tel (01387) 261218 *fax (01387) 264144*

McKenzie, R (team mgr) (based at 8)
Farrier, J (sw)
Sinclair, J (sw)
Radcliffe, S (sw)
McCall, S (snr clerical asst)

Courts

Dumfries Sheriff Court
Kirkcudbright Sheriff Court
Stranraer Sheriff Court
Dumfries & Galloway District Court at
Annan
Dumfries & Galloway District Court at
Dumfries
Dumfries & Galloway District Court at
Lockerbie
Dumfries & Galloway District Court at
Stranraer

DUNDEE CITY COUNCIL

Out of hours contact no: (01382) 436430
fax (01382) 436435

1 Friarfield House, Barrack Street
Dundee DD1 1PQ
tel (01382) 435001 *fax (01382) 435032*
direct dial (01382) 43 + ext

Jane, Martin (hd of cj service) ext 5017
Adam, Lorraine (secy) ext 5059
Rae, Kathryn (service mgr, cj) ext 1420
Lloyd Glyn (service mgr) ext 5507
Mellor, Charlaine (snr admin off, cj) ext 5058
Hendry, Mike Hendry (snr officer) ext 5084
Naeem, Shahida (planning off) ext 5084
Thomson, Nan (p, info asst) ext 5084

Team 2 (Probation)
O'Rourke, Mike (ssw) ext 5087
Barrie, Jackie (sw) ext 5076
Duncan, Susan (sw) ext 5005
Hinnrichs, Jill (sw) ext 5093
Reading Heidi (sw) ext 5050
Howitt, Elizabeth (sw) ext 5091
Greene, Brenda (sw) ext 5048
Vaughan, Ewan (sw) ext 5031
Wallace-King, Gwen (sw) ext 5060

Community Service/APEX
Patterson, Grant (ssw) ext 5015
Baird, Joanna (supt wrkr) ext 5002
Brewster Lesley (scja) ext 5008
 McLennan Brenda (supt wrkr) ext 5089
Galloway, Valerie (cjs asst) ext 5033
Leadbetter, Michelle (supt wrkr) ext 5007
Lyttle Claire (supt wrkr) ext 5044
Heid Haley(supt wrkr) ext 5043
Mortimer, Scott (supt wrkr) ext 5035

APEX Employability
fax (01382) 435055
Young, Julie (team leader) ext 5026
Alavuk Tanya (eda) ext 5026
Fowler, Vicky (eda) ext 5506
Ford, Shiona (admin apex) ext 5085

Pitt, Tom (unit mgr, inside out) ext 5079
Kenny Charlene (eda inside out) ext 5042
Dobie, June (KOT) ext 5040
Robertson Arlene (KOT) ext 5012
Yarwood Lyn (KOT) ext 5020
Geekie Lynsey (KOT) ext 5020
Black Cheryl (KOTY) ext 5094

Tay Project
Millar, Anna (ssw) ext 5054

Barrer, Lyn (sw) ext 5003
McDonald, Teresa (sw) ext 5037
Paton, Lisa (sw) ext 5075
Smith, Ron (sw) ext 5018
North, Joyce (supt wrkr) ext 5019

DTTO
Ramsay, Jacky (mgr) ext 5004
Barrow, Trisha (sw) ext 5029
Elder, Jill (sw) ext 5090
Hamilton Lizzie (sw) ext 5038
Whitehead Jim (sw) ext 5065
Russell, Tracey (sw) ext 5521
Campbell, Douglas (nurse) ext 5028
Harley, Pauline (nurse) ext 5047
Keay, Morag (nurse) ext 5030
Lindsay, Stuart (nurse) ext 5078
Stewart Grant (nurse) ext 5072
Murray, Angela (support) ext 5090

Public Protection Team
Lindsay, Stephen (ssw) ext 5046
Brodie, Carol (sw) ext 5069
Carnegie, Maureen (sw) ext 5074
McLean Susan (sw) ext 5057
Delaney, Fiona (sw) ext 5515
Leitch Mike (sw) ext 5516
McComiskie, Ron (sw) ext 5514
Milne, Janice (supt wrkr) ext 5048

2. **Flaxmill**
67 King Street, Dundee DD1 2JY
tel (01382 431400) *fax (01382) 431431*

Team 1 (Probation)
Sinclair, Rose (ssw) ext 1429
Dobson, Moira (sw) ext 1410
Dow, Ashley (sw) ext 1412
Lynch, Claire (sw) ext 1413
Nairn, Jill (sw) ext 1411
Reid, David (sw) ext 1415
Robertson, Nicole (sw) ext 1414
Garrigan, Helen (supt wrkr crt) ext 2188

Team 4 (Probation)
Kettles, Joyce(ssw) ext 1418
Blair, Rosie (sw) ext 1407
Campbell, Lesley (sw) ext 1403
Duff, Iain (sw) ext 1404
Higgins, Jill (sw) ext 1433
Hill, Alyson (sw) ext 1408
Scott, Rachel (sw) ext 1409
Sheridan, Margaret (sw) ext 1402
Walker, Debbie (sw) ext 1405

3. **East Port House**
65 King Street, Dundee DD4 1JY
tel (01382) 431450 *fax (01382) 435286*

Kidd, Jessie (mgr) ext 1442

Hendry, Mike (depute mgr) ext 1451

Resettlement Team
fax (01382) 431458
O'Rourke, Owen (snr supt wrkr) ext 1456
Brown, Colin (supt wrkr) ext 1439
Collings, Lesley (supt wrkr) ext 1461
Murray, Gill (supt wrkr) ext 1435
Muckersie-McIver, Karen (supt wrkr) ext 1457
Nelson, Dean (supt wrkr) ext 14

Female ISP
fax (01382) 431458
Millar, Avril (snr supt wrkr) ext 1465
Burns, Donna (supt wrkr) ext 1436
Henry, Gillian (supt wrkr) ext 1459
Robb, Nicky (supt wrkr) ext 1459
Mundie, Allan (nurse) ext 1464
Deevy Aisling (nurse) ext 1463

EAST AYRSHIRE COUNCIL

1. Social Work Headquarters
   John Dickie Street
   Kilmarnock KA1 1BY
   tel (01563) 576907/2, 576969, 576674
   fax (01563) 576654 & 576644

   Gilmour, Kay (acting exec head of sw)
   Fitzpatrick, Eugene (service mgr cj)

2. Social Work Department
   43/49 John Finnie Street
   Kilmarnock KA1 1BL
   tel (01563) 539888 *fax (01563) 538055*

   Millar, Morven (team mgr, cj service)

   Throughcare Team
   Kane, Terence (team mgr)

   Community Service Team
   Turner, Ian (cso)

3. 43a John Finnie Street
   Kilmarnock KA1 1BH
   tel (01563) 578484 *fax (01563) 578483*

   Watson, Evelyn (team mgr, youth justice)

4. Social Work Department
   Barrhill Road
   Cumnock KA18 1PG
   tel (01290) 428372 *fax (01290) 428380*

   McRoberts, Grace (team mgr, cj)

5. **Courts**
   Ayr Sheriff Court
   Sheriff Court House
   Wellington Square Ayr KA7 1EE
   tel (01292) 268474 *fax (01292) 282442*

   Hall, Drew (ssw)

   Kilmarnock Sheriff Court
   Sheriff Court House
   St Marnock Street
   Kilmarnock KA1 1ED
   tel (01563) 520211 *fax (01563) 543568*

   Hamilton, Jackie (ssw)

6. **Ayrshire Criminal Justice Partnership**
   Social Services, 4th Floor West Wing,
   Cunninghame House, Friarscroft,
   Irvine, KA12 8EE
   tel (01294) 317720 *fax (01294) 317701*

   MacKinnon, Fiona (mgr)

   Programme Delivery Team
   22 Portland Road
   Kilmarnock, KA1 2BS
   tel (01563) 553681

   MacKinnon, Fiona (prog mgr)

   inc the following teams
   Construct Team
   Walkerdine, Sue (treatment mgr)

   Programme Delivery Team
   Jones, Ray (treatment mgr)

   Training & Development
   Strachan, Fiona (co-ord)

Penal Establishment

7. Social Work Unit
   HM Prison, Mauchline Road
   Kilmarnock KA1 5JH
   tel (01563) 548851 *fax (01563) 548869*

   Haddow, Anita (team mgr)

Courts

Ayr Sherriff Court
Kilmarnock Sheriff Court
E Ayrshire District Court at Kilmarnock
E Ayrshire District Court at Cumnock

EAST DUNBARTONSHIRE COUNCIL

Out of hours standby service: Freephone 0800 811505

1. Communities Headquarters
    Tom Johnstone House
    Kirkintilloch G66 4TJ
    tel 0141-578 8000 *fax 0141-578 8470*

    Vacancy (chief exec)
    Simmons, John (corp director, community)

2. **Criminal Justice Unit**
    Unit 23, Fraser House
    Whitegates **Kirkintilloch** G66 3BQ
    tel 0141-578 8320 *fax 0141-578 0101*

    Fleming, John (service mgr)
    john.fleming@eastdunbarton.gov.uk
    Sexton, Jim (team leader)

    Offender Services
    Lynch, Tracy (sw)
    Cranston, Morven (sw)
    Chiang, Belinda (sw)
    Shearer, Alison (sw)
    Kier, Lynn (sw)
    Karpinski, Noel (cj asst)

    Community Service & Supervised Attendance
    Sutherland, Neil (cs officer)
    Nixon, Joseph (cs asst)
    Dickson, William (cs supvr)
    Coyne, Martin (cs supvr)

    Administration Section
    Watt, Karen (admin asst)
    Harvey, Janice (clerical off)
    Young, Lynn (clerical off)

Penal Establishment

3. Social Work Unit
    HM Prison **Lowmoss**
    Crosshill Road, Bishopbriggs
    Glasgow G62 2QB

    This prison is now closed for rebuilding.

Courts

These have been closed due to legislation changes

EAST LOTHIAN COUNCIL

Out of hours contact emergency social work service: freephone 0800 731 6969

e-mail jramsay@eastlothian.gov.uk

1. **Community Services**
    9-11 Lodge Street
    Haddington EH41 3DX
    tel (01620) 827413 *fax (01620) 824295*

    Ross, Dr Sue (director of community services)
    Millar, Gordon (acting head of adult social care)
    Ramsay, Jane (service manager)

2. **Criminal Justice Team**
    6-8 Lodge Street **Haddington**
    East Lothian EH41 3DX
    tel (01620) 826600 *fax (01620) 826345*

    Kaminski, Patricia (team ldr)
    Steel, Audrey (team ldr)
    Barbour, Carolyn (sw)
    Dudley, Susan (sw)
    Harvey, Steven (sw)
    Horne, Iain (sw)
    McFadzean, Frances (sw)
    Wilson, Julie (sw)

    Vacancy (sw th'care)
    Ellis, Duncan (voluntary th'care)

    Love, Robert (cs mgr)
    McAlpine, Owen (depute cs off)
    Hicks, Gary (cs asst)
    Kevan, Neill (cs asst)

    Laird, Scott (sao)
    Sharon Fitzpatrick (snr service supt)
    Cairns, Lesley (service support)
    Holm, Jean (service support)

3. **Youth Justice Team**
    Randall House
    Macmerry EH33 1RW
    tel (01875) 824090 *fax (01875) 612748*

    Coates, George (team ldr, youth justice)

Courts

Haddington Sheriff Court
E Lothian District Court at Haddington

EAST RENFREWSHIRE COUNCIL

Out of hours contact no: 0800 811 505

e-mail firstname.surname@eastrenfrewshire.gov.uk

1. East Renfrewshire Community Health & Care Partnership
   CHCP Headquarters
   1 Burnfield Avenue
   Giffnock G46 7TT
   tel 0141-577 3839 *fax 0141-577 3846*

   Murray, Julie (director of CHCP)
   Baxter, Safaa (chief sw officer/head of children's services and cj)

2. St Andrew's House
   113 Cross Arthurlie Street
   Barrhead G78 1EE
   tel 0141-577 8475 *fax 0141-577 3762*

   Hinds, Jonathan (service mgr - criminal justice)

3. 211 Main Street
   Barrhead G78 1SY
   tel 0141-577 8337/8 *fax 0141-577 8342*

   Criminal Justice Team
   Gaff, Les (team mgr - offenders)
   Craig, Dawn (snr sw pract)
   McDade, Karen (sw)
   Smith, Colin (sw)
   Vacancy (sw)
   Downie, Eddie (cj support worker)
   Kerr, Peter (cs supvr)
   Bell, Shona (admin asst)
   McQuade, Anne Marie (admin asst)

4. **Drug Treatment and Testing Order Project** (East Renfrewshire, Inverclyde & Renfrewshire)
   St Andrew's House
   113 Cross Arthurlie Street
   Barrhead G78 1EE
   tel 0141-577 8442 *fax 0141-577 3762*

   Buntrock, Christine (team leader)
   Cunningham, Neil (sw)
   Soper, Helen (sw)
   Murray, Patricia (sw)
   Brown, Craig (sw)
   Rush, Wendy (addiction wrkr)
   Barnes, Dr Rosalind (doctor)
   Nelis, Michael (snr addiction nurse)
   Lough, Jennifer (snr addiction nurse)

Vacancy (addiction nurse)
Denise Farrell (support wrkr)
Taylor, James (snr clerical asst)
McGettigan, Kerry (clerical asst)

5. **Forensic Community Mental Health Team** (East Renfrewshire, Inverclyde & Renfrewshire)
   Clutha House, 1st Floor
   120 Cornwall Street South, **Glasgow** G41 1AD
   tel 0141-427-8277/8260 fax 0141-427-8278

   e-mail firstname.surname@ggc.scot.nhs.uk

   Hendry, Shona (team leader)
   Bonini, Marina (snr sw pract)
   O'Donovan, Roberta (sw)
   Vacancy (sw assistant)
   McIntosh, Pauline (medical secretary)
   Lee, Shelley (medical secretary)
   Grierson, Lesley (forensic cpn)
   Murphy, Andrew (forensic cpn)
   O'Brien, Chris (forensic cpn)
   O'Neill, Denise (forensic cpn)
   Willsone, Nicola (forensic cpn)

Court

East Renfrewshire District Court at Giffnock

CITY OF EDINBURGH COUNCIL

Out of hours contact: emergency social work service: freephone 0800 731 6969

1. Health & Social Care Headquarters
   Level 1:8, Waverley Court, 4 East Market Street
   Edinburgh EH8 8BD
   tel 0131-553 82121 *fax 0131-529 6218*

   Gabbitas, Peter, (director)
   Brace, Sue (head of strategic planning & commissioning)
   Boyle, Monica, (head of quality & resources)

   Criminal Justice Services
   tel 0131-553-8212 *fax 0131-554-0838*

   Lancashire, Ron (cj services mgr)
   Robertson, Harry (acting service mgr, cj)
   Tyson, John (service mgr, cj)

Court Liaison Services

2. **Edinburgh**
   (District, Sheriff and High Courts)

4 Grindlay Street Court
Edinburgh EH3 9AR
tel 0131-469 3408 *fax 0131-229 8268*

District Criminal Justice Practice Teams

3. **Edinburgh North East**
Units C&D, Newkirkgate Shopping Centre
Edinburgh EH6 6DJ
tel 0131-553 3835 *fax 0131-553 6540*

Vacancy (acting practice team mgr)

4. **Edinburgh South East**
40 Captain's Road
Edinburgh EH17 8HN
tel 0131-529 5300 *fax 0131-529 5384*

Stewart, Ian (practice team mgr)

5. **Edinburgh North West**
34 Muirhouse Crescent
Edinburgh EH4 4QL
tel 0131-343 1991 *fax 0131-315 2172*

Fuller, Carey (practice team mgr)

6. **Edinburgh South West**
5 Murrayburn Gate
Edinburgh EH14 2SS
tel 0131-442 4131 *fax 0131-442 4842*

Pate, Kirsty (practice team mgr)

7. **Grindlay Court Community Justice Centre**
2-4 Grindlay Street Court
Edinburgh EH3 9AR
tel 0131-469 3408 *fax 0131-229 8628*

Fraser, Rona (practice team mgr)

Services include: bail info and assessment, diversion from prosecution, resettlement team, domestic violence probation project, sex offender intervention project, probation group programme

Crane Services (supported accom facility)
24 Broughton Place, Edinburgh EH1 3RT
tel 0131-556 9969 *fax 0131-558 1809*

Fraser, Dorothy (mgr)

Drug Treatment & Testing Orders
29-31 Alva Street
Edinburgh EH2 4PS
tel 0131-225-7788 *fax 225-9039*

Lawrie, Valerie (mgr)

Penal Establishment

8. Social Work Unit
HM Prison, 33 Stenhouse Road
Edinburgh EH11 3LN
tel 0131-444 3080 *fax 0131-444 3036*

Fraser, Dorothy (practice team mgr)

Courts

The High Court, Edinburgh
Edinburgh Sheriff Court
City of Edinburgh District Court

FALKIRK COUNCIL

1. Social Work Headquarters
Brockville, Hope Street **Falkirk** FK1 5RW
tel (01324) 506400 *fax (01324) 506401*

Birks, Janet (director of social work)
Anderson, Margaret (head of children & families, & cj)

Criminal Justice Service
tel (01324) 506464 *fax (01324) 506465*

Stirrat, Sharon (service mgr)
Duncan, Robin (research, information, & tr'ng off)

Probation & Throughcare Team
Burgess, Nick (team mgr)
Parnell, Anne Marie (team mgr)
Andrews, Carol (sw)
Boslem, Mary (sw)
Brodie, Andrew (sw)
Kostlin, Donna (sw)
Brown, Jacqueline (sw)
Dellamere, Allen (sw)
Goodwin, Anne-Marie (sw)
Kent, Gill (sw)
Marshall, Kay (sw)
McCartney, Lynn (sw)
Melvin, Shirley (sw)
O'Neill, Colin (sw)
Rodger, Claire (sw)
Boslem, Vicky (sw asst)
Brown, Nicola (sw asst)
Alexander, Maya (sw asst)
Thomson, Stephen (sw asst)

Community Service & Supervised Attendance Team
Hamilton, Mary (team mgr)
Howard, Fred (sw)
Deeley, Gillian (cs/sao)
Cooper, Dave (cs/sao)
Brockie, Clem (cs/sao)

Gardner, Melanie (cs/sao)
Adams, Gordon (cs/sao)

Accredited Programmes Team
(Also serving Clackmannanshire & Stirling
CJS)

McCormick, Jim (snr wrkr)
McDonald, Scott (sw)
Telford, Isobel (sw asst)
Begen, Margaret (sw asst)
Nicolson, John (sw asst)
Thomson, Laura (sw asst)

Administration
Cartwright, Sandra

Voluntary Organisation

2. **SACRO**
    Groupwork Service
    Restorative Justice Service
    Accommodation Service
    22 Meeks Road **Falkirk** FK2 7ET
    tel (01324) 627824 *fax (01324) 622006*

    Vacancy (service mgr)
    Conway, Bill (service team ldr, rest. just.)
    Madill, Stephen (service team ldr, gpwk)
    Easton, Craig (service team ldr, accom)
    Brown, Tony (intergenerational wrkr)

Youth Justice

3. Social Work Headquarters
    Brockville, Hope Street **Falkirk** FK1 5RW
    tel (01324) 506400 *fax (01324) 506401*

    Johnson, Sue (youth justice co-ordinator)

    Programme Providers

    Connect Youth Justice Service
    Unit 1, St John's Sawmill
    Etna Road **Falkirk** FK2 9EG
    tel (01324) 501060 *fax (01324) 501061*

    Hall, Gary (team mgr)
    Chapman, Gerry (sw)
    Halkett, Jane (sw)
    Kelly, Janet (sw)
    Vacancy (snr wrkr)
    Davies, Alan (com educn wrkr)
    Mullen, Lindsay (com educn wrkr)
    Vacancy (snr nurse prctnr)
    Hutton, Carolanne (subst wrkr)
    Moffat, Ginny (administration)

    Barnardo's Freagarrach Project
    4 Orchard Street, **Falkirk** FK1 1RF
    (temporary)
    tel (01324) 718277 *fax (01324) 503861*

Jones, Helen (children's services mgr)

Penal Establishment

4. Social Work Unit
    HM YOI **Polmont**
    Redding Road, Brightons
    Falkirk FK2 0AB
    tel (01324) 711708 *fax (01324) 722297*

    Whyte, Jackie (team mgr)
    Connolly, Kristine (snr wrkr)
    Berry, Ruth (sw)
    Chalmers, Jill (sw)
    Irvine, Anne (sw)
    Macfarlane, Bernadette (sw)
    Tait, Lee (sw)
    Walker, Natalie (sw)
    Wilson, Jim (sw)
    Archibald, Kathleen (snr clerical)
    Baillie, Lesley (clerical asst)

Courts

Falkirk Sheriff Court
Falkirk District Court

FIFE COUNCIL

Out of hours contact (08451 550099)

1. **Social Work Headquarters**
    Rothesay House, North Street
    Glenrothes, KY7 5LT
    tel (08451 555500) *fax* (01592) 583253

    Moore, Stephen (head of social work)
    Gaw, Alistair (snr manager)
    Kinnear, Bill (service mgr)
    Hopton, Steve (service mgr, planning &
    performance)

    Administration & Support Services
    Rodger, Gus (planning & perf off) (based

2. **Court Service Team (East/West)**
    21 St Catherine Street **Cupar** KY15 4TA
    tel (01334) 659356 *fax (01334) 659316*

    Reid, Aileen (team leader)
    Arthur, Jane (sw)
    Nicholson, Alex (sw)
    MacDonald, Andrew (sw)
    Robertson, Katie (sw)
    Anderson, Rachel (cja)
    Paterson, Carol (team ldr admin)
    Ashraf, Arif (admin supt)
    Smith, Janet (admin supt)

3. **Sheriff Court Social Work Services**

a. **Dunfermline Sheriff Court**
Carnegie Drive, Dunfermline KY12 7HJ
tel (08451 555555) 490102 *fax (01383) 602540*

Wishart, Lindsay (cja)
Bouglas, Dale (admin supt)
Fletcher, Betty (admin supt)
Rushford, Kelly (admin supt)

b. **Kirkcaldy Sheriff Court**
Whytescauseway, Kirkcaldy KY1 1XQ
tel (08451 555555) 470320 *fax (01592) 583197*

Gordon, Emma (cja)
Robson, Angela (cja)
Thomson, Christine (cja)
McGuire, Bernadette (admin supt)
Selbie, Michelle (admin supt)

c. **Cupar Sheriff Court**
21 St Catherine Street, Cupar KY15 4TA
tel (01334) 659356 *fax (01334) 659316*

Nicholson, Alex (sw)
Ashraf, Arif (admin supt)

d. **Bail Officer**
Broomlea, 1 Swan Road
Kirkcaldy KY1 1UZ
tel (01592) 583336 *fax (01592) 583198*

Callaghan, John (bail officer)

4. **Community Service by Offenders Scheme**

a. **Buckhaven Base**
96 Wellesley Road, Buckhaven KY8 1HT
tel (01592) 583335 *fax (01592) 583651*

Rose, Susan (team leader)
Melville, Archie (snr projects off)
Anderson, Shelley (cja)
Barclay, Jackie (cja)
Bernard, Caroline (cja)
Clachers, Audrey (cja)
Coull, Leah (cja)
Dunnett, Janette (cja)
Jamieson, Sharon (cja)
Lister, Lorraine (cja)
McGowan, Audrey (cja)
Ralph, Karen (system supt off)
Murray, Lynne (admin ass)
Armour, Cheryl (admin supt)

b. **Dunfermline Base**
Rannoch House, 2 Comely Park

Dunfermline KY12 7HU
tel (01383) 602354 *fax (01383) 312134*

Dunn, Mandy (cja)
Gallo, Joan (cja)
Green, Ralph (cja)
Hutt, Stephanie (cja)
Donald, Kimberley (admin supt)

5. **Court Services Team (Central)**
East Fergus Place, Kirkcaldy KY1 1XT
tel (01592) 583322 *fax (01592) 583263*

MacArthur, Stuart (team ldr, js)
Thompson, Susan (team ldr, js)
Black, Nadia (sw)
Clark, Kevin (sw)
Dewar, Mary (sw)
Gardner, Sybil (sw)
Sutherland, Yvonne (sw)
Kinnell, Beth (sw)
Nairn, Sandra (sw)
Nicholson, Karen (sw)
Reddick, Ailsa (sw)
Woodburn, Sarah (sw)
Brown, Carrie (admin supt)
Cook, Rebecca (admin supt)
Learmonth, Linda (admin supt)
Todd, Clair (admin supt)

6. **Probation Supervision Team (East)**

a. 96 Wellesley Road
Buckhaven KY8 1HT
tel (01592) 583335 *fax (01592) 583651*

Collins Margaret (team ldr)
Brown, Karen (sw)
Ferrol, Jean (sw) (based at 15)
Gilmour, Laura (sw) (based at 15)
Green, Angela (sw)
McKeown, Maurice (sw) (based at 15)
Mullen, Heather (sw)
Stillman, Matt (sw)
Brawley, Bryan (cja)
Barclay, Derek (sw)
Gilmour, Laura (sw)

Armour, Cheryl (admin supt)
Christensen, Brenda (admin supt)
Fyfe, Gillian (admin supt)
Leitch, Christine (admin supt)
Wigley, Felicity (admin supt)

b. 390 South Street
Glenrothes KY7 5NL
tel (01592) 583321 *fax (01592) 583262*

Bell, David (sw)
Hunter, Melanie (sw)

Lynch, Irene (sw)
Mitchell, Gill (sw)
Roy, Kelly (cja)
McPherson, Julie (admin supt)
Rook, Gayle (admin supt)

7. **Probation Supervision Team (East/West)**
Dunfermline Base
Rannoch House, 2 Comely Park
Dunfermline KY12 7HU
tel (01383) 602354 *fax (01383) 602539*

Myers, Ray (team ldr)
Chalmers, Moyra (sw)
Foy, Andrew (sw)
Hay, Alan (sw)
Nicol Ritchie, Kim (sw)
Ramage, Maureen (sw)
Roy, Catherine (sw)
Lucas, Richard (sw) (based at 2)
Francis, Gordon (sw) (based at 2)
Candish, Lesley (cja)
Dowell, Betty (admin ass)
Bouglas, Dale (admin supt)
Fletcher, Betty (admin supt)
Allan Galbraith (admin supt)
Rushford, Kelly (admin supt)

8. **Public Protection Team**
Broomlea, 1 Swan Road
Kirkcaldy KY1 1UZ
tel (01592) 583336 *fax (01592) 583198*

Simpson, Angela (team ldr)
McPake, Joanne (team ldr)
Henry, Carrie (snr pract)
Lamont, Louise (snr pract)
Dewar, Gillian (sw)
Hood, Christina (sw)
Munton, Richard (sw)
Quinn, Cathy (sw)
Ross, Suzanne (sw)
McGuinness, Odette (cja)
Balfour, Ashley (admin supt)
Somerville, Sharon (admin supt)

9. **MAPPA**
Police Headquarters, Detriot Road,
Glenrothes KY6 2JR
tel (01592) 411929 *fax (01592) 411920*

Sinclair, Nigel (MAPPA coordinator)
Candy, Laurence (cja) (based at 12)
Nicoll, Carole, (admin assist)
McKenzie, Lynne (admin supt)

Drug Court Supervision & Treatment Team
10. Fergus House
7 East Fergus Place
Kirkcaldy KY1 1XT
tel (01592) 583657 *fax (01592 583646)*

Thom, Martin (team ldr)
Burns, Lisa (sw)
Chalmers, Frank (sp)
Kay, Gill (sp)
McCallum, Ryan (sw)
McGovern, Tom (sp)
Mudie, Kath (sw)
Yule, John (sw)
Henderson, Linda (snr addiction wrkr)
Bell, Donna (addiction wrkr)
Craig, David (addiction wrkr)
Emmerson, Sara (addiction wrkr)
Peters, Helen (addiction wrkr)
Turner, Tracy (addiction wrkr)
Serbie, Carol (cja)
Stafford, Claire (cja)

NHS
Pitt, Ingrid (temp team leader)
Gray, Sarah (senior nurse)
McDonald, May (nurse)
McGurk, Gerry (nurse)
Mead, Stephen (nurse)
Milne, Amanda (nurse)
Smith, Laura (nurse)
Stewart, Dawn (nurse)
Waterman, Alan (nurse)
Barrie, Dave (project wrkr)
Haig, Barbara (project wrkr)
Mair, Sheila (project wrkr)

Smith, Gayle (admin asst)
Herd, Ashley (admin supt)
King, Dawn (admin supt)
McLean, Jenny (admin supt)
Pettigrew, Anne (admin supt)

11. **Throughcare Team**
a. Dunfermline Base
Rannoch House, 2 Comely Park
Dunfermline KY12 7HU
tel (01383) 602354 *fax (01383) 602539*

Rattray, Fiona (team ldr)
Maud, Lorna (sw)
Deeney, Catherine (sw)
Sinclair, Cheryl (sw)
Karin Stewart (cja)
Keenan, Dawn (cja)
Stephen, Ibby (cja)
Banning, Grant (admin supt)
Jennifer Nisbet (admin supt)
Simpson, Kay (admin supt)

b. Buckhaven Base
    96 Wellesley Road **Buckhaven** KY8 1HT
    tel (01592) 583335 *fax (01592) 414482*

    Mathews, Rory (snr practititoner)
    Black, Allison (sw)
    Slater, Stuart (sw)
    Kinnell, David (cja)
    Lee, Helen (sw)
    Holton, Anne (sw) (based between Cupar
    & Buckhaven)

Fife Courts

    Cupar Sheriff Court
    Dunfermline Sheriff Court
    Kirkcaldy Sheriff Court
    Fife District Court at Cupar
    Fife District Court at Dunfermline
    Fife District Court at Kirkcaldy

GLASGOW CITY COUNCIL

1. Social Work Headquarters
    3rd Floor, Nye Bevan House
    20 India Street, Glasgow G2 4PF
    tel 0141-287 8700 *fax 0141-287 8840*

    Crawford, David (director of social work
    services)

1a. **Criminal Justice Unit**
    Centenary House, 100 Morrison Street
    Glasgow G5 8LN
    tel 0141-420 5754
    fax 0141-420 5760/5957
    direct dial 0141-420 + number

    McQuillan, Raymund (head of service cj)
    5754
    Smith, Cath (principal officer cj) 5669
    McNulty, Mary (snr officer cj) 5899
    O'Donnell, John (snr officer cj) 5903
    Macmaster, Beth (resource wrkr cj) 5867
    Dunbar, Faith (research officer, cj) 287
    8748

*Note: CHCP Community Health + Care
Partnership. Community Service assessment/
supervision now located at relevant CHCP CJ
Team*

2. **East CHCP**
    The Newlands Centre
    871 Springfield Road
    Glasgow G31 4HZ
    tel 0141-565 0230 *fax 0141-565 0164*

    MacPhail, Meg (operations mgr cj)

    McAulay, Adrienne (pract team ldr cj)
    McLaughlin, Linda (pract team ldr cj)
    McLaughlin, Sandra (pract team ldr cj)
    Milne, Bruce (pract team ldr cj)
    Strong, Gordon (pract team ldr cj)

    East Criminal Justice
    Templeton Business Centre
    Unit 4A3, 62 Templeton Street
    Glasgow, G40 1DA
    tel 0141-276 1850 *fax 0141-276 1851*

    McAulay, Adrienne (pract team ldr cj)

3. **North CHCP**
    The Quadrangle, Unit 8b
    59 Ruchill Street, Glasgow, G20 9PY
    tel 0141-276 4560 *fax 0141-276 6222*

    Ross, Frances (ops mgr cj)
    Allan, Anne-Marie (pract team ldr cj)
    Bradley, Elizabeth (pract team ldr cj)
    Brittain, John (pract team ldr cj)
    Coyle, Martin (pract team ldr cj)
    MacDonald, Anne (pract team ldr cj)
    Singh, Arun (pract team ldr cj)

4. **South East Area CHCP**
    187 Old Rutherglen Road
    Twomax Building, Glasgow G5 0RE
    tel 0141-420 0070 *fax 0141-420 8004*

    Doherty, Liam (operations mgr cj)
    Conkie, Maria (pract team ldr cj)
    Donnelly, Kate (pract team ldr cj)

5. **South West CHCP**
    130 Langton Road, Glasgow G53 5DD
    tel 0141-276 2960 *fax 0141-276 2981*

    Kerr, Sandi (operations mgr, cj)
    Clarke, Dominic (pract team ldr cj)
    Lafferty, Caroline (pract team ldr cj)
    McNally, Lorraine (pract team ldr cj)
    Munro, Jean (pract team ldr cj)
    Sneddon, David (pract team ldr cj)
    Wylie, Rae (pract team ldr cj)

6. **West CHCP**
    Mercat House, 31 Hecla Square
    Glasgow G15 8NH
    tel 0141-276 4320 *fax 0141-276 4331*

    Reid, Tom (ops mgr cj)
    Campbell, Susan (pract team ldr cj)
    Edgely, Lynsey (pract team ldr cj)
    McCullough, Janet (pract team ldr cj)

7. **Homeless Persons Team**
    180 Centre Street

Glasgow, G5 8EE
tel 0141-287 1800 *fax 0141-287 1887*

Mearns, Gerry (operations mgr)
McShane, Tony (pract team ldr cj)

8. **Clyde Quay Project** (Sex Offenders)
85 Paisley Road
Glasgow G5 8LN
tel 0141-420 5868
fax 0141-420 5760/5957

Brown, Angelene (pract team ldr)
McDade, Alexis (pract team ldr)

9. **Multi Agency Public Protection Arrangements (MAPPA)**
Centenary House, 100 Morrison Street
Glasgow G5 8LN
tel 0141-420 5811

Hamilton, John (co-ord)

10. **Sex Offender Liaison Team**
Centenary House, 100 Morrison Street
Glasgow G5 8LN
tel 0141-420 5753

Asken, Stewart, (snr officer)
Bryden, John (snr officer)
Kennedy, Alison (snr officer)

11. **DTTO/Drug Court Team**
80 Norfolk Street, Glasgow G5 9EJ
tel 0141-274 6000 *fax 0141-274 6069*

Hendry, Paul (pract team ldr)

12. **Prison Throughcare Team**
80 Norfolk Street, Glasgow G5 9EJ
tel 0141-274 6000 *fax 0141-274 6095*

Ashworth, Mary (pract team ldr)
Kirk, Colin (pract team ldr)
Bell, David (pract team ldr)
Rodden, Louise (pract team ldr)
Bradley, Elizabeth (pract team ldr)
McCann, Peter (pract team ldr)

Courts

13. **Glasgow Sheriff Court**
1 Carlton Place, Glasgow G5 9DA
tel 0141-429 8888 *fax 0141-418 5244*

Social Work Unit
tel 0141-276 1845 *fax 0141-276 1846*

Fyfe, Robert (ops mgr)
Jamieson, Helen (pract team ldr)
Ross, Cath (pract team ldr)

14. **Glasgow & Strathkelvin Sheriff Court**
Social Work Unit, 80 Norfolk Street
Glasgow G5 9EJ
tel 0141 274 6000 *fax 0141 276 6088*

15. **City of Glasgow Stipendiary/ District Court**
21 St Andrews Street, Glasgow G1 5PW

Social Work Unit
68 Turnbull Street, Glasgow G1 5PW
tel 0141-552 8406/1671
fax 0141-552 5422

16. **Glasgow High Court**
1 Mart Street, Glasgow G1 5A
tel 0141-552 3795 *fax 0141-559 4519*

Social Work Unit
tel 0141-559 4529 *fax 0141-559 4528*

17. **Supervised Attendance Orders**
80 Norfolk Street, Glasgow G5 9EJ
tel 0141-274 6000 *fax 0141-274 6088*

Jamieson, Helen (pract team ldr)
Freeman, Ken (pract team ldr)

18. **Bail Services**
80 Norfolk Street, Glasgow G5 9EJ
tel 0141-274 6000 *fax 0141-274 6088*

Jamieson, Helen (pract team ldr)

Voluntary Organisations

19. **SACRO** (inc supported accommodation)
93 Hope Street, Glasgow G2 6LD
tel 0141-248 1763 *fax 0141 248 1686*

20. **Glasgow Council on Alcohol**
7th Floor, Newton House
457 Sauchiehall Street, Glasgow G2 3LG
tel 0141-353 1800 *fax 0141-353 1030*

21. **Victim Support (Glasgow)**
131-141 Saltmarket, Glasgow G1 5LF
tel 0141-553 2415 *fax 0141-553 2405*

22. **Victim Support (National Office, West)**
10 Jocelyn Square, Glasgow G1 5JU
tel 0141-553 1726 *fax 0141-552 3316*

23. **Dick Stewart Hostel (Crossreach)**
40 Circus Drive
Glasgow G31 2JE
tel 0141-554 0277 *fax 0141-554 6646*

24. **APEX (Scotland)**
3rd Floor, 45 Hope Street

Glasgow G2 6PH
tel 0141-248 4537 *fax 0141-248 4542*

25. **218 Service** (Turning Point)
218 Bath Street, Glasgow G2 4HW
tel 0141-331 6200 *fax 0141-331-6202*

26. **Phoenix Futures**
Drummond House
1st Floor, 1 Hill Street
Glasgow, G3 6RN
tel 0141-332 1900 *fax 0141-332 1249*

Penal Establishment

27. **HM Prison Barlinnie**
Lee Avenue, Smithycroft Road
Glasgow, G33 2QX
tel 0141-770 2000 *fax 0141-770 2060*

Social Work Unit
tel 0141-770 2123 *fax 0141-770 9808*

Reid, Tom (ops mgr)
Bryce, Helena (pract team ldr)
Tolmie, Brian (pract team ldr)

THE HIGHLAND COUNCIL

Out of hours contact no: 08457 697284

1. **The Highland Council Headquarters**
Glenurquhart Road, **Inverness** IV3 5NX
tel (01463) 702874 *fax (01463) 702855*

Dempster, Ms Harriet (director of social work)
Palin, Fiona (head of operations, cjs & central services)

1a. **Social Work Headquarters**
Kinmylies Building, Leachkin Road,
Inverness IV3 8NN
tel (01463) 703472 fax (01463) 713237

HQ Team
Maybee, James (principal off, cjs)
Nicholls, Pat (admin asst, cjs)
Odell, Kay (p, ca/typist, cjs)
Hall, Malcolm (p, info/research & QA off, cjs)

1b. **MAPPA Team**
Social Work Services
Inverness Area Command,
Burnett Road Police Station
Inverness IV1 1RL
tel (01463) 228505 *fax (01463) 228562*

Lyon, Ron (MAPPA co-ord)
Brown, Alana (admin asst)
Vacant, (ca/typist)

Criminal Justice Services

2. **Highland North Team**
a. **Caithness**
Social Work Services, Unit 27b
Airport Industrial Estate
Wick KW1 4QS
tel (01955) 603161 *fax (01955) 603164*

Donoghue, Terry (team mgr, North)
(2a&b)
Barr, Bob (sw)
Sarah Meldrum (sw)
Keith, Tracey (ca/typist)

b. **Sutherland**
Social Work Area Office
Drummuie **Golspie** KW10 6TA
tel (01408) 635369 *fax (01408) 634041*

MacPherson, Margaret (p, sw)
MacRae, Diane (ca/typist)

3. **Highland Central Team**
a. **Ross-shire**
Criminal Justice Services
Station Road, **Dingwall** IV15 9JX
tel (01349) 865600 *fax (01349) 865279*

Rainnie, Bill (team mgr, Central) (3a, b
& c)
Forbes, Bill (sw)
Mackay, Hilary (p, sw)
Morrison, Gail (p, sw)
Nicolson, Don (sw)
Redmond, Susie (p, sw)
Gerrard, Judith (ca/typist)
Lawless, Dawn (p, ca/typist)

b. **Skye**
Social Work Area Office, Top Floor
Tigh na Drochaid, Bridge Road
Portree Isle of Skye IV50 9ER
tel (01478) 612943 *fax (01478) 613213*

MacKinnon, Mary (sw)
MacPherson, Ann (p, ca/typist)

c. **H M Prison Porterfield**
CJS Unit, Porterfield Prison
Duffy Drive, **Inverness** IV2 3HH
tel (01463) 223489 *fax (01463) 243361*

McIvor, Alec (sw)
Vacant, (p, sw)
McRobert, Patricia (p, ca/typist)

4. **Highland South Team**

a. **Carsegate**
Carsegate House, Glendoe Terrace,
Inverness, IV3 8ED
tel (01463) 724022 *fax (01463) 724000*

Paulin, Jeremy (team mgr, South) (4a & b)
Botha, Mornay (sw)
Baxter, Stuart (sw)
Fletcher, Luisa (sw)
MacKenzie, Eileen (sw)
Ramsay, Isla (sw)
Young, Anne (sw)
Waller, Lesley (sw)
Murdoch, Sara (crts)
Fraser, Claire (ca/typist)
Lawless, Dawn (p, ca/typist)

b. **Lochaber**
Unit 4B1, Blar Mhor Industrial Estate
Caol **Fort William** PH33 7NG
tel (01397) 704668 *fax (01463) 700422*

Finnimore, Andrew (sw)
Bell, Trevor (p,sw)
Laing, Sara (ca/typist)

5. **Substance Misuse Team**

5a. **DTTO, Structured Deferred Sentence Diversion, Throughcare**
The Old Schoolhouse, 196 Culduthel Road
Inverness, IV2 4BH
tel (01463) 716324 *fax (01463) 712895*

Millar, Lynn (team mgr, subst misuse) (5a & b)
Sangster, Agnes (sw, DTTO)
Simpson, Fiona (p, s, DTTO)
Litster, Bob (p, DTTO addictions wrkr)
Murray, Lisa (cpn)
Vacancy (p, cpn)
MacRae, Margo (sw, div & th'care)
Linda Edmiston (TAS wrkr)
Mackay, Claire (sw, SDS)
Cascarino, Marie (ca/typist)
Blackley, Laura (p, ca/typist)

5b. **H M Prison Porterfield Addictions Unit**
CJS Unit, Porterfield Prison
Duffy Drive, Inverness IV2 3HH
tel (01463) 223489 *fax (01463) 243361*

Cameron, Mike, (sw)
McRobert, Patricia (p, ca/typist)

6. **Community Service, Supervised Attendance & Fiscal Work Orders**

CS Unit, The Old Schoolhouse
196 Culduthel Road **Inverness** IV2 4BH
tel (01463) 242511 *fax (01463) 716187*

Millar, Lynn (team mgr)
Boyd, David (cso)
Glen, Robert (sao)
Watt, Stewart (proj off)
Relph, Erin (fwo)
MacKenzie, Claire (ca/typist)
Vacancy (ca/typist)

7. **Community Service, Supervised Attendance**

a. **Ross-shire**
Unit 5, River Wynd
Teaninich Industrial Estate
Alness Ross-shire IV17 0PE
tel (01349) 884118 *fax (01349) 884158*

Rainnie, Bill (team mgr)
Cameron, Rod (cso)
Currie, Alistair (proj off)
Gell, Janice (p, ca/typist)

b. **Lochaber**
Unit 4B2, Blar Mhor Industrial Estate
Caol **Fort William** PH33 7NG
tel (01397) 704668 *fax (01397) 700422*

Paulin, Jeremy (team mgr)
MacKay, David (cso)
MacGillivray, Archie (p, proj off)
Laing, Sara (ca/typist)

c. **Caithness**
Unit 27b, Airport Industrial Estate
Wick KW1 4QS
tel (01955) 603161 *fax (01955) 603164*

Donoghue, Terry (team mgr) (7c & d)
Brass, Rodney (cso)
Sutherland, George (p, proj off)
Keith, Tracey (ca/typist)

d. **Sutherland**
Social Work Area Office
Drummuie **Golspie** KW10 6TA
tel (01408) 635369 *fax (01408) 634041*

Brass, Rodney (cso)
MacRae, Diane (p, ca/typist)

e. **Skye**
Social Work Area Office, Top Floor
Tigh na Drochaid, Bridge Road
Portree Isle of Skye IV50 9ER
tel (01478) 612943 *fax (01478) 613213*

Rainnie, Bill (team mgr, Central)

MacKinnon, Mary (sw)
MacPherson, Ann (p, ca/typist)

Voluntary Projects

8. **APEX (Employment Guidance)**
    17 Lotland Street, **Inverness** IV1 1ST
    tel & fax (01463) 717033

    McDonald, Alistair (team ldr)
    Tripp, Helen (team ldr)

9. **NCH (Intensive Probation)**
    2nd Floor, 46 Church Street, Inverness
    IV1 1EH
    tel (01463) 717227 *fax (01463) 236335*

    Mawby, Mike (mgr)
    Snedden, Iain (proj co-ord)

10. **SACRO (Supported Accomodation
    Bail Supervision)**
    Ballantyne House, Academy Street
    Inverness IV1 1LU
    tel (01463) 716325 *fax (01463) 716326*

    MacDonald, Alastair (mgr)
    Vacancy (mgr, supt accom service)
    Vacancy (proj wrkr)
    Scott, Brenda (p, proj wrkr)

11. **Venture Trust**
    Applecross, **Strathcanon** IV54 8ND
    tel (01520) 744332 fax (01520) 744306

    Barton, Greg (chief exec)
    Ashworth, Andy (resource mgr)

12. **Pulteney People's Project**
    (Homelink, Caithness)
    tel (01955) 606950

    MacNab, Katrina (mgr)

13. **Lifestyles Housing Support**
    46 The High Street, Fort William
    tel 01397 700740

    Powell, Bryan (mgr)
    McKenzie, Lizbeth (support wrkr)

Penal Establishment

15. HM Prison Porterfield, Duffy Drive,
    Inverness IV2 3HH
    tel (01463) 223489 fax (01463) 243361

    *See Highland Team Central at 3c or
    Substance Misuse Team at 5b above
    for CJS Contacts*

Courts

Dingwall Sheriff Court
Dornoch Sheriff Court
Fort William Sheriff Court
Inverness Sheriff Court
Portree Sheriff Court
Tain Sheriff Court
Wick Sheriff Court
Dingwall Justice of the Peace Court
Dornoch Justice of the Peace Court
Fort William Justice of the Peace Court
Inverness Justice of the Peace Court
Portree Justice of the Peace Court
Tain Justice of the Peace Court
Wick Justice of the Peace Court

INVERCLYDE COUNCIL

e-mail firstname.surname@inverclyde.gov.uk

1. Social Work Services
    Dalrymple House
    195 Dalrymple Street
    Greenock PA15 1LD
    tel (01475) 714000 *fax (01475) 714060*

    Murphy, Robert (head of service)

Criminal Justice Services

2. **Court Liaison/Fieldwork**
    2nd Floor Right, 99 Dalrymple Street
    Greenock PA15 1HU
    tel (01475) 714500 *fax (01475) 714515*

    Howard, Audrey (service mgr)
    Bradley, John (ssw)
    Thomson, Sharon (acting ssw)

3. **Greenock Sheriff Court**
    Social Work Office
    1 Nelson Street, Greenock PA15 1TR
    tel (01475) 715992 *fax (01475) 715993*

4. **Community Service**
    Unit 6, Kingston Business Park
    Port Glasgow PA14 5DR
    tel (01475) 715791 *fax (01475) 715794*

    Clark, Anne (cs org)

5. **Action for Children
    Gap Project**
    9 Terrace Road, Greenock PA15 1DJ
    tel & fax (01475) 727363
    and

    **Action for Children
    Integrated Criminal Justice Service**

7 Duncan Street
Greenock PA15 4JT
tel (01475) 723044 *fax (01475) 723045*

Bradbury, Carol (mgr)

6. **Supervised Attendance Order Scheme**
    Unit 6, Kingston Business Park
    Port Glasgow PA14 5DR
    tel (01475) 715791 *fax (01475) 723405*

    Laverty, Louise (sup att off)

7. **Through Care Team**
    Criminal Justice Team
    2nd Floor Right, 99 Dalrymple Street
    Greenock PA15 1HU
    tel (01475) 714500 *fax (10475) 714515*

    Aitken, Gordon (throughcare co-ord)
    *Area Covered: Inverclyde, Renfrewshire
    & East Renfrewshire*

8. **MAPPA**
    Greenock Police Station
    160 Rue End Street
    Greenock PA15 1HX
    mobile (07825) 584 634 (no land lines yet)

    Miller, Ann (co-ord)

Penal Establishments

9. Social Work Unit
    HM Prison **Greenock**
    Gateside, Greenock PA16 9AH
    tel (01475) 883323 *fax (01475) 883335*

    Booth, Gillian (ssw)
    Anderson, Susie (sw)
    Forsyth, Nicola (sw)
    McCue, Gillian (sw)
    Paterson, Joe (sw)

Courts

Greenock Sheriff Court
Inverclyde District Court at Greenock

MIDLOTHIAN COUNCIL

Out of hours contact: emergency social work
service: freephone 0800 731 6969

e-mail enquiries@midlothian.gov.uk

1. Social Work
    Fairfield House, 8 Lothian Road
    Dalkeith EH22 3ZH
    tel 0131-270 7500 *fax 0131-271 3624*

2. **Criminal Justice Team**
    Dalkeith Social Work Centre
    11 St Andrew Street **Dalkeith**
    Midlothian EH22 1AL
    tel 0131-271 3860 *fax 0131-660 6792*

    Neil, I (service mgr)
    e-mail ian.neil@midlothian.gsx.gov.uk
    Brewer, M (team leader)
    Jessup, J (team leader)
    Borowski, M (sw)
    Brewster, A (sw)
    Carr, R (sw)
    Duncan, F (sw)
    Pemble, I (sw)
    Scorgie, A (sw)
    Varndell, D (sw)
    Anderson, M (cso)
    Kane, F (cso)
    Brady, J (cs asst)
    Hicks, B (cs asst)
    Kerr, D (cs asst)

THE MORAY COUNCIL

Out of hours contact no: 08457 565656

Community Services Department

1. Council Office
    High Street **Elgin** IV30 1BX
    tel (01343) 543451 *fax (01343) 540183*

    Riddell, Sandy (director of community
    services & chief social work officer)
    Carney, John (head of children & families)

2. Criminal Justice Team
    11 North Guildry Street
    Elgin IV30 1JR
    tel (01343) 557200 *fax (01343) 557201*

    Dempsie, Blair (operations manager)
    Kelly, Jane (team mgr) (js)
    Richford, Tish (team mgr) (js)
    Anderson, Peter (sw)
    Dufficy, Fran (sw)
    Jamieson, Sean (sw)
    Reid, Ron (sw)
    Terry, Liz (p, sw)
    Westmacott, Jane (sw)

Other Social Work Teams

3. 1 Gordon Street
    Elgin IV30 1JQ
    tel (01343) 557222 *fax (01343) 541125*

Moray Central Child Care Team
Rizza, Graeme (team manager)

Moray North Childcare Team
Harkins, Gerry (team manager)

4. **Moray West Child Care Team**
Auchernack House, High Street
Forres IV36 1DX
tel (01309) 694000 *fax (01309) 694001*

Cotter, Mark (team manager)

5. **Moray East Child Care Team**
13 Cluny Square **Buckie** AB56 1AH
tel (01542) 837200 *fax (01542) 837201*

Gordon, Jennifer (team mgr)
Leitch, Robert (sw criminal justice)

Courts

Elgin Sheriff Court
Justice of the Peace Court at Elgin

NORTH AYRSHIRE COUNCIL

1. Social Services
4th Floor, West Wing, Cunninghame
House, Friars Croft **Irvine** KA12 8EE
tel (01294) 317700 *fax (01294) 317701*

Docherty, Bernadette M (corporate
director, social services)
Paterson, Sandra (hd of service, children &
families & cj)
MacKinnon, Fiona (mgr. Ayrshire cj social
work prtnrshp)
McCrae, James (mgr cj services)

2. Criminal Justice Services
157 New Street **Stevenston** KA20 3HL
tel (01294) 463924 *fax (01294) 471283*

Weaver A (team ldr cj services)
Hamilton J (team ldr cj services)

3. Community Service Team
Block 4, Unit 2, Moorpark Place Industrial
Estate, **Stevenston** KA20 3JT
tel (01294) 608900 *fax (01294) 608897*

Watson, M (team ldr cj services)

4. **DTTO Team** (Ayrshire CJ Services
Social Work Partnership)
60 Bank Street **Irvine** KA12 0AD
tel (01294) 273110 *fax (01294) 278795*

Kane, T (team ldr cj services)

5. Criminal Justice Services
Supporting People Team
1 Glebe Street **Stevenston** KA20 3EN
tel (01294) 475800 *fax (01294) 475810*

Corcoran, K (proj ldr cj services)

6. Social Work Unit
Kilmarnock Sheriff Court
St. Marnock Street **Kilmarnock** KA1 1ED
tel (01563) 570836 fax (01563) 570837

Courts

Kilmarnock Sheriff Court
N Ayrshire District Court at Irvine

NORTH LANARKSHIRE COUNCIL

1. Housing & Social Work Services
Scott House, 73/77 Merry Street
Motherwell ML1 1JE
tel (01698) 332000 *fax (01698) 332095*

Fegan, Mary (head of social work services
& chief social work officer)

Cringles, Lillian (mgr, justice services)
Coates, Liz (service mgr, justice services)
Gardner, Keith (snr officer, high risk
offenders)
Rodger, Kay (snr officer, cj)
McAuley, Iain, (service mgr, youth justice)

2. Social Work Services
Coats House, Gartlea Road
Airdrie ML6 6JA
tel (01236) 757000

Airdrie Locality
Barrie, Scott (ssw, justice services)

3. Social Work Services
Carron House
Town Centre, Cumbernauld G67 1DP
tel (01236) 784000

Cumbernauld Locality
Juttlay, Rajinder (ssw, justice services)

4. Social Work Services
8 Emma Jay Road
Bellshill ML4 1HX
tel (01698) 346666

Bellshill Locality
O'Neill, Terri (ssw, justice services)

5. Social Work Services
    122 Bank Street
    Coatbridge ML5 1ET
    tel (01236) 622100

    Coatbridge Locality
    Mitchell, Anthea (ssw, justice services)

6. Social Work Services
    Kings Centre, King Street
    Wishaw ML2 8BS
    tel (01698) 348200

    Wishaw Locality
    Gaffney, Mark (ssw, justice services)

7. Social Work Services
    Scott House, 73/77 Merry Street
    Motherwell ML1 1JE
    tel (01698) 332100

    Motherwell Locality
    Nicol, Karen (ssw, justice services)

8. **Throughcare**
    2 Hunter Street
    Bellshill ML4 1RN
    tel (01698) 346373

    Gilmartin, Jane (ssw)
    Ranacahan, Gerry (ssw)
    Meikle, Sandra (admin asst)

    Restorative Justice
    Hughes, Maureen (service mgr)
    MacDougall, Denham (ssw)

Penal Establishment

9. Social Work Unit
    HM Prison **Shotts**
    Newmill, Canthill Road
    Shotts ML7 4LE
    tel (01501) 824100

    Mary Reilly (ssw)

Courts

Airdrie Sheriff Court
N Lanarkshire District Court at Coatbridge
N Lanarkshire District Court at Cumbernauld
N Lanarkshire District Court at Motherwell

ORKNEY ISLANDS COUNCIL

Out of hours emergency contact: via Balfour
Hospital, Kirkwall (01856) 888000

e-mail jon.humphreys@orkney.gov.uk

1. Department of Community Social Services
    School Place **Kirkwall** KW15 1NY
    tel (01856) 873535

    Macaulay, Duncan (interim director of
    community social services)
    Mitchell, Joan (asst director, community
    care)
    Smee, Gill (interim asst director,
    children & families, cj)

2. **Criminal Justice Section**
    Council Offices, School Place
    Kirkwall KW15 1NY
    tel (01856) 873535 *fax (01856) 886453*

    Humphreys, Jon (service mgr)
    Banks, Andrea (sw)
    Larmouth, John (sw)
    Hall, Lindsay (cso)
    Vacancy (pt clerical asst)
    Wilson, Donna (clerical asst)

Court

Kirkwall Sheriff Court

PERTH & KINROSS COUNCIL

1. Housing & Community Care
    Perth & Kinross Council
    5 Whitefriars Crescent, **Perth** PH2 OPA
    tel (01738) 476700 *fax (01738) 476822*

    Burke, David (depute director & chief
    social work officer, community care)
    Dean, Jim (head of community care)

2. Criminal Justice Service
    Unit 45, St Martin's House North
    King Edward Street **Perth PH1** 5UT
    tel (01738) 444244 *fax (01738) 444250*

    Gilruth, John (lead officer, cj & addictions
    services)
    Newton, John (improvement mgr)
    Cranmer, Charlie (research & info officer,
    cj services)

    Paton, Mary (snr admin asst)(js)
    Patterson, Gillian (snr admin asst)(js)
    tel (01738) 472540/472555

e-mail Mpaton@pkc.gov.uk *or*
GTPatterson@pkc.gov.uk

Courts/ Community Service Team
Nisbet, Elizabeth (ssw)
Duncan, Brenda (cj asst, com ser)
McGregor, Shona (cj asst, com ser)
Moran, Audrey (cj asst, bail sup/sao)
Pow, Barbara (cj asst, com ser)
Bryson, Colin (cj asst, horticultural officer)

Probation/High Risk & Throughcare Team
Fairlie, Alison (ssw)
Banks, Pamela (sw)
Beck, Eddie (sw)
Bonthrone, Steve (cj asst, th'care supt)
Duncan, Robbie (sw)
Egan, Susan (sw)
Fraser, Gordon (sw)
Gavin, Anne (sw)
Geekie, Radley (cj asst, accom off)
Hatley, Nicola (sw)
Michie, Joy (sw)
Mortimer, Derek (sw)
Penman, Shirley (sw, progrs)
Thomson, Robert (sw)
Warren, Alasdair (sw)
Wilkinson, Anna (sw)

Youth Justice Team
Brown, Bill (ssw)
Dickson, Alan (sw)
Garland, Tracy (sw)
McClymont, Alastair (social care off)
Vannart, Alex (sw)
Scott, Sandra (social care off)
Wheeler, Sandra (social care off)

Admin Support
Gowans, Susan (admin asst)
Aitken Aimie (clerical asst, youth justice team)
Brand, Alison (clerical asst, mngmnt supt)
Briggs, Kathryn
Kelly, Jeri
McKean, Jennifer (snr clerical asst, MAPPA)
Pearson, Elaine (snr clerical asst, mngmnt supt)
Stevenson, Jacqueline (snr clerical asst)
Young, Pauline (clerical asst, reception)

3. **Community Service Workshop**
    Glover Street **Perth** PH2 0JD
    Tel (01738) 445793

    Johnston, Ken (cj asst, cso)
    Spark, John (cs supvr)
    Given, William (cs supvr)

4. Social Work Unit
    HM Prison, 3 Edinburgh Road
    Perth PH2 8AT
    tel (01738) 626883 *fax (01738) 625964*

    Rogerson, Nicola (ssw)
    Cassidy, Susan (sw)
    Geddes, Richard (sw)
    Hewitt, Elizabeth (sw)
    MacDonald, Flora (sw)
    McKay. Margaret (sw)
    Leishman, Gill (snr clerical asst)
    Smith, Holli (snr clerical asst)

5. Social Work Unit
    HM Prison **Friarton**
    Perth PH2 8DW
    tel (01738) 625885 *fax (01738) 630544*

    Chaplin, Sarah (sw)
    Whittet, Paula (sw)

6. Social Work Unit
    Scottish Prison Service Open Estate
    tel (01382) 319333

    Brown, Christina (team leader)

    Social Work Unit
    HMP **Castle Huntly**
    Longforgan, By Dundee DD2 5HL
    fax (01382) 360510

    Greig, Lex (snr pract)
    Henderson, Suzan (sw)
    Neville, Susan (sw)
    Ritchie, Jillian (sw)
    Lamond, Alice (snr clerical asst)

    Social Work Unit
    HM Prison Noranside
    Fern By Forfar
    Angus DD8 3QY
    fax (01356) 665255

    Vacancy (snr pract)
    Mollison, Harry (sw)
    Rennie, Diane (sw)

Courts

Perth Sheriff Court
Perth & Kinross District Court

RENFREWSHIRE COUNCIL

1. Social Work Headquarters
   3rd Floor, Renfrewshire House
   Cotton Street **Paisley PA1 1TZ**
   tel 0141-842 5158 *fax 0141-842 5144*

   Macleod, Peter (director of sw)
   Hawthorn, Dorothy (head of childcare & cj)
   Paterson, John (head of community care)

   Criminal Justice Section
   tel 0141-842 5130 *fax 0141-842-5144*
   Scott, Allison (principal off, cj & addictions)
   McCrae, Jackie (ssw)
   White, Rosemary (addictions co-ord)

2. **Community Service Team**
   62 Espedair Street, Paisley PA2 6RW
   tel 0141-840 1001 *fax 0141-849 0715*

   Connelly, Mike (ssw)
   Goodwin, Irene (cso)
   Hendry, George (cso)
   McCallum, Joe (cso)
   O'Hara, Catherine (cso)
   Skouse, Jake (csa)

3. **Community Alternatives Unit**
   20 Backsneddon Street
   Paisley PA3 2DF
   tel 0141-842 3020 *fax 0141-842 1078*

   Kelly, Julie (ssw)
   Vacancy (sw)
   McKenna, Barry (sw)
   Paterson, Willie (sw)
   Sheridan, Patricia (sw)
   Vacancy (sw)
   Aitchison, Karen (sw asst)
   Boylan, John (sw asst)

4. St James Street
   Paisley PA3 2HW
   tel 0141-889 0617 *fax 0141-848 9348*

   Paisley Sheriff Court
   Maloney, Liz (ssw)
   McNamara, William (sw)
   Kersten, Paul (sw, bail off)
   Brown, Jim (sw asst diversion)

   Supervised Attendance Order Team
   Crichton, John (sw, sao)
   Gillespie, Richard (resource officer)
   Jeffrey, Elizabeth (resource officer)

5. **Johnstone Area Team**
   Floorsburn House, Floors Street
   Johnstone PA5 8TL

   tel (01505) 342300 *fax (01505) 342380*
   Trainer, John (area mgr)
   Buchan, Anne (ssw)
   Graham, James (sw)
   Seager, Mandy (sw)
   Stewart, Mary (sw)
   Hutton, George (youth crime wrkr)

6. **Paisley Area Team**
   Kelvin House, River Cart Walk
   Paisley PA1 1YS
   tel 0141-842 5151 *fax 0141-842 4136*

   Beattie, Ian (area mgr)
   Georgeson, Caroline (asst area mgr)
   West, David (ssw)
   Cloherty, Tom (sw)
   Jamieson, Paula (sw)
   Lockhart, Robert (sw)
   McEwan, James (sw)
   Irving, Heather (sw)
   McNamara, William (sw)
   Matheson, Cathy (sw)
   Wright, Irene (sw)
   Graham, Caroline (drugs wrkr)

7. **Renfrew Area Team**
   6-8 Manse Street, Renfrew PA4 8QH
   tel 0141-886 5784 *fax 0141-886 8340*

   Wilson, David (area mgr)
   Buchan, Anne (ssw)
   Bryce, Sandy (sw)
   McAleer, Alice (sw)

8. **Renfrew Drug Service**
   10 St James Street, Paisley PA3 2HT
   tel 0141-889 1223 *fax 0141-848 9776*

   Boyle, Ailsa (project leader)
   Hamilton, David (snr project wrkr)
   Fitzpatrick, Elaine (snr project wrkr)
   Bogle, Susan (young persons wrkr)
   Smith, Jim (young persons wrkr)
   Gilhooley, Paul (project wrkr)
   Galloway, Louise (drugs wrkr)
   White, John (group wrkr)
   Stuart, Caroline (family devpt wrkr)
   Findlay, Michael (dual diagnosis wrkr)
   Adams, Joan (gp outreach wrkr)

   Health Board Trust Personnel
   Ferguson, Mandy (addctns nurse mgr, Ren & Inv)
   Perry, Angela (snr nurse)
   O'Hagan, Connie (snr nurse)
   Sommerville, Kate (snr nurse)
   Forrest, Jane (snr nurse)
   Moore, Robert (nurse)

McCrae, Kirstine (harm reductn charge nurse)
McLellan, Elaine, (harm reductn nurse)
Parkinson, Margaret (nurse specialist, dual diagnosis)
Watts, Sherilee (supt wrkr)
Gray, Jacquelyn (harm reductn nurse)

9. **Renfrew Council on Alcohol**
    Mirren House, Backsneddon Street
    Paisley PA3 2AF
    tel 0141-887 0880 *fax 0141-887 8063*

    Crawford, Dr Alec (chief exec)
    Patterson, Doreen (operations mgr)
    Bryson, Ros (sensing change mgr)
    Dooley, Gina (proj leader alcohol advice)

10. **Pathways Partnership Project**
    Kelvin House, River Cart Walk
    Paisley PA1 1YS
    tel 0141-842 4113/4188 *fax 0141-842 4132*

    Wilson, Lorna (proj leader, ssw)
    Clabby, Jim (sw)
    Marshall, Harry (sw)
    Vacancy (sw)
    Toland, Frances (sw)
    Mackenzie, Barbara, (swa)

11. **North Strathclyde Community Justice Authority**
    Unit 905, Mile End Mill
    12 Seedhill Road, Paisley PA1 1JS
    tel 0141-887 6133

    Hunter, Jim (chief officer)
    Kennedy, William (planning officer)

Courts
    Paisley Sheriff Court
    Renfrewshire District Court at Paisley

SCOTTISH BORDERS COUNCIL

1. Social Work Headquarters
    Newton St Boswells
    Melrose TD6 0SA
    tel (01835) 825080 *fax (01835) 825081*

    Lowe, Andrew (director of sw)
    Gray, Marian (group mgr, criminal justice)

2. Criminal Justice Team, Social Work
    13/14 Paton Street
    Galashiels TD1 3AT
    tel (01896) 661400 *fax (01896) 661401*

    McKenzie, Ishbel (team ldr, probn, dtto, crt)

Nichol, Diane (admin asst)
Grant, Brian (sw, dtto)
Campbell, Morag (sw, probn)
Grieve, Lisa (sw, probn)
McConchie, Geraldine (sw, probn)
Sobek, Anne (sw, probn)
Thomson, Stephen (sw, probn)
McDonald, Kathryn (cjo, crt/supvn/dtto)
Wood, Liz (cjo,crt/supvn)

3. Criminal Justice Team, Social Work
    Unit 6, Linglie Mill
    Levelcrossing Road **Selkirk** TD7,5ED
    tel (01750) 725255 *fax (01750) 725285*

    Keates, Dorothy (team ldr, th'care, solo, mappa, cs, sao)
    Scott, Eirin (admin asst)
    Cousin, Marilyn (sw, th'care)
    Robertson, Toni (sw, th'care)
    Matthews, Angela (cjo, crt/vol'care)
    Birse, Billy (cjo, cs/sao)
    Pretsel, Richard (cjo, cs/sao)
    Beck, Stewart (css)
    Farrell, Kevin (css)
    Heatlie,John (css)
    Kelly, Danny (css)
    White, Jimmy (css)

Courts
    Duns Sheriff Court
    Jedburgh Sheriff Court
    Peebles Sheriff Court
    Selkirk Sheriff Court
    Scottish Borders Justice of the Peace Court at Duns
    Scottish Borders Justice of the Peace Court at Jedburgh
    Scottish Borders Justice of the Peace Court at Peebles
    Scottish Borders Justice of the Peace Court at Selkirk

SHETLAND ISLANDS COUNCIL

Out of hours contact: duty social worker (01595) 695611

e-mail firstname.surname@sic.shetland.gov.uk

www.shetland.gov.uk

1. Department of Education & Social Care
    Social Work
    91-93 St Olaf Street
    Lerwick Shetland ZE1 0ES
    tel (01595) 744400 *fax (01595) 744460*

    Sutherland, Hazel (executive director)

Criminal Justice Social Work Unit
tel (01595) 744446 *fax (01595) 744445*

Morgan, Denise (criminal justice services mgr)
McKay, Shirley (ssw)
Morton, Fiona (sw)
Prittie, Francis (sw)
Alderman, Andy (cs supvr)
Gilfillan, Frank (cs supvr)
Halcrow, Julie (cj asst)
Black, Sarah (cj support worker)

Court

Lerwick Sheriff Court

SOUTH AYRSHIRE COUNCIL

e-mail nancy.mcneil@south-ayrshire.gov.uk

1. Social Work Headquarters
    Holmston House, Holmston Road
    Ayr KA7 3BA
    tel (01292) 262111 *fax (01292) 270065*

    Stewart, Ann (head of service)
    McNeil, Nancy (criminal justice mgr)

2. **Criminal Justice Team**
    MacAdam House
    34 Charlotte Street, Ayr KA7 1EA
    tel (01292) 289749 *fax (01292) 260065*

    Court Services, Fieldwork Services
    CS Scheme, Administration
    Gilmour, A (ssw)
    Brannan, T (ssw)
    Hall, D (ssw crts)
    Wilson, B (ssw cso)

3. **Supervised Attendance Team**
    Wellington House
    25 Wellington Square, Ayr KA7 1EZ
    tel (01292) 264493 *fax (01292) 290837*

    Hall, Susan (sao off)

Courts

Ayr Sheriff Court
S Ayrshire District Court at Ayr
S Ayrshire District Court at Girvan

SOUTH LANARKSHIRE COUNCIL

1. Social Work Headquarters
    Criminal Justice Services
    Council Offices, Almada Street
    Hamilton ML3 0AA
    tel (01698) 453700 *fax (01698) 453784*

    Stevenson, Harry (exec director social work resources)
    Brackenridge, Mairi (head of adults & justice services)
    (01698) 453715
    Moore, Brian (adults & justice services mgr)
    (01698) 453901
    McGregor, Hugh (cj services mgr)
    (01698) 453902

Area Teams

2. **East Kilbride Local Office**
    1st Floor, Civic Centre
    Andrew Street, East Kilbride G74 1AD
    tel (01355) 807000 *fax (01355) 264458*

    Finnegan, Hilary (team leader)
    Foster, Mary (sw)
    Glynn, Joe (sw)
    McGinn, Norma (sw)
    Tracey Warwick (sw)

3. **Rutherglen & Cambuslang Local Office**
    380 King Street
    Rutherglen G73 1DQ
    tel 0141-613 5000 *fax 0141-613 5075*

    McCarthy, Isobel (team leader)
    Mauchan, Kevin (sw)
    Cocozza, Caroline (sw)
    Robertson, David (sw)

4. **Blantyre Local Office**
    45 John Street, Blantyre G72 0JG
    tel (01698) 527400 *fax (01698) 527428*

    Johnson, Hazel (team leader)
    Crumley, Breda (sw)
    Tavendale, Juliette (sw)
    O'Donnell, Alex (sw)
    Prentice, Moira (sw)
    McMullan, Margaret (groupworker)

    Soones, Carol Anne (training & devpt)

5. **Hamilton Local Office**
    Brandongate, 1 Leechlee Road

Hamilton ML3 0XB
tel (01698) 455400 *fax (0698) 283257*

McTaggart, Ranald (team leader)
Fleming, Sheena (sw)
McEwan, Ronnie (sw)
Reid, Lennox (sw)
Shaw, Janice (sw)
Jeffrey, Carol (diversion co-ord)

6. **Clydesdale Local Office**
Council Offices, South Vennel
Lanark ML11 7JT
tel (01555) 673000 *fax (01555) 673401*

McKendrick, Alf (team leader)
Dunnery, Theresa (sw)
McTavish, Sarah (sw)
Mc Donald Stuart (sw)
Hutchison, Moira (sw)
Lochiel, Isobel (sw)

7. **Larkhall Local Office**
6 Claude Street, Larkhall ML9 2BU
tel (01698) 884656 *fax (01698) 307504*

Monaghan, Mary (team leader)
Paul Lockhart (sw)
Prescott, Karrie (sw)

8. **Community Service Unit**
Blantyre Local Office
45 John Street, Blantyre G72 0JG
tel (01698) 527484/527467/527408
fax (01698) 417428

English, Allan (team leader cs)
Canning, Tom (cs officer)
Boyle, Rosemarie (cs officer)
Harvey, John (cs officer)
McGeever, Mark (cs officer)
Muir, Jim (cs resource asst)
Pirrie, Andrew (cs resource asst)

Constable, Bill (cs officer)
tel 01555 673000
Lockhart, Brian (cs assist)
tel 01555 673000

9. **Community Service Workshop**
2/3a Third Road
High Blantyre Industrial Estate
High Blantyre GT2 0UP
tel (01698) 452030 *fax (01698 824799)*

Allan English (team leader)
O'Shea (sao officer)
Inness, John (sao officer)
Lamb, Ian (cs resource asst)
McKay, Stan (cs resource asst)

Court Units

10. **Hamilton Sheriff Court**
Beckford Street, Hamilton ML3 6AA
tel (01698) 282957

Social Work Court Unit
101 Almada Street
Hamilton ML3 0EX
tel (01698) 452050 *fax (01698) 457427*

Gorman, Tina (team leader)
Brady, John (sw)
Dempsey, Robert (sw)
Green, David (sw)
Murdoch, Caroline (sw)
Walker, Joyce (sw)
Adams, Janet (sw asst)
Borden, Claire (sw asst)
Hughes, Karen (sw asst)
Loudon, Jackie (sw asst)
Wilson, Sarah (sw, mental health)

11. **Lanark Sheriff Court**
Hope Street
Lanark ML11 7NQ
tel (01555) 661531

Social Work Unit
Council Offices, South Vennel
Lanark ML11 7JT
tel (01555) 673000 *fax (01555) 673401*

Brady, John (sw)

DTTO

12. High Patrick Street
Hamilton
tel (01698) 452800 *fax (01698) 452831*

Santosh, Dade (team leader)
Irvine, Alan (sw)
Young, Kelly (sw)

Youth Justice Team

13. Calder House, Bardykes Road
Blantyre G72 9UJ
tel (01698) 527230 *fax (01698) 527210*

McAllister, Marion (yj co-ord)
Simpson, Simpson (sw)
Dawson, Catherine (sw)
McCann, Marie Therese (sw)
Skeffington, Brenda (sw)
Kelly, Mary Ann (sw)
Ryan, Lindsay (sw)
Wright, Gillian (sw)
Welsh, Helen (sw)
James, Victor (groupworker)
McBride, Michael (groupworker)

Parenting Team
tel (01698) 527288 *fax (01698) 527210*

Grimley, Tricia (sw)
Gallagher, Deborah (family supt wrkr)
Gallagher, Robert (family supt wrkr)
Orr, Natalie (family supt wrkr)

Restorative Justice
tel (01698) 527288 *fax (01698) 527210*

Colvin, Rhoda (rest just co-ord)
Crawford, Chelsea (rest just wrkr)
McLachlan, Maggie (rest just wrkr)
Spence, Charlotte (rest just wrkr)

Courts

S Lanarkshire District Court at E Kilbride
S Lanarkshire District Court at Rutherglen

STIRLING COUNCIL

Out of hours contact: emergency duty team
(01786) 470500

1. Criminal Justice Services
    Wolfcraig, 1 Dumbarton Road
    Stirling FK8 2LQ
    tel (01786) 463812 *fax (01786) 443850*

    Criminal Justice Service
    Friel, Des (head of supt for people)
    Grassom, Michael (service mgr)

    Probation, & Throughcare Team
    Smillie, Alistair (team ldr)
    Haney, John (snr pract)
    Sanchez, Alexandra (sw)
    Whyte, Stephanie (sw)
    McDonald, Seona (sw)
    Russell, Bobby (sw)
    Casey, Carol (sw)
    McCartney, James (cj off)
    Shillington, Aileen (cj off)

    **Court, Community Service &
    Supervised Attendance Orders**
    Grinly, Helen (team ldr)
    Wilson, Jimmy (sw)
    Walls, Alison (sw)
    Kazemi, Sorour (sw)
    Kay, Linda (crt sw)
    Clark, Sarah (cj off)
    Gilmour, Norman (cj off)
    Lee, Michelle (cj off)

2. **Forth Valley Criminal Justice**
    Drug Services
    Drummond House, Wellgreen Place

Stirling FK8 2EG
tel (01786) 443900 *fax (01786) 443901*

Vacancy (team mgr)

DTTO Team
Mackie, Dot (snr pract)
Hillen, Robbie Anne (sw)
Cassells, Irene (charge nurse)
Parke, Paul (staff nurse)
Blair, Mary (sw asst)

Fast Track Team
Snell, Susan (charge nurse)
Neary, Denise (charge nurse)
Stewart, Norma (staff nurse)
Denholm, Anne (staff nurse)
Blair, Calum (sw asst)

Penal Establishment

3. Social Work Unit
    HM Institution **Cornton Vale**
    Cornton Road, Stirling FK9 5NY
    tel (01786) 885359 *fax (01786) 833597*

    Corvi, Elaine (team ldr)
    Thomas, Janet (team ldr)
    Stewart, Michael (snr pract)
    Murray, Ian (sw)
    Travers, Jane (sw)

Courts

Stirling Sheriff Court
Stirling District Court

WEST DUNBARTONSHIRE COUNCIL

Out of hours contact no: 0800 811 505

1. Social Work Headquarters
    Social Work and Health
    Council Offices, Garshake Road
    Dumbarton G82 3PU
    tel (01389) 737000 *fax (01389) 737513*

    Clark, William (executive director)

2. Social Work and Health
    Criminal Justice Services
    Municipal Buildings, Station Road
    Dumbarton G82 1NR
    tel (01389) 738484 *fax (01389) 738480*

    Firth, Norman (partnership mgr)

    Assessment Team
    Steven, Craig (ssw)
    Beattie, Graham (sw)
    McLaughlin, Marielaine (sw)

Ritchie, Allan (sw)
Robertson, Helen (sw)
Currie, Anne (bail officer)

Probation Team
Dady, Philip (ssw)
Brown, Janice (sw)
Carruthers, Donna (sw)
Petrina Traynor (sw)
Sellars, Connie (sw)
Wrigley, Lorraine (women's supt off, domestic abuse)
McVey, Grace (women's supt off, domestic abuse)

Groupworkers
Ferguson, Marianne (groupworker)
Gallagher, Michael (groupworker)
Haggerty, Eddie (groupworker)
Johnstone, Alex (groupworker)

Throughcare Team
Livingstone, Maureen (ssw)
McGroggan, Isobel (sw)
McGuire, John (sw)
MacKenzie, Valerie (sw)
Rivero, Rita (sw mental health)

Community Service
Ruth Pryce (temp cs manager)
Monaghan, Seamus (cso)
Swanson, Alistair (cso)
Freeland, Bill (asst cso)
Catherine Carr (sao)

Nicola Taylor (temp sao)

DTTO
Joanna Dowall (ssw)
Boag, Chris (sw)

Courts

Dumbarton Sheriff Court
W Dunbartonshire District Court at Dumbarton
W Dunbartonshire District Court at Clydebank

WEST LOTHIAN COUNCIL

Out of hours contact no: (01506) 777401

e-mail Tim.Ward@westlothian.gov.uk (non-secure)
Tim.Ward@westlothian.gsx.gov.uk (secure)

1. Social Policy
    Strathbrock Partnership Centre
    189a West Main Street
    Broxburn EH52 5LH

tel (01506) 777000 *fax (01506) 771827*
Blair, Grahame (head of social policy)

2. Lomond House, Beveridge Square
    Livingston EH54 6QF
    tel (01506) 775900 *fax (01506) 775925*
    criminaljusticeteam@westlothian.gov.uk

Criminal Justice Services
Ward, Tim (criminal justice mgr)
Oghene, Gillian (group mgr)

Court & Assessment Team
Streater, Paul (team mgr)
Creighton, John (snr pract)
Foster, Lynne (snr pract)
Hogg, Edith (snr pract)
Gilchrist, Jim (snr pract)
Kenny, Ada (snr pract)
Aien, Alison (sw)

Probation Supervision Team
Ferguson, Linda (team mgr)
Carter, Kevin (snr pract)
Kelly, Patrick (snr pract)
Murphy, Viv (snr pract)
Gittens,Simon (sw)
Vacancy (sw)
Wilson, Cameron (sw)
Paxton, Chris (sw)
McBain, Amy (cj asst)

Throughcare Team
Probka, Linda (team mgr)
Conacher, Moira (snr pract)
Holmes, Stephen (snr pract)
Morton, Andrew (snr pract)
Timpany, David (sw)
Graham, Nik (cj asst)

Community Work Order Team
Probka, Linda (team mgr)
Hughson, Brian (cwo off)
Young, David (cwo off)
Millar, Lesley (cwo asst)
Moore, Joanne (cwo asst)
Reynolds, Pauline (cwo asst)

Drug Treatment & Testing Orders Team
Oxley, Sharon (team mgr)
Campbell, Caroline (sw)
Pritchard, Geoff (proj wkr)
Carroll, Dr Jason
Mckechnie, Julie (nurse)
Vanbeck, Pauline (nurse)

Courts

Linlithgow Sheriff Court
Livingston Sheriff Court

NACRO – THE CRIME REDUCTION CHARITY

Head Office

Park Place, 10-12 Lawn Lane
London SW8 1UD
tel 020-7840 7200 *fax 020-7840 7240*
www.nacro.org.uk
Nacro is registered as a charity, no. 226171
e-mails: unless otherwise stated all emails
are firstname.lastname@nacro.org.uk

Websites

Corporate: www.nacro.org.uk
Disclosure service: www.nacrodisclosures.
org.uk
Mental health: www.nacromentalhealth.
org.uk
Safer Society magazine: www.safersociety.
org.uk

National Helpline

Resettlement *Plus* Helpline
Information and advice for ex-offenders,
their families and people working with
them
tel 020-7840 6464 *fax 020-7735 4666*
Freephone 0800 0181 259 for ex-offenders,
their family and friends only
e-mail helpline@nacro.org.uk

Board of Directors

Paul Cavadino (chief exec)
tel 020-7840 7208 *fax 020-7840 7238*

Liz Walker (acting director finance &
resources)
Head Office
tel 020-7840 7210 *fax 020-7840 7240*
Birmingham
tel 0121-380 4879 *fax 0121-359 3510*

Val Todd (director HR)
Head Office
tel 020-7840 7231 *fax 020-7840 7242*
Birmingham
tel 0121-380 4884 *fax 0121-359 3510*

Claire Bassett (director operations)
Head Office
tel 020-7840 7210 *fax 020-7840 7240*
Birmingham
tel 0121-250 5233 *fax 0121-359 3510*

Jackie Worrall (director policy & public
affairs)
tel 020-7840 7209 *fax 020-7840 7240*
mobile 07976 715340

Tim Bell (director housing)
Nottingham
tel 0115-962 8942 *fax 0115-962 8949*

Central Services

Communications

Melior Whitear (head of communications)
tel 020-7840 7214 *fax 020-7840 7240*

Cynthia Sutherland (bookings)
tel 020-7840 7219 *fax 020-7840 7240*

Caroline Fuller (conference enquiries)
tel 07974 406 673
e-mail events@nacro.org.uk

Sally Burnell (media relations mgr)
tel 020-7840 7216 *fax 020-7840 7240*
e-mail media@nacro.org.uk

Cynthia Sutherland (publications mgr)
tel 020-7840 7219 *fax 020-7840 7240*
e-mail publications@nacro.org.uk

Finance

Liz Walker (acting director finance)
Head Office
tel 020-7840 7210 *fax 020-7840 7240*
Birmingham
tel 0121-380 4879 *fax 0121-359 3510*

Finance team

Challenge House,148-150 High Street
Aston, Birmingham B6 4US
tel 0121-380 4879 *fax 0121-359 3510*

Fundraising

Head Office
tel 020-7840 7224 *fax 020-7840 7240*

Equality and Diversity

Kulbir Shergill (head of equality strategy)
PO Box 142, Fishponds, Bristol BS16 7WG
tel/fax 0117 910 4990
e-mail kulbir.shergill@nacro.org.uk

Health and Safety

Rocco Zitola (head of resources)
tel 0121-250 5250 *fax 0121 359 3510*

HR Directorate (and pensions)

Val Todd (director HR)
Head Office
tel 020-7840 7231 *fax 020-7840 7242*
Birmingham
tel 0121-380 4884 *fax 0121-359 3510*

Internal Audit and Risk

Richard Hollands (head of audit &

risk review)
Challenge House,148-150 High Street
Aston, Birmingham B6 4US
tel 0121-380 4844 *fax 0121-359 3510*

IT

Anthony Bezuidenhout (head of ICT)
Challenge House, 148-150 High Street
Aston, Birmingham B6 4US
tel 0121-380 4864 *fax 0121-270 2324*

Resources

Challenge House, 148-150 High Street
Aston, Birmingham B6 4US
tel 0121-380 4847 *fax 0121-359 3510*

Rocco Zitola (head of resources)
tel 0121-250 5250

John Roberts (national procurement mgr)

tel 0121-380 4852

Tony Eaton (facilities mgr)
tel 07711 129680

Dionne Foster (legal & insurance officer)
tel 0121-380 4849

Operational Directorate Structures

Housing

Tim Bell (director Housing)
16 Vivian Avenue, Sherwood Rise
Nottingham NG5 1AF
tel 0115-962 8942 *fax 0115-962 8949*

Performance and Planning

Helen O'Connor (Assistant Director)
1 Hastings Street, Normanton
Derby DE23 6QQ
tel (01332) 272414 *fax (01332) 273910*

Dean Hall (Acting Quality and Training
mgr)
tel 0161-860 2009 *fax 0161-860 7555*

Steven Bambrough (Performance Review)
16 Vivian Avenue, Sherwood Rise
Nottingham NG5 1AF
tel 0115-985 7744 *fax 0115-962 8948*

Property and Development

Dave McCarthy (Assistant Director)
567a Barlow Moor Road
Chorlton-cum-Hardy, Manchester M21
8AE
tel 0161-860 7444 *fax 0161-860 7555*

John Frame (Senior Surveyor)
1 Hastings Street, Normanton, Derby
DE23 6QQ

tel (01332) 273703 *fax (01332) 273910*
e-mail maintenance.helpdesk@nacro.org.uk

National Business Development Mgrs

Hilary Hare Duke & Una Mulrenan
16 Vivian Avenue, Sherwood Rise
Nottingham NG5 1AF
tel 0115-985 7744 *fax 0115-962 8948*

Resettlement, North

Paul Phillips (asst director)
tel 0115-985 7744
Kanwaljit Singh (area mgr, Midlands)
16 Vivian Avenue,Sherwood Rise
Nottingham NG5 1AF
tel 0115-985 7744 *fax 0115-962 8948*

Patsy Davis (area mgr, North West)
567a Barlow Moor Road
Manchester M21 8AE
tel 0161-860 7444 *fax 0161-860 7555*

Sara Bain (area mgr, Lincolnshire &
Newark)
12 Melville Street, Lincoln LN5 7HW
tel (01552) 525383 *fax (01552) 878381*

Vin Murtagh (area mgr, N Wales &
Cheshire)
1 Trinity Square, Llandudno LL30 2PY
tel (01492) 860437 *fax (01492) 878703*

Resettlement, South

John Lowery (Assistant Director)
tel (01245) 606010

Brendan O'Mahony (area mgr, Essex &
Herts)
Rosebery House, 41 Springfield Road
Chelmsford CM2 6QZ
tel (01245) 606010 *fax (01245) 606011*

Joe Hellawell (area mgr, London)
159 Clapham Road, London SW9 0PU
tel 020-7840 6480 *fax 020-7840 6481*

Operations

Claire Bassett (director operations)
Head Office
tel 020-7840 7210 *fax 020-7840 7240*
Birmingham
tel 0121-250 5233 *fax 0121-359 3510*

National Delivery Team

Fenland House, The Chase, Chapel Road
Wisbech, Cambridgeshire PE13 1RH
Linda Goult (head of operational delivery)
tel (01945) 587 898 *fax (01945) 582 670*

For national delivery standards officer
enquiries, contact Linda Goult (see above)

National Programme Devpt Team

Simon Evans (head of business devpt)
Challenge House, 148-150 High Street
Aston, Birmingham B6 4US
tel 0121-250 5232 *fax 0121-359 3510*
mobile 07776 207 332

Ian Hands (business devpt mgr, East)
1 Hastings Street, Derby DE23 6QQ
tel (01332) 273 703 *fax (01332) 273 910*
mobile 07815 858 497

Chris Dare (business devpt mgr, Midlands)
Challenge House, 148-150 High Street
Aston, Birmingham B6 4US
tel 0121-380 4855 *fax 0121-359 3510*
e-mail youthactivities@nacro.org.uk

Michelle Hill (business devpt mgr, North
West)
The Cuthbert Centre (Unit 1)
877 Ashton Old Road, Openshaw
Manchester, M11 2NA
tel 0161-223 3568 *fax 0161-223 9599*

Ian Sorrell (business devpt mgr, North)
Aldenstone, Townhead, Alston
Cumbria CA9 3SL
tel 01434 381 429 and 07768 631 187

Gordon Murray (business devpt mgr,
South)
tel 07980 941 367

Sophie Haines (business devpt mgr, South)
tel 07977 936 989

Ashish Poddar (business devpt mgr, Wales)
Bridge Chambers, 1 Godfrey Road,
Newport NP20 4NX
tel (01633) 213 434 *fax (01633) 213 435*

Austin Riley (ntnl peer mentoring co-ordtr)
Challenge House, 148-150 High Street
Aston, Birmingham B6 4US
tel 0121-380 4858 *fax 0121-359 3510*

Amandeep Shukla (research & info officer)
Challenge House, 148-150 High Street
Aston, Birmingham B6 4US
tel 0121-380 4857 *fax 0121-359 3510*

Regional offices

East

Susan Crampton (regional mgr)
Fenland House, The Chase, Chapel Road
Wisbech, Cambridgeshire PE13 1RH
tel (01945) 587 898 *fax (01945) 582 670*

Midlands

Charlie Duffin (regional mgr)
Apollo House, Rounds Green Road
Oldbury B69 2DF
tel 0121-552 9589 *fax 0121-552 1786*

North

Brian Rowcroft (regional mgr)
Hutchinson Street
Stockton-on-Tees TS18 1RW
tel (01642) 615554 *fax (01642) 611050*

South

Nigel Good (regional mgr)
Golden Arrow House
237a Queenstown Road
London SW8 3NP
tel 020-7978 3000 *fax 020-7978 3001*

West and Wales

Val Metcalf (regional mgr)
201 Kensington, Liverpool L7 2RF
tel 0151-260 4072 *fax 0151-260 4322*

Wales

Anne Newhall (area mgr)
63 High Street, Bangor LL57 1NR
tel (01248) 354602 *fax (01248) 353400*

Policy and Public Affairs

Jackie Worrall (director Policy and Public
Affairs)
tel 020-7840 7209 *fax 020-7840 7240*
mobile 07976 715340

Debra Clothier (national policy devpt mgr)
tel 020-7840 1205 *fax 020-7840 1213*
mobile 07854 543 783

Jackie Lowthian (national policy devpt
mgr)
mobile 07968 477 984 *fax 020-7840 7240*

Melior Whitear (head of communications)
tel 020-7840 7214 *fax 020-7840 7240*

Mervyn Barrett (head of resettlement info)
tel 020-7840 6432 *fax 020-7840 6420*

Sally Wentworth James (national devpt
advisor, research & evaluation)
mobile 07714 099155
e-mail sally.james@nacro.org.uk

Services for organisations and partnerships

Housing Services to CJ agencies

Dave McCarthy
567a Barlow Moor Road
Chorlton-cum-Hardy, Manchester M21
8AE
tel 0161-860 7444 *fax 0161-860 7555*

Mental Health
General enquiries and consultancy
services
Park Place, 10-12 Lawn Lane, London
SW8 1UD
tel 020-7840 1209 *fax 020-7840 1213*
e-mail mentalhealth@nacro.org.uk
Lucy Smith
website www.nacromentalhealth.org.uk

Operations services to CJ agencies
(ISSPs, YIPs, NOMS, learning and skills)
See National Devpt Team (above)
For general enquiries contact Amandeep
Shukla (research & info officer)
tel 0121-380 4857 *fax 0121-359 3510*

Prison and Resettlement Services
Prisons and Resettlement Team
Contact to find out about developing new
services, training for prison officers or
Nacro's existing resettlement services
in prisons in England and Wales.

General enquiries and mail to
Challenge House,148-150 High Street
Aston, Birmingham B6 4US
tel 0121-380 4870 *fax 0121-359 3510*
e-mail naomi.byron@nacro.org.uk

Prison and Resettlement Managers
Angela Hughes
tel 0121-380 4870 or 07976 715 359

Sue Howes
tel (01924) 339154 or 07967 177 890
e-mail sue@howes16.fsnet.co.uk

Judith Ford
tel (01299) 269218 or 07976 711987
e-mail judith.ford@nacro079.easynet.co.uk

Resettlement Information Division
tel 020-7840 6432 *fax 020-7840 6420*
159 Clapham Road, London SW9 0PU
Contact Mervyn Barrett

Disclosure Service
www.nacrodisclosures.org.uk
159 Clapham Road, London SW9 0PU
tel 020-7840 6475 *fax 0207 735 4666*
e-mail nacro.disclosures@nacro.org.uk

Resettlement **Plus** *Helpline*
159 Clapham Road, London SW9 0PU
tel 020-7840 6464 *fax 020-7840 6420*
or Freephone 0800 0181 259

e-mail helpline@nacro.org.uk

Resettlement Service Finder
*information database for probation
services and prisons*
Louis Anson
tel 020-7840 6461 *fax 020-7840 6420*

Equality and diversity
General enquiries
Park Place, 10-12 Lawn Lane, London
SW8 1UD
tel 020-7840 1203 *fax 020-7840 1213*
e-mail raceunit@nacro.org.uk

Consultancy services
tel 07711 667 241
Contact James Riches

Research services
tel 07773 343 984
Contact Neena Samota

Youth Crime
Consultancy, development, training
& research services

General enquiries
Park Place, 10-12 Lawn Lane, London
SW8 1UD
tel 020-7840 1203 *fax 020-7840 1213*
e-mail youth.crime@nacro.org.uk

Nacro Cymru Youth Offending Unit
c/o Neath Port Talbot Youth Offending
Team
Cramic Way, Port Talbot SA13 1RU
tel 07968 315072
Contact Sue Thomas
e-mail suebthomas@btinternet.com

Services for individuals and communities

Amlwch

Nacro Cymru Youth Activities Projects
Contact via Bangor Eductn and
Employmt Services address

Bangor

Nacro Cymru Housing in N Wales
106-108 High Street, Bangor LL57 1NS
tel (01248) 371192 *fax (01248) 371925*
e-mail alison.jones@nacro.org.uk or
julie.simonsen@nacro.org.uk

**Nacro Cymru Educn & Emplt
Services in North Wales and DIP**
63 High Street, Bangor LL57 1NR
tel (01248) 354602 *fax (01248) 353400*
e-mail anne.newhall@nacro.org.uk

Nacro Cymru Operations
117 High Street, Bangor LL57 1NT
tel/fax (01248) 354667

Barnsley

Nacro Grimethorpe Training Centre
The Old Library, Elizabeth Street
Barnsley S72 7HZ
tel (01226) 780961 *fax (01226) 711483*
e-mail janice.wilson@nacro.org.uk

Barrow-in-Furness

**Nacro Educn & Emplt Junior
and Snr YIP, and MOVES Project**
Hindpool Community Centre
Nelson Street
Barrow-in-Furness LA14 1NF
tel (01229) 871420 *fax (01229) 432697*
e-mail helen.bunting@nacro.org.uk

Basildon

Nacro Housing in Essex and Herts
Suite 2, 2nd Floor, Eastgate Business
Centre, Southernhay, Basildon SS14 1EB
tel (01268) 282822 *fax (01268) 282860*
e-mail angela.martin@nacro.org.uk

Bedford

Bedford Score Project
Room B211, Riverside House
Bedford Borough Council, Town Hall,
St Paul's Square, Bedford MK40 1SJ
mobile 07920 571586
e-mail john.jones@nacro.org.uk

Bethesda

Nacro Educn & Emplt Services
10-12 High Street
Bethesda Becws Pesda
Gwynedd LL57 3AF
tel/fax (01248) 605289
e-mail sharon.mostyn-williams
@nacro.org.uk

Bexley

Nacro Bexley Young Persons Foyer
1 James Watt Way, Erith
Kent DA8 1FN
tel (01322) 333520
e-mail nola.saunders@nacro.org.uk

Birmingham

**Nacro Educn & Emplt Services
in Birmingham**
Southside Centre
13 Griffins Brooks Lane
Bournville, Birmingham B30 1QN
tel 0121-477 5863 *fax 0121-477 5862*
e-mail info.birmingham@nacro.org.uk

Nacro Housing in Birmingham
Suite 2, 1st Floor, Alma House
Newtown Shopping Centre, Aston
Birmingham B19 2SS
tel 0121-333 6795 *fax 0121-359 4213*
e-mail surinder.kapur@nacro.org.uk

Blackburn

**Nacro Educn & Emplt Services
in Lancashire**
Units 3 & 4, Walker Street
Blackburn BB1 1BG
tel/fax (01254) 695653
e-mail alan.baybutt@nacro.org.uk

Blackpool

Nacro Tenancy Support in Lancs
Marquis House, 273 Church Street
Blackpool FY1 3PF
tel (01253) 625204 *fax (01253) 620458*
e-mail paula.rutherford@nacro.org.uk

Bolton

Nacro Educn & Emplt Services
Ruth Street, off St George's Road
Bolton BL1 2QA
tel (01204) 381656 *fax (01204) 559952*
e-mail paula.telford@nacro.org.uk

Boston

'Get Involved' Sports Project
14-16 High Street, Boston PE21 8SH
tel (01205) 359664 *fax (01205) 311441*
e-mail 'Get Involved':
get.involved@nacro.org.uk

Nacro Housing in Boston
34 Middlecott Close, Boston PE21 7RD
tel (01205) 310718 *fax (01205) 367966*
e-mail penny.lait@nacro.org.uk

Bradford

**Nacro Bradford Intensive Supvn &
Surveillance Prog, Resettlement
& Aftercare Prog, Custody
Leaver Supt Prog, Volunteer Prog**
Bank House, 41 Bank Street

Bradford BD1 1RD
tel (01274) 436060 *fax (01274) 436061*
e-mail jim.brady@bradford.gov.uk

**Nacro Bail Support Scheme in
Yorkshire and Humberside**
Contact via the Leeds office

Braintree

Nacro Community Sports Project
c/o Braintree District Council,
Causeway House, Braintree CM7 9HB
tel (01376) 552525 ext 2342
fax (01376) 557726
e-mail jamesm@braintree.gov.uk

**Nacro Housing in Essex and Herts
(Trinity House)**
Contact via Chelmsford office

Bridport

Nacro Educn & Emplt Services
Contact via the Poole office

Brighton

**Nacro Educn & Emplt
Services Sussex**
Unit D5, Enterprise Point
Melbourne Street
Brighton BN2 3LH
tel (01273) 704010 *fax (01273) 704028*
e-mail melany.jovic@nacro.org.uk

Broxbourne

Nacro Sports Project
c/o Community Services (Leisure)
Broxbourne Borough Council
Bishops College, Churchgate
Cheshunt EN8 9XF
tel (01992) 785555 ext 5908
fax (01282) 455458
e-mail alex.hepton@nacro.org.uk

Burnley

**Nacro Youth Inclusion Project
Graft Football Project
V Involved Volunteer Project**
Parkside Methodist Church
Myrtle Avenue, Burnley BB11 5AH
tel (01282) 455457 *fax (01282) 455458*
e-mail rebecca.keville@nacro.org.uk

Burton-on-Trent

**Nacro Eductn and Employmt
Services in Staffordshire**
4 Hawkins Lane

Burton-on-Trent DE14 1PT
tel/fax (01283) 546727
e-mail jenny.harvey@nacro.org.uk

Bury

Nacro Educn & Emplt Services
Unit 3, Birch Business Park
Todd Street, Bury BL9 5BQ
tel 0161-763 5566 *fax 0161-763 3233*
e-mail elizabeth.simpson@nacro.org.uk

Carlisle

Nacro Extra-Time Football Project
c/o Culture, Leisure and Sport Services
Carlisle City Council, Civic Centre
Carlisle CA3 8QG
tel (01228) 817371 or 07816 522147
fax (01228) 817369
e-mail steve.torre@nacro.org.uk

**Nacro Educn & Emplt Services
and Junior YIP**
Stanley Street, Workington CA14 2JG
tel (01900) 604488 *fax (01900) 65131*

Castleford

**Nacro Castleford & Knottingley YIPs
and Gaps Football Project**
Hilltop Community Centre
Airedale City Business Park
Kershaw Avenue, Airedale WF10 3ES
tel (01977) 604932 *fax (01977) 604824*
e-mail helen.duke@nacro.org.uk

Chatham

**Nacro Educn & Emplt Services
in Kent & Medway**
Newbridge House, 18 New Road Avenue
Chatham ME4 6BA
tel (01634) 818305 *fax (01634) 812727*
e-mail vanessa.austin@nacro.org.uk

Chelmsford

Nacro Housing in Essex and Herts
Rosebery House, 41 Springfield Road
Chelmsford CM2 6QZ
tel (01245) 606010 *fax (01245) 606011*
e-mail jackie.leno@nacro.org.uk

Nacro Community Sports Project
Chelmsford Sport and Athletics Centre
Salerno Way, Chelmsford CM1 2EH
tel (01245) 605665 *fax (01245) 491851*
e-mail Sports Project
david.streetley@nacro.org.uk

Chester

Nacro Housing in Cheshire
2 Handels Court, Northgate Street
Chester CH1 2HT
tel (01244) 318555 *fax (01244) 318858*
e-mail rachel.richards@nacro.org.uk

Nacro Milestones Housing Project
16 Canalside, Chester CH1 3LH
tel (01244) 318232/340794
fax (01244) 314009
e-mail rachel.richards@nacro.org.uk

Clacton-on-Sea

**Nacro Educn & Emplt Services
in East Anglia, Football
Foundation Project**
102 Oxford Road
Clacton-on-Sea CO15 3TH
tel (01255) 431877 *fax (01255) 224129*
e-mail E&E: diane.boyd@nacro.org.uk
e-mail Football Foundation Project
bryan.mcmanus@nacro.org.uk

Nacro Housing in Essex & Herts
Contact via Chelmsford office

Colchester

Nacro Housing in Essex & Herts
Suite 2, Unit 6, Challenge Way
Colchester CO1 2LY
tel (01206) 864209 *fax (01206) 866586*
e-mail robert.harper@nacro.org.uk

Colwyn Bay

Nacro Cymru Youth Choices
23a Abergele Road
Colwyn Bay LL29 7RS
tel/fax (01492) 534674
e-mail anne.newhall@nacro.org.uk

Nacro Cymru DAWN
35-37 Princes Drive
Colwyn Bay LL29 8PD
tel (01492) 523690 *fax (01492) 523691*

Nacro Cymru DIP
The DIP Building, 13 Princes Drive
Colwyn Bay LL29 8HT
tel (01492) 536672 *fax (01492) 535069*
e-mail anne.newhall@nacro.org.uk

Nacro Cymru Housing in N Wales
Contact via Llandudno office

Corby

**Nacro Corby Sports Project
(Positive Programmes)**
Connaughty Centre, Cottingham Road

Corby, Northants NN17 1SY
tel (01536) 275860 *fax (01536) 275866*
e-mail dean.tams@nacro.org.uk

Coventry

Nacro Housing in Coventry
Rooms 13 and 14, 1st Floor
Koco Building, Arches Industrial Estate
Spon End, Coventry CV1 3JQ
tel 024-7671 5113 *fax 024-7671 1693*
e-mail heather.horton@nacro.org.uk

Darlington

**Nacro Educn & Emplt Services
in Tees Valley**
John Street, Darlington DL1 1LG
tel (01325) 245587 *fax (01325) 242599*
e-mail valerie.cooper@nacro.org.uk

Denbigh

**Nacro Cymru Housing in N Wales
(Symud Ymlaen and NEST)**
15A Bridge Street, Denbigh LL16 3LF
tel/fax Symud Ymlaen (01745) 814123
tel/fax NEST (01745) 815739
e-mail Symud Ymlaen
dawn.barraclough@nacro.org.uk
e-mail NEST
becky.torrington@nacro.org.uk

Derby

Nacro Housing in Derby
1 Hastings Street, Normanton
Derby DE23 6QQ
tel (01332) 273703 *fax (01332) 273910*
e-mail dale.nicholson@nacro.org.uk

Nacro Osmaston Family Project
28-30 Varley Street, Allenton
Derby DE24 8DE
tel (01332) 384414 *fax (01332) 203679*
e-mail margaret.woodbridge@nacro.org.uk

Nacro Educn & Emplt Services
8 Siddals Road, Derby DE1 2PW
tel (01332) 360113 *fax (01332) 347159*
e-mail joel.booth@nacro.org.uk

Dudley

**Nacro Educn & Emplt Services
in the Black Country**
Maple House, Rear of 12-14 High Street
Pensnett, West Midlands DY6 8XD
tel (01384) 276020 *fax (01384) 276021*
e-mail mark.guy@nacro.org.uk

Epping

Nacro & Epping Forest Community Sport and Leisure Project
Ongar Youth Centre, The Gables
Fyfield Road, Ongar ÇM5 0GA
tel 07709 402008 *fax (01993) 564120*
e-mail john.manning@nacro.org.uk

Nacro Housing in Essex and Herts
Contact via Harlow office

Gainsborough

Nacro Housing in Lincolnshire
3 North Street, Gainsborough DN21 2HP
tel (01427) 617757 *fax (01427) 678012*
e-mail jamie.wrath@nacro.org.uk

Gateshead

Nacro Football Project
Highfield Community Centre
Whinfield Way, Highfield
Rowlands Gill, Gateshead NE39 1EH
tel (01207) 549759
e-mail anne.hayes@nacro.org.uk

Grantham

Nacro Housing in Lincolnshire
35 Westgate, Grantham NG31 6LY
tel (01476) 578503 *fax (01476) 592935*
e-mail ruth.baker@nacro.org.uk

Harlow

Nacro Housing in Essex and Herts
Shield House, Elizabeth Way
The Pinnacles, Harlow CM19 5AR
tel (01279) 443303 *fax (01279) 443304*
e-mail christine.mckie@nacro.org.uk

Hartlepool

Nacro Educn & Emplt Services in Tees Valley
Unit 2, Hartlepool Workshops
Usworth Road, Hartlepool TS25 1PD
tel (01429) 863335 *fax (01429) 860960*
e-mail barry.hockborn@nacro.org.uk

Hartlepool Drugs Team
Hartlepool Community Drug Centre
Whitby Street,Hartlepool TS24 7AB
tel (01429) 852836 *fax (01429) 285001*
e-mail samantha.mudd@nacro.org.uk

Harwich

Nacro Housing in Essex & Herts
tel/fax (01244) 240981

Holyhead

Nacro Cymru Housing in N Wales
Unit 12, Enterprise Park
Holyhead LL65 2HY
tel/fax (01407) 762026
e-mail wendy.williams@nacro.org.uk

Hull

Nacro Bail Support Scheme in Yorkshire and Humberside
Contact via Leeds office

Huntingdon

Nacro Educn & Emplt Services in East Anglia
Orchard House, 1 Orchard Lane
Huntingdon PE29 3QT
tel (01480) 377045 *fax (01480) 356063*
e-mail jane.storey@nacro.org.uk

Ipswich

Nacro Edun & Emplt Services in E Anglia (including the Ride for Life Project) & East Anglia Prison Resettlement Team
247 Felixstowe Road, Ipswich 1P3 9BN
tel (01473) 729230 *fax (01473) 729216*
e-mail E&E: susannah.waters@nacro.org.uk
e-mail Ride for Life Project nicholas.soar@nacro.org.uk

Leeds

Nacro Educn & Emplt Services in Leeds, Nacro Bail Support Scheme in Yorkshire and Humberside
Valley Mills Trading Estate
334 Meanwood Road, Meanwood
Leeds LS7 2JF
tel 0113-239 2674 *fax 0113-237 9499*
e-mail E&E
christopher.morgan@nacro.org.uk
e-mail Bail Support Scheme
reena.puri@nacro.org.uk

Nacro Middleton Youth Inclusion Progr, 'Engage' Project and Leeds Football Community Link Project
c/o Middleton Skills Centre
110 Middleton Park Avenue
Middleton, Leeds LS10 4HY
tel 0113-272 3428 *fax 0113-271 8677*
e-mail elaine.holden@nacro.org.uk

Leicester

Nacro E2E Project
18 Slater Street, Leicester LE3 1AY
e-mail naida.begum@nacro.org.uk

Nacro Braunstone Sports Project
ASB Project
Braunstone Community Association
Units 3 and 4, Forest Business Park
Oswin Road. Braunstone
Leicester LE3 1HR
tel *Sports Project* 08701 706955
tel *ASB Project* 08701 706942
fax 08701 706999
e-mail Sports Project
dean.tams@nacro.org.uk
e-mail ASB Project
jo.adams@braunstone.com

Lincoln

Nacro Housing in Lincolnshire
12 Melville Street, Lincoln LN5 7HW
tel (01552) 525383 *fax (01552) 870178*
e-mail beverley.johnson@nacro.org.uk

Liverpool

West and Wales Regional office
201 Kensington, Liverpool L7 2RF
tel 0151-260 4072 *fax 0151-260 4322*
e-mail audrey.cooper@nacro.org.uk

Nacro Housing on Merseyside
Flat 1, 2-4 The Elms, Dingle, Liverpool
L8 3SS
tel 0151-7273537 *fax 0151-726 8475*
e-mail paul.huston@nacro.org.uk

Nacro Kensington Youth Inclusion
Project (YIP), Junior YIP and
MOVES Project
201 Kensington, Liverpool L7 2RF
tel 0151-260 3768 *fax 0151-260 4322*
e-mail kensingtonyip@btconnect.com

L4 (YIP) Project
Unit B1, Tetlow Way
Langham Street Industrial Estate
Kirkdale, Liverpool L4 4QS
tel 0151-298 9195 *fax 0151-207 6900*
e-mail carole.ellis@nacro.org.uk

Nacro Liverpool Youth Sport Project
c/o Liverpool Sports Action Zone, Job Bank
4 Tunnel Road, Liverpool L7 6QD
tel 0151-233 6142 *fax 0151-233 6144*
e-mail rhiannon.brown@liverpool.gov.uk

Llandudno

Nacro Cymru Housing in N Wales
1 Trinity Square, Llandudno LL30 2PY
tel (01492) 860437 *fax (01492)* 878703
e-mail vin.murtagh@nacro.org.uk

Llangefni

Nacro Cymru (DIP, DAWN, Housing &
Youth Choices)
1 Glanhwfa Road, Llangefni LL77 7EN
tel/fax DIP (01248) 751092
tel DAWN and Youth Choices (01248)
750732
fax (01248) 750975
tel Housing: (01248) 724906 *fax (01248)*
750975

London

Nacro Creekside Foyer
14 Stowage, London SE8 3ED
tel 020-8694 8143 *fax* 020-8694 8162
e-mail amanda.mensah@nacro.org.uk

Nacro Educn & Emplt Services
in S London
Unit 16, The Windsor Centre
Windsor Grove, West Norwood
London SE27 9NT
tel 020-8761 6242 *fax 020-8761 1825*
e-mail sam.sykes@nacro.org.uk

Golden Arrow House
237a Queenstown Road, Battersea
London SW8 3NP
tel 020-7978 3000 *fax 020-7978 3001*
e-mail john.johnson@nacro.org.uk

Nacro Housing in London
159 Clapham Road, London SW9 0PU
tel 020-7840 6480 *fax 020-7840 6481*
e-mail housing.london@nacro.org.uk

Nacro South London ISSP, and
Community Remands Project
c/o Southwark Yot, 1 Bradenham Close
London SE17 2QA
tel 020-7525 0536 *fax 020-7525 7876/7940*
e-mail emily.gumb@southwark.gov.uk

Nacro North London ISSP
c/o Haringey Yot, 476 High Road
Tottenham, London N17 9JF
tel 020-8489 1508/1523 *fax 020-8489 1588*
e-mail gareth.mellens@nacro.org.uk

Nacro Wandsworth Community
Sports Project, Greenwich
Youth Activities Project
c/o Battersea Youth and Sports Project

Hope Street, London SW11 2DA
tel 07950 923258/020-7801 9290
e-mail paul.davis@nacro.org.uk

**Nacro Resettlement Info
and Advice Service**
C Wing, Landing 1, HM Prison Brixton
PO Box 369, Jebb Avenue, London SW2
5XF
tel 020-8588 6032/6078 *fax 020-8588 6362*
e-mail joyce.headley@hmps.gsi.gov.uk

Loughton

Nacro Housing in Essex and Herts
Contact via Harlow office

Luton

**Nacro Educn & Emplt Services
in E Anglia, Sports Project**
47 Cardiff Road, Luton LU1 1PP
tel (01582) 458965 *fax* (01582) 728953
e-mail melanie.lowe@nacro.org.uk

Nacro Project Turnaround (YISP)
Manor Family Resource Centre
Chase Street, Luton LU1 3QZ
tel/fax (01582) 481623
e-mail jackie.palmer@nacro.org.uk

Macclesfield

Nacro Steps Project
c/o Police Station, Brunswick Street
Macclesfield SK10 1HQ
tel (01244) 613481 *fax (01244) 614473*
e-mail christopher.shannon@
cheshire.pnn.police.uk

Maldon

Nacro Housing in Essex and Herts
Contact via Chelmsford office

Manchester

**Nacro Discus (YIP, Families Support
Project Duke of Edinburgh Award
Scheme) and Salford Safe Project**
The Cuthbert Centre (Unit 1)
877 Ashton Old Road, Openshaw
Manchester M11 2NA
tel 0161-223 3568 *fax 0161-223 9599*
e-mail Discus discusproject@nacro.org.uk
e-mail Safe Project
natalie.radcliffe@nacro.org.uk

**Nacro East Manchester 'Respect'
Sports Project, Engage Project
and NEET Project**
The Cuthbert Centre (Unit 1)

877 Ashton Old Road, Openshaw
Manchester M11 2NA
tel 0161-223 3568 *fax 0161-223 9599*

Youth Intervention
Parkway Green Housing Trust
460 Palatine Road, Northenden
Manchester M22 4DJ
tel 0161-946 6312 *fax 0161-998 8710*
e-mail lee.isherwood@nacro.org.uk

Nacro Housing in G Manchester
567a Barlow Moor Road
Chorlton-cum-Hardy, Manchester M21
8AE
tel 0161-860 7444 *fax 0161-860 7555*
e-mail joanne.mack@nacro.org.uk

Middlesbrough

**Nacro Educn & Emplt Services in
Tees Valley**
123 Marton Road, Middlesbrough TS1
2DU
tel (01642) 223551 *fax* (01642) 254244
e-mail maureen.burton@nacro.org.uk

Milton Keynes

Nacro Positive Futures Sports Project
c/o Milton Keynes Council Sports
Development Team
Saxon Court, 502 Avebury Boulevard
Milton Keynes MK9 3HS
tel 07920 571588
e-mail robin.osborn@nacro.org.uk

Newark

Nacro Housing in Nottinghamshire
Newark Foyer and Dispersed House
Elmhurst, 42/44 Lombard Street
Newark NG24 1XP
tel 0115-844 3610 *fax (01636) 679538*
e-mail elaine.compton@nacro.org.uk

Newbury

c/o West Berkshire Council Cultural
Services
Avonbank House, West Street
Newbury RG14 1BZ
Mobile 07793 881107
e-mail robert.guy@nacro.org.uk

Newcastle-upon-Tyne

**Nacro Educn & Emplt Services
in Newcastle, Tyne & Wear Youth
Activities Project, Community
Football Project**
29 Welbeck Road, Byker

Newcastle-upon-Tyne NE6 2HU
tel 0191-265 8164 *fax 0191-224 1400*
e-mail E&E: anne.hayes@nacro.org.uk

Newport

**Nacro Cymru Educn & Emplt
Services in South Wales**
Bridge Chambers, 1 Godfrey Road
Newport NP20 4NX
tel (01633) 213434 *fax (01633) 213435*
e-mail sharon.mostyn-williams@nacro.org.uk

Northampton

**CASPAR + NR (Community Safety
Project)**
2 St Luke, Low Harding Street
Springborough, Northampton NN1 2JJ
tel (01604) 607045 *fax (01604) 607012*
e-mail lucy.lisowiec@lha.asra.org.uk

Nottingham

**Nacro Housing in Nottinghamshire
Nacro Nottingham Mediation Service**
16 Vivian Avenue, Sherwood Rise,
Nottingham NG5 1AF
tel 0115-985 7744 *fax 0115-962 8948*
e-mail Housing gaynor.clark@nacro.org.uk
e-mail Mediation julie.o'farrell@nacro.
org.uk

**Nacro Nottingham Young People and
Families Centre including Filling the
Gap**
29-31 Aston Drive, Bulwell
Nottingham NG6 8BG
tel 0115-979 7847 *fax 0115-979 4096*
e-mail dave.mulligan@nacro.org.uk

**Nacro Parenting Solutions
Project and Junior YIP**
Queensberry Baptist Church, Queensberry
Street
Basford, Nottingham NG8 9DG
tel 0115-978 4778 *fax 0115-942 4779*
e-mail ted.kavanagh@nacro.org.uk

Ollerton

**Nacro County High Risk Floating
Support,
Bassetlaw Floating Support,
Drug Intervention, Bassetlaw
& Ashfield Supported Housing**
First Floor Office, Forest Road
New Ollerton, Newark NG22 9PL
tel (01623) 863699 *fax* (01623) 861649

e-mail marie.beedall@nacro.org.uk

Peterborough

**Nacro Educn & Emplt Services
in E Anglia Youth Activities
Project, and Football Project**
Unit 7, Cavell Court, North Street
Peterborough PE1 2AB
tel (01733) 890088 *fax (01733) 890437*
e-mail jackie.wilson@nacro.org.uk
e-mail Football carina.greenaway@nacro.org.uk

Poole

**Nacro Educn & Emplt Services
in Dorset, Bournemouth
Football Project**
The Lion Works, 543 Wallisdown Road
Poole BH12 5AD
tel (01202) 539966 *fax (01202) 539986*
e-mail E&E tom.lund@nacro.org.uk
e-mail Football dominic.weir@nacro.org.uk

Portland

Milestones (formerly On-side
Resettlement Project)
Nacro office, HM YOI Portland
Grove Road, Portland DT5 1DL
tel (01305) 825694/5
e-mail john.bayley@hmps.gsi.gov.uk

Preston

Nacro Preston YIP
3 Hazel Grove, Ribbleton, Preston PR2
6PT
tel (01772) 651300 *fax (01772) 654017*
e-mail karen.robinson@nacro.org.uk
Nacro East Preston Centre for Restorative
Justice and National Centre for Restorative
Justice
Winckley Chambers, 30 Winckley Square
Preston PR1 3JJ
tel (01772) 556752 *fax (01772) 556831*
e-mail deborah.air@nacro.org.uk

Reading

Nacro Sport & Angling Project
Palmer Park Lodge, Wokingham Road
Reading RG6 1LF
tel 0118-901 5713 *fax 0118-939 0472*
Mobile 07971 308586
e-mail daniel.williams@nacro.org.uk

Retford

Nacro Bassetlaw Footballing Chance
Bassetlaw Sports Development Unit

17B The Square, Retford DN22 6DB
tel (01777) 713889 *fax (01909) 534529*
e-mail matt.handley@bassetlaw.gov.uk

Nacro Housing Floating Support in Notts
Contact via Ollerton housing office

Rhyl

Nacro Cymru Housing in North Wales
8a Bodfor Street, Rhyl LL18 1AU
tel (01745) 331586 *fax (01745) 354550*
e-mail Ex-offender housing
peter.harrington@nacro.org.uk
or jessica.hymus-gant@nacro.org.uk
e-mail YOT housing
david.thomas@nacro.org.uk
or cora.jevams@nacro.org.uk

Nacro Cymru DAWN, and Skillbuild
Contact the Bangor office

Nacro Cymru DIP
Dewi Sant Centre, Clwyd Buildings
Clwyd Street, Rhyl LL18 3LA
tel (01745) 345900 *fax (01745) 345248*
e-mail sharon.mostyn-williams@nacro.org.uk

Nacro Night Shelter and Resettlement and Advice
1 Crescent Road, Rhyl LL18 1TF
tel (01745) 361728 *fax (01745) 345928*
e-mail chloe.marshall@nacro.org.uk

Nacro Roof & Rhyl Floating Support
Clwyd Buildings, Clwyd Street
Rhyl LL18 3LU
tel (01745) 345929 *fax (01745) 369538*
e-mail chloe.marshall@nacro.org.uk

GIFT and Prevention of Homelessness Denbigh
FF2, Morfa Hall, Bath Street
Rhyl LL18 3EB
tel/fax (01745) 340046
e-mail GIFT john.bennett@nacro.org.uk
e-mail Prevention of homelessness
glenda.hailwood@nacro.org.uk

Roydon

Nacro Housing in Essex and Herts
Contact via Harlow office

St Helens

Nacro St Helens YIPs
Parr Stocks Fire Station, Parr Stocks Road
Parr, St Helens WA9 1NU
tel (01744) 675169 *fax (01744) 675156*
e-mail sue.gregory@nacro.org.uk

Nacro St Helens Action for Football Enterprise (SHAFE)
Nacro St Helens Alternative Motor Project (STAMP)
Parr Stocks Fire Station
Parr Stocks Road, Parr
St Helens WA9 1NU
tel SHAFE (01744) 675170 fax (01744) 675156
e-mail SHAFE
jonathan.hayhurst@sthelens.gov.uk
tel STAMP
(01744) 675169 *fax (01744) 675156*
e-mail STAMP
gillian.webster@nacro.org.uk

Salford

Nacro Salford Sports Project
2 Paddington Close, Off Churchill Way
Salford M6 5PL
tel/fax 0161-736 4150
e-mail natalie.radcliffe@nacro.org.uk

Nacro Salford Resettlement & Aftercare Project (RAP)
c/o Youth Offending Team
10-12 Encombe Place, Salford M3 6FJ
tel 0161-607 1930
e-mail duane.mccamon@salford.gov.uk

Sandwell

Nacro Educn & Emplt Services in the Black Country
Apollo House, Rounds Green Road,
Oldbury B69 2DF
tel 0121-552 9589 *fax 0121-552 1786*
e-mail nacrosandwell@nacro.org.uk

Nacro Housing in Birmingham and the Black Country
Contact via Birmingham office

Scarborough

Nacro Bail Support Scheme in Yorkshire and Humberside
Contact via Leeds office

Sheffield

Nacro Educn & Emplt Services Kick-off Football Project and Nacro Bail Support Scheme in Yorkshire and Humberside
70 Earl Street, Sheffield S1 4PY
tel 0114-272 2319 *fax 0114-272 4103*
tel *Kick-off Project* 07967 028864
e-mail E&E

sheffieldtraining@nacro.org.uk
e-mail Kick-off
matthew.bray@nacro.org.uk
Bail Support Scheme:
contact via Leeds office

Shotton

**Nacro Cymru Youth Choices
Skills for Life Flintshire Doorstop
Project**
72 Chester Road West, Shotton CH5 1BZ
tel/fax Youth Choices (01244) 812643
e-mail andy.watson@nacro.org.uk
tel/fax Doorstop Project (01244) 816515
e-mail nia.parry@nacro.org.uk

Nacro Cymru DIP
10-12 Salisbury Street, Shotton CH5 1DR
tel (01244) 845920 *fax (01244) 838483*
e-mail sharon.mostyn-williams@nacro.org.uk

Shrewsbury

**Nacro Educn & Emplt Services
in Shropshire**
10 Shoplatch, Shrewsbury SY1 1HL
tel (01743) 364582 *fax (01743) 235063*

Skegness

Nacro Housing in Lincolnshire
Contact via Boston office

Southampton

Getting Active Football Project
c/o Southampton ISSP, Wheatsheaf House
24 Bernard Street, Southampton SO14
3AY
tel 07841 118707
e-mail paul.walshe@hants.gov.uk

Southend

**Nacro Housing in South East Essex
(Southend-on-Sea, Castle Point
and Rochford & Rayleigh)**
1st Floor, 33-37 Hamlet Court Road
Westcliff-on-Sea SS0 7EY
tel (01702) 437183 *fax (01702) 392719*
e-mail helene.leader@nacro.org.uk

Spalding

**Nacro Educn & Emplt Services
in Lincolnshire**
Unit 12, Broadgate House
Westlode Street, Spalding
Lincolnshire PE11 2AF
tel (01775) 718679 *fax (01775) 725051*

e-mail tracey.hitchborn@nacro.org.uk

Stafford

Nacro Housing in Staffordshire
Unit 305, St. Albans House
Enterprise Centre, St Albans Road
Stafford ST16 3DP
tel/fax (01785) 255467
e-mail dale.nicholson@nacro.org.uk

Staines

**Nacro Educn & Emplt Services
in Surrey**
1st floor offices, 11-17 Kingston Road
Staines TW18 4QX
tel (01784) 492192 *fax (01784) 492101*
e-mail christina.williams@nacro.org.uk

Stamford

**Nacro Educn & Emplt Services
in Lincolnshire**
13 Radcliffe Road, Stamford
Lincolnshire PE9 1AP
tel (01780) 757402 *fax (01780) 753428*
e-mail tracey.hitchborn@nacro.org.uk

Stevenage

Nacro Housing in Essex and Herts
14-16 High Street, Old Stevenage
Stevenage SG1 3EJ
tel (01438) 313132 *fax (01438) 313134*
e-mail sheila.day@nacro.org.uk

Stockton-on-Tees

**Nacro Educn & Emplt Services in
Tees Valley, Pyramid (Prison and
Community Resettlement) Project**
Hutchinson Street
Stockton-on-Tees TS18 1RW
tel (01642) 615554 *fax (01642) 611050*
e-mail E&E:
shirley.courtney-sinclair@nacro.org.uk
tel *Pyramid Project*
(01642) 615071
e-mail Pyramid Project:
gordon.fenwick@nacro.org.uk

Pathway Project
32-34 William Street
Stockton-on-Tees TS18 1DN
tel (01642) 356088 *fax (01642) 356084*

Stoke-on-Trent

**Nacro Educn & Emplt Services
in Staffordshire**
3 Spring Garden Road, Longton
Stoke-on-Trent ST3 2QN
tel (01782) 332699 *fax (01782) 596314*
e-mail elaine.pollard@nacro.org.uk

Meir YIP
Meir Youth Centre, Sandon Road, Meir
Stoke on Trent ST3 7DJ
tel (01782) 342028 *fax (01782) 816200*
e-mail amy.taylor@nacro.org.uk

Stanfields YIP
13 Sherwin Road, Stanfields
Stoke on Trent ST6 7BQ
tel (01782) 834891 fax (01782) 816200
e-mail marjorie.caviglia@nacro.org.uk

Tamworth

**Nacro Educn & Emplt Services
in Staffordshire**
59-60 Church Street, Tamworth B79 7DF
tel (01827) 56420 *fax (01827) 51587*
e-mail staffordshirenct@nacro.org.uk

Telford

**Nacro Educn & Emplt Services in
Shropshire, and School Pathways
and Springboard Project**
11 Tan Bank, Wellington, Telford TF1 1HJ
tel (01952) 243689 *fax (01952) 245445*
e-mail deepa.freebury@nacro.org.uk
e-mail School Pathways
samantha.lindsay@nacro.org.uk

Nacro Adult Substance Misuse Services
6A Bagley Drive, Wellington
Telford TF1 3NP
tel (01952) 248221 *fax (01952) 248255*
e-mail tara.pond@nacro.org.uk

**Nacro Adult Substance Misuse
Services Revolution**
Unit 1, Stafford Park 12, Telford TF3 3BJ
tel (01952) 385179
e-mail martin.woodall@nacro.org.uk

Thurrock

Nacro Housing in Essex & Herts
Contact via Chelmsford office

Nacro Thurrock Sports Project
Sport and Leisure Development
Thameside Complex, Orsett Road
Grays RM17 5DX
tel (01375) 413567 *fax (01375) 385504*

e-mail NAFarrell@thurrock.gov.uk

Wakefield

**Nacro Wakefield Prevention Services
inc Junior and Senior YIPs,
Bikeshed Project, Volunteering and
Mentoring Service and Positive
Futures Sports Project**
Suite 2, Trinity Buildings
Calder Vale Road, Wakefield WF1 5PE
tel (01924) 378399 *fax* (01924) 378388
e-mail alison.rowe@nacro.org.uk
e-mail Project Co-ordinator
colin.mallinder@nacro.org.uk
e-mail Positive Futures
gareth.hamlet@nacro.org.uk

Walsall

**Nacro Educn & Emplt Services in the
Black Country, Positive Futures Proj
YIPs (Junior and Senior), DIP, MOVES,
Supt and Achievement Progr,
Young Mums to be Programme,
and Floating Support**
Bath House, Bath Street
Walsall WS1 3DB
tel (01922) 625060 *fax* (01922) 625101
e-mail E&E zoe.marsh@nacro.org.uk
e-mail Positive Futures
kate.jones@nacro.org.uk
*e-mail YIP, MOVES, Support &
Achievement Programme*
hobby.rahman@nacro.org.uk
e-mail DIP dawn.morris@nacro.org.uk
e-mail Young Mums to be Programme
elizabeth.gavin@nacro.org.uk
e-mail Floating Support
dave.griffiths@nacro.org.uk

Waltham Abbey

Nacro Housing in Essex and Herts
Contact via Chelmsford office

Wisbech

**Nacro Eductnand Employmt
Services in E Anglia**
1 Hill Street, Wisbech PE13 1BA
tel (01945) 467254 *fax (01945) 467855*
e-mail susan.gillies@nacro.org.uk

Witham

**The Bridge Project
(Community Sentence Mentoring)**
Essex Probation HQ, Cullen Mill
Braintree Road, Witham CM8 2DD

tel (01376) 500841 *fax (01376) 503058*
e-mail mark.grindall@nacro.org.uk

Woking

Nacro Surrey Probation Area IAG,
Skills for Life Projects
Woking Probation Centre
White Rose Court, Oriental Road
Woking GU22 7PJ
tel (01483) 776262 *fax (01483) 727244*
e-mail sam.sykes@nacro.org.uk

Wokingham

Nacro Street Games Project
Wokingham Borough Council
Sports Development Unit, Civic Offices
Shute End, Wokingham RG40 1BN
tel 0118-914 6265
e-mail adam.tombs@nacro.org.uk

Workington

Nacro Educn & Emplt Services
in Cumbria, Workington Junior YIP
Stanley Street, Workington CA14 2JG
tel (01900) 604488 *fax (01900) 65131*
e-mail rebecca.wilson@nacro.org.uk

Wrexham

Nacro Cymru Housing in N Wales
21 Grosvenor Road, Wrexham LL11 1BT
tel/fax (01978) 364416
e-mail wendy.hayes@nacro.org.uk

Nacro Cymru Youth Choices
35 Chester Street, Wrexham LL13 8AH
tel/fax (01978) 314313
e-mail dee.rigby@nacro.org.uk

Nacro Cymru DIP and Housing
Hafod, 21 Grosvenor Road
Wrexham LL11 1BT
tel/fax (01978) 364416

York

Nacro Bail Support Scheme in
Yorkshire and Humberside
Contact via Leeds office

SACRO

National Office Services

1. **National Office**
   1 Broughton Market
   Edinburgh EH3 6NU
   info@national.sacro.org.uk
   tel 0131-624 7270 *fax 0131-624 7269*

   Administration
   Finance & Payroll
   Service Development & Research
   Human Resources
   Operations Support
   IT Management & Support
   Publicity & Media Services

   Criminal Justice Advisor
   Tim Richley
   trichley@cja.sacro.org.uk

2. **Community Mediation Consultancy**
   & Training Service
   21 Abercromby Place
   Edinburgh EH3 6QE
   info@cmconsultancy.sacro.org.uk
   tel 0131-624 9200 *fax 0131-557 2102*

3. **Learning and Development**
   109 Hope Street **Glasgow** G2 6LL
   info@staffdev.sacro.org.uk
   tel 0141-847 0738 *fax 0141-847 0736*

   Learning & development
   Staff & volunteer induction
   Continuing professional devpt
   SVQ centre

Aberdeen & Aberdeenshire

4. 110 Crown Street
   Aberdeen AB11 6HJ
   info@aberdeen.sacro.org.uk
   tel (01224) 560560 *fax (01224) 560 551*

   Supported Tenancies
   Supported Accommodation
   tel (01244) 560550

   Restorative Justice Services
   Youth Justice Services
   tel (01244) 560560

   Community Mediation
   Street Mediation
   tel (01244) 560570

   Groupwork Services
   Intensive Supt & Monitoring
   Youth Justice Services

Youth Justice Strategy co-ord
tel (01244) 560560

Angus

5. Unit E, Market Mews
Market Street, Dundee DD5 4AA
tel (01382) 459252 *fax (01382) 459318*
info@dundee.sacro.org.uk

Community Mediation

Argyll & Bute

6. c/o Leven Valley Enterprise
Room 1.9, Castlehill Road
Dumbarton G82 5BN
tel (01389) 772031 *fax (01389) 772033*
info@argyllbute.sacro.org.uk

Youth Justice Service

Ayrshire

7. 60 Bank Street
Kilmarnock KAI 1ER
info@ayrshire.sacro.org.uk
tel (01563) 525815 *fax (01563) 525328*

Youth Justice Services
Bail Supervision

8. 146 High Street **Irvine** KA12 8AH
tel (01294) 314020 *fax (01294) 314021*
info@irvine.sacro.org.uk

Community Mediation

Clackmannanshire/Falkirk/Stirling

9. 22 Meeks Road
Falkirk FK2 7ET
info@groupworkservices.sacro.org.uk
tel (01324) 627824 *fax (01324) 622006*

Groupwork Service (Domestic Abuse)
Groupwork Service (Sexual Offenders)
info@groupworkservices.sacro.org.uk
Supported Accommodation
info@falkirksas.sacro.org.uk

Youth Justice Service
info@falkirk.sacro.org.uk

Dumfries & Galloway

10. Children's Services, Council Offices
Dryfe Road **Lockerbie** DG11 2AP
SamL@dumgal.gov.uk
tel (01576) 205070 *fax (01576) 204411*

Youth Justice Services (East)

11. Unit 4, Castle Court
8 Castle Street **Stranraer** DG9 7RT
info@stranraer.sacro.org.uk
tel (01776) 706287 *fax (01776) 706287*

Supporting People Services

Community Mediation
tel (01776) 706283

12. Youth Justice, Dunbae House
Church Street **Stranraer** DG9 7JG
tel (01776) 702151 *fax (01776) 707282*
PaulineBa@dumgal.gov.uk

Youth Justice Services (West)

13. 75 Buccleuch Street, **Dumfries** DG1 2AB
tel (01387) 731270 *fax (01387) 731271*
info@dumfries.sacro.org.uk

Community Mediation

Dundee

15. Suite E, Market Mews
Market Street, Dundee DD1 3LA
info@dundee.sacro.org.uk
tel (01382) 459252 *fax (01382) 459318*

Community Mediation

16. Suite F, Market Mews
Market Street, Dundee DD1 3LA
info@dundee.sacro.org.uk
tel (01382) 524758 *fax (01382) 524757*

Youth Justice

East Dunbartonshire

17. **East Dunbartonshire Youth Justice**
c/o Social Work, 1 Balmuildy Road
Bishopbriggs G64 3BS
tel 0141-772 6384 *fax 0141-762 4677*

18. E Dunbartonshire Community Mediation
Broomhill Industrial Estate, Kilsyth Road
Kirkintilloch G66 1TF
tel 0141 574 5771 *fax 0141 574 5742*
community.mediation@eastdunbarton.
gov.uk

East Renfrewshire

19. East Renfrewshire Council
1 Balmuidy Road **Bishopbriggs** G64 3BS
tel 0141-772 6384 *fax 0141-762 4687*

Youth Justice Services

20. East Renfrewshire Council
Broomhill Industrial Estate
Kilsyth Road **Kirkintilloch** G66 1TF
tel 0141-574 5771 *fax 0141 574 5742*
community.mediation@eastrenfrewshire.
gov.uk

Community Mediation

East Lothian

21. 18 Bridge Street
Musselburgh EH21 6AG
info@eastlothian.sacro.org.uk
tel 0131-653 3421 *fax 0131-653 3071*

Community Mediation
Homeless Mediation

Edinburgh

22. Community Links Centre
25 Nicolson Square
Edinburgh EH8 9BX
info@lothiancjs.sacro.org.uk
tel 0131-622 7500 *fax 0131-622 7525*

Criminal Justice Services
Supported Accommodation
Bail Supervision Service
Alcohol Education Probation Service
Arrest Referral
Throughcare
Supported Accommodation
'Another Way' Service for Street Sex
Workers
Travel Service
Restorative Justice Service

23. 21 Abercromby Place
Edinburgh EH3 6QEinfo@edincm.sacro.
org.uk
tel 0131-557 2101 *fax 0131-557 2102*

Community Mediation
infor@lothianmedrep.sacro.org.uk
tel 0131 557 2101

24. 73 Boswall Parkway
Edinburgh EH5 2PW
info@pilton.sacro.org.uk
tel 0131-551 1753 *fax 0131-551 1677*

Community Mediation

Fife

25. 24 Hill Street
Kirkcaldy **Fife** KY1 IHX
info@fife.sacro.org.uk
tel (01592) 593100 *fax (01592) 593133*

Youth Justice Services
Community Mediation
Peer Mediation in Schools
Transition to High School Training
Effective Communication Training

Glasgow

26. Central Chambers, 93 Hope Street
Glasgow G2 6LD
info@glasgow.sacro.org.uk
tel 0141-248 1763 *fax 0141-248 1686*

Bail Service
Intensive Support & Monitoring
Supported Accommodation
Throughcare Service
Travel Service
Youth Justice Services

Highland

27. Ballantyne House, 84 Academy Street
Inverness IV1 1LU
info@highland.sacro.org.uk
tel (01463) 716325 *fax (01463) 716326*

Supported Accommodation
Intensive Support & Monitoring
Bail Supervision
Community Mediation
Youth Justice Services

28. Unit 5D, Airport Industrial Estate
Wick KW1 4QS
info@wick.sacro.org.uk
tel (01955) 606873

Youth Justice Services

29. Youth Action Team Office
Lochaber High School
Carmaghael, Fort William PH33 7ND
info@lochaber.sacro.org.uk
tel (01397) 704129

Youth Justice Services

Midlothian

30. 4/3 Lothian Street
Dalkeith Midlothian EH22 IDS
info@midlothian.sacro.org.uk
tel 0131-454 0841 *fax 0131-454 0982*

Youth Justice Services

North & South Lanarkshire

31. 11 Merry Street
Motherwell ML1 1JJ
info@nslanarkshire.sacro.org.uk

tel (01698) 230433 *fax (01698) 230410*

Supervised Bail
Restorative Justice Services
Arrest Referral
Family Group Conferencing
Youth Justice Services

Moray

32. 2/2 Ballantyne House, 84 Academy Street
Inverness IV1 1LU
tel (01463) 716325 fax (01463) 716326
info@highland.sacro.org.uk

Youth Justice Services

Orkney

33. 4b Laing Street
Kirkwall Orkney KW15 1NW
info@orkney.sacro.org.uk
tel & fax (01856) 875815

Supported Accommodation
Youth Justice Services
Drink Drive Programme
Streetwise Programme
Community Mediation
Adult Diversion
Adult Cognitive Programmes

Perth & Kinross

34. Suite D, Moncrieff Business Centre
Friarton Road
Perth PH2 8DG
tel (01738) 445753 *fax (01738) 627563*
info@perthcm.sacro.org.uk

Community Mediation

35. Suite 3c, Kinnoull House
Riverview Business Park
Friarton Road **Perth** PH2 8DG
tel (01738) 580582 *fax (01738) 622992*
info@perth.sacro.org.uk

Youth Justice Services

West Dunbartonshire

36. c/o Leven Valley Enterprise
Room 1.9, Castlehill Road
Dumbarton G82 5BN
tel (01389) 772032 *fax (01389) 772033*
info@dumbarton.sacro.org.uk

Youth Justice Services

SOVA

Central Administration

1. **SOVA Head Office**
1st Floor Chichester House
37 Brixton Road London SW9 6DZ
tel 020-7793 0404 *fax 020-7735 4410*

Gill Henson (chief exec)
Janet Crowe (natnl director operations)
Jennie Spanton (snr finance mgr)
Louise Castello (devpt director)
Susan Cooper (director of learning &
quality)
Steve Lally (learning & quality co-ord)
David Barlow (dir of operations, South)
Ineke Burke (area co-ord, South)
Diana Clough (personnel director)
Tom Tolhurst (personnel officer)
Marjorie Reid (personnel officer)
Clare Bunnell (pa)
Tony Savage (head of ICT)
Steve McPartland (IT mgr)
Coral Evans (IT mgr)
Val Abraham (ore admin South)

2. **Regional Office (Sheffield)**
St Silas House
18 Moore Street, Sheffield S3 7UW
tel 0114-270 3700 *fax 0114-270 3701*

Julia Stanley (dir of operations, North)
Andy Whitehead (regnl mgr, North)
Sam Dumoulin (regnl mgr, North)
Gina Carter (regnl mgr, North)
Gary Kernaghan (new business director)
Keith Osborne (snr finance mgr)
Mohammad Aklim (snr finance mgr)
Ann Naylor (finance officer)
Lynne Spamer (finance officer)
Sam Briggs (finance officer)
June Graham (personnel mgr)
Heather Eyre (core admin, North)
Kerry Halsall (area co-ord, North)
Sarah Browne (PASS supt officer)

3. **SOVA Birmingham Office**
Scala House, Suites F6 F7 FS
5th Floor, Scala House, 36 Holloway Circus
Queensway, Birmingham, B1 1EQ
tel 0121-643 7400 *fax 0121-643 7454*

Sophie Wilson (operations director,
Midlands)
Sarah Whitehouse (area co-ord, Midlands)

4. **SOVA Newtown Wales Office**
2nd Floor, Ladywell House
Newtown, Powys SY16 1JB
Tel (01686) 623873 *fax (01686) 623875*

Chris Arnold (director of operations, Wales)
Martin Jones (area co-ord, Wales)
Teresa Lewis (admin asst)

5. **Regional Office (Lincoln)**
SOVA Volunteer Centre
Lamb Gardens, Lincoln LN2 4EG
tel (01522) 540251 *fax (01522) 537490*

Amanda Marshall (supt off)

Projects

6. **FC Scott Foundation (Lancaster Farms)**
HMP/YOI Lancaster Farms
SOVA Mentoring Link Building
Far Moor Lane, Stone Row Head
Off Quermore Road, Lancaster LA1 3QZ
tel (01524) 563828 *fax (01524) 563833*

Becky Bland (co-ord (volunteers))

7. **HMP YOI Askham Grange**
Askham Richard, York YO2 3FT
tel (01904) 772000 *fax (01904) 772001*

Adele Bilson (key wrkr)
Dee Pandya (emplt supt wrkr)

8. **HMP Garth**
Ulnes Walton Lane
Leyland, Preston PR26 8NE
tel (01772) 443585

Imraan Hussain (housing officer)
Emily Keogh (housing co-ord)

9. **HMP Kirkham**
Freckleton Road, Preston
Lancashire PR4 2RN
tel (01772) 6754000 *fax (01772) 675600*

Jamie Sweet (housing officer)
Tara Smallshaw (housing co-ord)

10. **Hull Independent Visitors**
Stonefield House
Young Peoples Support Service
Stonefield House
16/20 King Edward's Street
Hull HU1 3SS
tel (01482) 331004 *fax (01482) 318356*

Louise Brown (proj mgr)

Richard Mullins (co-ord (volunteers))

11. **Norfolk Probation Partnership**
SOVA Norfolk
Centenary House, 2nd Floor
19 Palace Street, Norfolk NR3 1RT
tel (01603) 303018

Anna Haggith (proj mgr)

12. **North Yorkshire NPS Circles**
c/o SOVA Regional Office, St Silas House
18 Moore Street, Sheffield, S3 7UW
tel 0114-270 3703 *fax 0114-270 3703*

Ann Powell (proj mgr)
Kerry Halsall (area co-ord)

13. **Sheffield Mentoring Services**
VAS, the Circle, 33 Rockingham Lane
Sheffield S1 4FW
tel 0114-253 6755 *fax 0114-253 6756*

Dennis Ward (supt off)
Rosie Chitty (proj mgr)

14. **SOVA Barnsley ETE**
2nd Floor, Central Chambers
74-75 Eldon Street, Barnsley S70 2JN
tel (01226) 215257 *fax (01226) 215262*

Lorna Szkliniarz (co-ord)
Libby Wood (admin & monitoring officer)
Sasha Lawrence (supt off)
Carol Guest (supt off)
Helen Swift (proj mgr)
John Parker (admin asst)

15. **SOVA Barnsley Youth Justice**
BMBC Youth Offending Team
Crookes Street, Barnsley S70 6BX
tel (01226) 774986 *fax (01226) 774968*

Tim Hawkins (proj mgr)
Helen Walker (supt off)
Gillian Grainger (bail & remand officer)

16. **SOVA Bexley**
c/o Leaving Care Team
Howbury Centre
Slade Green Road
Erith, Kent DA8 2HX
tel (01322) 356463 *fax (01322) 356473*

Chrissie Wild (proj mgr)
John Young (Looked After Children's Right officer)
Philip Erswell (supt off)
Jenny Hudson (supt wrkr)
Julie Clark (proj mgr)

17. **SOVA Camden YOT Mentoring**
Third Floor, Crowndale Centre
218-220 Eversholt Street
London NW1 1BD
tel 0207-974 6173 *fax 0207-974 4163*

Danielle Tuorn (proj mgr)
Michael Sojirin (supt off)
Helen Merryweather (supt off)

18. **SOVA Canolfan Dewi Sant**
Clwyd Buildings, Clwyd Street
Rhyl, Wales LL18 3LA
tel (01745) 362429 *fax (01745) 362434*

Brian Davies (supt off)
Imogene Elie (supt wrkr)
Wyn Roberts (supt wrkr)
Natalie Lewis (admin asst/supt officer)
Ruth Cole (proj mgr)

19. **SOVA CAST**
Leaving Care Team
92-98 Queen Street, Sheffield S1 1WU
tel 0114-293 0034 *fax 0114-275 2357*

Thelma Whittaker (proj mgr)
Christian Dixon (supt wrkr)

20. **SOVA Croydon Young People**
Cornerstone House, 14 Willis Road
Croydon CR0 2XX
tel 0208-665 5668 *fax 0208-665 1972*

Pauline McGrath (snr proj mgr)
Ally McKinlay (proj mgr)
Angela Pryce (supt off)
Angela Sinclair (supt off)
Grace Williams (supt off)

21. **SOVA Deerbolt**
HMP Deerbolt, Bowes Road
Barnard Castle, Co Durham DL12 9BG
tel (01833) 633200 *fax (01833) 633395*

Erica Jones (supt off)
Andrew Heron (supt off)

22. **SOVA Derby Community Safety Partnership & Appropriate Adults**
2nd Floor, St Peters House
Gower Street, Derby DE1 9BK
tel (01332) 256826 *fax (01332) 256830*

Kelly Buswell (proj mgr)
Alan Keeton (proj co-ord)
Clive Topley (supt off)
Martin Cooper (supt off)
Helen Stretton (victim liaison supt officer)
Katie Peirce (admin asst)

23. **SOVA Derby Engage**
Suite 30, Beaufort Business Centre
Beaufort Street, Derby DE21 6AH
tel 07947 126189 *fax (01332) 256830*

Martin Cooper (supt off)

24. **SOVA Ealing**
2 Cheltenham Place
Acton, Ealing, London W3 8JS
tel 0208-896 0042 *fax 0208-752 2179*

Jean-Michel Jordan (proj mgr)
Khurm Islam (practical skills co-ord)
Simone Hill (supt off)

25. **SOVA Essex**
The Probation Office
4th Floor Ashby House
Brook Street, Chelmsford CM1 1UH
tel (01245) 287154 *fax (01245) 491321*

Peter Brown (proj mgr)

26. **SOVA Essex DAT Mentoring**
Moulsham Mill, Parkway
Chelmsford, Essex CM2 7PX
tel (01245) 608200 *fax (01245) 608310*

Alison Battersby (proj mgr)
Brian Hunt (supt off)

27. **SOVA Herts**
25d Alma Road
St Albans, Herts AL1 3AR
tel (01727) 867 800

Anne Regan (proj mgr)
Carol Hudson (supt wrkr)
Sharon Ahmad (supt off)
Barbara Bathurst (supt off)

28. **SOVA Humberside NPS Employment Project**
Liberty House, Liberty Lane
Hull HU1 1RS
tel (01482) 480241

Hayley Cullen (co-ord ETE)
Kevin Carrick (proj mgr)
Dennis Margerison (admin)
Kenny Ross (supt wrkr)
Sam Dale (admin/supt wrkr)
Nanette Tuck (supt off)

29. **SOVA Invest to Save Bail Support Scheme**
Valley Mills Trading Estate
334 Meanwood, Leeds LS7 2JF
fax 0113-237 9499

Debbie Harding (co-ord (volunteers))
07809 587 167
Claire Sowerby (supt off) 07973 480839

30. **SOVA Lincolnshire IV and Befrienders**
Lamb Gardens, Lincoln LN2 4EG
tel (01522) 567711 *fax (01522) 537490*

Colin Russell (proj mgr)
Helen Caskie (supt off)
Valerie Milstead (supt off)
Carrie Flint (supt off)

31. **SOVA Lincolnshire Mentoring**
SOVA Volunteer Centre
Lamb Gardens, Lincoln LN2 4EG
tel (01522) 567711 *fax (01522) 537490*

Maureen Keddy (proj mgr)
Amanda Marshall (supt off)
Carrie Flint (supt off)
Elaine Harwin (volunteer co-ord)
Jane Buchanan (admin/supt wrkr)

32. **SOVA Newham Mentoring Project**
Newham DIP
2nd Floor, 409 High Street
Stratford, London E15 4QZ
020-8430 6633

Justine Wilsher (proj mgr)

33. **SOVA North Wales Drug Initiatives**
Priory Offices, 8-10 Priory Street
Wrexham, Clwyd LL11 1SU
tel (01978) 262223 *fax (01978) 263332*

Sheree Davies (proj mgr)

34. **SOVA New Dawn**
137 High Street, Bangor LL57 1NT
tel (01248) 352974 *fax (01248) 364755*

Maria Woolley (supt wrkr)

35. **SOVA New Dawn**
The Dawn Centre
35-37 Princes Drive
Colwyn Bay, Conway LL29 8PD
tel (01492) 523695 *fax (01492) 523691*

Catherine Farley (proj mgr)
Melanie Newport (supt wrkr)
Oxana Jones (admin asst)

36. **SOVA NEWID**
137 High Street
Bangor LL57 1NT
tel (01248) 352974 *fax (01248) 364755*

Nigel Brooks (supt officer)

37. **SOVA Cardiff Refugee Services**
Marine House
23 Mount Stuart Square
Cardiff, Wales CF10 5DP
tel 029-2049 5281 *fax 029-2049 2148*

Glyn Parry (proj mgr)
Rachel Owens (admin asst)

38. **SOVA Rotherham**
Bank Courtyard, 2a Wellgate
Rotherham S60 2NN
tel (01709) 839579 *fax (01709) 515111*

Aileen Housley (co-ord)
Janette Walker (proj mgr)
Michelle Marshall (co-ord)
Margo Middleton (supt wrkr)
Jenny Mattrick (supt off)
Jonathan Ferguson (emplt supt officer)
Paula Martin (Spec Mgr)
Philip Clough (supt off)
Michelle Griffin (supt wrkr)
Michelle Smith (supt off)

39. **SOVA Sheffield Youth Justice Project**
7 St Peters Close
Sheffield S1 2EJ
tel 0114-228 8545 *fax 0114-228 8500*

Darren Smith (proj mgr)
Fahreen Khan (supt wrkr)
John Graham (supt wrkr)

40. **SOVA Staffordshire Leaving Care**
Stafford Area Office
Madford Retail Park
Foregate Street
Stafford ST16 2PA
tel (01785) 276984

Margaret Collier (supt off)
Hannah Evans (supt off)
Michelle Elliot (proj asst)

41. **SOVA Thames Valley Mentoring
Project**
Units C/D, Agora Centre
47-49 Church Street
Wolverton MK12 5LD
tel (07809) 587005

Kathleen Power (proj mgr)

42. **SOVA Transform**
5th Floor, Scala House
36 Holloway Circus
Queensway, Birmingham B1 1EQ
tel 0121-643 7400 *fax 0121-643 7454*

John Leach (snr proj mgr)
Stephen Ashton (volunteer supt officer)
Tarah Inniss (volunteer supt officer/
cover supt wrkr)
Anesta Benjamin (supt wrkr)
Leslie Rennocks (emplt supt wrkr)
Claire Evans (emplt supt wrkr)

43. **SOVA Young London**
London – Cornerstone House
Cornerstone House, 14 Willis Road
Croydon CR0 2XX
tel 0208-665 5668 *fax 0208-665 1972*

Joanne Freeman (proj mgr)

44. **v involved**
VAS, The Circle
33 Rockingham Lane, Sheffield S1 4FW
tel 0114-253 6755 *fax 0114-253 6756*

Nicola Kidston (youth volunteer devpt
mgr)
Jonathan Tyrell (supt off)
Tamar Wharam (supt off)

45. **SOVA Wales New Deal**
137 High Street, Bangor LL57 1NT
tel (01248) 352974 *fax (01248) 364755*

Urtha Felda (snr proj mgr)
Soo Paul (Trainer)
Lesley Haggis (supt wrkr)
Demi Rowe (supt wrkr)

46. **SOVA Wales New Deal**
Marine House
23 Mount Stuart Square
Cardiff CF10 5DP
tel 029-2049 5281 *fax 029-2049 2148*

Sandra Taylor (snr proj mgr)
Christopher Collins (training mgr)
Jennifer Winters (supt officer (training))
Malcolm Evans (supt off)
Alex Tyler (supt off)
Ruth Hawkins (supt off)
Lorraine Owens (supt off)

47. **SOVA Wales New Deal**
The Dawn Centre, 35-37 Princes Drive
Colwyn Bay, Conway LL29 8PD
tel (01492) 523695 *fax (01492) 523691*

Melanie Newport (supt off)

48. **SOVA Wales New Deal**
2nd Floor, Ladywell House
Newtown, Powys SY16 1JB
tel (01686) 623873 *fax (01686) 623875*

Martin Jones (area co-ord)

49. **SOVA Wales New Deal**
33 Heathfield, Swansea SA1 6EJ
tel 01792 463597 *fax 01792 461884*

Elizabeth Beguin (proj mgr)
Lesley Evans (admin asst)

50. **SOVA Wales New Deal**
Wrexham – Priory Offices
Priory Offices, 8-10 Priory Street
Wrexham LL11 1SU
tel (01978) 262223 *fax (01978) 263332*

Samantha Blaze (supt off)
Becky Cotton (admin asst)

51. **SOVA Yorkshire Prisons ETE**
HMP Everthorpe, Brough
East Yorkshire HU15 1RD
tel (01430) 426577 *fax (01430) 426501*

Audra White (supt wrker)
Michelle Hilton (co-ord)
Philip Marsham (supt wrkr)

52. **SOVA Yorkshire Prisons ETE**
HMP Lindholme, Bawtry Road
Hatfield Woodhouse
Doncaster DN7 6EE
tel (01302) 524625 *fax (01302) 524849*

Vicky Wooller (co-ord)
Fiona Ross (proj mgr)

53. **SOVA Yorkshire Prisons ETE**
HMP/YOI Moorland
Bawtry Road, Hatfield Woodhouse
Doncaster DN7 6BW
tel (01302) 523000 ext 3009
fax (01302) 350896

John Taylor-Jones (co-ord (ETE))
Audra White (supt wrkr)

54. **SOVA Yorkshire Prisons ETE**
HMP /YOI New Hall
Dial Wood, Flockton
Wakefield, W4 4XX
tel (01924) 844200 *fax (01924) 844201*
Maxine Rudram (co-ord (ETE))

55. **SOVA Yorkshire Prisons ETE**
HMP/YOI Northallerton
East Road, Northallerton DL6 1NW
tel 01609 785193 *fax (01609) 785318*

Anne Mableson (co-ord (ETE))
Craig Milner (co-ord (ETE)/monitoring
officer)

56. SOVA Yorkshire Prisons ETE

HMP Wealstun, Wetherby
West Yorkshire
tel (01937) 444586 *fax (01937) 444766*

Rachel Atha (co-ord (ETE))
Greg Robinson (co-ord (ETE))
Rosemary Delderfield (co-ord (ETE))
Mark Wilkinson (co-ord (ETE))
Philip Marsham (supt wrkr)

RAINER CRIME CONCERN

Rectory Lodge, High Street, Brasted Kent
TN16 1JF
tel (01959) 578200 *fax (01959) 561891*
e-mail mail@raineronline.org
www.raineronline.org

Rainer and Crime Concern have now merged as one charity.

Rainer has worked with the probation service since it was first founded, with the original police court missionaries (as probation officers were then called) funded through a donation by Frederic Rainer. Building on over 200 years experience, Rainer now runs around 55 services and projects nationally, working with thousands of under-supported young people each year.

Work includes learning and employability services, mentoring, supported accommodation, restorative justice and resettlement/through the gate work with offenders. These are delivered by professional staff in accordance with a national performance management framework. Key examples include:

Many of these services are working with young adults subject to supervision by the probation service. All of Rainer's work is underpinned by a clear commitment and expertise in the use of volunteers and mentors recruited from communities locally. This work is facilitated through the delivery of nationally accredited models for mentor and volunteer training. Rainer is also the lead agency in RESET, an EQUAL-funded national partnership that aims to identify, develop and disseminate effective resettlement practice for young people and young adults in the custodial estate.

Many of the young people have been involved with the criminal justice system, are in or leaving care, homeless, may be young parents or are facing serious deficits in their education affecting their employment prospects. Often they are facing a combination of these issues.

Rainer focuses on the following areas that affect young people

Supported accommodation Rainer can give young people a home, teach them how to live there, and let them stay as long as they need.

Learning & employability Rainer know that young people without an education struggle to find work and are much more likely to commit crime, suffer from depression or become homeless. Engaging with education and employment dramatically reduces the risk of offending and means they can make a valuable contribution to society and their community. It gives opportunities to young people who either missed out on schooling in their earlier years, or who have found it difficult to engage with mainstream education.

Tackling crime Crime or persistent offending is easy for some young people who do not have the right support. Rainer helps these young people to find their feet and give them a fresh start in life. It works intensively with young people who persistently offend, tackling offending behaviour and working with them to deal with the consequences of their crime, both for their own benefit and for the community in which they live.

Supporting young people and their families Many of our young people have struggled through life without the care of parents and family. Rainer sees young people and their families at a point of crisis when emotions are high with feelings of failure, anger and helplessness. Its work can often help families find solutions for themselves. Helping young people rebuild their relationships with their families, even if they cannot go back home to live, is an important part of establishing a support network around them. And if young people become young parents, when they can often find it hard to offer the care a baby needs, it supports them with their parenting, as this is the best way of preventing problems later on in life.

ST MUNGO'S
OFFENDER SERVICES

Services Provided

Housing Advice Service provides housing advice for new prisoners with problems that can arise from a prison sentence. Works with prisoners to plan for their discharge, by finding accommodation for the day of release. Focuses on post-release needs so that young clients have the best chance of sustaining a crime-free life back in their community.

Includes support and information to the families with concerns about the release of a family member with accommodation issues. Provides a mediation service to try to rebuild relationships between clients and their families to enable a return to the family home. The team liaises with the Probation Service, solicitors, social workers and court officials. They will provide support at court hearings when required

Assessment & Referral Service provides an initial screening assessment of all new prisoners within 4 days of entering the prison to identify needs and make referrals to all of the relevant agencies working within the prison. The assessment identifies housing, substance use, alcohol, health, children and family, finance and debt, attitude and behavioural needs.

Muslim Resettlement project at HMP Pentonville for prisoners from a Muslim background. Builds links with a range of Muslim agencies and services in the prison and the community to improve resettlement prospects for these prisoners.

Floating Support dovetails with prison based services and local probation and homelessness agencies. It is developing best practice in meeting the housing needs of Probation clients, in the context of community based orders and drug requirements.

Offender Work and Learning Service provides support to male and female ex-offenders over 18 who want training to improve their work skills. Provides coaching to help in finding employment. Helps people who wish to set up their own businesses, including support finding grants and specialist business planning advice. It offers workshops on personal

development and skills training, and a chance to develop business idea. Offers personal one-to-one careers and job coaching, supporting clients to obtain funding for training and education, opportunities to volunteer, advice on disclosure of convictions and help with planning. Support is provided with setting up bank accounts and applying for passports or other ID. Access to computers with internet access to job sites and use of telephones, photocopier and fax. Offers specific support to women, on issues such as building self confidence, assertiveness, and sharing experiences with other women.

1. **HM Prison & YOI Feltham**
   Housing Advice, Resettlement & Post-Release Floating Support Service
   Sam Cowie, Manager
   tel 020-8844 5374
   Samantha.cowie@hmps.gov.gsi.uk
   samc@mungos.org

   Eligibility criteria
   Serving or remand prisoners. Aged 18+
   No geographic restrictions

2. **HMP Pentonville**
   Housing Advice, Resettlement Service
   Sam Cowie, Manager
   tel 020-7023 7320
   Samantha.cowie@hmps.gov.gsi.uk
   samc@mungos.org

   Eligibility criteria
   Serving or remand prisoners. Aged 18+
   No geographic restrictions

   Muslim Resettlement Service
   Ahmed Patel, Service Co-ordinator
   tel 07791 7212781
   ahmedpatel@mungos.org
   Eligibility criteria
   Serving or remand Muslim prisoners.
   Aged 18+
   No geographic restrictions, although the service focuses on Muslim prisoners from East London

3. **HMP Wormwood Scrubs**
   Housing Advice, Resettlement Service
   Eligibility criteria
   Serving or remand prisoners. Aged 18+
   No geographic restrictions

Assessment and Referral Service
Eligibility criteria
All new prisoners

Michael Kenny, Manager
tel 020-8588 3649
michael.kenny@hmps.gov.gsi.uk
samc@mungos.org

4. **HMP Latchmere House**
Housing Advice, Resettlement Service
Michael Kenny, Manager
tel 020-8588 3649
michael.kenny@hmps.gov.gsi.uk
samc@mungos.org

Eligibility criteria
Serving or remand prisoners. Aged 18+
No geographic restrictions

5. **Tower Hamlets Resettlement Service**
(The Looking Out Project)
Sam Cowie, Manager
tel 020-8844 5374
Samantha.cowie@hmps.gov.gsi.uk
samc@mungos.org

Eligibility criteria
Serving or remand prisoners preparing for
discharge to LB of Tower Hamlets. Aged
18+

6. **Harrow Probation Housing Advice
Service**
Brian Stevenson, Manager
tel 020-8762 5500
BStevenson@mungos.org

Eligibility criteria
Clients of Harrow Probation or prisoners
returning to the borough. Aged 18+

7. **Hillingdon Offender Housing Floating
Support**
Brian Stevenson, Manager
tel 020-8762 5500
BStevenson@mungos.org

Eligibility criteria
Clients of Hillingdon Probation or
prisoners returning to the borough.
Aged 18+

8. **Brent Probation Housing Advice
and Floating Support**
Rachel Kerr, Co-ordinator
tel 0208 451 7537
rkerr@mungos.org

Eligibility criteria
Offenders living in the LB of Brent. Aged
18+

9. **Offender Work & Learning Services**
Graham Burton, Manager
tel 020-7549 8200
grahamb@mungos.org

Eligibility criteria
Ex-offenders, particularly disabled and
female

Accommodation

10. **Larix Annexe** (London Borough of Brent)
The Manager
tel 020-8965 4763

Eligibility criteria
Offenders with complex needs in the LB
of Brent

Referrals via
Probation Officer, Brent Council

7 bed supported housing project for
clients with complex needs including
mental health and substance misuse, (dual
diagnosis). There is a multi-disciplinary
team including a supported housing officer,
activity worker, resettlement worker that
facilitates access to drug, alcohol and
mental health services.

11. **Pound Lane** (London Borough of
Hackney)
115 Pound Lane, London NW10 2HU
tel 020-8809 7241

Eligibility criteria
Male ex-offenders

Referrals via
Brent Probation

The hostel has 46 bed spaces that
currently houses about 15 ex-offenders
referred by the Probation Service, from
our Brent ex-offender floating support
service and from Wormwood Scrubs.

12. **Accommodation in Haringey**
188 Vartry Road, London N15 6HA
tel 020-8809 5742

Eligibility criteria
Mixed gender, no couples

Referrals via
Vulnerable Adults Team, Haringey Council

Mixed 23 bed first stage hostel where 30% of the residents are ex-offenders and live in self-contained flats. Has attached peripatetic mental health worker, substance use worker, and resettlement worker.

14 Weston Park, Crouch End, London N8 9TJ
tel 020 8341 0258

Eligibility criteria
Males only Persistent Prolific Offenders

Referrals via
Referrals strictly through PPO structures from Probation, the council, and Drug Intervention Partnerships.

8 beds, providing semi-independent accommodation. A substance use worker is attached to the project. A senior project worker with specialist knowledge of the criminal justice system is being recruited. Available at any point post release.

13. **Accommodation in Islington**
35 Tollington Road, London N7 6PB
tel 020-7700 2402
(or contact 155 Tufnell Park Road 020-7609 4773)

Eligibility criteria
Mixed gender, ex-offenders

Referrals via
Referrals from the Islington Supporting People Referral Coordinator

An 8 bed semi-independent accommodation project. Has self contained studio flats for clients with low to medium support needs. . A link worker will available to assist clients search for work. Has a health worker, a project worker and senior project worker with specialist knowledge of the criminal justice system. Available at any point post release.

127 Huddleston Road, London N7 0EH
tel 020-7281 4261
(or contact 155 Tufnell Park Road 020-7609 4773)

Eligibility criteria
Males only, ex-offenders.

Referrals via
Referrals from the Islington Supporting People Referral Coordinator

7 bed medium support semi-independent accommodation project. Rooms are single occupancy with shared bathroom and kitchen. A link worker will available to assist clients search for work. Has a health worker, a project worker and senior project worker with specialist knowledge of the criminal justice system. Available at any point post release.

14. **Accommodation in Hackney**
178 Glyn Road, London E5 0JE
tel 020-8533 8305

Eligibility criteria
Ex-offenders, those at risk of offending, going through courts, on suspended sentence or probation order

Referrals via
Referrals through London Probation, the council or the Drug Intervention Programme or from ex-offenders previously referred into Mare Street hostel or directly from St Mungo's Prison Services Team.

5 bed semi-independent housing project, mixed gender. For progressively independent living prior to independent living. Links into local external services. Access available at any time post release. The project is being remodelled to support ex-offenders with complex needs. Specialist senior project workers and substance use workers with a knowledge of the criminal justice system will be recruited.

27 Kenworthy Road, London E9 5PB
tel 020-8533 8305

Eligibility criteria
Ex-offenders, those at risk of offending, going through courts, on suspended sentence or probation order

Referrals via
Referrals are through London probation, the council or the Drug Intervention Programme or directly from St Mungo's Prison Services Team.

5 bed semi-independent housing project for men. Access available at any time post release. The project is being remodelled to support ex-offenders with complex needs. Specialist senior project workers and substance use workers with a knowledge of the criminal justice system will be recruited.

Confidential address
tel 020-7249 5294

Eligibility criteria
Females only

Referrals via
Direct from prison, or from Hackney
Probation and Drug Intervention
Programmes.

First stage direct access 29 bed hostel.
Access available at any time post release.
There is a full time substance use worker,
resettlement worker, and project workers,
the latter having specialist knowledge of
the criminal justice system.

Mental Health Team Services

15. **Neighbourhood link worker Scheme**
tel 020-7549 8236
neighbourhoodlink@mungos.org

Eligibility criteria
Clients must live in Islington, 18-65 with
a mental health need (including needs that
do not meet statutory services' criteria)

Referrals via
Self referral, SNTs and other agencies.

A pilot project that pioneers a partnership
working with the Metropolitan Police's
Safer Neighbourhood Teams in Islington.
Aims to contact and provide support to
vulnerable adults at the earliest point in
the criminal justice system, and prevent
an escalation of their mental health needs
and offending. The experience from the
Scheme will be used to produce a model
suitable for national replication across the
Neighbourhood Policing network.

16. **Prison Link Worker Scheme**
    HMP Holloway
    tel 07764 958 916

Eligibility criteria
Black & minority ethnic women with
mental health needs (including needs that
do not meet statutory services' criteria).

Referrals via
Self referral, Inreach Mental Health
Team, Prison Resettlement Teams and St
Mungo's.

Support for black & minority ethnic
women who are in contact with the
criminal justice system and have mental
health needs that are not met by statutory

mental health services. Offers emotional
& practical support in helping women link
into the community services & resources
(including primary & secondary care,
housing and benefits).

Outreach Service

17. **Drug Intervention Programme**
    Assertive Outreach Programme
    Great Guildford Business Square, 30 Great
    Guildford Street, London SE1 0HS
    tel 020-7525 0830

Referral not needed

Provide assertive street-based outreach
to locate individuals who have disengaged
from Drug Intervention Programmes.
Undertakes intensive, time limited
interventions with ex-service users to re-
engage with them.

Drug & Alcohol Services

18. **Cedar's Road Hostel**
    113-117 Cedar's Road, SW4 0PJ
    tel 020-7720 7377

Eligibility criteria
Must be resident at the hostel

Referrals via
Hostel project workers, or self referral

This 120 bed first stage mixed gender
hostel has four substance use workers,
and links with local DIP and Probation
Services. Additionally. The service offers
a women's worker and a Portuguese
speaking worker. Provides in-house
methadone scripting services, moving
scripts from different boroughs, referrals
for detox, rehab and community day
programmes, individual sessions,
acupuncture and Women's Relaxation
Group as well as Blood Borne Virus
testing.

19. **Pagnell Street Hostel**
    Exeter Way, New Cross, SE14 6LL
    tel 020-8692 3454

Eligibility criteria
Must be resident at hostel

Referrals via
Hostel project workers, or self referral

At 43 bed first stage mixed gender hostel
there is access to one substance use
worker. The following services are offered:

one to one sessions, referrals to detox, rehab, DIP, day programmes and onsite Blood Borne Virus testing.

VICTIM SERVICES

The information in this section has largely been supplied by Victim Support. The editor wishes to express his thanks for this help.

NOMS Victim Helpline

NOMS Victim Helpline, PO Box 4278, Birmingham B15 1SA
0845 7585 112
Part of the National Offender Management Service in the Home Office

Head of Unit, A K Jones 0121 626 2208
Team leader 0121 626 3331
Information available at www.hmprisonservice.gov.uk

Victim Support

National Office, Victim Support National Centre, Hallam House, 56-60 Hallam Street, London W1W 6JL
020-7268 0200 *fax 020-7268 0210* helpline 0845 30 30 900
email contact@victimsupport.org.uk
www.victimsupport.org.uk

Co-ordinates the work of local community-based branches providing services to victims of crime and their families, also co-ordinates the Witness Service which supports witnesses in every criminal court in England and Wales.

Victims' Voice

P.O. Box 21, Fairford GL7 4WX
07984 078918
victimsvoice@hotmail.com *www.victimsvoice.co.uk*

Victims' Voice is an umbrella charity which provides a 'voice' for its affiliated organisations and individual members. It raises issues that arise when people are bereaved by sudden and traumatic death and have to cope with the involvement of police, coroners, mortuaries, hospitals and the courts.

Witness Service

Central Criminal Court, Old Bailey, London EC4M 7EH
020-7192 2423 *fax 020-7192 2142*

CCWS.CentralCriminalCourt@vslondon.org

The Witness Service is a free and confidential service, available at every criminal court in London, which helps witnesses, victims and their families before, during and after a trial.

Organisations offering bereavement support

A Different Journey

Care for the Family, Garth House, Leon Avenue, Cardiff CF15 7RG
029 2081 0800
adifferentjourney@cff.org.uk
www.careforthefamily.org.uk/adj

Offers support to those suffering bereavement or family breakdown, together with any children.

Bereaved Parents Network

Bereaved Parents Network, Care for the Family, Garth House, Leon Ave, Cardiff F15 7RG
029 2081 0800
bereavedparentsnetwork@cff.org.uk
www.careforthefamily.org.uk/bpn

Offers support to those who have been bereaved of a child (including adult children), together with siblings.

Cruse Bereavement Care

Cruse House, 126 Sheen Road, Richmond, Surrey TW9 1UR
020-8939 9530 *fax 020-8940 7638*
helpline 0844 477 9400 helpline@cruse.org.uk
(for young people) 0870 167 1677 info@rdforu.org.uk
www.cruse.org.uk (for young people)
www.rd4u.org.uk

The only national organisation that helps and supports anyone who has been bereaved. It provides advice, bereavement support and information on practical matters for bereaved people entirely free of charge. Its support is delivered through a network of 180 branches across the UK. It also offers training, support, information and publications to those working to care for bereaved people.

The Candle Project

St Christopher's Hospice, 51-59 Lawrie Park Road, Sydenham, London SE26 6DZ
tel 0208 768 4500
f.kraus@stchristophers.org.uk

The Candle project provides one to one and group bereavement support for children, young people and families in the South East London area. It also offers a telephone advice service for parents, carers and professionals nationwide. This is a free service for those who need it.

The Child Death Helpline
York House, 37 Queen Square, London WC1N 3BH
020-7813 8416(admin) 020-7813 8550(volunteering) *fax 020 7813 8516*
contact@childdeathhelpline.org
www.childdeathhelpline.org.uk

Helpline 0800 282 986 open throughout the year every evening 7pm to 10pm, Monday to Friday mornings 10am to 1pm, Wednesday afternoons 1pm to 4pm. This is a lifelong freephone listening service of emotional support for anyone affected by the death of a child.

The Compassionate Friends
53 North Street, Bristol BS3 1EN
0845 1203785 helpline 0845 123 2304 (local rate), day/evening 365 days a year
info@tcf.org.uk helpline@tcf.org.uk
www.tcf.org.uk

The Compassionate Friends was founded in 1969 as an organisation of bereaved parents and their families helping each other through their grief.

Winston's Wish
Westmoreland House, 80-86 Bath Road, Cheltenham, Glos GL53 7JT
01242 515157 *fax 01242 546187* helpline 08452 03 04 05 (open Mon-Fri, 9am to 5pm)
info@winstonswish.org.uk *www.winstonswish.org.uk*

Winston's Wish provides support for bereaved children and young people up to the age of 18. They also support parents and carers. Whether the death was sudden or expected they work closely with children and families in a variety of practical and creative ways to create an atmosphere where they can share their thoughts and feelings and meet others.

Organisations offering specialist trauma care

ASSIST Trauma Care
Assistance, Support & Self Help in Surviving Trauma, 11 Albert St, Rugby CV21 2RX
(01788) 551919 *fax (01788) 553726*
www.traumatic-stress.freeserve.co.uk
helpline, Mon-Fri 10am-4pm, (01788) 560800.

Provides therapeutic support and counselling to probationers, prisoners and all those involved in the prison system, who have been affected by trauma, including their friends and families. Specialist treatment for those suffering from Post Traumatic Stress and Post Traumatic Stress Disorder.

Disaster Action
No 4, 71 Upper Berkeley Street, London W1H 7DB
01483 799066 (office is open on a part time, answer phone outside office hours)
pameladix@disasteraction.org.uk
www.disasteraction.org.uk
Survivors and bereaved people from major UK and overseas disasters founded Disaster Action in 1991 as a British Based Charity. All their members have direct personal experience of surviving and or being bereaved in a wide variety of disasters of different origin including terrorist attacks, transport and natural disasters.

Organisations helping after murder or manslaughter

SAMM (Support After Murder and Manslaughter),
First floor, Scotia House, 33 Finsbury Square, London EC2A 1PL,
020-7638 4040, helpline 0845 3440 *fax 020-7638 4050*
support@samm.org.uk *www.samm.org.uk*

An independent voluntary organisation offering help and support to families and friends bereaved as a result of murder and manslaughter. All their support volunteers have been similarly bereaved and can share what it feels like to have a loved one taken in this violent and tragic way. They are also involved in training, research, raising public awareness and increasing the understanding of organisations that work with bereaved families, particularly with the criminal justice system. Please contact the National Office for details of local groups.

SAMM Abroad 0845 123 2384 e-mail info@sammabroad.org
Support group for people who are bereaved through murder or manslaughter abroad.

MAMAA
e-mail info@mama.org *www.mamaa.org*

MAMAA (Mothers Against Murder and Aggression) is a national registered charity that provides support to families and friends of victims of murder, manslaughter and unlawful killing.

North of England Victims' Association,
PO Box 111, Jarrow, Tyne & Wear NE32 4SE
0191-4232210 e-mail n.e.v.a@blueyonder.co.uk

Helps those in the North East of England who are suffering or who have suffered, as a result of serious crimes, such as murder and manslaughter, by the provision of financial assistance, advice, counselling and support services.

Scotland

PETAL Support Group (People Experiencing Trauma and Loss)
29 Clydesdale Street, Hamilton ML3 0DD
01698 324502
help@petalsupportgroup.fslife.co.uk
www.petalsupport.com

PETAL provides practical, emotional and confidential support, advocacy, group support and counselling for the families and friends of murder and suicide victims. The level of practical and emotional support provided by PETAL differs from the support available from other agencies since the membership consists of the families and friends of murder and suicide victims. The Support Provision by PETAL centres on practical and emotional support and assists people to come to terms with the implications of these traumatic events. Clients can attend Fortnightly Support Meetings at PETAL and use PETAL as a Drop-in Centre for Support or get One to One Counselling. Telephone support and counselling can be provided to those families outwith a reasonable travelling distance.

Families of Murdered Children (F.o.M.C) 99 Wood Crescent, Motherwell ML1 1HQ
fomcuk@yahoo.co.uk *www.fomc.org.uk* or *www.fomcuk.org*
helpline 01698 336646 and the 24 hour contact number is 0777 562 6779

A non-religious, charitable organisation providing support, information, advice and advocacy to anyone who has lost a loved one as a result of murder, culpable homicide or unlawful killing regardless of age, sex, religion or sexual orientation. Services including a Helpline, a 24 hour contact number, home visits, court support, weekly meetings and a secure internet group (by invitation only) including secure chat room facilities.

Victims of Crime Trust
PO Box 999, Twickenham, Middlesex TW1 3TB
0870 842 8467
info@victimsofcrimetrust.com
www.victimsofcrimetrust.com

Victims of Crime Trust provides service to anyone bereaved through homicide especially initial advocacy assistance to victims when they are too vulnerable to cope with the tragedy by themselves, supporting them until they are stronger.

Organisations offering support after a road death

BrakeCare
PO Box 548, Huddersfield HD1 2XZ
(01484) 559909 *fax (01484) 559983* helpline
0845 603 8570
helpline@brake.org.uk *www.brake.org.uk*

This division of Brake the national road safety charity supports people who have been bereaved and injured in road crashes and assists professionals working with road crash victims. It provides emotional support and practical information to road crash victims.

Campaign Against Drinking & Driving (C.A.D.D.)
PO Box 62, Brighouse HD6 3YY
0845 123 5541/3 helpline 0845 603 8570 (9am to 9pm 365 days)
e-mail cadd@scard.org.uk *www.cadd.org.uk*

The Campaign Against Drinking and Driving (CADD) was set up in 1985 to support all victims of drunk or drugged drivers throughout the UK.

RoadPeace
PO Box 2579, London NW10 3PW
020-8838 5102 helpline 0845 4500 355, open 7 days, 9am to 9pm
info@roadpeace.org & helpline@roadpeace.org
www.roadpeace.org

RoadPeace is UK's specialist charity for road traffic victims with headquarters in London and 10 local groups throughout the country. RoadPeace offers dedicated support to people bereaved and injured through a road crash and represents their interests.

S.C.A.R.D. (Support & Care After Road Death & Injury)
PO Box 62, Brighouse HD6 3YY

0845 123 5541 helpline 0845 123 5542, open 7 days, 9am to 9pm
info@scard.org.uk *www.scard.org.uk*

Inspired by the tragic death of the founder's son at the hands of a drunk and illegal driver, S.C.A.R.D. is a registered charity, which exists to provide emotional and practical support to the people affected by road tragedies all over the United Kingdom.

Other Organisations offering support

DAMN (Deaths After Medical Negligence)
Mrs Lilly Lewy, tel 020-8205 4985
lhl005@londonmet.ac.uk

Formally RAID: Rigorous Analysis of Iatrogenic Death – when the cause of death is given as 'Natural Causes' yet the cause was through negligence.

Samaritans
www.samaritans.org
UK Telephone number 08457 90 90 90 or Text 07725 90 90 90
Republic of Ireland 1850 60 90 90 or Text 0872 60 90 90
For the deaf or hard of hearing there are minicom numbers: UK 08457 90 91 92 Republic of Ireland 1850 60 90 91
jo@samaritans.org *www.samaritans.org*

ARTS FOR OFFENDERS

Anne Peaker Centre for Arts in Criminal Justice
Neville House, 90/91 Northgate, Canterbury, Kent CT1 1BA
(01227) 470629 e-mail info@apcentre.org.uk
www.apcentre.org.uk

The national umbrella organisation that promotes and supports the use of arts in criminal justice. Seeks to influence policy through closely liaising with government and to provide training for creative professionals working in criminal justice. Aims to demonstrate the value of the arts through undertaking and analysing research, and sources and disseminates clear information, advice and support to the sector.

Aside from its main website, the Centre promotes two other online resources *www. joiningthedots.co.uk* (an interactive online resource providing details of experienced practitioners and workshop ideas, soon to

hold Europe-wide information) and *www. artsontheout.co.uk* (a web based resource for offenders and ex-offenders).

Professional membership offers enhanced access to useful resources, networking and promotional opportunities, discounted training and other valuable support for creative professionals working in the arts in the criminal justice sector.

A comprehensive listing of arts projects can be found on the two web sites listed above. Below is a selection of directly relevant projects, including some that may not appear on the web sites.

Rideout (Creative Arts for Rehabilitation)
The Roslyn Works, Uttoxeter Road, Stoke on Trent ST3 1PQ
(01782) 32555 e-mail admin@rideout.co.uk
www.rideout.org.uk

Rideout specialise in drama, theatre and multi-artform projects in prisons. The aim of the company's work is to aid prisoners' rehabilitation through the provision of a range of arts activities. These include both long-term drama-based workshops exploring multiple aspects of offending behaviour, and theatre and multi-artform projects that allow for the development of creativity and self-expression, as well as a number of inter- and intra-personal skills.

Art Alive Trust
Creative Centre for the Arts, Unit 6A, Clapham North Arts Centre, 26-32 Voltaire Road, Clapham, London, SW4 6DH
020-7622 0441 mobile 07944 476 459 *fax 020-7622 0441*
e-mail info@artalive.org.uk *www.artalive.org.uk*

Promotes rehabilitation of offenders and ex-offenders, with particular but not exclusive reference to young offenders from an ethnic minority background. Art-Alive Arts Trust offers arts education and mentoring, with the aim of assisting (ex)offenders to re-integrate into the community and to acquire creative skills that will assist them in avoiding re-offending, and gaining employment.

Burnbake Trust
29 North Street, Wilton, Wilts SP2 0HE
(01722) 744178 Tues & Fri, between 08.00 - 15.00 e-mail eva.burnbaketrust@yahoo.co.uk

The trust provides prisoners with art materials, and invites them to return the work produced in order that it can be sold for them. Prisoners then receive the profits of the sales and are encouraged to purchase new materials with them.

Clean Break Theatre Company
2 Patshull Road London NW5 2LB
020-7482 8600 fax 020-7482 8611 e-mail general@cleanbreak.org.uk
www.cleanbreak.org.uk

The UK's only women's theatre education and new writing company for ex-offenders, prisoners, ex-prisoners and women at risk of offending due to drug or alcohol use or mental health issues. Clean Break produces theatre that engages audiences in the issues faced by women whose lives have been affected by the criminal justice system. Their belief is that engaging in theatre can create new opportunities for these women and develop their personal, social, artistic and professional skills.

The Comedy School
15 Gloucester Gate, London NW1 4HG
020-7486 1844 e-mail@thecomedyschool.com
www.thecomedyschool.com
Practical and realistic approaches to stand-up comedy in prisons nationally. Believes that comedy is a powerful tool that can be used to help people gain the motivation to learn.

Dance United
United House, 39-41 North Road, London, N7 9DP
tel 020 7502 6570 fax 020 7502 6571 e-mail info@dance-united.com
www.dance-united.com

Plays a part in helping marginalised or excluded people to transform the way they see themselves and the way they are viewed by society. Through the dance process offenders are able to research their identity as a community and as individuals.

Escape Artists
Studio 24, 7-15 Greatorex Street, London, E1 5NF and The Cambridge Resource Centre, 47-51 Norfolk Street, Cambridge, CB1 2LD
020 7655 0909 e-mail info@escapeartists.co.uk
www.escapeartists.co.uk

Provides NOCN accredited arts based programmes and pre-employment training courses specifically designed for use within the criminal justice sector. Also offers a project management service providing a wide range of services from financial and administrative support to project delivery and funding advice.

Fine Cell Work
PO Box 44779, London, SWIW OXH
tel 020-7931 9998 e-mail enquiries@finecellwork.co.uk www.finecellwork.co.uk

A registered charity that teaches needlework to inmates and pays them for their work so they can accumulate a nest egg and sells their products. The inmates are taught by volunteers from the Embroiderers Guild, the Royal School of Needlework and the world of professional design. The prisoners do the work in their cells and the earnings give them hope, skills and independence.

Geese Theatre Company
Woodbridge House, 9 Woodbridge Road, Birmingham B13 8EH |
0121-449 6222 *fax 0121-449 1333*
mailbox@geese.co.uk *www.geese.co.uk*

A team of specialised theatre practitioners working within the criminal justice system. Geese design and deliver performances, workshops, groupwork programmes and creative residencies with offenders and young people at risk of offending both in a custodial and a community setting. Geese also provides staff training and consultancy with criminal justice system staff and bespoke performances at criminal justice conferences

Good Vibrations Gamelan in Prisons Project
39 St Gerards Close, London, SW4 9DU
020 867305367
e-mail gamelannetwork.co.uk
www.gamelannetwork.co.uk
Well over 500 prisoners, in a wide variety of prisons across the UK, have taken part in Good Vibrations projects. Projects last one or two weeks and culminate in an informal performance. Every participant receives a professionally-produced CD of their group's work. Prison staff have observed striking improvements in people's ability to work together, their ability to listen to each other, and their levels of concentration and sense of self-worth. They have found the workshops to be very effective at engaging prisoners who have not previously participated in anything and who do not respond well to more "traditional" forms of education. Most of the prisons use the workshops as a way of helping participants work towards Basic and Key Skills qualifications. Good Vibrations uses a specially-developed

workbook to enable people to get accredited for Communications Skills Level 1 purely through our workshops and without having to set foot in a classroom.

Irene Taylor Trust

Music in Prisons, Unit 401, Bon Marche Centre, 241Ferndale Road, London SW9 8BJ
tel 020-7733 3222
e-mail info@musicinprisons.org.uk
www.musicinprisons.org.uk

Through music and high quality arts activities, the Trust aims to teach artistic and personal skills that participants will be able to draw on in everyday life. By working in conjunction with prison education departments, the Trust enables prisoners to achieve recognised accreditation in key skills. The Trust continues to raise the profile of music and arts in prisons through the evaluation and dissemination of its working practices

Koestler Trust Arts Centre

168a Du Cane Road, London W12 0TX
020-8740 0333
e-mail info@koestlertrust.org.uk
www.koestlertrust.org.uk
A prison arts charity, founded by Arthur Koestler in 1962. Its annual competition and exhibition, that has grown in recent years to be a high profile event, promotes and encourages the arts and creativity in UK prisons, YOIs, high security hospitals, secure units and probation.

Safe Ground Productions

PO Box 11525, London SW11 5ZW
020-7228 3831 *fax 020-7228 3885* e-mail safeground@aol.com

Produces projects and programmes of education using drama, design and film. Also focuses on peer education and parenting projects, and mapping key skills.

Synergy Theatre Project

Hyde Park House, 5 Manfred Road, London SW15 2RS
020-8870 2112
e-mail info@synergytheatreproject.co.uk
www.synergytheatreproject.co.uk

Runs theatre based projects in prisons and creates drama opportunities for ex-offenders on their release.

The Theatre in Prison and Probation Centre (TIPP)

The Martin Harris Building, University of Manchester, Oxford Road, Manchester M13 9PL
0161-275 3047 *fax 0161-275 3877* e-mail admin@tipp.org.uk
www.tipp.org.uk

Uses theatre to explore issues (drugs, anger management, employment, etc) with socially excluded groups; particularly within the criminal justice system. Also provides specialist training.

Valley and Vale Community Arts

Sardis Media Centre, Heol Dewi Sant, Betws, Bridgend CF32 8SU
(01656) 729246
e-mail mail@valleyandvale.co.uk
www.valleyandvale.co.uk

Valley and Vale offer access to Community Arts and media workshops as well as projects in video, animation, dance, drama, forum theatre, photography, visual and digital arts, multimedia, music and design. They connect groups and communities through outreach, cross-generational projects and local and international cultural exchange.

The Writers in Prisons Network

PO Box 71, Welshpool SY21 0WB
tel (01938) 810402 e-mail info@ writersinprisonnetwork.org
www.writersinprisonnetwork.org

Supports a wide range of prison-based projects (and in the wider Criminal Justice system) that use creative writing, oral storytelling, publishing, video, radio, theatre, reading and music to address issues such as adult literacy, parenting, journalism and personal development. Writers in residence are placed in prisons to work for 2.5 days a week for up to three years. The scheme is jointly funded by Arts Council England, the Learning & Skills Council and individual establishments. Lord Longford Prize Winner 2004.

EDUCATION FOR PRISONERS

Prisoners' Education Trust

Wandle House, Riverside Drive, Mitcham, Surrey CR4 4BU
tel 020-8648 7760 *fax 020-8648 7762*
www.prisonerseducation.org.uk
e-mail info@prisonerseducation.org.uk

A national charity that aims to extend and enrich educational opportunities available to prisoners and promote debate about offender learning policy. It offers grants to prisoners with at least six months to serve (or a good chance of completing the course before release) to enable them to study by distance learning. Courses that have been studied range from GCSEs, A levels, Open University Degrees to subjects such as fitness, counselling, computing, navigating and horticulture. Prisoners are advised to discuss their plans with their prison's education department, complete an application form (the education department has copies), and write a short letter to the Trust outlining their aims and stating how the course they have chosen will help meet them. Applications are normally processed within 6 to 8 weeks. The Trust also runs projects that strengthen support for prisoner learning.

Haven Distribution - Books to Prisoners
Haven Distribution, 27 Old Gloucester Street, London WC1N 3XX
www.havendistribution.org.uk

Haven Distribution is a small charity that provides free educational books to prisoners in the UK & Republic of Eire who are currently attending educational courses in prison, such as Open University, NVQ, etc. It also supplies dictionaries to prisoners in their chosen language. To apply for an application form, write to Haven Trust or download application form from the website.

RELIGIOUS ORGANISATIONS OFFERING SERVICES TO PRISONERS

Chaplain General of the Prison Service, William Noblett, Chaplaincy, HQ NOMS, Room 410, Abell House, John Islip Street, London SW1P 4LH. 020-7217 8201 (admin) *fax 020-7217 8980*

Angulimala, The Buddhist Prison Chaplaincy Organisation, The Forest Hermitage, Lower Fulbrook, Nr Sherbourne, Warwickshire CV35 8AS. phone (01926) 624385. e-mail Angulimala@foresthermitage.org.uk Angulimala is the Buddhist Religious Consultative Service to HM Prison Service and provides visiting Buddhist prison chaplains and advises the Prison Service on Buddhist matters. Ven. Ajahn Khemadhammo O.B.E., the Spiritual Director, is the Buddhist Adviser to

the Prison Serevice & NOMS - Ajahn. Khemadhammo@hmps.gsi.gov.uk

The Baptist Union of Great Britain, Baptist House, PO Box 44, 129 Broadway, Didcot, Oxon OX11 8RT (01235) 517705. Contact The Ministry Support Administrator, Ministry Department.

Churches Criminal Justice Forum, 39 Eccleston Square, London SW1V 1BX 020-7901 4878 *fax 020-7901 4874* info@ccjf.org.uk A national, ecumenical group that seeks to raise awareness of criminal justice concerns among people of faith. It encourages people to get involved in the criminal justice system in ways that will improve it, and also urges politicians to address those aspects of social disadvantage that lie behind crime.

The Church of Jesus Christ of Latter Day Saints, Office of Area Presidency, 751 Warwick Road, Solihull, West Midlands B91 3DQ. 0121-712 1200. Members of the church are sometimes known as 'Mormons' or 'Latter Day Saints'.

IQRA Trust Prisoners' Welfare, 3rd Floor, 20 East Churchfield Road, London W3 7LL 020-8354 4460 *fax 020-8354 4465*. *www. iqraprisonerswelfare.org* Promotes better understanding of Islam in Britain. It supports prisoners through its Prisoners' Welfare Directorate by providing books, religious clothing and special foods. It can also train people who are working with Muslim inmates. For their publications phone 020-7838 7987 or e-mail info@iqratrust.org

The National Council for the Welfare of Muslim Prisoners, 20 East Churchfield Road, London W3 7LL 020-8354 4460 *fax 020-8354 4465*. Gen Secretary Salah El Hassan

The Jewish Prison Chaplaincy, Rev Michael Binstock, United Synagogue, 8/10 Forty Avenue, Wembley, Middx HA9 8JW 020-8385 1855 *fax 020-8385 1856.* michael@aje.org.uk

The Methodist and Free Churches Prison Ministry. Contact Rev Alan Ogier, Superintendent Methodist Chaplain, NOMS, Horseferry House, Dean Ryle Street, London SW1P 2AW 020 7217 8048 *fax 020 7217 8980* e-mail alan.ogier@hmps.gsi.gov.uk In collaboration with the Prison Service Chaplaincy, is responsible for appointing, training and giving pastoral support to Methodist/Free Church chaplains in every prison in England and Wales.

The Pagan Federation, c/o Suzanne White, National Manager for Visiting Pagan Ministers, BM Box 7097, London WC1N 3XX. e-mail suzanne@prisonministry.org. uk Covers all areas of Paganism including Wicca, Druidry and the Northern Tradition. Can supply information and reading lists for inmates as well as providing visiting Ministers

Prison Fellowship *England & Wales*, PO Box 945, Maldon, Essex CM9 4EW. (01621) 843232 *fax 01621 843303* e-mail info@ prisonfellowship.org.uk Web *www.pfew.org.uk Northern Ireland*, 39 University Street, Belfast BT7 1FY tel/fax 028-9024 3691, e-mail info@pfni.org *Scotland*, 110 St James Street, Glasgow G4 0PS tel/fax 0141-552 1288 e-mail prisonfellowship@lineone.net A Christian ministry providing practical and spiritual support to prisoners and their families. Volunteer based organisation with local groups throughout UK that work closely with prison chaplaincy teams and local churches.

The Prison Phoenix Trust, PO Box 328, Oxford OX2 7HF. *www.prisonphoenixtrust.org.uk* Supports prisoners of any faith or none in their spiritual lives by teaching the disciplines of meditation and yoga, working with silence and the breath. It sends out free books *We're All Doing Time, Freeing the Spirit, Becoming Free Through Meditation and Yoga* etc. and CDs, and supports prisoners by regular correspondence, newsletters and by establishing weekly prison yoga classes. The trust also works with prison officers.

Religious Society of Friends (Quakers), Quaker Prison Ministry Group, QPSW, Friends House, 173 Euston Road, London NW1 2BJ. 020-7663 1035 *fax 020-7663 1001*. e-mail qpsw@quaker.org.uk The group supports about 100 Quaker prison ministers throughout Britain.

Seventh-day Adventist Church, Search Prison Ministries, 25 St John's Road, Watford, Herts WD17 1PZ (01923) 232728 *fax (01923) 250582*. North England Conference of Seventh-day Adventists, 22 Zulla Road, Mapperley Park, Nottingham NG3 5DB Welsh Mission, Ty Capel, Twyn Road, Ystrad Mynach, Caerphilly CF82 7EU Scottish Mission, Gwydyr Road, Crieff,

Perthshire PH7 4BS Irish Mission Office, 9 Newry Road, Bambridge, Co Down, N Ireland BT32 3HF Provides spiritual help and counselling to oprisoners and their families. Teams of volunteers in London and other large cities.

HIGH SECURITY HOSPITALS

1.   **Ashworth Hospital**
     Mersey Care NHS Trust
     Parkbourn, Maghull, Liverpool L31 1HW
     tel 0151-473 0303 *fax 0151-526 6603*

     Social Care
     tel 0151-471 2312/473 2713
     fax 0151- 473 2720
     e-mail name@merseycare.nhs.uk

     McLean, Robert (head of forensic social care, nominated officer safeguarding children)
     Corbishley, Angela (pa)
     0151-473 2808

     Anson, Sue (forensic social care mgr)
     Hicks, Douglas (forensic social care mgr)
     Appleton, Phil (ssw)
     Brown, Katharine (ssw)
     Caffrey, Karen (ssw)
     Carroll, Jane (ssw)
     Goodridge, Elizabeth (ssw)
     Heywood, Lynne (ssw)
     Hughes, Dennis (ssw)
     McBride, Amanda (ssw)
     O'Mara, Joyce (ssw)
     Shea, Nicholas (ssw)
     White, Lesley (ssw)
     Whittred, Stephanie (ssw)
     Warwick, Anne (child protection liaison mgr)
     Tunstall, Neil (vol sector & carers liaison mgr)
     Francis, Irene (admin mgr)

2.   **Broadmoor Hospital**
     Crowthorne, Berks RG45 7EG
     tel (01344) 773111 fax (01344) 754625

     Social Work Services
     tel (01344) 754523 *fax (01344) 754421*

     Frost, Carol (sw mgr)
     Townsend, Ruth (acting asst mgr)
     Allen, Martine
     Barker, Denis
     Chalk, Pat

White, Anne
Davies, Gareth
Hames, Carol
Heffernan, Susan
Hulin, Gillian
Kelly, Gareth
Kenworthy, Frances
Mukasa, Paul
Nijjar, Daljit
Pearce, Clive
Phillips, David
Ainsworth, Janice (locum)
Kruger, Arnold (locum)

3. **Rampton Hospital**
(Forensic Division, Nottinghamshire
Healthcare NHS Trust)
Retford, Notts DN22 0PD
tel (01777) 248321 *fax (01777) 248442*

Forensic Social Care Service
11/12 Galen Avenue, Rampton Hospital,
Retford, Notts DN22 0PD
tel (01777) 247354 *fax (01777) 247259*

Gardner, Julie (Trust Associate Director of
Social Care
Nominated Officer children's safeguarding)
Wendy Cove (pa/admin manager)
Clayton, Amanda (children's safeguarding
mgr)
Jane Brown (children's safeguarding
admin)
sfswp snr forensic social wk practitioners

Learning Disability Directorate
Clayton, Amanda (sw mgr)
Bryson, Beverley (sfswp)
Cowling Stephen (sfswp)
McNeil, Kevin (sfswp)

Mental Health Directorate
Parkinson, John (sw mgr)
Singh, Janga (sfswp)
Page, Clare (sfswp)
Johnson, Lynn (sfswp)
Wray, Corrina (sfswp)
Greenwood, Julie (sfswp)
Lanfranchi, Elizabeth (sfswp) (natnl deaf
service)

Peaks Unit
Corcoran, Lynne (sw mgr)
Bryson, Beverley (sfswp)
Cochrane, David (sfswp)
Adamson, Lyn (sfswp)
Robertson, Kim (sfswp)

Personality Disorder Directorate
Corcoran, Lynne (sw mgr)

Hahn, Gill (sfswp)
Humphries, Gail (sfswp)
Oliver, Sonia (sfswp)

Women Services Directorate
Cochrane, Sarah (sw mgr)
Briggs, Myra (sfswp)
Garrib, Aasra (sfswp)

Volunteer Co-ordination
Phillips, Janet (volco mgr)
Strawson, Val (volunteer co-ord)

Visitors Centre/Family Support
Christian, Carmel (family supt manager)
Bridge, Karen (family supt wrkr)
Weaver, Helen (family supt wrkr)

SPECIALIST ACCOMMODATION FOR OFFENDERS

*Individual projects are not generally listed,
only those organisations which take referrals
nationally.*

Carr-Gomm Society

Duke House, 6-12 Tabard Street,
London SE1 4JU
020-7397 5300 *fax 020-7397 5301*

info@carr-gomm.org.uk *www.carrgomm.org.uk*

A charitable housing association that provides
supportive environments for single people
with a range of needs, including physical
and mental health, ex-alcohol, drug users,
ex offenders and those who cannot live on
their own without support, referred by social
services or housing departments

To find out more about the services or the
referral process email info@carr-gomm.org.uk
or contact one of the Support Officers below:

North & North East: Joel Clarke-Davey
0161 877 8847

North-West & Midland: Sarah Spindler
0161 877 8847

Soth-West & South Central: Jemila Ellis
020 8253 8591

London, Home Counties & South East:
Joe Ashdown
020 8253 8590

Carr-Gomm Scotland

Craigmillar Social Enterprise & Arts Centre
(SPACE), 11 Harewood Road, Edinburgh EH16
4NT 0131-659 4777 *fax 0131-659 4787*
info@carrgommscotland.org.uk
www.carrgommscotland.og.uk
An independent charity fulfilling a similar role
to the Carr-Gomm society.

Gordon House Association

see section on services for problem gamblers

Langley House Trust

Central Services: PO Box 181, Witney,
Oxfordshire OX28 6WD
(01993) 774075 *fax (01993) 772425*
e-mail info@langleyhousetrust.org
www.langleyhousetrust.org

A national Christian charity and Registered
Social landlord providing specialist resettlement
accommodation for those who are hard to place
(ex-offenders and those at risk of offending). 16
projects and associated move-on provision.

Referrals direct to the chosen project or via
Witney office

Drug Rehabilitation Centres *(Registered Care Homes)*

Chatterton Hey, Exchange Street, Edenfield,
Ramsbottom, Lancashire BL0 0QH. (01706)
829895 *fax (01706) 828761*
Chatterton@langleyhousetrust.org

Murray Lodge, 1 Whitley Village, Coventry
CV3 4AJ.
024-7650 1585 *fax 024-7650 5759*
Murray@langleyhousetrust.org

Fresh Start Projects

Ashdene. Provision for adult ex-offenders and
has some places for wheelchair users.
29 Peterson Road, Wakefield, West Yorkshire
WF1 4DU
(01924) 291088 *fax (01924) 366529*
Ashdene@langleyhousetrust.org

Box Tree Cottage. Provision for adult male ex-
offenders including those with complex needs
110 Allerton Road, Bradford, West Yorkshire
BD8 0AQ
(01274) 487626 *fax (01274) 543612*
BoxTree@langleyhousetrust.org

Langdon House. Provision for male ex offenders
age 25 and above.
66 Langdon Road, Parkstone,
Dorset BH14 9EH

(01202) 747423 *fax (01202) 256718*
Langdon@langleyhousetrust.org

The Shrubbery. Provision for male ex offenders
age 18 and above.
35 Frindsbury Road, Strood, Rochester, Kent
ME2 4TD
(01634) 717085 *fax (01634) 291049*
Shrubbery@langleyhousetrust.org

Park View. Provision for male ex-offenders and
homeless men aged 21 and over
85 Warrenhurst Road, Fleetwood, Lancashire
FY7 6TP
(01253) 872162 *fax (01253) 879345*
ParkView@langleyhousetrust.org

Residential Training Centres

Elderfield. Works with full range of male ex-
offenders
Main Road Otterbourne, Winchester,
Hampshire S021 2EQ
(01962) 712163 *fax (01962) 711174*
Elderfield@langleyhousetrust.org

House of St Martin. Provision for men and
women. Offers training leading to recognised
qualifications
1 Langford Lane, Norton Fitzwarren, Taunton,
Somerset TA2 6NU
(01823) 275662 *fax (01823) 352455*
StMartin@langleyhousetrust.org

Wing Grange. Provision for male ex-offenders
aged 18 and over. Specialises in working with
those with mental health problems of learning
and behavioural difficulties.
Preston Road, Wing, Oakham, Rutland LE15
8SB
(01572) 737246 *fax (01572) 737510*
WingGrange@langleyhousetrust.org

Resettlement Projects These projects cater
for residents requiring a high degree of support
who might otherwise reoffend, Training
programmes form part of the working week.

Bedford Project. Provision for men and women
over 18.
PO Box 395, Bedford MK43 6AD
(01234) 855515 *fax (01234) 843137*
Bedford@langleyhousetrust.org

Rothera. Women only over 18
 PO Box 977, Bradford BD5 9YJ
(01274) 603664 *fax (01274) 605677*
Rothera@langleyhousetrust.org

Kent Resettlement Project. Provision for men
and women over 18.
35 Frindsbury Road, Strood, Rochester, Kent
ME2 4TD

(01634) 723200 *fax (01634) 723244*
KentProject@langleyhousetrust.org

Homeless Project
The Torbay Project, 46 Newton Road, Torquay,
Devon TQ2 6AA (some direct access places)
NB The project will move to Factory Rd, Torbay
in summer 2009. Telephone and email will be
unchanged.
(01803) 212234 *fax (01803) 203830*
Torbay@langleyhousetrust.org

Registered Care Homes
The Knole. Provision for men over 30.
23 Griffiths Avenue, Cheltenham,
Gloucestershire GL51 7BE
(01242) 526978 *fax (01242) 237504*
Knole@langleyhousetrust.org

Longcroft, Provision for men over 18. Can cater
for individuals with complex needs.
58 Westbourne Road,
Lancaster LA1 5EF
(01524) 64950 *fax (01524) 844082*
Longcroft@langleyhousetrust.org

Nacro

Nacro has a number of specialist housing
projects. These are listed in the Nacro Section.

Penrose Housing Association

Head Office: 356 Holloway Road,
London N7 6PA
020-7700 0100 *fax 020-7700 8133*
www.penrose.org.uk
Chief Executive: Janice Horsman

Specialist housing association providing
supported housing and resettlement service
for homeless male and female offenders in the
London area. All housing is shared ranging from
2 bedroomed flats to 14 bed hostel. Assured
short hold tenancies are issued. Move-on for
most tenants through public and private sector
accommodation with resettlement support.

Women: women only housing provided in small
shared flats and self-contained flats using high
care and floating support.

Priority: lifers and other long term prisoners.
Exclusions: Penrose operates no blanket
exclusions.

All enquiries to head office or the relevant
project. Applications can only be accepted from
probation officers in the London Area or other
approved referral soources.

Penrose also operates separate accommodation
for mentally disordered offenders.

St Mungo's

St Mungo's has a number of specialist housing
projects. These are listed in the St Mungo's
Section

Stepping Stones Trust

Referrals to: Suffolk House, George Street,
Croydon CR0 1PE 020-8253 0450 *fax 0208 680
8077*
e-mail info@steppingstonestrust.org.uk
referrals@steppingstonestrust.org.uk
www.steppingstonestrust.org.uk

Park View, 51 Clapham Common West Side,
London SW4 9AS tel & fax 020-7228 0863
Hope House, 14a St Augustine's Ave, South
Croydon CR2 6BS

Supported housing for ex-prisoners or referrals
from probation services. No local connection
necessary. Our focus is on helping residents find
employment and move-on accommodation and
providing spiritual support (from a Christian
perspective) for people who feel this would help
them stay clear of crime. Residents must be
clean of drugs, accept a curfew (11 pm to 7 am)
and want support.

Bridge House, PO Box 3209, London SW8. 020-
7720 6421 *fax 020 7622 1864*

Accommodation and care for Christian male sex
offenders. For the unemployed, rent covered
by DSS and Housing Benefit. Residents will
usually stay for up to two years and can receive
psychiatric assessment and treatment through
the NHS. NOTE: before making any referral
please contact SPO, 217a Balham High Road,
London SW17. 020-8767 5905

Stonham

Head Office, Malt House, 281 Field End Road,
Eastcote, Ruislip, Middlesex HA4 9XQ
0208 868 9000 stonham@homegroup.org.uk
www.stonham.org.uk

Stonham, a division of the Home Group, is
England's largest specialist provider of housing
with support for socially excluded people. It
runs 545 directly managed services, working
in partnership with local authorities, health
care providers, probation services and others,
delivering services to over 15,000 people
each year. Stonham works with ex-offenders,

including those with mental health problems, drug and/or alcohol addiction and basic skills needs. There are over 100 Stonham projects for ex-offenders around England.

Regional offices
North
Key contact: Sally Parsons (Operations Director)
Meridian House, Artist Street, Armley Road, Leeds LS12 2EW
0113-246 8660 e-mail sally.parsons@homegroup.org.uk

West
Key contact: Alan Ryan (Operations Director)
2nd Floor, High Point, Thomas Street, Taunton, Somerset TA2 6HB
01823 327388
e-mail alan.ryan@homegroup.org.uk

East
Key contact: Molly Newton (Operations Director)
Malt House, 281 Field End Road, Eastcote, Ruislip, Middlesex, HA4 9XQ.
0208 868 9000
e-mail molly.newton@homegroup.org.uk

SERVICES FOR DRUG & ALCOHOL USERS

This list is not comprehensive. Further information on local treatment services is available in a directory from DrugScope 020-7928 9500 *Drug Problems: where to get help* a comprehensive, fully updated directory of drug treatment services across the whole of the UK; including prison drug services, £35.00 or use their online data base *Helpfinder* accessed from their website www.drugscope.org.uk.

HELPLINES

Alcoholics anonymous helpline 0845 769 7555

Drinkline helpline 0800 917 8282 Best time to ring 9am-11am Mon-Fri

Frank (national drugs helpline) 0800 77 66 00

Narcotics Anonymous 0845 3733366 or 020 7730 0009

National AIDS Helpline 0800 567 123

Release 0845 4500 215 Advice on drug related legal problems

National organisations & head offices in alphabetical order

ADFAM
25 Corsham Street, London N1 6DR
tel 020-7553 7640 *fax 020-7253 7991*
www.adfam.org.uk
National charity supporting families and friends of drug users. Specialist support for prisoners' families.

Alcohol Concern
64 Leman Street, London E1 8EU
tel 020-7264 0510 *fax 020-7488 9213*
e-mail contact@alcoholconcern.org.uk *www.alcoholconcern.org.uk*
National voluntary agency working on alcohol misuse. Library, information service, can refer caller to local agencies, produces a variety of literature and directory of local services.

The Alliance
32 Bloomsbury Street, London WC1B 3QJ
tel 020-7299 4304 helpline 0845 122 8608 (10am-5pm,weekdays except bank holidays)
info@m-alliance.org.uk *www.m-alliance.org.uk*
The Alliance is a user led organisation that provides advocacy, training and helpline services to those currently in drug treatment, those who have accessed drug treatment in the past and those who may access drug treatment in the future.

Aquarius
16 Kent Street, Birmingham B5 6RD
tel 0121-622 8181 *fax 0121-622 8189*
e-mail headoffice@aquarius.org.uk
www.aquarius.org.uk
Drug, alcohol and gambling projects in the Midlands, providing information, training, counselling, residential and day services. Also delivers the Alcohol and Offending Programme in partnership with W Midlands Probation Area in Solihull, Wolverhampton, Walsall, Sandwell and Dudley; and alcohol arrest referral programmes in Dudley and Sandwell.

C.O.C.A.
Unit 8, 5 Durham Yard, London E2 6QF
tel 020-7729 5513 info@ coca.org.uk
www.coca.org.uk
Provides support and information services for professionals working with issues of crack and cocaine dependence.

Compass - Services to tackle problem drug use
Langton House, 5 Priory Street, York YO1 6ET
tel (01904) 636374 *fax (01904) 632490*

e-mail info@compass-uk.org
www.compass-uk.org
Provides a range of community services in York
and North Yorkshire, Hull, Nottingham and the
East Midlands, and Milton Keynes. Services
include structured day programmes, young
people's services, throughcare aftercare and
resettlement, progress2work, arrest referral,
substitute prescribing, and tier 2 and 3 adult
services.

Cranstoun Drug Services
1st Floor, St Andrew's House, 26-7 Victoria
Road, Surbiton, Surrey KT6 4JX
tel 020-8335 1830 fax 020-8399 4135
email info@cranstoun.org.uk *www.cranstoun.org*
Major NGO provider of a range of services for
substance misusers in the UK. Encompasses
high care residential services, supported
housing, community drug agencies and specific
criminal justice services.

Crime Reduction Initiatives (CRI)
140-142, Kings Cross Road, London WC1X 6DS
(Regional offices in Leeds and Brighton)
tel 020-7833 7975 *fax 020-7833 0863*
www.cri.org.uk
Leading national charity focused on crime
reduction, rehabilitation and community safety.
Services include: DIP; prison drug treatment
programmes (CARAT, P-ASRO etc); DRRs and
ATRs; supported housing for ex-offenders;
street outreach; domestic abuse services;
parenting support services and interventions for
young offenders.

DrugScope
Prince Consort House,Suite 204 (2nd
Floor),109/111Farringdon Road
London EC1R 3BW
tel 020-7520 7550 *fax 020-7520 7555*
information & library enquiry line 08707-743-
682
e-mail info@drugscope.org.uk
web site www.drugscope.org.uk
UK's leading centre of expertise on drugs. Its
aim is to inform policy and reduce drug related
risk. Provides information, promotes effective
responses to drug taking, undertakes research
at local, national and international levels,
advises on policy making, encourages informed
debate and speaks for member bodies working
on the ground.

Frank
Drugs information and help service.
24 hour national drugs helpline, 0800 77 66 00
email frank@talktofrank.com Informative
website *www.talktofrank.com*

HIT
3 Paramount Business Park, Wilson Road,
Liverpool L36 6AW
tel 0844 412 0972/0844 412 0974
e-mail customerservice@hit.org.uk
www.hit.org uk
Provide training and information on drug related
issues. Provides a library and information
service, training courses, publications and
campaigns. The main distributor of DrugScope
publications.

Langley House Trust
The Langley House Trust has two dry
rehabs. See their entry under the Specialist
Accommodation for Offenders Section.

Lifeline Manchester
101-103 Oldham Street, Manchester M4 1LW
tel 0161-839 2054 *www.lifeline.org.uk*
Helps drug users and their families in the
North of England. Offices in Manchester, East
Lancashire, West Yorkshire and Calderdale
provide a range of services for drug users and
those affected by drug use.

Mainliners
1 London Bridge, London SE1 9BG
tel 020-7022 1890 *www.mainliners.org.uk*
2762 Bath Street Glasgow G2 4JR Tel:
0141- 353 6969

Working with users affected by, or at risk of HIV,
Hepatitis and other blood borne viruses. Offers
a range of services both locally and nationally.
All frontline services can provide sterile
injecting equipment and condoms.

SMART Services, 9 Mitcham Lane, London
SW16 6LQ
tel 020 8677 9541 *fax 020 8664 6017* e-mail
smart@mainliners.org.uk
A Mainliners street drugs agency working
with people with drug issues in Lambeth and
surrounding areas. Can help in addressing the
effects of drug use and withdrawal, treatment
choices and referrals in relation to stabilisation,
maintenance/reduction prescribing or stopping
use of drugs. Can also advise around safer drug
use, safer sexual practices, HIV/AIDS, Hepatitis
and other issues.

Phoenix Futures (formerly Phoenix House)
3rd Floor, Asra House, 1 Long Lane, London
SE1 4PG
tel 020-7234 9740 *fax 020-7234 9770*
e-mail info@phoenix-futures.org.uk
www.phoenix-futures.org.uk
National referral number for adult & family
residential rehab services: 0845 600 7227

e-mail intake@phoenixfutures.org.uk
Offers structured rehabilitation services,
designed around the needs of people with
drug and alcohol problems. Largest UK
provider of residential rehabilitation services
for single adults and families and structured
community day services. Extensively involved
in resettlement, aftercare, supported housing,
tenancy sustainment services and education and
retraining services. Work in partnership with
probation and prison services in England and
Scotland delivering a full range of intervention
services.

**RAPt (Rehabilitation for Addicted
Prisoners Trust)**
Riverside House, 27-29 Vauxhall Grove, London
SW8 1SY
tel 020 7582 4677 *fax 020 7820 3716*
e-mail info@rapt.org.uk *www.rapt.org.uk*
National charity with full accreditation from the
joint Prisons and Probation Accreditation Board.
Provides intensive abstinence based treatment
and supportive counselling and CARAT services
to substance users in the CJ system. Services
include prison based 12 step treatment and
CARAT services, a community based DIP
team and community based residential and day
treatment programmes.

Release
388 Old Street, London EC1V 9LT
tel 020-7729 9004 (office) *fax 020-7729 2599*
helpline 0845 4500 215 Weekdays 11am-1.0pm,
2pm-4pm.
ask@release.org.uk *www.release.org.uk*
Advice on legal drug related problems.

Scottish Drugs Forum
91 Mitchell Street, Glasgow G1 3LN
tel 0141-221 1175 *fax 0141-248 6414*
email enquiries@sdf.org.uk *www.sdf.oorg.uk*
Scottish Drugs Forum is the national, voluntary
sector and membership-based drugs policy
and information agency with regional offices
throughout Scotland. It work to reduce
drugs harm through improving awareness
and understanding of drugs use issues,
and developing, promoting, and supporting
improvements to the range and quality of
services to all drug users. Provides an on-line
directory of Scottish drug services.

Turning Point
Standon House, 21 Mansell Street, London
E1 8AA
tel 020-7481 7600
info@turning-point.co.uk
www. turning-point.co.uk
Turning Point is a leading social care

organisation. It provides services for people
with complex needs, including those affected by
drug and alcohol abuse, mental health problems
and those with a learning disability.

Solvents

Re-Solv
30a High Street, Stone, Staffs ST15 8AW
tel (01785) 817885 *fax (01785) 813205*
free national helpline 01785 810762 (9am-5pm,
weekdays except bank holidays)
information@resolv.org.uk *www.re-solv.org.uk*
National charity with regional offices. Deals
with all aspects of solvent and volatile substance
abuse (that currently kills an average of 6
young people a month). Research, educational
materials, training & community projects.

Self help organisations

Narcotics Anonymous
UK Service Office, 202 City Road, London
EC1V 2PH
Organisation for recovering adults
tel 020 7251 4007 *fax 020 7251 4006* e-mail
ukso@ukna.org *www.ukna.org*
helplines 0845 373 3366 or 020 7730 0009
e-mail: helpline@ukna.org Public Information
e-mail pi@ukna.org

Alcoholics Anonymous
PO Box 1, 10 Toft Green, York YO1 7NJ
tel (01904) 644026 helpline 0845 769 7555
www.alcoholics-anonymous.org.uk

Cocaine Anonymous
PO Box 46920, London E2 9WF
tel 0800 612 0225
info@cauk.org.uk *www.cauk.org.uk*
A fellowship of men and women who share their
experience, strength and hope so that they may
solve their common problem and help others
recover from addiction.

Al-Anon Family Groups
61 Great Dover Street, London SE1 4YF
tel 020-7403 0888(10am-10pm daily confidential
helpline)*fax 020-7378 9910*
e-mail enquiries@al-anonuk.org.*uk*
www.al-anonuk.org.uk
Al-Anon is worldwide and offers understanding
and support for families and friends of problem
drinkers, whether the alcoholic is still drinking
or not. Alateen, a part of Al-Anon, is for young
people aged 12-20 who have been affected
by someone else's drinking, usually that of a

parent. For details of meetings throughout UK and Eire, please contact the helpline.

Families Anonymous
Doddington & Rollo Community Association
Charlotte Despard Avenue, Battersea, London
SW11 5HD
tel 0207-498 4680 help line 0845 1200 660 (local)
e-mail office@famanon.org.uk
www.famanon.org.uk
Free and confidential support groups for families and friends of drug users. Office and helpline staffed Mon–Fri 1pm to 4.00pm, 6pm-10pm, weekends 2pm-10pm.

PADA (Parents Against Drug Abuse)
12-14 Church Parade, Ellesmere Port, Cheshire
CH65 2ER
admin & fax 0151-356 1996 helpline 08457 023 867
e-mail admin@pada.org.uk *www.pada.org.uk*
A national network of local support groups offering help and support to parents and families of drug users. Helpline (confidential) staffed 24hrs 365 days a year, calls charged at local rate.

Campaigns

Transform Drug Policy Foundation
Easton Business Centre, Felix Road, Easton, Bristol BS5 0HE
tel 0117-941 5810 *fax 0117-941 5809*
email info@tdpf.org.uk *www.tdpf.org.uk*
The leading drug policy reform charity in the UK aiming to create a just, humane and effective drug policy. It campaigns for an effective system of regulation and control to replace the failed policy of prohibition through advocating reform at national and international levels.

Health issues

HIV/AIDS

National AIDS Trust
New City Cloisters, 196 Old Street, London
EC1V 9FR
tel 020-7814 6767 *fax 020-7216 0111*
info@nat.org.uk *www.nat.org.uk*
Strategic body campaigning for effective prevention, the development of vaccines, quality treatment and care and an end to discrimination against people with HIV and AIDS.

The Terrence Higgins Trust
314-320 Gray's Inn Road, London WC1X 8DP

tel 020-7812 1600 *fax 020-7812 1601*
info@tht.org.uk *www.tht.org.uk*
Has several local offices. Offers a buddying service, information, advice and counselling on the law, welfare, housing and insurance for people affected by HIV/AIDS.

HEPATITIS C

UK Hepatitis C Resource Centre
276 Bath Street, Glasgow G2 4JR
tel 0141-353 6969 fax 0141-331 2552
195 New Kent Road, London SE1 4AG
tel 020-7378 5495 *fax 020-7378 5489*
helpline 0870 242 2467 *www.hepccentre.org.uk*
Provide information to people living with hepatitis C, healthcare professionals, the public and media. Also provides a peer perspective on experiences of HCV positive individuals regarding day-to-day living, treatment, alternative therapies and support.

SERVICES FOR PROBLEM GAMBLERS

The following information has been supplied by GamCare

National Organisations

GamCare
2nd Floor, 7-11 St Johns Hill, Clapham, London
SE11 1TR
helpline 0845 6000 133 (8am to 12 midnight Mon-Sun)
info@gamcare.org.uk *www.gamcare.org.uk*.

Provides free advice, information and counselling to problem gamblers, their family and friends. Offers a national helpline and on-line support services as well as free face to face counselling from the London office and via a network of national partner organizations. Also provides training and literature to organizations working with problem gamblers and their families.

Gamblers Anonymous
PO Box 88, London SW10 0EU.
24 hour Helpline numbers
London 020-7384 3040; Glasgow 08700 508 88; Sheffield 0114 2620026; Birmingham 0121 231335; Ulster 0287 1351329
info@gamblersanonymous.org.uk
prison liaison plo@gamblersanonymous.org.uk
www.gamblersanonymous.org.uk

GA is a self help fellowship of men and women who have joined together to do something about their own gambling problem and to help other compulsive gamblers to do the same. Over 200 groups throughout the UK and in many prisons.

Gam-Anon
address as GA above
Helpline 08700 508880 *www.gamanon.org.uk*

'Sister' organisation to GA, providing advice and support to the spouses and parents of compulsive gamblers.

Residential/Rehabilitation

Gordon House Association
114 Wellington Rd, Dudley, West Midlands, DY1 1UB
01384 241292 email help@gordonhouse.org.uk
www.gordonhouse.org.uk

Counselling and discussion of gambling problems. Website also offers instant online chat

Also offers residential facility for men & women 18+, including offenders on court orders or ex-prison. Therapeutic environment, individual and group counselling and support whilst at hostel and after. Catchment area is national.

Groups & Organisations with Local Projects

England

Cumbria Alcohol & Drug Advisory Service (CADAS)
17a West Tower St, Carlisle, CA3 8QT
01228 544140 *www.cadas.co.uk*

Provides a telephone and one-to-one counselling service to problem gamblers and their relatives/friends.

Off The Record
Freephone 0808 801 0724
www.off-the-record.org.uk

Drop in centres
250 Fratton Road, Portsmouth PO1 5HH & Threeways, Client Line 023 9247 4724

138 Purbrook Way, Leigh Park, Hampshire PO9 3SU. Client Line 023 9281 5322

Point of contact for young people, 11-25, who wish to receive counseling, support and information in Hampshire regarding problem gambling.

North East Council on Addiction (NECA)
Derwent Point, Clasper Way, Swalwell,

Newcastle upon Tyne N16 3BE (head office)
0191-414 6446 e-mail headoffice@neca.co.uk
www.neca.co.uk

Centres in Newcastle, South Tyne, Gatehead, Durham, Consett, Peterlee, Hartlepool, Washington, Stanley, Mid Tyne, Chester le Street, Sunderland, Bishop Auckland, Seaham, Sedgefield, Darlington. All centres provide telephone and one-to-one counselling to problem gamblers and their relatives/friends. Addresses and phone numbers from head office.

Alcohol Problems Advisory Service (APAS)
36 Park Row, Nottingham NG1 6GR
0115-948 5770 or Lo-call 0845 7626 316
www.apas.org.uk

Provides advice, information and counselling service to problem gamblers, drinkers and drug takers and for people affected by someone else's dependency on alcohol, drugs and gambling. Drop in service.

Options (Southampton)
64 Ironside Court, Homtun Street, Southampton SO14 2BB
02380 631796 *fax 02380 634716*

Well established agency on the South coast provides one-to-one counselling, information and guidance for problem gamblers, their families and friends who are affected by gambling dependency.

Wales

Islwyn Drug & Alcohol Project
Bryn Road, Markham, Nr Blackwood, Caerphilly, Gwent
(01495) 229299

Provides information, advice and one-to-one counselling to problem gamblers and their relatives/ friends who are affected by a gambling dependancy as part of a community project within South Wales and surrounding districts.

Scotland

Renfrew Council on Alcohol
Mirren House, Back Sneddon Street, Paisley PA3 2AF
0141-887 0880

In conjunction with other services, also offers information, advice, and one-to-one counselling to problem gamblers, their relatives and friends affected by gambling dependency as a part of a community project.

VOLUNTARY WORK

CSV (Community Service Volunteers)
237 Pentonville Road, London N1 9NJ
020-7278 6601   volunteer line 0800374 991
email volunteer@csv.org.uk *www.cvs.org.uk*

CSV Scotland
Wellgate House, 200 Cowgate, Edinburgh EH1 1NQ
0131 622 7766

CSV Wales
CSV House, Williams Way, Cardiff CF10 5DY
029 20 415717

CSV provides opportunities for people to volunteer in the community.

CSV offers full time volunteering opportunities to those aged 16 and over who are able to volunteer full time and away from home at hundreds of social care and community projects throughout Britain. Volunteers receive a weekly allowance plus free accommodation and food. CSV also works through service and contract agreements (e.g. with the probation services) to involve volunteers as mentors to young offenders and also places as volunteers in their local area young people at risk of offending.

Volunteering with CSV gives young people greater self-confidence and provides them with a range of workplace skills such as team working and decision making. Of special interest to probation officers based in YOIs, Cat C and Cat D prisons is CSVs partnership with HM Prison Service. CSV offers, as part of an effective resettlement process, one month full time away from home volunteering opportunities to young people usually in their last month prior to release.

Voluntary Service Overseas
317 Putney Bridge Road, London SW15 2PN
tel 020-8780 7200
www.globalxchange.org.uk

Runs many different programmes such as **The Global Xchange Programme**, a partnership between the British Council, Community Service Volunteers (CSV) and Voluntary Service Overseas (VSO). An international youth exchange programme aimed at building active global citizens. Nine young adults from the UK are paired with nine from an African/Asian country (all aged 18-25) to live and to carry out voluntary work in host communities, three months in the UK and three months in the exchange country. Global

Xchange is open to all UK/EEA citizens who are resident in the UK, regardless of skills, experience and educational background. The Global Xchange Programme covers the costs of participation – all travel, food, accommodation, medical expenses and insurance, training and support.

INSURANCE SERVICES FOR EX-OFFENDERS

When obtaining insurance, non-disclosure, or giving false information about any criminal convictions, will almost certainly mean that the policy will be declared void in the case of a claim. It must be remembered that a criminal conviction is a *material fact* and must be declared. By giving false information another crime is being committed. When disclosing their convictions the majority of ex-offenders will find getting insurance for home, building and contents, motor and business cover, practically impossible.

N.B. The editor accepts no responsibility for any of the statements below. They have been supplied by the companies listed.

Specialist insurance for ex-offenders is available through:

Fresh Start
Vinpenta House, 4 High Causeway, Whittlesey, Peterborough PE7 1AE
01733 208278
e-mail johnc@culpeck.co.uk
www.culpeck.co.uk/fresh

Fresh Start is supported and recommended by Nacro, the Probation Service, CABs, Banks, Building Societies, Insurance and Mortgage Brokers throughout the UK. Fresh Start believes it is well placed to offer a comprehensive choice of cover (in particular providing cover for those people seeking buildings and contents insurance when looking for a mortgage) along with premium instalment facilities for buildings, home contents and business insurance packages. A fully comprehensive, supportive and confidential service is provided by experienced staff offering the best service and cover at the most competitive premiums. Regulated by the Financial Services Authority.

Fairplay Insurance Services
Charter House, 43 St Leonards Road, Bexhill-on-Sea, East Sussex TN40 1JA

01424 220110 e-mail cover@bureauinsure.co.uk *www.bureauinsure.co.uk-insurance*

Fairplay Insurance Services, part of the Bureau Insurance services Group, authorised and regulated by the FSA, was established solely to promote Household and Motor Insurance for proposers with criminal convictions. Fairplay guarantees that each applicant will be dealt with in a sensitive, non-judgmental and helpful way. Every proposer will be treated with respect and in total confidence, regardless of previous convictions. Fairplay has been in existence for several years and is confident in its ability to provide household and motor insurance for ex-offenders.

The Fairplay scheme is endorsed by the British Insurance Brokers' Association and is their officially appointed scheme provider. Fairplay works closely with the home office, Unlock, NACRO, the Probation Service etc. The Fairplay proposal form notes that spent convictions need not be declared and they provide information that will show when a conviction is spent.

MISCELLANEOUS ADDRESSES

Descriptions of the organisations are those provided by themselves; the publisher takes no responsibility for these statements. Any information about other organisations that might usefully be included will be welcomed. Please send it to Owen Wells, 23 Eaton Road, Ilkley LS29 9PU (01943) 602270 e-mail o.r.wells@gmail.com

Prisoners' Families Helpline 0808 808 2003 *www.prisonersfamilieshelpline.org.uk* free confidential,national helpline that provides information and support for prisoners' families and friends.

Action for Prisoners' Families Unit 21, Carlson Court, 116 Putney Bridge Road, London SW15 2NQ 020-8812 3600 *fax 020-8871 0473* e-mail: info@actionpf.org.uk or The Lenton Centre, Willoughby Street, Lenton, Nottingham, NG7 1RQ, 0115-905 2736, e-mail: rosemary@actionpf.org.uk or info@actionpf.org.uk *www.prisonersfamilies.org.uk* National umbrella organisation speaking for, and encouraging the development of organisations that provide assistance for prisoners' families. Publishes a National Directory and other resource material

including a series of children's books. Provides details of local support services.

Advisory Service for Squatters, Angel Alley, 84b Whitechapel High Street, London E1 7QX. 020-3216 0099 (phone first, Mon-Fri 2-6pm) 0845 644 5814 (local rate) *fax 020-3216 0098.* e-mail advice@squatter.org.uk *www.squatter.org.uk* Legal and practical advice for squatters and homeless people.

The Aldo Trust, c/o NACRO, 169 Clapham Road, London SW9 0PU. 020-7582 6500. Charitable small grants to prisoners in England and Wales only, no applications direct from prisoners.

Alternatives to Violence Project, contact AVP London, Grayston Centre, 28 Charles Square, London N1 6HT. 0207-324 4757 e-mail info@avpbritain.org.uk *www.avpbritain.org.uk* Works to relieve those afflicted by violence or abuse, whether they are victims or aggressors or both. Provides group experiential workshops that develop people's ability to resolve difficult situations without resorting to violence. These are delivered across the UK in prisons, for charities and the public. AVP also trains prisoners, ex-offenders and members of the community to become workshop facilitators and volunteers for AVP.

Apex Trust, 7th Floor, No.3 London Wall Buildings, London Wall, London EC2M 5PD, 020-7638 5931, *fax 020-7638 5977,* email jobcheck@apextrust.com, *www.apextrust.com* Helps people with a criminal record obtain jobs, self employment, training or further education through its projects in England providing direct advice and guidance to ex-offenders. Provides employers with information about the best ways of recruiting and retraining people with a criminal record. Operates a national telephone helpline 0870 608 4567 offering confidential information on issues relating to employment and having a criminal record:.

ARC (Antenatal Results & Choices), 73 Charlotte Street, London W1T 4PN phone & fax 020-7631 0280 helpline 020-7631 0285, *www.arc-uk.org* Offers non-directive, specialised support to parents who discover that their unborn baby may have an abnormality, gives support to parents making a decision about ante-natal testing and offers support regardless of the future of the pregnancy.

ARX (Advocacy Resource Exchange), ARX Unit 3, 60 Duke Street, Liverpool, L1 5AA, 0151-734 3047, email joe@advocacyresource.net *www.advocacyresource.net* Maintains a national database of independent advocacy schemes and provides information, training & publications on advocacy.

Asian Family Counselling Service, Suite 51, Windmill Place, 2-4 Windmill Lane, Southall UB2 4NL 020-8571 3933 020-8813 9714 *fax 020-8571 3933* e-mail info@asianfamilycounselling.org.uk *www.asianfamilycounselling.org.uk* Offers family, marital and individual counselling to the Asian community.

Association for Shared Parenting, PO Box 2000, Dudley, West Midlands DY1 1YZ. (01789) 751157. helpline 01789 750891 (evenings) email spring-cott@btopenworld.com *www.sharedparenting.org.uk* Seeks to promote the rights and needs of children following separation or divorce, through promoting view that children have the right to receive love and nurture from both parents. Offers support workshops for parents and a child contact centre for families.

Black Prisoners Support Groups, POPS, Valentine House, 1079 Rochdale Road, Blackley, Manchester M9 8AJ. tel/fax 0161-740 3679. email info@nbpsg.org *www.nbpsg.co.ku*

Brook, 421 Highgate Studios, 53-79 Highgate Road, London NW5 1TL. 020-7284 6040 *fax 020-7284 6050 www.brook.org* Offers young people under 25 free confidential advice on health and contraception. For immediate information about contraception (inc emergency), pregnancy testing, abortion, sexually transmitted infections. Helpline (9-5 Mon-Fri). Recorded 24 hour information 020-7950 7755 or 'Ask Brook' at *www.brook.org.uk* for a confidential response to an enquiry. Contact brook@adc-uk.com for info on Brook publications.

Cambridge Family Mediation Service, 3rd Floor, Essex House, 7 Regent Street, Cambridge CB2 1AB (01223) 576308 (info & answerphone) *fax (01223) 576309.* email families@cambridgefms.co.uk *www.cambridgefms.co.uk* Specialist family mediation service for divorcing or separating couples. Has free counselling service for under 19s.

The Centre for Crime and Justice Studies,

King's College, Strand, London WC2R 2LS, 020-7848 1688 or 1677, *fax 020-7848 1689,* email ccjs.enq@kcl.ac.uk *www.crimeandjustice.org.uk* An independent charity that informs and educates about all aspects of crime and criminal justice. Provides information, produces research and carries out policy analysis to encourage and facilitate an understanding of the complex nature of issues concerning crime. A membership organisation working with practitioners, policy makers, academics and students, the media and voluntary sector offering programmes of events, publications and online resources.

The Child Bereavement Trust, Aston House, High Street, West Wycombe, Bucks HP14 3AG (01494) 446648 *fax (01494) 440057* enquiries@childbereavement.org.uk *www.childbereavement.org.uk* Cares for bereaved families by offering specialised training and support to the professional carer, also offers resources for families and professionals (e.g. videos and books).

ChildLine, 42 Curtain Road, London EC2A 3NH. address for children Freepost NATN1111, London E1 6BR. admin 020-7650 3200 *fax 020-7650 3201* helpline 0800 1111 24 hr national telephone helpline for children and young people in trouble or danger. Calls free from landlines or mobiles. Informative website *www.childline.org.uk* The service is free and confidential. e-mail info@childline.org.uk (cannot answer problems or offer counselling online).

Child Poverty Action Group, 94 White Lion Street, London N1 9PF. 020-7837 7979 *fax 020-7837 6414 www.cpag.org.uk.* For details of CPAG and training courses and membership schemes contact above address. Welfare rights enquiries (advisors only): Citizens' Rights Office 020-7833 4627, 2-4pm Mon-Fri Promotes action for relief, directly or indirectly, of poverty among children and families with children. Works to ensure that those on low incomes get their full entitlement to welfare benefits. Aims to eradicate the injustice of poverty.

Children's Legal Centre, University of Essex, Wivenhoe Park, Colchester, Essex CO4 3SQ (01206) 872466 (admin + publications) *fax (01206) 874026.* e-mail clc@essex.ac.uk *www.childrenslegalcentre.com* Free and confidential advice and information service covering all aspects of law affecting young people including refugees. Publishes 'Childright' and other publications. Education law helpline 0845 456 6811.

Citizens Advice, 115-123 Pentonville Road, London N1 9LZ. 020-7833 2181 (admin) *fax 020-7833 4371* (admin) *www.citizensadvice. org.uk* The independent national charity and membership organisation for Citizens Advice Bureaux, providing free, confidential, and impartial advice to anyone on all subjects. Citizens Advice monitors the problems that CAB clients are experiencing and reports these findings to show where services and policies are failing both locally and nationally. The address and telephone number of local offices can be found in the telephone directory or on the website. For CAB information advice online see *www. adviceguide.org.uk*

CLAPA, Cleft Lip & Palate Association, 1st Floor, Green Man Tower, 332B Goswell Road, London EC1V 7LQ 020-7833 4883 *fax 020-7833 5999* e-mail info@clapa.com *www. clapa.com* Offers information and support to all people affected by cleft lip or palate. bottles and teats available by mail order.

CoDA (Co-dependents Anonymous), CoDA UK, PO Box 2365, Bristol BS6 9XJ *www. coda-uk.org* An informal Twelve Step fellowship of men and women, whose common problem is an inability to maintain functional relationships with self and others as a result of co-dependency in their lives. CoDA uses the Twelve Steps, as a part of its suggested programme of recovery and for building healthy relationships, in a safe and confidential environment.

Criminal Cases Review Commission, Alpha Tower, Suffolk Street Queensway, Birmingham B1 1TT. 0121-633 1800 *fax 0121-633 1823* e-mail ccrc@gtnet.gov.uk An independent public body reviewing alleged miscarriages of justice with power to refer convictions and sentences to the appeal courts.

Criminal Injuries Compensation Authority, Tay House, 300 Bath Street, Glasgow G2 4LN. 0800 358 3601 *fax 0141-331 2287 www.cica. gov.uk* Administers the government funded-scheme to provide compensation to innocent victims of violent crime in Great Britain.

Depression UK, Self Help Nottingham, Ormiston House, 32-36 Pelham Street, Nottingham NG1 2EG 0870 774 4320 *fax*

0870 774 4319 e-mail info@depressionuk. org *wwwdepressionuk.org* Self help organisation for people with depression (and relatives). Members receive 4 newsletters a year, can join penfriend/phonefriend schemes. Some local self help groups. Information line open to anyone at anytime

Down's Syndrome Association, Langdon Down Centre, 2a Langdon Park, Teddington TW11 9PS. 0845 230 0372 *fax 0845 230 0373.* e-mail info@downs-syndrome.org. uk *www.downs-syndrome.org.uk* Helpline 0845 230 0372 Exists to support parents and carers of people with Down's Syndrome and to improve the lives of those with the condition.

Dyspel, 88 Clapham Road, London SW9 0JR 020-7793 3722 *fax 020-78203577* email info@dyspel.org.uk A project that helps dyslexic offenders and offers training in the screening of dyslexia to probation officers and partnership staff.

Eating Disorders Association, 1st Floor, 103 Prince of Wales Road, Norwich, Norfolk NR1 1DW admin only 0870 770 3256 *fax (01603) 664915.* helpline 0845 634 1414 (weekdays 10.30am-8.30pm, sat 1pm-4.30pm), youth helpline 0845 634 7650 (up to 18yrs, weekdays 4.30pm-8.30pm, sat 1pm-4.30pm) e-mail help@b-eatco.uk. *www.b-eat.co.uk.* Provides information, help and support for people affected by eating disorders and, in particular, anorexia and bulimia nervosa.

Epilepsy Action, New Anstey House, Gate Way Drive, Leeds LS19 7XY. 0113-210 8800 *fax 0113-391 0300* helpline 0808 800 5050 e-mail epilepsy@epilepsy.org.uk *www.epilepsy.org.uk* Advice and information on all aspects of living with epilepsy.

Equality & Human Rights Commission, Helplines hours Mon, Tues, Thurs Fri 9am-5pm; contacts: England 0845 604 6610, email info@equalityhumanrights.com Scotland 0845 604 5510 email scotland@ equalityhumanrights.com, Wales 0845 604 8810 email wales@equalityhumanrights. com Wed 9am-7.45pm. London Office: 3 More London, Riverside Tooley Street SE1 2RG 020-3117 0235 *fax (01925) 884 275 www.equalityhumanrights.com* Cardiff: 3rd floor, Capital Tower, Greyfriars Road, Cardiff CF10 3AG. 029-2044 7010 *fax 029-2044 7013* Helpline 0845 604 0845 Glasgow: The Optima Building, 58 Robertson Street,

Glasgow, G2 8DU, 0141-228 5910, *fax 0141-228 5912* Manchester: Arndale House, The Arndale Centre, Manchester, M4 3AQ 0161-829 8100 *fax (01925) 884 000* The Commission took over the responsibilities of the former Commission for Racial Equality (CRE), Disability Rights Commission (DRC) and Equal Opportunities Commission (EOC), with new responsibilities for sexual orientation, age, religion and belief, and human rights.

Fairbridge, 207 Waterloo Road, London SE1 8XD 020-7928 1704 *fax 020-7928 6016.* e-mail info@fairbridge.org.uk *www.fairbridge. org.uk* National youth charity working with people aged 13-25 in 15 disadvantaged areas of UK. Many are ex-offenders or are at risk of offending. Using a combination of challenging activities and long term support, young people are encouraged to re-engage with mainstream opportunities in education training and employment.

Families Need Fathers, 134 Curtain Road, London EC2A 3AR 020-7613 5060. helpline 08707 607496 Mon-Fri 6-10pm. *www.fnf.org. uk* National network of voluntary contacts. Keeping children and parents in contact after separation or divorce. Regular meetings are held around the country.

Family Action, 501-505 Kingsland Road, London E8 4AU. 020-7254 6251 *www.family-action. org.uk* Provides a range of social care services including community mental health services, activity based resource centres, family centres, grants to people in need, and grants advice for students undertaking vocational courses.

FPA (Family Planning Association), 50 Featherstone Street, London EC1Y 8QU 020-7608 5240. Publications 0845 122 8600 Helpline 0845 122 8690 (mon-fri 9am-6pm) providing information and advice on contraception, sexual health, planning a pregnancy and pregnancy choices, and family planning and sexual services.

Family Rights Group, The Print House, 18 Ashwin Street, London E8 3DL. 020-7923 2628 *fax 020-7923 2683.* office@frg.org.uk Telephone advice service: mon-fri 10am-12pm & 1.30-3.30pm, freephone 0800 731 1696. *www.frg.org.uk* Provides a phone and written advice service for parents, relatives and carers who have children in care, on the child protection register, or who are receiving services from social services departments.

Female Prisoners' Welfare Project/Hibiscus, FPWP/ Hibiscus, 12 Angel Gate,,320 City Road, London EC1V 2PT, 020-7278 7116, Email fpwphibiscus@aol.com *www. hibiscuslondon.org.*uk Charity providing advice and support to women in prison, their children and families. Visits and supports British and foreign national women also group sessions for foreign nationals including Spanish speaking women. Provides Home Circumstance Reports for the Courts via an office in Jamaica. Staff speak a wide range of languages.

Gingerbread see One Parent Families

Headway – the brain injury association, 7 King Edward Court, King Edward Street, Nottingham NG1 1EW 0115-924 0800 *fax 0115-958 4446* helpline 0808 800 2244 *www.headway.org.uk* Exists to promote the understanding of all aspects of brain injury and to provide information, support and services to people with brain injury, their family and carers.

Homeless Link, 1st Floor, 10-13 Rushworth Street, London SE1 0RB 020-7960 3010 *fax 020-7960 3011* e-mail info@homelesslink. org.uk *www.homeless.org.uk* Membership body for local organisations and individuals providing services and support to homeless people. Also runs the Homeless Services Unit which brings together front line workers in the resettlement and emergency accommodation fields.

Howard League, 1 Ardleigh Road, London N1 4HS. 020-7249 7373 *fax 020-7249 7788.* e-mail info@howardleague.org *www. howardleague.org* A charity working for humane and effective reform of the penal system.

Institute of Criminology, University of Cambridge, Sidgwick Avenue, Cambridge CB3 9DT (01223) 335360. *fax (01223) 335356.* e-mail enquiries@crim.cam. ac.uk A centre for teaching and research in criminology and criminal justice matters, a biennial senior course for practitioners in the criminal justice system, and a part-time masters degree course for senior corrections officials and police officers.

Irish Commission for Prisoners Overseas. 50-52 Camden Square, London NW1 9XB 020-7482 5528 *fax 020-7482 4815.* e-mail icpolondon@hotmail.com Fr Gerry

McFlynn. ICPO is a subsection of the Bishops' Commission for Emigrants. It cares for all Irish prisoners abroad, regardless of faith, offence or prison status, and their families when requested. ICPO works to ensure that minimum levels of human rights for Irish migrants, refugees and prisoners abroad are respected and enforced. As an NGO, ICPO operates on a not for profit basis to represent the needs of Irish individuals imprisoned overseas.

Joint Council for the Welfare of Immigrants, 115 Old Street, London EC1V 9RT. 020-7251 8708 (admin) *fax 020-7251 8707.* email info@jcwi.org.uk *www.jcwi.org.uk* An independent national organisation that exists to campaign for justice in immigration, nationality and refugee law and policy. It undertakes strategic casework and acts as an expert training resource for others who work in this field.

Justice, 59 Carter Lane, London EC4V 5AQ 020-7329 5100 *fax 020-7329 5055* e-mail admin@justice.org.uk *www.justice.org.uk* Justice is a law reform and human rights group. It cannot deal with individual cases, but has produced 'How to Appeal' a simple guide to the criminal appeal process. This is currently out of print but available from the website as a pdf file. When in print it is free to prisoners (send sae 9"x6" with 34p stamp). It is available to others at £2.50 inc p&p.

KIDSCAPE, 2 Grosvenor Gardens, London SW1W 0DH. 020-7730 3300. *www.kidscape. org.uk* Provides books, posters, videos, teaching materials and training about prevention of child sexual abuse and school bullying. Helpline 08451 205 204 for parents of children bullied at school.

Law Society, 113 Chancery Lane, London WC2A 020-7242 1222. *www.lawsociety.org. uk* The representative body and regulator of solicitors in England & Wales.

Lincolnshire Action Trust, Beech House, Witham Park, Waterside South, Lincoln LN5 7JH (01522) 806611 *fax (01522) 806619 www.lincolnshire-action-trust.org.uk* Employment, training and education advice and guidance, etc for offenders in community and prison Lincolnshire and surrounding area. Also provides assistance to employers considering recruitment of people with a criminal record.

Men's Advice Line 0808 801 0327 a helpline for male victims of domestic violence info@mensadviceline.org.uk or *www. mensadviceline.org.uk*

Message Home helpline P O Box 28908, London SW14 7ZU, 0800 700 740 e-mail messagehome@missingpeople.org.uk *help@messagehome.org.uk* operated by National Missing Persons Helpline for missing adults allowing them to pass a message home.

MENCAP, 123 Golden Lane, London EC1Y 0RT. 020-7454 0454 *fax 020-7608 3254,* e-mail help@mencap.org.uk *www. mencap.org.uk* The largest charity for people with learning difficulties.

Mind (Nat Assn for Mental Health), Granta House, 15/19 Broadway, Stratford, London E15 4BQ 020- 8519 2122 *fax 020-8522 1725* Mind*info*Line 0845 7660163. e-mail contact@mind.org.uk Mind is the leading mental health charity in England and Wales and works for a better life for everyone with experience of mental distress. There are over 220 local Mind associations. Call 020-8215 2122 or log on to *www.mind.org.uk* to find the nearest one.

Missing People, Roebuck House, 284 Upper Richmond Road West, London SW14 7JE 020-8392 4545 *fax 020-8878 7752* national helpline 0500 700 700 e-mail info@ missingpeople.org *www.missingpeople.org* The UK's only charity dedicated to finding missing people and supporting those left behind. Supports the work of the police, Social Services and works in partnership with other agencies in the field. It registers all types of missing persons and can help to publicise medium-high risk cases and offers ID and reconstruction services too. Missing people can send a message home Freefone 0800 700 740 or email messagehome@ missingpeople.org.uk

Muslim Youth Helpline, 2nd Floor, 18 Rosemont Road, London NW3 6NE 020 7435 8171, *fax 0870 774 3519* e-mail info@myh.org.uk helpline (freephone) 0808 808 2008 mon-fri 6pm-12am sat/sun 12pm-12am e-mail (admin) info@myh.org.uk (helpline) help@ myh.org.uk A free confidential counselling and befriending service for young Muslims in need.

National Association of Child Contact Centres, Minerva House, Spaniel Row, Nottingham

NG1 6EP. 0845 4500 280 *fax 0845 4500 420*
e-mail contact@naccc.org.uk *www.naccc.
org.uk* Promotes safe child contact within a
national framework of child contact centres.
These exist to provide neutral meeting
places where children of a separated family
can enjoy contact with one or both parents,
and sometimes other family members, in
a comfortable and safe environment where
there is no viable alternative.

National Association of Official Prison Visitors,
32 Newham Avenue, Bedford MK41 9PT
tel/fax (01234) 359763 e-mail info@napov.
com *www.napov.org.uk*

Napac (National Association for People Abused
in Childhood, NAPAC, 42 Curtain Road,
London EC2A 3NH, *www.napac.org.uk*,
Support Line 0800 085 3330

National Children's Bureau, 8 Wakley Street,
London EC1V 7QE. 020-7843 6000 *fax
020-7278 9512. www.ncb.org.uk* Identifies
and promotes the interests of children and
young people through policy, research and
practice development. The Bureau is multi
disciplinary, working with professional
across all sectors.

National Youth Agency, Eastgate House, 19-23
Humberstone Road, Leicester LE56GJ.
0116-242 7350 *fax 0116-242 7444* General
enquiries: dutydesk@nya.org.uk *www.nya.
org.uk* Information, advice and support for
those working with young people. Validates
qualifying training for youth and community
work.

New Bridge, 27a Medway Street, London
SW1P 2BD, 020-7976 0779 e-mail info@
newbridgefoundation.org.uk *www.
newbridgefoundation.org.uk* New Bridge
runs a wide range of resettlement advisory
services in prisons; covering housing,
debt advice, education and mentoring. The
keynote service (which has been running
for over 50 years) is the friendship and
support given by 200+ volunteers. Every
volunteer knows his or her prisoner client
as an individual with their own personality,
problems and potential and values them
as such. Also runs 'Family Matters'
parenting education courses in prisons and a
subsidiary company publishes *'Inside Time'*
the national newspaper for prisoners.

New Bridge Prison Liaison Project, 4 & 5
Laurel Business Centre, 15 Laurel Road,
Liverpool L7 0LJ 0151-254 2558 *fax 0151-
254 2559* e-mail info@prisonlisaisonproject.
co.uk *www.prisonliaisonproject.co.uk*
Provides services and information working
with offenders who will be settling in
Liverpool.

NORCAP – supporting adults affected by
adoption, 112 Church Road, Wheatley,
Oxon OX33 1LU (01865) 875000. e-mail
enquiries@norcap.org *www.norcap.org.uk*
Provides support, guidance and sympathetic
understanding to adult adopted people and
their birth and adoptive relatives. Contact
Register. For members: telephone helpline,
intermediary role for those seeking renewed
contact, advice on searching and research
service, comprehensive research pack.

NSPCC, 42 Curtain Road, London EC2A 3NH.
020-7825 2500 *fax 020-7825 2525*. 24hr
child protection helpline 0808 800 5000
e-mail help@nspcc.org.uk *www.nspcc.
org.uk* The NSPCC is the UK's leading
charity specialising in child protection and
prevention of cruelty to children. It exists to
prevent children from suffering significant
harm as a result of ill treatment; to help
protect children who are at risk from such
harm; to help children who have suffered
abuse overcome the effects of such harm;
and to work to protect children from further
harm.

One Parent Families/Gingerbread, 255 Kentish
Town Road, London NW5 2LX. 020-7428
5400. Helpline for lone parents 0800 018
5026 e-mail info@oneparentfamilies.org.uk
www.oneparentfamilies.org.uk Information
service for lone parents, other organisations,
local authorities and the media. Providing
consultancy on employment initiatives for
lone parents and rights based training for
professionals working with lone parents.
Campaigning and lobbying to change the law
and improve provision for lone parents and
their children.

Papyrus, Lodge House, Thompson Park,
Ormerod Road, Burnley, Lancashire, BB11
2RU. (01282) 432555 admin@papyrus-
uk.org *www.papyrus-uk.org* helpline
(HopelineUK) 0800 068 4141 Mon-Fri
10am-5pm and 7pm-10pm weekends 2pm-
5pm. Aims to prevent young suicide by
providing support to families, friends, carers
and professionals, and helpline for them and
for suicidal youngsters.

Parentline Plus, 520 Highgate Studios, 53-79

Highgate Road, Kentish Town, London NW5 1TL. 020-7284 5500 Helpline 0808 800 2222, Textphone 0800 783 6783 e-mail parentsupport@parentlineplus.org.uk (for parents, not general enquiries) *www. parentlineplus.org.uk* National charity offering help and information for parents and families via a range of services including a free 24 hour confidential helpline, workshops, courses, leaflets and website. Works to recognise and to value the different types of families that exist and expand services available to them; understands that children's needs cannot be separated from the needs of parents/carers, believes that it is normal for all parents to have difficulties from time to time.

Partners of Prisoners Families Support Group, POPS, Valentine House, 1079 Rochdale Road, Blackley, Manchester M9 8AJ. tel/fax 0161-702 1000. e-mail mail@partnersofprisoners.co.uk *www. partnersofprisoners.co.uk* Offers a wide range of services to anyone who has a loved one in prison. Advice, information, emotional support is available to families from arrest to release. POPS is Manchester based but operates nationally. Manages the Black Prisoner Support Project that provides services to black offenders.

The POW Trust, 295a Queenstown Road, Battersea, London SW8 3NP 020-7720 9767 *fax 020-7498 0477. http://powtrust. org/* Devoted to helping the socially excluded, especially assisting inmates and ex-offenders, to fit back into society with a 'second chance'.

The Prince's Trust, 18 Park Square East, London NW1 4LH. 020-7543 1234 *fax 020-7543 1200* General enquiries freephone 0800-842 842 website *www.princes-trust. org.uk* Helps 14-30 year olds to develop confidence, learn new skills, move into work and start businesses. It offers training, personal development opportunities, business start up support, mentoring and advice. The Trust has four priority target groups - unemployed, educational under achievers, offenders/ex-offenders, and those leaving care.

Prison Advice & Care Trust (PACT), Suite C5, 196 Old Street, London EC1V 9FR 020-7490 3139 helpline 0808 808 2003 e-mail info@ pact.uk.net *www.prisonadvice.org.uk* Provides services for families including

information, advice and support. Visits Centres in London, South West and at HMP Woodhill. First night in custody schemes at HMP Holloway and HMP Exeter.

Prison Dialogue, PO Box 44, Chipping Campden, Glos GL55 6YN (01386) 849186 *fax (01386) 840449.* e-mail enquiries@ prisondialogue.org.uk *www.prisondialogue. org.uk* Relationship based approach to organisational and therapeutic issues in the criminal justice system. Work is targeted across the criminal justice continuum from high security to local prisons and into the community.

Prison Link, 29 Trinity Road, Aston, Birmingham B6 6AJ 0121-551 1207 *fax 0121-554 4894* e-mail pl@ueponline.co.uk *wwwueponline.co.uk* Specialist prisoners' families support service, Counselling/ individual support.

Prison Link Cymru (PLC) operated by Shelter Cymru and Trothwy Cyf, delivering a national Prison Link service throughout Wales. Shelter Cymru, 23 Abbot Street, Wrexham, LL11 1TA, 01978 317914, e-mail prisonlink@sheltercymru.org.uk Provides information to local authorities in Wales about homeless prisoners due to be discharged to their area and to facilitate the provision of appropriate housing and support. The service operates across the four Welsh prisons and Altcourse, Walton, Risley, Styal, Stoke Heath, Eastwood Park and Ashfield prisons in England.

POA, The Professional Trades Union for Prison, Correctional and Secure Psychiatric Workers, Cronin House, 245 Church Street, London N9 9HW. 020-8803 0255 Trade Union and professional staff association for workers in penal institutions and secure psychiatric units in England, Wales, Scotland and Northern Ireland.

Prison Reform Trust, 15 Northburgh Street, London EC1V 0JR. 020-7251 5070 *fax 020-7251 5076.* e-mail prt@prisonreformtrust. org.uk *www.prisonreformtrust.org.uk* Runs a research and publishing programme, and offers advice and information on all aspects of penal policy, publishes a quarterly magazine 'Prison Report'. Jointly (with HM Prison Service) publishes "Prisoners' Information Book".

Prisoners Abroad, 89-93 Fonthill Road, Finsbury Park, London N4 3JH. 020-7561

6820 Helpline 0808 172 0098 *fax 020-7561 6821.* e-mail info@prisonersabroad.org. uk *www.prisonersabroad.org.uk* The only UK charity providing information, advice and support to British citizens detained overseas, to their families and friends, and to released prisoners trying to re-establish themselves in society. Prisoners Abroad makes no moral judgement about its clients: it helps convicted and unconvicted, guilty or innocent, solely on the basis of need.

Prisoners' Advice Service, PO Box 46199, London EC1M 4XA. 020-7253 3323 *fax 020-7253 8067* helpline 0845 430 8923 The PAS is an independent charity that offers free confidential advice and information to prisoners in England & Wales, particularly concerning prisoners' rights and the application of Prison Rules. Publishes a quarterly bulletin "Prisoners' Rights".

Prisoners' Families and Friends Service, 20 Trinity Street, London SE1 1DB. 020-7403 4091 *fax 020-7403 9359.* free helpline for families 0808 808 3444 e-mail info@ prisonersfamiliesandfriends.org.uk *www. prisonersfamiliesandfriends.org.uk* Advice and information service for prisoner's families. Other facilities available in the London area.

Prisoners' Families Helpline 0808 808 2003 weekdays 9am-5pm, Sats 10am-3.pm free confidential, national helpline providing information and support for prisoners' families and friends info@ prisonersfamilieshelpline.org.uk *www. prisonersfamilieshelpline.org.uk*

Probation Managers Association, AMICUS, Hayes Court, West Common Road, Bromley, Kent BR2 7AU. 0845 850 4242 e-mail info@ probationmanagers.co.uk *www.amicustheunion.org*

Repetitive Strain Injury Association, has now ceased to exist, RSI advice is provided as a free service by Keytools Ltd, Abacus House, 1 Spring Crescent, Southampton SO17 2FZ, 023 8029 4500, e-mail rsia@keytools.com *www.keytools.co.uk*

Respect Phoneline 0845 122 8609 an information and advice line for domestic violence perpetrators, their (ex)partners as well as frontline workers. phoneline@respect.uk.net *www.changeweb.org.uk/respect.htm*

Rethink (formerly National Schizophrenia Fellowship), 5th Floor, Royal London House,

22-256 Finsbury Square, London EC2A 1DX, 020-7840 3188 advice 0845 456 0455 (10am to 3pm Monday, Wednesday & Friday; 10am to 1pm Tuesday & Thursday) or e-mail info@rethink.org *www.rethink.org* A national voluntary organisation that helps people with a severe mental illness, their families and carers and provides training for professionals.

The Rights Shop 296 Bethnal Green Road, London E2 0AG, 020-7739 4173 *fax 020-7613 3758;* open Mon & Wed 9am-1.30pm (drop-in service), Tues & Thurs 9am-2pm (appt only). Drop-in welfare rights/housing advice/money advice.

Royal National Institute of the Blind (RNIB), 105 Judd Street, London WC1H 9NE. 020-7388 1266 *fax 020-7388 2034.* Helpline 0845 766 9999 *www.rnib.org.uk* General enquiries: RNIB Resource Centre, London; benefit rights; education; employment and leisure enquiries; services for local societies; health, social and environmental services; reference library; advice on wills and legacies; enquiries on multiple disability; physiotherapy support.

RNID - for deaf and hard of hearing people, 19-23 Featherstone Street, London EC1Y 8SL. 0808 808 0123 (telephone), 0808 808 9000 (textphone), *helpline fax 020-7296 8199.* e-mail informationline@rnid.org.uk *www.rnid.org.uk* The RNID is the largest charity working to change the world for the 9 million deaf and hard of hearing people in the UK. As a membership charity it aims to achieve a radically better life for deaf and hard of hearing people. It does this by campaigning and lobbying, by raising awareness, by providing services and through social, medical and technical research.

Runaway Helpline PO BOX 28908, London SW14 7ZU, 0808 800 7070 operated by National Missing Persons Helpline for young people under 18, to call who are away from home or care help@runawayhelpine.org.uk *www.runawayhelpline.org.uk*

SANDS (Stillbirth And Neonatal Death Charity), 28 Portland Place, London W1B 1LY. Admin 020-7436 7940, *fax 020-7436 3715,* helpline 020-7436 5881 e-mail support@uk-sands. org *www.uk-sands.org* Support and advice for parents and families whose baby dies before, during or after birth.

SANE, 1st Floor, Cityside House, 40 Adler Street, London E1 1EE 020-7375 1002 *fax 020-7375 2162* Saneline (helpline) 0845 767 8000 (1pm-11pm everyday) SANEmail sanemail@sane.org.uk *www.sane.org.uk* SANEline A national mental health helpline for anyone with a mental health problem, their friends, families, carers and interested professionals. Can offer emotional support and information on local and national services, illnesses, medications, therapies and mental health law.

Shelter (National campaign for homeless), 88 Old Street, London EC1V 9HU. 08454584590, e-mail info@shelter. org.uk *www.shelter.org.uk* Freephone emergency advice 0808 800 4444 (8am-12pm 7 days per week). Runs a network of housing aid centres providing advice and advocacy to people who are, or are threatened with, homelessness, and campaigns on their behalf.

SITRA, 3rd Floor, 55 Bondway, London SW8 1SJ 020-7793 4710 *fax 020-7793 4715* e-mail sitrahelpline@sitra.org *www.sitra. org.uk* Training, advice, policy information and consultancy on all supported housing and supporting people matters. Monthly journal 'SITRA Bulletin' goes to all SITRA members.

Survivors UK, 12A Evelyn Court, Grinstead Road, LONDON, SE8 5AD 020 7357 6222 (mon-fri 9.30am-5.30pm) *fax 020-8357 7766* helpline (Tues & Thurs 7-10pm) 0845 122 1201 e-mail info@survivors.org.uk *www.survivors.org* Provides information, support and counselling to men who have experienced any form of sexual abuse, and to advance public education about all matters relating to the sexual abuse of men.

Together, 12 Old Street, London EC1V 9BE 020-7780 7300 *fax 020-7780 7301* e-mail contactus@together-uk.org *www.together-uk.org* A national charity providing a wide range of high quality community and hospital based services for people with mental health needs and their carers; including advocacy, assertive outreach schemes, community support, employment schemes, forensic services, helplines/information, respite for carers, social clubs, supported accommodation including 24 hour care.

Women in Prison, 1a Aberdeen Studios, 22 Highbury Grove, London N5 2EA.

020-7226 5879 *fax 020-7354 8005. www. womeninprison.org.uk* Established as a support and campaigning group for women prisoners, visits women prisoners and offers practical advice on a range of welfare issues, particularly accommodation, education and training. WIP has a mother and child grant fund for women in mother and baby units or the carers of the children of women prisoners. It produces a national magazine for women in custody and co-ordinates volunteer mentors for women leaving prison.

Women's Aid Federation of England Ltd, PO Box 391, Bristol BS99 7WS. national co-ordinating office telephone 0117-944 4411 e-mail info@womensaid.org.uk *www. womensaid.org.uk* Freephone 24hr National domestic violence helpline 0808 2000 247 (run in partnership between Women's Aid & Refuge) helpline@womensaid.org.uk. Public information, publications and training on domestic violence. National helpline for women and children experiencing domestic violence. Co-ordinates work of women's refuges in England.

Workaholics Anonymous, PO Box 394, Witney OX28 9BR *www.workaholics-anonymous*.org 12 step self help programme for compulsive workers. Free literature in return for an s.a.e.

Zito Trust, 16 Castle Street, Hay on Wye, Hereford HR3 5DF. (01497) 820011. e-mail zitotrust@btinternet.com *www.zitotrust.co.uk* A registered mental health charity that seeks to provide advice and support for victims of community care breakdown and to carry out research into services for the severely mentally ill and disordered.

HM INSPECTORATE OF PRISONS

1st Floor, Ashley House, 2 Monck Street,
London SW1P 2BQ
tel 020-7035 + ext *fax 020-7035 2140*

HM Chief Inspector of Prisons: Ms Anne Owers
ext 2102
HM Deputy Chief Inspector of Prisons: Nigel
Newcomen ext 2104

Functions:
By statute to inspect and report to the
Secretary of State on Prison Service
establishments in England and Wales,
Immigration Removal Centres in England,
Wales and Scotland. By invitation to inspect
and report to the relevant Secretary of State
on prisons in Northern Ireland, the Channel
Isles, the Isle of Man and other Commonwealth
territories; and on immigration short term
holding centres and the Military Corrective
Training Centre. In particular, to report on (a)
conditions of those establishments; (b) the
treatment of prisoners and other inmates and
the facilities available to them; (c) such other
matters as the Secretary of State may direct

HM PRISON SERVICE

HM Prison Service Headquarters, Cleland
House, Page Street, London SW1P 4LN
tel 020-7217 6000 *fax 020-7217 6403*
Website: www.hmprisonservice.gov.uk

Director General: Phil Wheatley. tel 020-7217
6777
Chief Operating Officer: Michael Spurr. tel 020-7217 6393
Director of Finance: Ann Beasley. tel 020-7217
6822
Director of High Security Prisons: Steve
Wagstaffe. tel 020-7217 6397
Director of Human Resources: Robin Wilkinson.
tel 020-7217 2944
Director of Prison Health: Richard Bradshaw. tel
020-7972 4767
Director of Probation: Roger Hill. tel 020-7217
0650
Director of Capacity Programme: Colin Allars. tel
020-7035 4091
Director of Commissioning & Operational Policy:
Ian Poree. tel 020-7217 2964

AREA OFFICES

Eastern
Area Manager: Drayton Old Lodge, 146 Drayton
High Road, Drayton, Norwich NR8 6AN
tel 01603 264100 *fax 01603 264111*

Responsible for:
HMP Bedford, HMP Blundeston, HMP
Bullwood Hall, HMP/YOI Chelmsford, HMP
Edmunds Hill, HMP Highpoint, HMP/YOI
Hollesley Bay Colony, HMP Littlehey, HMP
The Mount, HMP/YOI Norwich, HMP/YOI
Warren Hill, HMP Wayland

East Midlands
Area Manager: Empriss House, Unit C,
Harcourt Way, Meridian Business Park,
Leicester LE19 1WP
tel 0116 281 4000 *fax 0116 281 4060*

Responsible for:
HMP Ashwell, HMP/YOI Foston Hall, HMP
Gartree, HMYOI/RC Glen Parva, HMP
Leicester, HMP Lincoln, HMP Morton Hall,
HMP North Sea Camp, HMP Nottingham,
HMP/YOI Onley, HMP Ranby, HMP Stocken,
HMP Sudbury, HMP Wellingborough, HMP
Whatton

Kent & Sussex
Area Manager: 80 Sir Evelyn Road, Rochester,
Kent ME1 3NF
tel 01634 673000 *fax 01634 673048*

Responsible for:
HMP Blantyre House, HMP Canterbury, HMP/
YOI Cookham Wood, HMIRC Dover, HMP/YOI
East Sutton Park, HMP/YOI Elmley, HMP
Ford, HMP/YOI Lewes, HM Prison Maidstone,
HMYOI Rochester, HM Prison Standford Hill,
HM Prison Swaleside

London
Area Manager: Room 726, Cleland House, Page
Street, London SW1P 4LN
tel 020-7217 6180 *fax 020-7217 2893*

Responsible for:
HMP Brixton, HMYOI/RC Feltham, HMP
Holloway, HMP Latchmere House, HMP
Pentonville, HMP Wandsworth, HMP
Wormwood Scrubs

North East
Area Manager: 2 Artemis Court, St Johns Road,
Meadowfield, Durham DH7 8XQ
tel 0191 378 6000 *fax 0191 378 6001*

Responsible for:
HMP Acklington, HMYOI Castington, HMYOI
Deerbolt, HMP Durham, HMP Holme House,
HMP Kirklevington, HMP Low Newton

North West
Area Manager: Stirling House, Ackhurst Business Park, Foxhole Road, Chorley PR7 1NY
tel 01257 248600 *fax 01257 248604*

Responsible for:
HMP Buckley Hall, HMP Garth, HMP Haverigg, HMP/YOI Hindley, HMP Kennet, HMP Kirkham, HMP Lancaster Castle, HMYOI Lancaster Farms, HMP Liverpool, HMP Preston, HMP Risley, HMP/YOI Styal, HMYOI Thorn Cross, HMP Wymott

South Central
Area Manager: 2nd Floor, White Rose Court, Oriental Road, Woking, Surrey GU22 7PJ
tel 01483 716607

Responsible for:
HMP Albany, HMP/YOI Aylesbury, HMP Bullingdon, HMP Camp Hill, HMP Coldingley, HMP Downview, HMP Grendon/Springhill, HMIRC Haslar, HMP High Down, HMP Huntercombe, HMP Kingston, HMP Parkhurst, HMP/YOI Reading, HMP Send, HMP Winchester

South West
Area Manager: 1 Tortworth Road, Leyhill, Wotton under Edge, Gloucestershire GL12 8BQ
tel 01454 264053 *fax 01454 264065*

Responsible for:
HM Prison Bristol, HM Prison Channings Wood, HM Prison Dartmoor, HM Prison Dorchester, HM Prison Eastwood Park, HM Prison Erlestoke, HM Prison Exeter, HM Prison Gloucester, HMP/YOI Guys Marsh, HM Prison Leyhill, HMYOI Portland, HM Prison Shepton Mallett, HM Prison The Verne

NOMS Cymru
Director of Offender Management: 102 Maryport Street, Usk, Gwent NP15 1AH
tel 01291 674855 *fax 01291 674865*

NOMS Cymru, Ground Floor East, Welsh Assembly Building, Cathays Park, Cardiff CF10 3NQ

Responsible for:
HM Prison Cardiff, HMP/YOI Parc, HM Prison Swansea, HM Prison Usk, HM Prison Prescoed

West Midlands
Area Manager: P.O. Box 458, HM Prison Shrewsbury, The Dana, Shrewsbury, Shropshire SY1 2WB
tel 01743 284543 *fax 01743 280051*

Responsible for:
HM Prison Birmingham, HMYOI Brinsford,

HMP/YOI Drake Hall, HM Prison Featherstone, HM Prison Hewell, HM Prison Shrewsbury, HM Prison Stafford, HMYOI Stoke Heath, HMYOI Swinfen Hall, HMYOI Werrington,

Yorkshire and Humberside
Area Manager: 2 Marston House, Audby Lane, Wetherby, West Yorkshire LS22 7FD
tel 01937 544500 *fax 01937 544501*

Responsible for:
HM Prison Askham Grange, HM Prison Everthorpe, HM Prison Hull, HM Prison Leeds, HM Prison Lindholme, HM Prison Moorland Closed, HM Prison Moorland Open, HM Prison New Hall, HMRC Northallerton, HM Prison Wealstun, HMYOI Wetherby

Directorate of High Security
Director: Room 512/513, Cleland House, Page Street, London SW1P 4LN
tel 020-7217 2888 *fax 020-7217 6664*

Responsible for:
HM Prison Belmarsh, HM Prison Frankland, HM Prison Full Sutton, HM Prison Long Lartin, HM Prison Manchester, HM Prison Wakefield, HM Prison Whitemoor, HM Prison Woodhill,

Office for National Commissioning
Area Manager: Elizabeth House, Unit 2, Forder Way, Cygnet Park, Hampton, Peterborough PE7 8GX
tel 01733 440400 *fax 01733 440455*

Responsible for:
HM Prison Altcourse, HM Prison Ashfield, HM Prison Bronzefield, HMP Buckley Hall, HMYOI Doncaster, HM Prison Dovegate, HMYOI Forest Bank, HMP Hewell, HM Prison Lowdham Grange, HM Prison Peterborough, HM Prison Rye Hill, HM Prison The Wolds

ALPHABETICAL LIST OF PRISONS IN ENGLAND & WALES

Acklington
The Governor, HM Prison Acklington, Nr. Morpeth, Northumberland NE65 9XF
tel (01670) 762300 *fax (01670) 762301*

Albany
The Governor, HM Prison Albany, 55 Parkhurst Road, Newport, Isle of Wight PO30 5RS
tel (01983) 556300 *fax (01983) 556362*

Altcourse
The Director, HM Prison Altcourse, Higher Lane, Fazakerley, Liverpool L9 7LH
tel 0151-522 2000 *fax 0151-522 2121*

Ashfield
The Director, HMYOI, Shortwood Road,
Pucklechurch, Bristol BS16 9QJ
tel (0117) 303 8000 *fax (0117) 303 8001*

Ashford
see Bronzefield

Ashwell
The Governor, HM Prison Ashwell, Oakham,
Leics LE15 7LF
tel (01572) 884100 *fax (01572) 884101*

Askham Grange
The Governor, HM Prison and YOI Askham
Grange, Askham Richard, York YO23 3FT
tel (01904) 772000 *fax (01904) 772001*

Aylesbury
The Governor, HMYOI, Bierton Road,
Aylesbury, Bucks HP20 1EH
tel (01296) 444000 *fax (01296) 444001*

Bedford
The Governor, HM Prison, St Loyes Street,
Bedford MK40 1HG
tel (01234) 373000 *fax (01234) 273568*

Belmarsh
The Governor, HM Prison Belmarsh, Western
Way, Thamesmead, London SE28 OEB
tel 020-8331 4400 *fax 020-8331 4401*

Birmingham
The Governor, HM Prison, Winson Green Road,
Birmingham B18 4AS
tel (0121) 345 2500 *fax (0121) 345 2501*

Blakenhurst
The Governor, HM Prison Blakenhurst, Hewell
Lane, Redditch, Worcs B97 6QS
tel (01527) 400500 *fax (01527) 400501*

Blantyre House
The Governor, HM Prison Blantyre House,
Round Green Lane, Goudhurst, Kent TN17
2NH
tel (01580) 213223 *fax (01580) 213201*

Blundeston
The Governor, HM Prison Blundeston,
Lowestoft, Suffolk NR32 5BG
tel (01502) 734500 *fax (01502) 734501*

Brinsford
The Governor, HMYOI & Remand Centre, New
Road, Featherstone, Wolverhampton WV10 7PY
tel (01902) 532450 *fax (01902) 532451*

Bristol
The Governor, HM Prison, Cambridge Road,
Horfield, Bristol BS7 8PS
tel (0117) 372 3100 *fax (0117) 372 3153*

Brixton
The Governor, HM Prison, PO Box 369, Jebb
Avenue, Brixton, London SW2 5XF
tel 020-8588 6000 *fax 020-8588 6296*

Brockhill
The Governor, HM Prison Brockhill, Hewell
Lane, Redditch, Worcestershire B97 6RD
tel (01527) 552650 *fax (01527) 552651*

Bronzefield
The Director, HM Prison, Woodthorpe Road,
Ashford, Middx TW15 3JZ
tel (01784) 425690 *fax (01784) 425691*

Buckley Hall
The Governor, HM Prison, Buckley Hall Road,
Rochdale, Lancs OL12 9DP
tel (01706) 514300 *fax (01706) 514399*

Bullingdon
The Governor, HM Prison Bullingdon, PO Box
50, Bicester OX25 1WD
tel (01869) 353100 *fax (01869) 353101*

Bullwood Hall
The Governor, HM Prison Bullwood Hall, High
Road, Hockley, Essex SS5 4TE
tel (01702) 562800 *fax (01702) 562801*

Camp Hill
The Governor, HM Prison Camp Hill, Newport,
Isle of Wight PO30 5PB
tel (01983) 554600 *fax (01983) 554799*

Canterbury
The Governor, HM Prison, Longport,
Canterbury, Kent CT1 1PJ
tel (01227) 862800 *fax (01227) 862801*

Cardiff
The Governor, HM Prison, Knox Road, Cardiff
CF2 0UG
tel (029) 2092 3100 *fax (029) 2092 3318*

Castington
The Governor, HMYOI Castington, Morpeth,
Northumberland NE65 9XG
tel (01670) 382100 *fax (01670) 382101*

Channings Wood
The Governor, HM Prison Channings Wood,
Denbury, Newton Abbot, Devon TQ12 6DW
tel (01803) 814600 *fax (01803) 814601*

Chelmsford
The Governor, HM Prison, 200 Springfield
Road, Chelmsford, Essex CM2 6LQ
tel (01245) 272000 *fax (01245) 272001*

Coldingley
The Governor, HM Prison Coldingley,
Shaftesbury Road, Bisley, Woking, Surrey GU24
9EX

tel (01483) 804300 *fax (01483) 804427*

Cookham Wood
The Governor, HM Prison & YOI Cookham
Wood, Sir Evelyn Road, Rochester, Kent ME1
3LU
tel (01634) 202500 *fax (01634) 202501*

Dartmoor
The Governor, HM Prison Dartmoor,
Princetown, Yelverton, Devon PL20 6RR
tel (01822) 322000 *fax (01822) 322001*

Deerbolt
The Governor, HYOI Deerbolt, Bowes Rd,
Barnard Castle, Co. Durham DL12 9BG
tel (01833) 633200 *fax (01833) 633201*

Doncaster
The Director, HM Prison, Marshgate,
Doncaster, S Yorks DN5 8UX
tel (01302) 760870 *fax (01302) 760851*

Dorchester
The Governor, HM Prison, North Square,
Dorchester, Dorset DT1 1JD
tel (01305) 714500 *fax (01305) 714501*

Dovegate
The Director, HM Prison Dovegate, Uttoxeter,
Staffs ST14 8XR
tel (01283) 829400 *fax (01283) 820066*

Downview
The Governor, HM Prison Downview, Sutton
Lane, Sutton, Surrey SM2 5PD
tel 020-8929 6300 *fax 020-8929 6301*

Drake Hall
The Governor, HM Prison and YOI Drake Hall,
Eccleshall, Stafford ST21 6LQ
tel (01785) 774100 *fax (01785) 774010*

Durham
The Governor, HM Prison, Old Elvet, Durham
DH1 3HU
tel 0191-332 3400 *fax 0191-332 3401*

East Sutton Park
The Governor, HM Prison and YOI East Sutton
Park, Sutton Valance, Maidstone, Kent ME17
3DF
tel (01622) 845000 *fax (01622) 845001*

Eastwood Park
The Governor, HM Prison, Falfield, Wotton-
under-Edge, Gloucestershire GL12 8DB
tel (01454) 382100 *fax (01454) 382101*

Edmunds Hill
The Governor, HM Prison Edmunds Hill,
Stradishall, Newmarket, Suffolk CB8 9YN
tel (01440) 743100 *fax (01440) 743560*

Elmley
The Governor, HM Prison, Church Road,
Eastchurch, Sheerness, Kent ME12 4DZ
tel (01795) 882000 *fax (01795) 882001*

Erlestoke
The Governor, HM Prison Erlestoke, Devizes,
Wiltshire SN10 5TU
tel (01380) 814250 *fax (01380) 814273*

Everthorpe
The Governor, HM Prison Everthorpe, Beck
Road, Brough, E Yorks HU15 1RB
tel (01430) 426500 *fax (01430) 426501*

Exeter
The Governor, HM Prison, 30 New North Road,
Exeter, Devon EX4 4EX
tel (01392) 415650 *fax (01392) 415691*

Featherstone
The Governor, HM Prison, New Road,
Featherstone, Wolverhampton WV10 7PU
tel (01902) 703000 *fax (01902) 703001*

Feltham
The Governor, HMYOI and Remand Centre,
Bedfont Road, Feltham, Middx TW13 4ND
tel 020-8844 5000 *fax 020-8844 5001*

Ford
The Governor, HM Prison Ford, Arundel, West
Sussex BN18 0BX
tel (01903) 663000 *fax (01903) 663001*

Forest Bank
The Governor, HM Prison Forest Bank,
Agecroft Road, Pendlebury, Manchester M27
8FB
tel 0161-925 7000 *fax 0161-925 7001*

Foston Hall
The Governor, HM Prison Foston Hall, Foston,
Derbyshire DE65 5DN
tel (01283) 584300 *fax (01283) 584301*

Frankland
The Governor, HM Prison Frankland, Brasside,
Durham DH1 5YD
tel 0191-332 3000 *fax 0191-332 3001*

Full Sutton
The Governor, HM Prison Full Sutton, York
YO41 1PS
tel (01759) 475100 *fax (01759) 371206*

Garth
The Governor, HM Prison Garth, Ulnes Walton
Lane, Leyland, Preston, Lancs PR26 8NE
tel (01772) 443300 *fax (01772) 443301*

Gartree
The Governor, HM Prison Gartree, Gallow

Field Road, Market Harborough, Leics LE16
7RP
tel (01858) 436600 *fax (01858) 436601*

Glen Parva
The Governor, HMYOI, 10 Tigers Road,
Wigston, Leics LE18 4TN
tel 0116-228 4100 *fax 0116-228 4000*

Gloucester
The Governor, HM Prison, Barrack Square,
Gloucester GL1 2JN
tel (01452) 453000 *fax (01452) 453001*

Grendon
The Governor, HM Prison Grendon, Grendon
Underwood, Aylesbury, Bucks HP18 0TL
tel (01296) 443000 *fax (01296) 443001*

Guys Marsh
The Governor, HM Prison Guys Marsh,
Shaftesbury, Dorset SP7 0AH
tel (01747) 856400 *fax (01747) 856401*

Hatfield
see Moorland

Haverigg
The Governor, HM Prison Haverigg, Millom,
Cumbria LA18 4NA
tel (01229) 713000 *fax (01229) 713001*

Hewell Grange
The Governor, HM Prison Hewell Grange,
Redditch, Worcs. B97 6QQ
tel (01527) 552000 *fax (01527) 552001*

Highdown
The Governor, HM Prison, Highdown Lane,
Sutton, Surrey SM2 5PJ
tel 020-7147 6300 *fax 020-7147 6301*

Highpoint
The Governor, HM Prison Highpoint,
Stradishall, Newmarket, Suffolk CB8 9YG
tel (01440) 743100 *fax (01440) 743092*

Hindley
The Governor, HM Prison, Gibson Street,
Bickershaw, Wigan, Lancs WN2 5TH
tel (01942) 663000 *fax (01942) 663101*

Hollesley Bay
The Governor, HM Prison & YOI Hollesley Bay,
Hollesley, Woodbridge, Suffolk IP12 3JW
tel (01394) 412400 *fax (01394) 412758*

Holloway
The Governor, HM Prison & YOI, Parkhurst
Road, Holloway, London N7 0NU
tel 020-7979 4400 *fax 020-7979 4401*

Holme House
The Governor, HM Prison, Holme House Road,

Stockton-on-Tees, Cleveland TS18 2QU
tel (01642) 744000 *fax (01642) 744001*

Hull
The Governor, HM Prison, Hedon Road, Hull
HU9 5LS
tel (01482) 282200 *fax (01482) 282400*

Huntercombe
The Governor, HMYOI, Huntercombe Place,
Nuffield, Henley-on-Thames, Oxon. RG9 5SB
tel (01491) 643100 *fax (01491) 643101*

Kingston
The Governor, HM Prison, 122 Milton Road,
Portsmouth, Hants. PO3 6AS
tel 023-9295 3100 *fax 023-9295 3181*

Kirkham
The Governor, HM Prison Kirkham, Freckleton
Road, Preston, Lancs PR4 2RN
tel (01772) 675400 *fax (01772) 675401*

Kirklevington Grange
The Governor, HM Prison Kirklevington
Grange, Yarm, Cleveland TS15 9PA
tel (01642) 792600 *fax (01642) 792601*

Lancaster Castle
The Governor, HM Prison, The Castle,
Lancaster LA1 1YL
tel (01524) 565100 *fax (01524) 565101*

Lancaster Farms
The Governor, HMYOI & Remand Centre
Lancaster Farms, Far Moor Lane, off
Quernmore Rd, Lancaster LA1 3QZ
tel (01524) 563450 *fax (01542) 563451*

Latchmere House
The Governor, HM Prison Latchmere House,
Church Road, Ham Common, Richmond, Surrey
TW10 5HH
tel 020-8588 6650 *fax 020-8588 6698*

Leeds
The Governor, HM Prison, 2 Gloucester
Terrace, Armley Road, Leeds, W. Yorks LS12
2TJ
tel (0113) 203 2600 *fax (0113) 203 2601*

Leicester
The Governor, HM Prison, Welford Road,
Leicester LE2 7AJ
tel 0116-228 3000 *fax 0116-228 3001*

Lewes
The Governor, HM Prison, Brighton Road,
Lewes, East Sussex BN7 1EA
tel (01273) 785100 *fax (01273) 785101*

Leyhill
The Governor, HM Prison Leyhill, Wotton-

under-Edge, Gloucestershire GL12 8BT
tel (01454) 264000 *fax (01454) 264001*

Lincoln
The Governor, HM Prison, Greetwell Road,
Lincoln LN2 4BD
tel (01522) 663000 *fax (01522) 663001*

Lindholme
The Governor, HM Prison, Bawtry Rd, Hatfield
Woodhouse, Doncaster, S. Yorks DN7 6EE
tel (01302) 524700 *fax (01302) 524750*

Littlehey
The Governor, HM Prison Littlehey, Perry,
Huntingdon, Cambs. PE28 0SR
tel (01480) 333000 *fax (01480) 333070*

Liverpool
The Governor, HM Prison, 68 Hornby Road,
Liverpool L9 3DF
tel 0151-530 4000 *fax 0151-530 4001*

Long Lartin
The Governor, HM Prison Long Lartin, South
Littleton, Evesham, Worcs. WR11 8TZ
tel (01386) 835100 *fax (01386) 835101*

Lowdham Grange
The Director, HM Prison Lowdham Grange,
Lowdham, Notts. NG14 7DA
tel 0115-966 9200 *fax 0115-966 9220*

Low Newton
The Governor, HM Prison & Y.O.I. Low
Newton, Brasside, Durham DH1 5YA
tel 0191-376 4000 *fax 0191-376 4001*

Maidstone
The Governor, HM Prison, County Road,
Maidstone, Kent ME14 1UZ
tel (01622) 755300 *fax (01622) 755301*

Manchester
The Governor, HM Prison, Southall Street,
Manchester M60 9AH
tel 0161-817 5600 *fax 0161-817 5601*

Mount, The
The Governor, HM Prison, Molyneaux Avenue,
Bovingdon, Hemel Hempstead, Herts. HP3 0NZ
tel (01442) 836300 *fax (01442) 836301*

Moorland (Open)
The Governor, HMYOI Moorland Open, Thorne
Road, Hatfield, Doncaster, DN7 6EL
tel (01405) 746500 *fax (01405) 746501*

Moorland (Closed)
The Governor, HM Prison, Bawtry Road,
Hatfield Woodhouse, Doncaster DN7 6BW
tel (01302) 523000 *fax (01302) 523001*

Morton Hall
The Governor, HM Prison Morton Hall,
Swinderby, Lincoln LN6 9PT
tel (01522) 666700 *fax (01522) 666750*

New Hall
The Governor, HM Prison and YOI New Hall,
Dial Wood, Flockton, Wakefield, West Yorks
WF4 4XX
tel (01924) 803000 *fax (01924) 803001*

Northallerton
The Governor, HMYOI, East Road,
Northallerton, North Yorks DL6 1NW
tel (01609) 785100 *fax (01609) 785101*

North Sea Camp
The Governor, HM Prison North Sea Camp,
Freiston, Boston, Lincs PE22 0QX
tel (01205) 769300 *fax (01205) 769301*

Norwich
The Governor, HM Prison, Knox Rd, Norwich,
Norfolk NR1 4LU
tel (01603) 708600 *fax (01603) 708601*

Nottingham
The Governor, HM Prison, Perry Road,
Sherwood, Nottingham NG5 3AG
tel 0115-872 3000 *fax 0115-872 3001*

Onley
The Governor, HM Prison & YOI Onley,
Willoughby, Rugby, Warcs CV23 8AP
tel (01788) 523400 *fax (01788) 523401*

Oxford
see Bullingdon

Parc
The Governor, HM Prison & YOI, Heol Hopcyn
John, Bridgend, Mid Glam CF35 6AR
tel (01656) 300200 *fax (01656) 300201*

Parkhurst
The Governor, HM Prison Parkhurst, Newport,
Isle of Wight PO30 5NX
tel (01983) 554000 *fax (01983) 554001*

Pentonville
The Governor, HM Prison Pentonville,
Caledonian Road, London N7 8TT
tel 020-7023 7000 *fax 020-7023 7001*

Peterborough
The Director, HM Prison, Saville Road,
Westfield, Peterborough PE3 7PD
tel (01733) 217500 *fax (01733) 217501*

Portland
The Governor, HMYOI, Easton, Portland,
Dorset DT5 1DL
tel (01305) 715600 *fax (01305) 715601*

Portsmouth
see Kingston

Prescoed
The Governor, HM Prison, Prescoed, Coed-y-Paen, Nr. Pontypool, Torfaen NP14 0TB
tel (01291) 675000 *fax (01291) 675158*
(Linked with Usk. Please send all correspondence to Usk address)

Preston
The Governor, HM Prison, 2 Ribbleton Lane, Preston, Lancs PR1 5AB
tel (01772) 257734 *fax (01772) 886810*

Ranby
The Governor, HM Prison Ranby, Retford, Notts. DN22 8EU
tel (01777) 862000 *fax (01777) 862001*

Reading
The Governor, HM Prison, Forbury Road, Reading, Berks. RG1 3HY
tel 0118-908 5000 *fax 0118-908 5001*

Risley
The Governor, HM Prison, Warrington Road, Risley, Cheshire WA3 6BP
tel (01925) 733 000 *fax (01925) 733001*

Rochester
The Governor, HMYOI, 1 Fort Road, Rochester, Kent ME1 3QS
tel (01634) 803100 *fax (01634) 803101*

Rye Hill
The Director, HM Prison Rye Hill, Onley, Willoughby, Rugby, Warwickshire CV23 8SZ
tel (01788) 523300 *fax (01788) 523311*

Send
The Governor, HM Prison, Ripley Road, Send, Woking, Surrey GU23 7LJ
tel (01483) 471000 *fax (01483) 471001*

Shepton Mallet
The Governor, HM Prison, Cornhill, Shepton Mallet, Somerset BA4 5LU
tel (01749) 823300 *fax (01749) 823301*

Shrewsbury
The Governor, HM Prison, The Dana, Shrewsbury, Shropshire SY1 2HR
tel (01743) 273000 *fax (01743) 273001*

Spring Hill
The Governor, HM Prison, Grendon Underwood, Aylesbury, Bucks HP18 0TL
tel (01296) 443000 *fax (01296) 443001*

Stafford
The Governor, HM Prison, 54 Gaol Road, Stafford ST16 3AW

tel (01785) 773000 *fax (01785) 773001*

Standford Hill
The Governor, HM Prison Standford Hill, Church Road, Eastchurch, Sheerness, Kent ME12 4AA
tel (01795) 884500 *fax (01795) 884638*

Stocken
The Governor, HM Prison, Stocken Hall Rd, Stretton, Nr. Oakham, Rutland LE15 7RD
tel (01780) 795100 *fax (01780) 410767*

Stoke Heath
The Governor, HM Prison Stoke Heath, Market Drayton, Shropshire TF9 2JL
tel (01630) 636000 *fax (01630) 636001*

Styal
The Governor, HM Prison & YOI Styal, Wilmslow, Cheshire SK9 4HR
tel (01625) 553000 *fax (01625) 553001*

Sudbury
The Governor, HM Prison, Sudbury, Ashbourne, Derbyshire DE6 5HW
tel (01283) 584000 *fax (01283) 584001*

Swaleside
The Governor, HM Prison Swaleside, Brabazon Road, Eastchurch, Isle of Sheppey, Kent ME12 4AX
tel (01795) 804100 *fax (01795) 804200*

Swansea
The Governor, HM Prison, Oystermouth Road, Swansea SA1 3SR
tel (01792) 485300 *fax (01792) 485430*

Swinfen Hall
The Governor HMYOI Swinfen Hall, Lichfield, Staffs. WS14 9QS
tel (01543) 484000 *fax (01543) 484001*

Thorn Cross
The Governor, HMYOI, Arley Rd, Appleton Thorn, Warrington, Cheshire WA4 4RL
tel (01925) 805100 *fax (01925) 805101*

Usk
The Governor, HM Prison, 47 Maryport Street, Usk, Monmouthshire NP5 1XP
tel (01291) 671600 *fax (01291) 671752*

Verne, The
The Governor, HM Prison The Verne, Portland, Dorset DT5 1EQ
tel (01305) 825000 *fax (01305) 825001*

Wakefield
The Governor, HM Prison, Love Lane, Wakefield, West Yorks WF2 9AG
tel (01924) 246000 *fax (01924) 246001*

Wandsworth
The Governor, HM Prison, PO Box 757,
Heathfield Road, Wandsworth, London SW18
3HS
tel 020-8588 4000 *fax 020-8588 4001*

Warren Hill
The Governor, HMYOI, Warren Hill, Hollesley
Bay, Woodbridge, Suffolk IP12 3JW
tel (01394) 412400 *fax (01394) 412767*

Wayland
The Governor, HM Prison Wayland, Griston,
Thetford, Norfolk IP25 6RL
tel (01953) 804100 *fax (01953) 804220*

Wealstun
The Governor, HM Prison Wealstun, Wetherby,
West Yorks LS23 7AZ
tel (01937) 440000 *fax (01937) 440001*

Weare, The
now closed

Wellingborough
The Governor, HM Prison, Millers Park,
Doddington Road, Wellingborough, Northants
NN8 2NH
tel (01933) 232700 *fax (01933) 232701*

Werrington
The Governor, HMYOI, Werrington, Stoke-on-
Trent, Staffs ST9 0DX
tel (01782) 463300 *fax (01782) 463301*

Wetherby
The Governor, HMYOI, York Road, Wetherby,
West Yorks LS22 5ED
tel (01937) 544200 *fax (01937) 544201*

Whatton
The Governor, HM Prison, New Lane, Whatton,
Notts NG13 9FQ
tel (01949) 803200 *fax (01949) 803201*

Whitemoor
The Governor, HM Prison Whitemoor, Longhill
Road, March, Cambs PE15 0PR
tel (01354) 602350 *fax (01354) 602351*

Winchester
The Governor, HM Prison, Romsey Road,
Winchester, Hants SO22 5DF
tel (01962) 723000 *fax (01962) 723001*

Wolds
The Director, HM Prison Wolds, Sands Lane,
Everthorpe, Brough, E. Yorks HU15 2JZ
tel (01430) 428000 *fax (01430) 428001*

Woodhill
The Governor, HM Prison Woodhill, Tattenhoe
Street, Milton Keynes, Bucks. MK4 4DA

tel (01908) 722000 *fax (01908) 867063*

Wormwood Scrubs
The Governor, HM Prison Wormwood Scrubs,
PO Box 757, Du Cane Road, London W12 0AE
tel 020-8588 3200 *fax 020-8588 3201*

Wymott
The Governor, HM Prison Wymott, Ulnes
Walton Lane, Leyland, Preston PR5 8LW
tel (01772) 442000 *fax (01772) 442001*

SPECIAL HOSPITALS (DoH)

Broadmoor Hospital
Crowthorne, Berks. RG11 7EG
tel 01344 773111 *fax 01344 754848*

Rampton Hospital
Retford, Notts. DN22 0PD
tel 01777 248321 *fax 01771 248442*

Ashworth Hospital
Parkbourn, Maghull, Liverpool L31 1HW
tel 0151 473 0303 *fax 0151 526 6603*

NORTHERN IRELAND PRISON SERVICE

Headquarters
Prison Service Headquarters, Dundonald
House, Upper Newtownards Road, Belfast BT4
3SU
tel 028 9052 2922 *fax 028 9052 4330*

Prison Service College
Head of Training and Development, Prison
Service College, Woburn House, Millisle, Co.
Down BT22 2HS
tel 028 9186 3000 *fax 028 9186 3022*

Prisons

Maghaberry
The Governor, Maghaberry Prison, Old Road,
Ballinderry Upper, Lisburn, Co. Antrim BT28
2PT
tel 028 9261 1888 *fax 028 9261 9516*

Magilligan
The Governor, Magilligan Prison, Point Road,
Limavady, Co. Londonderry BT49 0LR
tel 028 7776 3311 *fax 028 7775 0819*

Young Offenders Centre And Prison

Hydebank Wood
The Governor, Hydebank Wood Young
Offenders Centre and Prison, Hospital Road,
Belfast BT8 8NA
tel 028 9025 3666 *fax 028 9025 3668*

SCOTTISH PRISON SERVICE

Headquarters
Calton House, 5 Redheughs Rigg, Edinburgh
EH12 9HW
tel 0131-244 8745 *fax 0131-244 8774* e-mail
gaolinfo@sps.gov.uk.

Scottish Prison Service College
Head of College, Scottish Prison Service
College, Newlands Road, Brightons, Falkirk,
Stirlingshire FK2 0DE
tel Polmont (01324) 710400 *fax 01324 710401*

Prisons

Aberdeen
The Governor, H.M. Prison, Craiginches, 4
Grampian Place, Aberdeen AB11 8FN
tel 01224 238300 *fax 01224 896209*

Barlinnie
The Governor, H.M. Prison, Barlinnie, Glasgow
G33 2QX
tel 0141-770 2000 *fax 0141-770 2060*

Castle Huntly
The Governor, HMP Open Estate, Castle
Huntly, Longforgan, Near Dundee DD2 5HL
tel 01382 319333 *fax 01382 319350*

Cornton Vale
The Governor, H.M. Prison, Cornton Vale,
Cornton Road, Stirling FK9 5NU
tel 01786 832591 *fax 01786 833597*

Dumfries
The Governor, H.M. Prison, Terregles Street,
Dumfries DG2 9AX
tel 01387 261218 *fax 01387 264144*

Edinburgh
The Governor, H.M. Prison, Edinburgh, 33
Stenhouse Road, Edinburgh EH11 3LN
tel 0131-444 3000 *fax 0131-444 3045*

Glenochil
The Governor, H.M. Prison, King O'Muir Road,
Tullibody, Clackmannanshire FK10 3AD
tel 01259 760471 *fax 01259 762003*

Greenock
The Governor, H.M. Prison, Gateside,
Greenock PA16 9AH
tel 01475 787801 *fax 01475 783154*

Inverness
The Governor, H.M. Prison, Porterfield, Duffy
Drive, Inverness IV2 3HH
tel 01463 229000 *fax 01463 229010*

Kilmarnock (Serco Home Affairs)
The Director, H.M. Prison, Bowhouse,
Mauchline Road, Kilmarnock KA1 5AA
tel 01563 548800 *fax 01563 548845*

Noranside
The Governor, H.M.P. Open Estate, Noranside,
Fern, by Forfar, Angus DD8 3QY
tel 01382 319333 *fax 01356 650245*

Perth
The Governor, H.M. Prison, 3 Edinburgh Road,
Perth PH2 8AT
tel 01738 622293 *fax 01738 630545*

Peterhead
The Governor, H.M. Prison, Peterhead,
Aberdeenshire AB42 2YY
tel 01779 479101 *fax 01779 470529*

Shotts
The Governor, H.M. Prison, Scott Drive,
Shotts, Lanarkshire ML7 4LE
tel 01501 824000 *fax 01501 824001*

Young Offender Institutions

Cornton Vale
The Governor, H.M. Y.O.I., Cornton Vale,
Cornton Road, Stirling FK9 5NU
tel 01786 832591 *fax 01786 833597*

Polmont
The Governor, H.M. Y.O.I., Brightons, near
Falkirk, Stirlingshire FK2 0AB
tel 01324 711558 *fax 01324 714919*

State Hospital

State Hospital, Carstairs Junction, Lanark ML11
8RP
tel 01555 840024 *fax 01555 840100*

Residential Schools

Ballikinrain School
Balfron, Glasgow G63 0LL (34)
Junior, Intermediate School
Head: Mr Chris McNaught tel (01360) 440244
& 440645
Correspondent: Mr A Staff, Director of Social
Care, Crossroach, Church of Scotland, Charis
House, 47 Milton Road East, Edinburgh EH15
2SR. tel (0131) 657 2000

Geilsland School
Beith, Ayrshire KA15 1HD (35)
Residential School for senior boys
Head: Mr Ranald Mair tel (01505) 504044
Correspondent: The Official Correspondent for
Residential Schools, Church of Scotland, Board
of Social Responsibility, Church of Scotland,

Charis House, 47 Milton Road East, Edinburgh
EH15 2SR tel (0131) 657 2000

St Mary's
Kenmure, Bishopbriggs, GLASGOW G64 2EH
(34)
Secure facility providing care and education for
both boys and girls
tel (0141) 586 1200 *fax (0141) 586 1224*
E-mail: administrator@stmaryskenmure.org.uk
Correspondents: Messrs J. McSparran &
McCormick, S.S.C., Waterloo Chambers, 19
Waterloo Street, Glasgow G2 6AH. tel (0141)
248 7962/226 5203

Kibble Education & Care Centre
Goudie Street, Paisley, Renfrewshire PA3 2LG
tel 0141 889 0044 *fax 0141 887 6694*
e-mail: mailbox@kibble.org (50+40)
Provides residential and day care for boys aged
12–17
Chief Executive: Mr G. Bell. tel (0141) 889 0044
Correspondent: D. Nairn, Messrs. Milne, Craig
and Corson, 79 Renfrew Road, Paisley PA3 4DA

Oakbank School
Aberdeen AB15 5XP (72)
School for 40 adolescent boys and girls,
residential and day
Principal: Jane C. Arrowsmith tel (01224)
313347

Rossie Secure Accommodation Services
Montrose, Angus DD10 9TW (28)
Secure accommodation service provides care
and education for boys and girls between the
ages of 12 and 18
Chief Executive and Official Correspondent: Mr
Richard Murray tel (01674) 820204 *fax (01674)
820249*

St Philip's School
Plains, Airdrie, Lanarkshire ML6 7SF (62)
Junior/Intermediate School for boys with social,
emotional and behavioural difficulties.
Head: Mr P. K. Hanrahan
Correspondents: Messrs. J. McSparrow, J.
McCormick tel (01236) 765407

Springboig St John's School
Glasgow G33 4EH
Senior School for boys.
Head: Mr W. Fitzgerald tel (0141) 774 9791
Correspondents: Messrs. J. McSparran &
McCormick, S.S.C., Waterloo Chambers, 19
Waterloo Street, Glasgow G2 6AH. tel (0141)
248 7962

Wellington School
Peebles Road, Nr. Penicuik, Midlothian EH26
8PT
School for boys aged 13–16, any denomination.
Up to 16 residents and 34 day places.
Head and Official Correspondent: Mr R. Wells.
tel (01968) 672515

ISLE OF MAN, JERSEY, GUERNSEY

Isle of Man Prison
99 Victoria Road, Douglas,
Isle of Man IM2 4RD
tel (01624) 621306 *fax (01624) 628119*
special visits (01624) 663813

HMP La Moye, Jersey
La Moye, St Brelade, Jersey,
Channel Islands JE3 8HQ
tel (01534) 441800 *fax (01534) 441880*

Guernsey Prison
Les Nicolles, Baubigny, St Sampson
Guernsey, Channel Islands GY2 4YF
tel (01481) 248376 *fax (01481) 247837*
admin fax (01481) 200949

IRISH PRISON SERVICE

IDA Business Park, Ballinalee Road, Longford,
Co. Longford
tel 043 35100 *fax 043 35371* (from UK dial 00
353 and omit first 0)
info@irishprisons.ie

Arbour Hill Prison
Arbour Hill, Dublin 7.
tel 01 6719333 *fax 01 6799518*

Castlerea Prison
Harristown, Castlerea, Co. Roscommon
tel/fax 094 962 5277

Cloverhill Remand Prison
Cloverhill Road, Clondalkin, Dublin 22.
tel 01 6304530/01 6304531 *fax 01 6304580*

Cork Prison
Rathmore Road, Cork City, Cork.
tel 021 4518800

Dochas Centre
North Circular Road, Dublin 7.
tel 01-8858987

Limerick Prison
Mulgrave Street, Limerick.
tel 061 204700 *fax 061 415116*

Loughan House Open Centre
Blacklion, Co. Cavan.
tel 072-53020 *fax 072-53234*

Midlands Prison
Dublin Road, Portlaoise, Co. Laois.
tel 0502 72110/72100 *fax 0502 72219*

Mountjoy Prison
North Circular Road, Dublin 7.
tel 01 8062800

Portlaoise Prison
Dublin Road, Portlaoise, Co. Laois.
tel 0502 21318 *fax 0502 20997*

Shelton Abbey
Arklow, Co. Wicklow.
tel 0402 32140 *fax 0402 39924*

St. Patrick's Institution
North Circular Road, Dublin 7.
tel 01 8062896 *fax 01 8307705*

The Training Unit
Glengarriff Parade, North Circular Road,
Dublin 7.
tel 01 8062890

Wheatfield Prison
Cloverhill Road, Clondalkin, Dublin 22.
tel 01 6260011

Under development
Thornton Hall
Kilworth

INDEX OF OFFICE NAMES

Offices are indexed by Area Name and reference number, not page numbers, i.e to find Andover, look up Hampshire office number 4